The Petroleum Handbook

Shell International Petroleum Company Limited London 1966

This book has been compiled by members of the staff of companies
of the Royal Dutch/Shell Group of Companies

Fifth edition

The Petroleum Handbook

First edition 1933
Second edition 1938
Third edition 1948
Fourth edition 1959

Printed in Great Britain by
Balding & Mansell Limited
Wisbech Cambridgeshire England

Foreword

by L. E. J. Brouwer

It is seven years since the publication of the last edition of this Handbook. During that time things moved very fast in both the petroleum and chemical industries, and it has been our aim in this new edition to reflect the major changes that have occurred. More space has been devoted to chemicals; the new discoveries of natural gas, the increased activity in under-water operations, new manufacturing processes and the focus on marketing techniques, resulting from the increasingly competitive nature of both the oil and chemical markets, have all been included.

It is indeed extremely difficult in a book of this nature to keep fully abreast of developments; apologies are due for any minor obsolescences that may be evident now.

The anonymous authors of the various chapters, all members of the Shell staff, have once again given generously of their time, and much painstaking effort has been expended in the preparation of the illustrations. I should like to thank all of them for their co-operation.

Contents

Acknowledgements

The Editor would like to thank the following organizations for supplying illustrations for this Handbook

Avery-Hardoll Limited, *Fig. 240*
Babcock & Wilcox (Operations) Limited, *Fig. 129*
Bristol Aero Engines Limited, *Fig. 118*
Bristol Aeroplane Plastics Limited, *Fig. 185*
Carel Blazer, *Figs 246 and 252*
Clarbat Limited, *Fig. 133*
Conch Methane Services Limited, *Figs 68, 70 and 216*
Eileen Ramsay, *Fig. 195*
Hoe, R. & Crabtree Limited, *Fig. 178*
Hughes Tool Company, *Fig. 35*
Imperial Chemical Industries Limited, *Figs 176, 183, 184, 194 and 201*
Lubrizol International Laboratories, *Fig. 162*
Plastona (John Waddington) Limited, *Fig. 146*
Rolls Royce Limited, *Fig. 117*
Ruston and Hornsby Limited, *Fig. 125*
Stanhope Engineering Company Limited, *Fig. 167*
The Oil Well Engineering Company Limited, *Fig. 38*
United Kingdom Atomic Energy Authority, *Fig. 144*
Vickers Armstrong (Shipbuilders) Limited, *Fig. 177*
Zwicky Limited, *Fig. 231*

Preface

The Editor

The reception given to the fourth edition of the Handbook, and the continuing demand for copies, have encouraged the production of this new edition. In view of the complete revision effected in the fourth edition, it has been thought undesirable to make any radical alteration in the general scheme of the book. All sections have, however, been updated and, in some instances, edited in order to save space and so allow the inclusion of new material.

The new format has also helped to permit the inclusion of extra material without appreciably increasing the overall size of the volume. Moreover, it is believed that readers will find the new edition easier to handle and more convenient as a source of reference.

In presenting production and manufacturing data the editor has accepted that the oil industry keeps records in a system, barrels per day or per year, that is peculiar to itself. Those readers who find it difficult to grasp the significance of such data will find it helpful to know that

1 barrel = 42 US gallons = 35 UK gallons (approx) = 160 litres (approx)

1 barrel per day approximates to 50 metric tons per year, the exact equivalent depending on the specific gravity of the material.

In giving British and metric equivalents, realistic equivalents rather than exact conversions are given except where the latter are essential, e.g. in physical properties of materials. Thus, in describing processes, the equivalent of 500 °C is given as 930 °F and not as 932 °F, and the equivalent of 100 kg/cm^2 is given as 1400 lb/in^2 and not as the exact 1422 lb/in^2.

The editor gratefully acknowledges his indebtedness to all those members of the staffs of Shell companies who have so readily assisted him either as authors or in the submission of materials for illustrations. He is also grateful to those designers outside the company whose assistance in designing the book and preparing the illustrations has been invaluable.

Throughout the book the words Shell and Group are used collectively in relation to companies associated together under the name of the Royal Dutch/Shell Group of Companies.

The petroleum industry

The world petroleum industry

The Royal Dutch/Shell Group of Companies

The world petroleum industry

Petroleum

All over the world, at various depths beneath land and sea, there are accumulations of hydrocarbons formed long ago by decomposition of animal and vegetable remains. Hydrocarbons are compounds of hydrogen and carbon that, at normal temperatures and pressures, may be gaseous, liquid or solid according to the complexity of their molecules. The natural deposits are correspondingly gaseous, liquid or solid depending on the relative proportion of the various hydrocarbons present in the mixture.

In its widest sense 'petroleum' embraces all hydrocarbons occurring naturally in the earth. In its narrower, commercial sense, 'petroleum' is usually restricted to the liquid deposits – crude oil, the gaseous ones being known as 'natural gas' and the solid ones as 'bitumen', 'asphalt' or 'wax' according to their composition.

Most crude oils, although liquid as such, contain gaseous and solid hydrocarbons in solution. The gases come out of solution either on the release of pressure as the crude oil is produced or during the first stages of refining, and contribute to the total natural gas production. Some of the solids are recovered during refining as bitumen and wax, some stay in solution in the liquid oil products. Natural gas is also found associated with crude oil as a gas cap above the oil or on its own, unassociated with oil.

Crude oil and natural gas are the raw materials of the petroleum industry. It is the business of the industry to find them, to win them from the ground, to manufacture technically useful products from them and to sell the products in the markets of the world.

Historical

Petroleum had been used for many centuries in Mesopotamia, Egypt, Persia and elsewhere for heating, lighting, roadmaking and building. Various materials recorded in the Bible under a variety of names as having been used in the construction of the Tower of Babel, Noah's Ark and Moses' basket were most probably natural bitumens obtained from local seepages. Bitumen was used in Persia as far back as 4000 BC and is still found in Babylonian monuments.

In Europe the northern Italian town of Salsomaggiore, near which an issue of natural gas was known, adopted the crest of a burning salamander in 1226. A small oil accumulation was discovered in 1498 at Pechelbronn in Alsace and 'earth balsam' was mentioned in Poland in 1506. Marco Polo noted 'oil springs' at Baku on the Caspian Sea towards the end of the thirteenth century.

In the Americas, Raleigh reported on the Trinidad Pitch Lake in 1595 and there are accounts of visits by a Franciscan to 'oil springs' in New York in 1632 and by a Russian traveller to those in Pennsylvania in 1748.

In Burma, oil has long been used and was being produced from hand dug wells in substantial quantities by the end of the eighteenth century.

Nevertheless, until the middle of the nineteenth century, almost all illuminating oil used in the world came from animal or vegetable sources and early machines were lubricated with castor or whale oil. In 1850 James Young of Glasgow introduced a process for the production of lamp oil by the distillation of coal or shale and this was taken up in the USA where by 1855 several factories were making 'coal oil' for use in lamps.

In 1859 Drake drilled the first well to be sunk specifically for oil and struck oil at $69\frac{1}{2}$ ft in Pennsylvania. This is generally taken as the start of the modern petroleum industry although small quantities of oil were being produced in Russia by 1856 and in Romania by 1857. Developments followed in other countries and by 1900 commercial production was averaging just over 400 000 barrels daily, made up as in Table 1.

Table 1 World production of petroleum in 1900

Country	Barrels/day
Russia	206 310
USA	173 830
East Indies	9 090
Poland	6 410
Romania	4 920
India and Burma	2 950
Japan	2 380
Canada	1 940
Germany	980
Peru	830
Italy	30
Total	409 670

In those early days kerosine, as illuminating oil, was the important product and the main object of refining was to extract as much of it as possible from the crude. Lubricants and some fuel oil were also sold, but gasoline was burnt off as unwanted and bitumen was a useless nuisance.

After 1900 expansion was more rapid; Mexico became a producing country in 1901, followed by Argentina in 1907 and Trinidad in 1908. An international trade developed, undertaken by American, British and Dutch companies, and the names of Rockefeller of Standard Oil, Deterding of Royal Dutch and Samuel of Shell became well known.

By 1910 world production had grown to some 900 000 barrels/day of which the USA produced 560 000 and Russia 200 000 barrels/day. The Middle East came into the picture with Iran where oil was found in 1908 and exports began in 1911. Production started in British Borneo in 1911 and in Venezuela in 1914. The internal combustion engine provided a use for gasoline, now becoming a major product, and World War I caused a greatly increased demand for all types of oil, including fuel for shipping.

Through the 1920s and 30s demand continued to grow, especially for gasoline which would have been difficult to supply in the quantities required but for improvements in refining methods and the introduction of cracking. A demand for bitumen developed for the construction of roads to cope with the increasing needs of the motorist. The USA remained far in the lead and was responsible for most of the expansion in production, supplying its own needs and exporting large quantities. Russia remained largely self supporting but the rest of the world became more and more dependent on the international trade in oil in which the Caribbean (mainly Venezuela) was the chief supplier, followed by the USA and the Middle East, where Iraq became a producer in 1927 and Saudi Arabia in 1938, exports beginning in 1934 and 1939 respectively. The chemical side of the industry was born and began to develop, chiefly in the USA, in the 1930s.

Since World War II expansion has been still more striking and world consumption is now three times its 1938 level. Great efforts were necessary after 1945 to supply, refine and transport the increased output, which was facilitated by improved methods of exploration and refining.

Major changes have taken place in the pattern of international trade in recent years. Consumption in the USA has risen even faster than production and since 1948 the USA has been a net importer of oil. Output in the Caribbean has risen with an increased proportion absorbed by North America. Middle East production has increased dramatically and now plays the chief part in supplying Europe and much of the eastern hemisphere. More recently, large discoveries of oil have been made in North and West Africa from where increasing quantities are being supplied to Europe. Russia continues to absorb most of its greatly increased production but is again making exports to numerous countries.

The post-war years have seen the establishment and expansion of the chemical side of the industry in many countries. Crude oil and natural gas are being increasingly used as raw materials for chemical manufacture.

With great activity in exploration and production in the last decade and the building of new refineries, supply has more than caught up with demand and the prospect for some time to come is one of abundant oil in search of a market. Competition, already severe, is likely to become still more so.

However, the world's demand for oil continues to grow and is likely to double in the next fifteen years. With this growth in demand all over the world and with the increasing manufacture of chemicals from petroleum, the industry seems certain to continue to grow and to supply a great part of the world's energy requirements.

Thus in little more than a hundred years the industry has grown from almost nothing to one of the most important in the world, remarkable for its size, complexity and geographical extent.

In 1850 world petroleum production was negligible; in 1900, 900 000 barrels/day; in 1964, 29 million barrels/day. In 1900 the world had 20 000 motor vehicles; in 1964 about 160 million. In 1914, 3% of the world's ships consumed fuel oil; in 1964, 97%; and of course the number of ships has increased enormously, from 24 000 in 1914 to 41 000 in 1964. In 1920 oil and natural gas supplied only 15% of the world's total effectively used energy; in 1964 they provided 54%. In the early days of the industry the number of products was small, virtually only gasoline, kerosine and fuel oil; today in addition to several grades of each of these commodities a very wide and still expanding range of oil products, from petroleum gases to bitumens and waxes, must be produced to satisfy technical progress in many fields. And in addition there is the enormous range of chemicals of many types, from solvents to agricultural chemicals. The finding and handling of the vast quantities and many different types of oil necessary to provide these products makes the industry today a very complex one.

Oil production and manufacture are now carried out in more than sixty countries, and the marketing of products in all parts of the world. The international trade is of great importance, oil is now the largest single commodity carried between countries, and tankers account for a third of all merchant tonnage.

Structure of the industry

The structure of the oil industry is largely the outcome of four fundamental characteristics of its basic commodity. Crude oil is an inflammable liquid; it is not found in a form in which it can be immediately used; it is not found where it is mainly wanted; it is difficult to find at all. There are exceptions to all these statements but in general they are true.

The finding of oil involves great effort and expense and is fraught with a large element of uncertainty. When oil is found it requires complex processing in expensive plants to produce technically useful and marketable products. Outside the USA, oilfields are mostly far from the main consuming countries and many of these have little local production. An international trade has therefore grown up. Finally oil requires specialized transport and storage in all its stages from crude oil to marketed product.

The oil industry therefore falls naturally into divisions responsible for exploration, production, manufacture, transport, marketing, and research each of which will be briefly reviewed in general outline in the present chapter and in more technical detail in the rest of the book.

The need for marketers to secure supplies of products, for refiners to secure both supplies of crudes and markets for refined products, for producers to secure outlets for their crudes and for each to ensure adequate transport and storage facilities, with all the inter-related problems of co-ordination and timing, has led to a considerable degree of integration of these various activities by the more important oil companies. These have become large enough to finance the very costly operations, to accept the necessary risks and, in many cases, to operate on an international scale.

By no means the whole of the industry, however, is thus vertically integrated. There are many smaller independent organizations that may be of considerable local importance; this is especially marked in the USA where in addition to some thirty large vertically integrated companies there are several thousand smaller producers and many independent refining, transport and marketing organizations.

Exploration

Continuous exploration for new sources of oil and to extend knowledge of known oil-bearing formations is essential to ensure future supplies to meet increasing demands. It is a long-term operation; from five to ten or even twenty years may elapse between initial examination and commercial production. This time is spent in surface and sub-surface exploration, wildcat drilling, proving the extent of discovered accumulations, and the building of pipelines and other facilities for the movement of the crude.

Exploration is an extremely costly and uncertain business and costs are rising as remoter areas and under-sea formations come to be investigated. Modern techniques are improving in speed and accuracy but there is still no certain way of predicting oil in a new locality. The petroleum geologist can do no more than indicate the likely existence of a structure that may bear oil; drilling is necessary to prove it.

The number of wells drilled in 1963 in the world outside the Sino-Soviet spheres and in selected countries is shown in Table 2; by far the greatest number was in the USA, about nine out of every ten. The proportion of dry holes varies greatly from area to area. In the USA, where something approaching one and a quarter million wells have been drilled since 1859 and development has been intensive, more than one in every three is dry and of the purely exploratory or wildcat wells, only about one in eight is productive. Table 3 shows the number of wells drilled in the USA from 1920 onwards and the increasing proportion of dry holes, reflecting the fact that the oilfields that could be found and developed relatively easily have long since been drilled up. Elsewhere, in an established Middle East field such as the Burgan field in Kuwait for example, a dry hole would be an exception; in a relatively new area (such as Libya or Australia) a dry hole would be more likely than a producer.

With the long odds against striking oil and the necessity of drilling, exploration is inevitably costly. Moreover, large sums have to be paid for licences to prospect and frequently the remoteness of operations means heavy expenditure on transport and services. Actual drilling costs vary widely between the extremes of a deep exploratory well in a remote area and a development well in a known formation. For example one exploratory well in Pakistan took 334 days to drill 12 007 ft, and cost £1 300 000, while a development well in a known formation may cost only a few thousand pounds. Underwater exploration may be less expensive than land surveys owing to easier movement but drilling and development under water may cost three or four times more than on land. An exploration well in Lake Maracaibo in 1959 took 135 days to drill 13 900 ft, and cost £1 062 000.

The total cost of exploration can therefore be very heavy. In Ecuador, Shell, in partnership with an American company, spent £9 million on a six-year search for oil which was abandoned in 1950 without result. In Colombia another American company spent $21 million between 1916 and first discovery in 1933 and a further $39 million in the next six years before the first oil was marketed in 1939. In the Zubair fields in Iraq £18 million was spent in six years before production began in 1961.

As a result of continual exploration more oil has been discovered world-wide, year after year, than has been taken out of the ground. Table 4 shows the increase in the world's proven oil reserves. 'Proven oil reserves' means the quantity of oil known with reasonable certainty to be present in oilfields already discovered, and to be commercially recoverable by today's techniques.

Table 2 Drilling completions (1963): exploration and development wells

Country	Wells completed Total	Oil	Gas	Distillate	Dry	Average depth ft
World (excluding Sino-Soviet spheres)	51 156	24 403	5377	1 798	19 578	4520
USA	43 126	20 135	4570	1 659	16 762	4312
Canada	3119	1 524	395	75	1 125	4779
Venezuela	503	425	—	5	73	6393
Iran	42	37	—	—	5	9433
Iraq	7	7	—	—	—	1 621
Kuwait	54	35	—	1	18	6296
Saudi Arabia	20	12	1	5	2	6691
Abu Dhabi	24	21	—	—	3	10 032
Algeria	193	111	12	27	43	7306
Libya	349	147	1	—	201	6851
Nigeria	50	35	3	—	12	10 909
Australia	125	5	9	—	111	5169

Table 3 USA drilling completions: exploration and development wells

Year	Wells completed Oil	Gas	Dry	Total	% Dry	Producing oil wells at end of year
1920	24 273	2274	7364	33 911	22	251 000
1930	11 640	2866	6734	21 240	32	331 070
1938	18 598	2066	6141	26 805	23	369 640
1946	15 851	3090	8047	26 988	30	421 460
1950	24 272	2972	14 778	42 022	35	467 776
1955	31 567	3613	20 742	55 922	37	524 010
1960	23 470	5149	18 212	46 831	39	599 977
1963	21 794	4570	16 762	43 126	39	587 777

Table 4 Total world production and proven oil reserves

Year	Crude oil production million barrels	Proven reserves million barrels	Ratio reserves : production
1930	1450	26000	18
1935	1650	24000	14
1940	2145	35000	16
1945	2590	67000	26
1950	3795	80000	21
1955	5625	155000	27
1960	7663	300000	39
1963	9477	327000	35

There are undoubtedly vastly greater ultimately recoverable reserves awaiting discovery outside the proven areas and, since present techniques permit on average the extraction of only 25–30% of oil known to exist in a field, there is fair margin for improvement in methods of extraction and increase in proven reserves.

The distribution of the world's proven reserves at the end of 1963 is shown in Table 5. See also Fig. 11, p. 22.

Table 5 Location of total world's proven oil reserves at end 1963

Area	Proven reserves %
North America	11·8
South America	7·0
USSR and Eastern Europe	10·2
Western Europe	0·5
Middle East	62·7
Far East	3·2
Africa	4·6
Total world	100·0

Production

Nearly 90% of the current world crude oil and natural gasoline production comes from four areas – North America (mainly USA), the Middle East, the Caribbean and the USSR; there are also important production areas in North and West Africa and in the Far East. In all there is now production in more than fifty countries. Table 6 shows the growth of crude oil and natural gasoline production from 1920 and how the proportions provided by the various areas have fluctuated over the years.

The USA has always been the predominant producing country (except for the years 1898–1901 when Russia took the lead) and in 1964 still provided 30% of world production. During the 1920s the USA contributed more than 70% of world production but the proportion has declined steadily in recent years.

The outstanding feature of post-war production has been the rise of the Middle East. Kuwait only became a producer in 1946 but by 1953 had risen to fourth in the world, overtaking Saudi Arabia, where production had started in 1938. Newer areas outside the major producing countries of Iraq, Iran, Saudi Arabia and Kuwait are rapidly developing their crude oil resources, and Abu Dhabi has reached a level of nearly 200 000 barrels/day in two and half years.

The bulk of the African production comes from Libya and the Algerian Sahara. These countries are now seventh and eighth major producers although commercial production did not start until 1958 and 1961 respectively.

Natural gas has long been an important source of energy in the USA, and more recently in the USSR and Canada. Elsewhere developments have been limited to gasfields situated close to areas of high consumption but recent discoveries of vast deposits of natural gas in Europe and the Sahara are completely changing the picture in Europe, and deposits in other parts of the world are likely to be exploited in the near future.

Manufacture

Manufacture covers all the operations necessary to convert crude oil and natural gas into marketable oil products and chemicals. The first stage is the refining of crude oil in refineries, to produce a number of basic refined oil products. Some of these can be marketed with little or no further treatment, others, particularly lubricating oils, undergo further blending with other ingredients to sometimes quite complex formulations to produce a great variety of marketable products. From various refinery products, particularly the byproducts of cracking operations, and from natural gas, chemicals are manufactured in chemical plants quite distinct from the refineries.

Table 6 World crude oil and natural gasoline production

Year	North America (including Mexico)	Caribbean	Middle East	Africa	Far East	Sino-Soviet spheres	Rest of world	Total production
	Percentage output							'000 b/d
1890	61·8	—	—	—	0·5	37·7	—	210
1900	42·9	—	—	—	3·4	53·2	0·5	410
1910	65·2	—	—	—	5·9	28·1	0·8	900
1920	87·1	0·4	1·9	—	4·0	5·8	0·8	1910
1930	65·8	11·1	3·2	—	3·7	14·5	1·7	4130
1940	66·2	10·6	4·7	—	3·6	12·7	2·2	6030
1950	56·7	15·1	16·5	—	2·2	7·7	1·8	10910
1960	40·1	14·2	24·1	1·3	2·5	15·0	2·8	21870
1964	33·6	13·2	25·7	5·6	2·1	16·8	3·0	29200

Oil products

Refinery capacity is therefore a basic need of the industry. The total world crude oil refining capacity is shown in Table 7 from 1938 onwards. To meet the growth in demand, capacity by 1950 was nearly twice that in 1938 and by 1964 capacity was nearly three times that in 1950.

There have been important changes in the location of refineries. Before World War II the usual practice was to site refineries in or near crude-producing areas and to ship the refined products to the consuming areas. The post-war trend has been to build refineries in the consuming areas to suit local markets and to ship crude to them from the producing areas, and much of the post-war expansion has been on these lines. This change has been brought about by a combination of economic, technical and political factors. In the economic sphere the growth in demand in consuming areas has made it possible to build large refineries which can operate more economically than smaller units, and the relative cost of transporting crudes and refined products has changed in favour of the former. On the technical side, with new processes and plant, refineries can now be constructed substantially to tailor their products to the local needs. On the political side governments have encouraged home refining for a variety of reasons; security, to save foreign currency (crude being less expensive than finished products), and sometimes to exploit locally produced crude oil that had not previously been developed.

This changed pattern of location of refineries is demonstrated in Table 7. The USA still holds the dominant position with over 30% of the world's refining capacity but this is a marked reduction from their 56% in 1950. Correspondingly there has been a large increase in refining capacity in Western Europe (rising from 8% in 1950 to 23% in 1964) where there are major refining industries in France, Italy, the Netherlands, the UK and Western Germany and where virtually every country has now at least one refinery. This has been matched by growth in the Far East, largely as a result of expansion in Japan and Australia. In the Far East and Africa particularly, the development of refineries in the smaller consuming areas has been accompanied by an increase of refineries jointly owned by a number of companies whose individual sales are not large enough to justify economically any one of them building a plant for their own use.

In the larger consuming areas of Europe the second phase of refinery development has begun with the erection of facilities inland (in France, Switzerland and Western Germany) close to areas of consumption and fed by large diameter pipelines from the North Sea (Rotterdam and Wilhemshaven) or the Mediterranean (Marseilles and Genoa).

The increase in refining capacity has been accompanied by an increase in the use of cracking, reforming and desulphurization processes whereby refiners can more readily tailor their end products to the local needs – and to changes in demand.

Refinery construction is very expensive and is affected by size, type and location. A refinery of 15 000 barrels/day capacity may cost half as much again per barrel of capacity as a refinery of 40 000 barrels/day alike in all respects except size. The quality and number of products required determine the number and size of the various processing plants and hence the cost. Refineries may vary in type from those designed for minimum cost and few products to those with a high degree of flexibility in crude and finished product. Cracking and reforming plants, necessary for the latter type of refinery, are especially expensive; one catalytic cracker can cost £10 million. Location affects cost because of differences in harbour, power, water, housing, local labour and building facilities not only from country to country but also within an individual country.

No general figure can be given, but some examples are of interest. The complex and flexible refinery at Bombay, opened in 1955 with a throughput of 2 million tons/annum, cost £23 million, i.e. £11/ton; a simple refinery may cost less than £5/ton. In 1951–5 total capital expenditure on refineries in the world (excluding the Sino-Soviet spheres) has been estimated at over £1900 million, of which £1000 million was spent in the USA. No figures are available for Western Europe but OEEC estimates for capital expenditure on refinery construction in that area between 1945–54 were over £700 million.

Chemicals

The manufacture of chemicals from petroleum is a rapidly growing and integral part of the chemical industry. Its history dates back to the 1920s, or perhaps a little earlier, but its really dramatic growth has taken place since World War II. Today, it is firmly established in North America, Western Europe, Japan and elsewhere, and there still appears to be tremendous scope for future expansion.

The early developments took place largely within the

Table 7 Total world crude oil refining capacity

	Refining capacity: thousands barrels/day				
Area	1938	1950	1955	1960	1964
USA	4510	6960	8630	10010	10750
Caribbean	580	1230	1450	2080	2640
Rest of western hemisphere	400	750	1450	2060	2440
Middle East	320	1070	1080	1390	1730
Western Europe	320	1030	2550	4330	7800
Sino-Soviet spheres	930	970	1600	3260	4920
Africa	20	70	120	190	610
Rest of eastern hemisphere	280	320	790	1430	2780
Total	7360	12400	17670	24750	33670

USA where, in the 1920s, the petroleum industry met the great increase in demand for gasoline by developing new cracking processes, which also produced large quantities of gases. Traditionally refinery gases had been flared off, but as the quantities grew the oil companies and some chemical manufacturers developed processes for converting certain of them to useful chemicals.

The principal development in the early 1930s was the production of chemical solvents for use in paints and lacquers. At the same time the manufacture of ammonia and hence nitrogenous fertilizers was begun, using the cheap and abundant natural gas available from many oilfields in the USA.

World War II gave the manufacture of chemicals from petroleum a new impetus but progress was still confined almost entirely to the USA. Apart from the additional demand for chemicals for military purposes, it was necessary to replace a number of essential materials whose supply had been reduced or cut off. This led to the large scale manufacture of synthetic rubber, alcohol and detergents from petroleum raw materials.

Since the war there has been an enormous increase not only in the total quantity but also in the variety of chemicals produced from petroleum. Not surprisingly, petroleum has made its main contribution to the organic chemicals sector, although the petroleum-derived world production of three inorganic chemicals, ammonia, sulphur and carbon black, now amounts to several million tons per year.

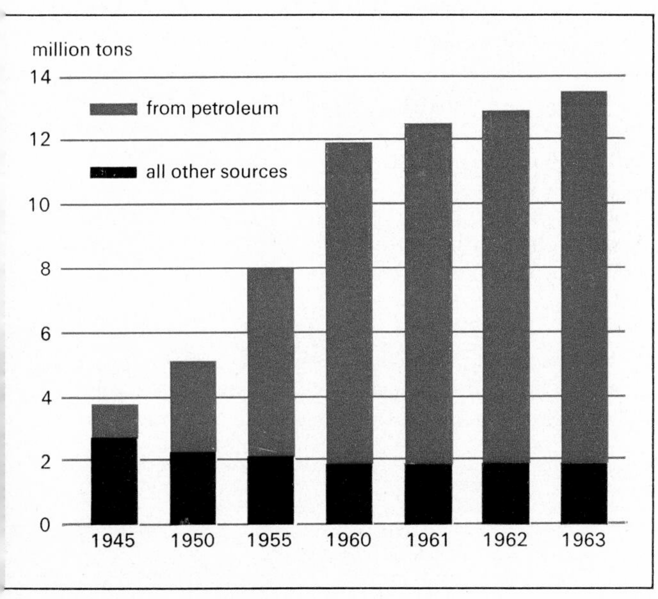

Fig. 1 USA production of organic chemicals

Fig. 1 shows that in the USA the production of organic chemicals from petroleum grew from about 1 million tons in 1945 to about 11·5 million tons in 1963, over 85% of the total US organic chemical output from all sources in that year. Thus, the growth of the US organic chemicals production in this period has been based almost entirely on petroleum.

Outside the USA, Western Europe is the main producing area. Although output of petroleum based organics did not reach the 100 000 tons/year mark in Western Europe until 1950, subsequent progress has been remarkable, as shown

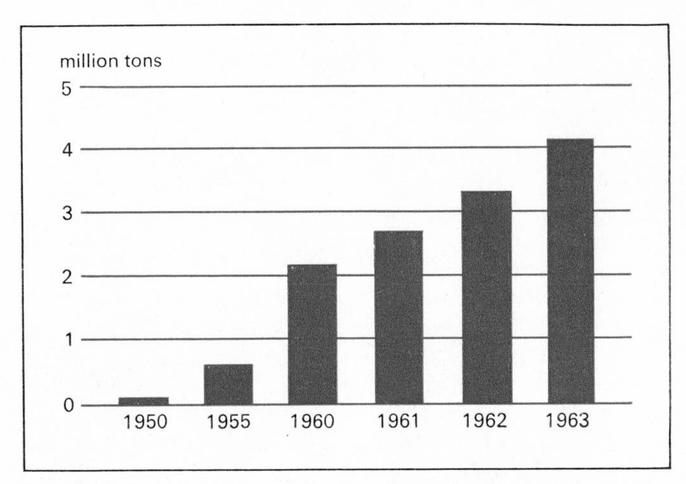

Fig. 2 Western European production of organic chemicals from petroleum

in Fig. 2, and the production of over 4 million tons in 1963 accounted for approximately 50% of all organics manufactured in the area. The manufacture of chemicals from petroleum in Japan and Canada is on a large and growing scale, and manufacture has been started in a number of other countries.

Although, in some instances, petroleum has replaced the older-established raw materials (e.g. coal, vegetable products) for organic chemical manufacture, in general it is truer to say that it has supplemented them. The tendency has been for petroleum to satisfy the new raw material needs of the rapidly developing branches of the organic chemical industry, notably synthetic resins, rubbers and fibres.

The ever-growing demand for organic chemicals is mainly due to their ever-widening use in the more advanced kinds of consumer goods, such as cars, refrigerators, etc.

The production of chemicals from petroleum began later in Western Europe than in the USA, mainly because European mass consumer markets for their end-products developed only during the post-war years. This coincided with the installation of large refinery capacity in Western Europe but the chemical industry's requirements for petroleum raw materials have grown so fast that they have to be met mainly through the special cracking of liquid petroleum fractions. This contrasts with the situation in the USA, where special cracking of liquid fractions is a comparatively recent development, the main sources of raw material being the much more abundant and suitable refinery gases, as well as natural gas, which has been available for much longer than in Western Europe.

Although the manufacture of chemicals from petroleum has the advantage of a relatively low and stable cost of raw materials, complex and expensive plants are often required. Thus in the initial stages of the development of a product there is usually a heavy burden of operating costs which acts as a strong incentive to achieve the economies of larger-scale manufacture – hence the need for large markets previously mentioned. This factor, combined with the growing importance of the outlets in the more advanced consumer goods, explains the concentration of the industry so far in the industrially advanced countries.

A very considerable amount of capital has been invested in this petroleum-based sector of the chemical industry. For example, up to the end of 1963 over £900 million had been invested in organic petroleum-based chemical plants in the UK and the European Economic Community countries. The heavy investment involved in establishing manufacturing capacity on a worthwhile scale, means that petroleum chemical production is very much the preserve of large concerns – primarily major chemical companies and oil companies. On an investment basis oil companies and their subsidiaries account for only about one-third of petroleum chemical capacity in the world outside North America and the Sino-Soviet spheres. Thus the manufacture of chemicals from petroleum is by no means the private preserve of the oil companies.

It seems certain that world demand for organic chemicals will continue to grow rapidly for many years, and that by far the greater part of this new demand will have to be satisfied by petroleum raw materials. In the areas outside North America and the Sino-Soviet spheres for example, it is estimated that total output of petroleum-based organic chemicals will rather more than double during the next five years. This should create few major raw material problems, since at present chemicals manufacture accounts for little more than 2 % of world consumption of crude oil and natural gas.

Transport

Many main producing areas of crude oil and natural gas are remote from the main consuming areas of the world. The efficient movement of oil over great distances is therefore an integral part of the oil business. Oil and oil products are transported in bulk mainly by tankers and pipelines.

Tankers

Water transport is normally much cheaper than other means, and tankers are used whenever possible. The growth of world tanker tonnage since World War II has been enormous, corresponding with the increased demand for oil, and is expected to continue steadily in the future. Fig. 3 shows the growth not only in tonnage but also in size, an important development in recent years permitting considerable economies in freighting costs.

As stated earlier, oil is much the largest single commodity in international seaborne trade. In 1964, the total was approximately 800 million tons, and iron ore came second and well below with 160 million tons. It is estimated that on any day an average of more than 30 million tons of oil cargoes are at sea valued at well over £200 million.

The pattern of this seaborne trade has changed in two ways since pre-war days. Firstly, the change from refining near source to refining near point of consumption has resulted in a preponderance of crude over refined products in the cargoes. Secondly, the development of production in the Middle East and the changed role of the USA from a net exporter to a net importer has entirely changed the quantity and direction of oil movement as shown in Figs 4 and 5. The pre-war flow of exports (mainly products) to Europe from the USA and the Caribbean has been largely, though not entirely replaced by an enormous increase in the flow of exports (mainly crude oil) from the Middle East to Europe.

Pipelines

Pipelines provide the only form of long distance continuous transport for oil and gas. Their main uses are to gather crude oil from producing points and transport it to shipping or refining centres, and to carry refined products and natural gas to consumers.

The economics of pipelines are such that unit costs fall as throughputs and capacities increase. At present the practicable limit for pipe diameters is 42 in., corresponding to a throughput of 40–50 million tons/year, but the future may bring still larger sizes.

Extensive networks of pipelines have existed for many years in North America and the Middle East, whilst in recent years their development in Europe and other areas has been rapid and is expected to continue. For certain landlocked oilfields (Canada, the Middle East, North Africa) pipelines furnish the only access to the sea; similarly large inland refineries are unthinkable without pipelines from the coast.

Other means

Apart from this international bulk transport of crude and refined products on a large scale, the delivery of oil products to the consumer entails the smaller scale use of bulk transport by road, rail and water within the consuming area, for which special facilities and equipment have to be provided. Here too there has been an enormous increase in the amount of material transported and great developments in equipment.

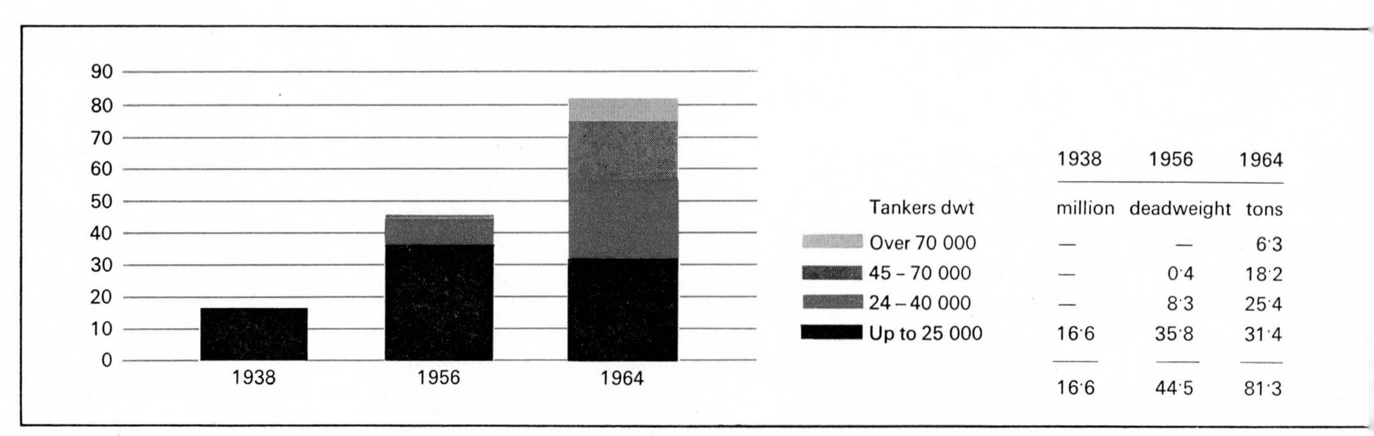

Fig. 3 Growth of world tanker tonnage

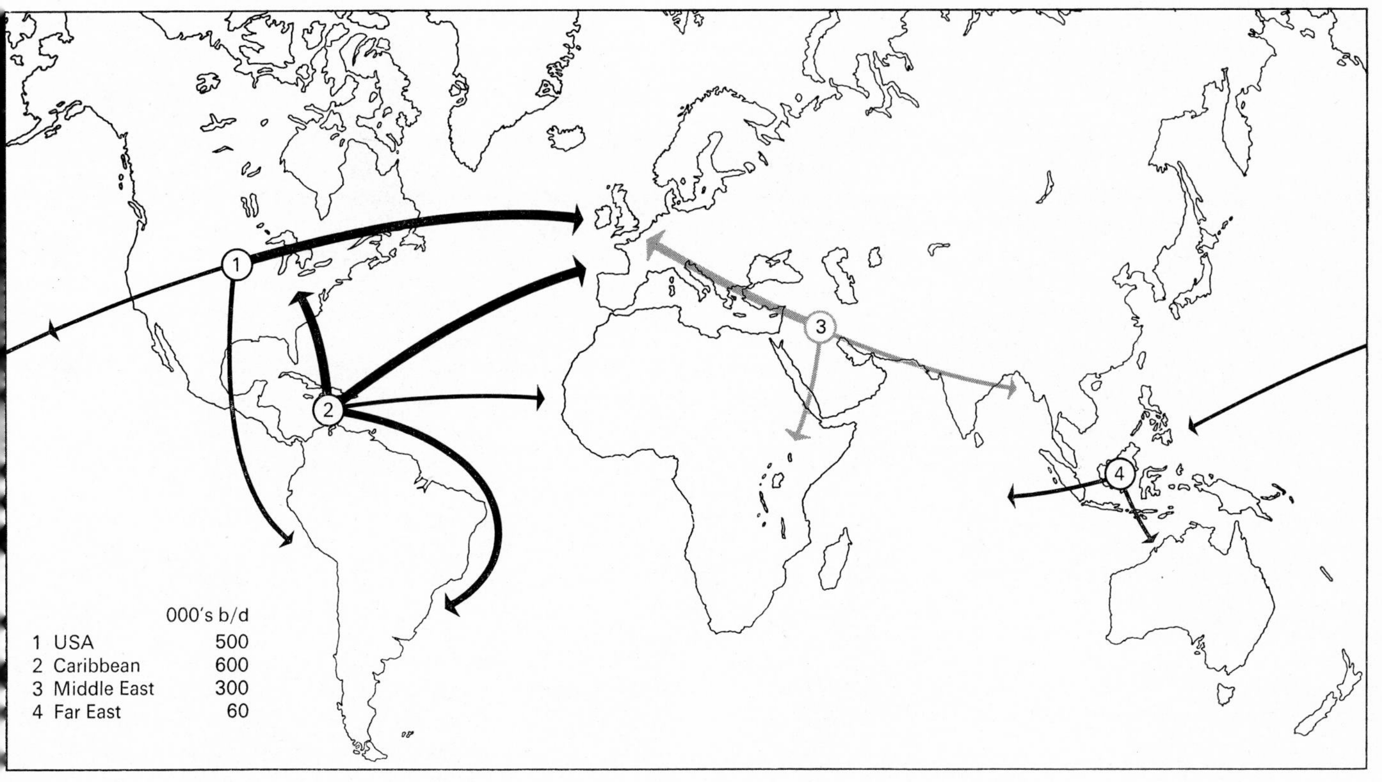

Fig. 4 International movements from major oil producing centres, 1938

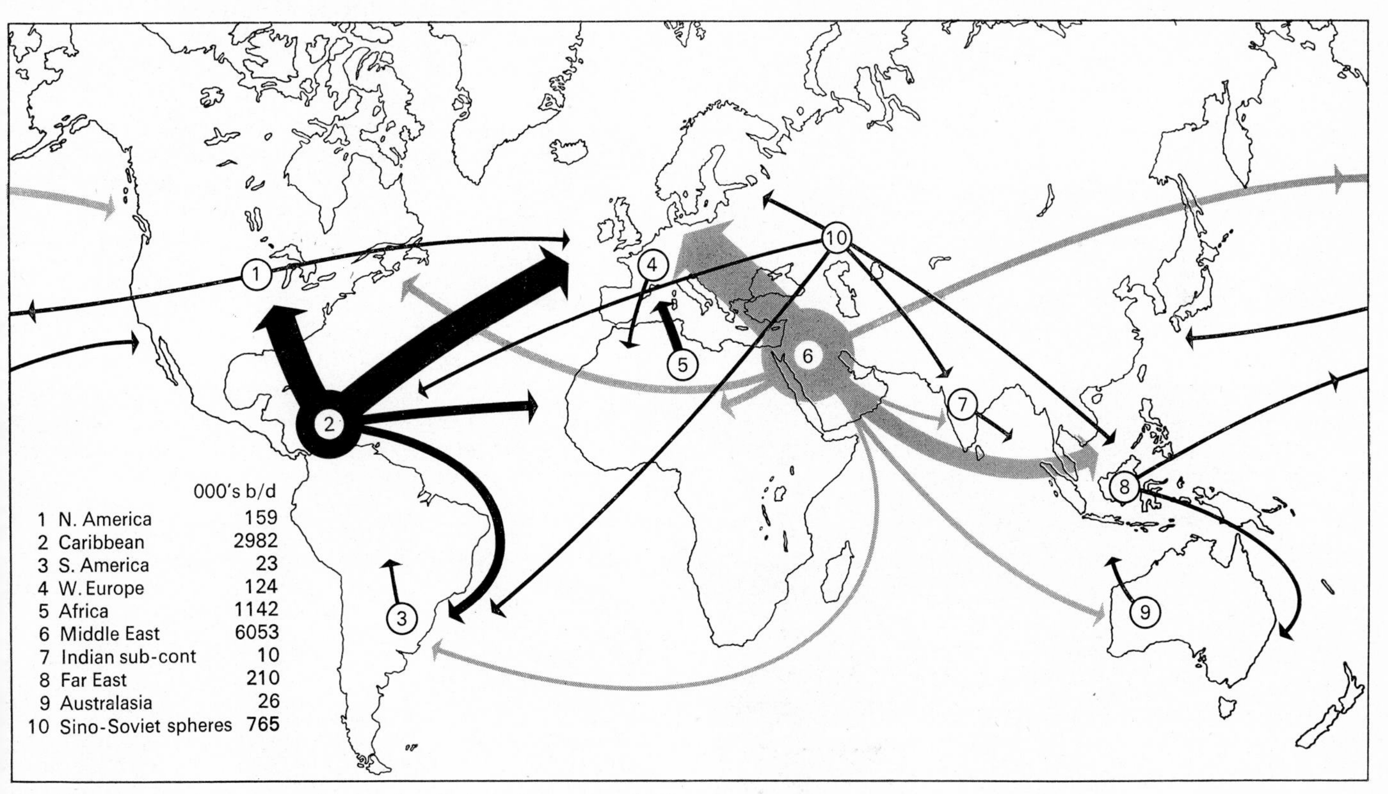

Fig. 5 International movements from major oil producing centres, 1963

Marketing

Marketing – the selling and delivery of oil products and chemicals to the customer – is the ultimate link in the long chain of oil operations which starts with exploration. Moreover, it earns the revenue that finances all other phases of the business and provides a surplus for further investment.

Marketing in the petroleum industry is not merely selling what is produced; it is more concerned with satisfying the customers' needs. It thus has a dual responsibility; to the customer in finding out and satisfying his needs, to the industry in informing the manufacturing side of what the customer requires or is likely to require and of ensuring long-term and profitable outlets for its products.

The consumer needs in the petroleum industry are dictated more by technical needs than by the whims of fashion and, as might be expected, demand follows general industrial and technological development in quantity, quality and type of product. Whereas in the early days of the industry a very few products sufficed to meet demands, an enormous range of products is required today. Moreover the quality of today's products has to be far superior to the quality of corresponding products that sufficed in pre-war days.

Demand for petroleum products

The world demand for petroleum products is given in Fig. 6, which shows that growth in demand since World War II has been strongest in the eastern hemisphere, notably in Western Europe and Japan.

The total number of products in demand has been put as high as 1000; it is obviously impossible to describe all these and their end uses but they may be divided into a smaller number of types which will be described in later chapters. The amounts of major products expressed as percentages of the total sales in the world outside the Sino-Soviet spheres are shown in Table 8.

Table 8 World product sales (excluding Sino-Soviet spheres)

Product	Proportion of total sales %w 1938	1950	1964
Gasolines	46	39	33
Kerosines	6	6	6
Gas oil/diesel fuel	13	18	22
Fuel oils	28	29	27
Other products	7	8	12
	100	100	100

In the years since 1938 gasoline has remained the chief product in demand though the relative demand for it has declined even in the USA. Fuel oil is next in importance and in Western Europe has become the leading product. A general increase in the demand for gas oil and diesel fuel is apparent, due to their increased use in industry, central heating, road and rail transport. The demand for kerosine has been maintained partly because of its continued widespread use in less developed countries, partly because of its increased use in aviation fuels and domestic heating. There has been a strong growth in the demand for black oils (gas oil, diesel and fuel oils), notably on the inland market, compared with the slower development of the ocean bunkers. The category 'other products' includes, *inter alia*, lubricants, bitumen, liquefied petroleum gas and naphtha-type feedstocks for the manufacture of chemicals and town gas. In contrast to the relatively slow rate of growth for lubricants and bitumen, there has been a phenomenal expansion in the demand for LPG and feedstocks.

The growth in the demand for energy tends to go hand-in-hand with general industrial and technological development and since a large proportion of oil products is supplied for the production of energy, the demand for petroleum is linked to the growth of world energy requirements and its ability to compete with other sources of energy – solid fuels, hydro-electricity, natural gas and nuclear power. Fig. 7 shows the growth and the changing pattern of total energy supplies since 1938.

Although still the major source of energy, coal's contribution has fallen relatively within a total which has increased by nearly 200% since 1938. Most of the increase has been provided by petroleum fuels and natural gas; this pattern of development is expected to continue. The volume of coal supplies is unlikely to be expanded at a rate demanded by growing energy needs and coal's relative importance must be expected to decline further. It is unlikely that hydro-electricity development as a whole will be a major factor in the expanding energy picture, and although nuclear power is almost certain to make a significant contribution, it is not expected to become a main source in the immediate future. It seems therefore that petroleum fuels and natural gas are certain to provide the bulk of the additional supplies for some considerable time.

Research

The oil industry has changed in the last fifty years from a rather crude art to a great scientific industry, one of several in the modern world. The pace of change, expansion and development and the need to anticipate future technical requirements have made it necessary for the major oil com-

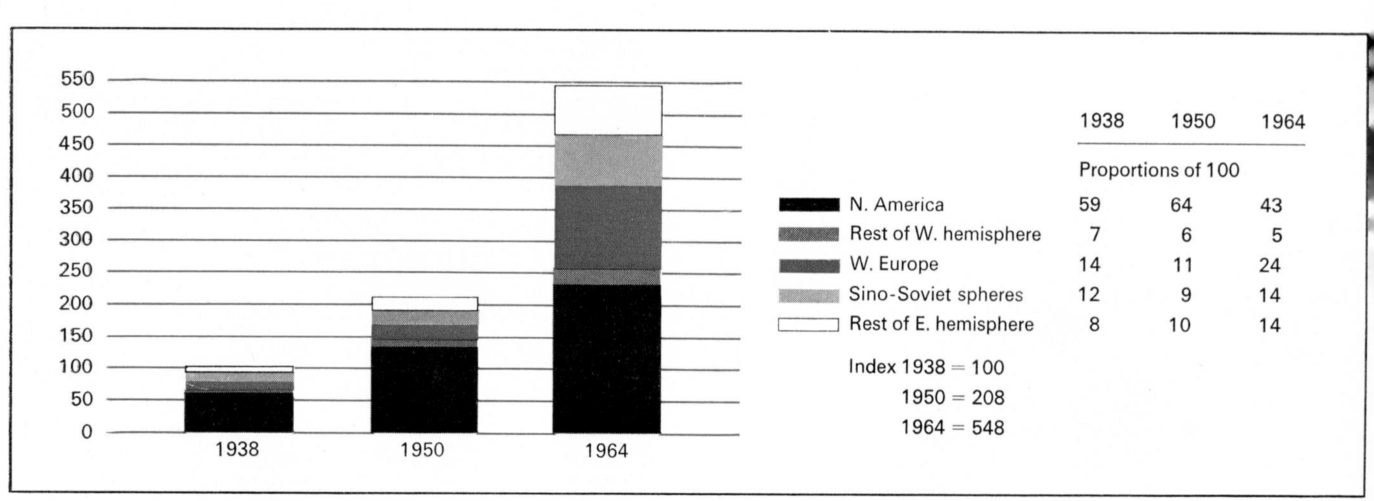

Fig. 6 World demand for petroleum products

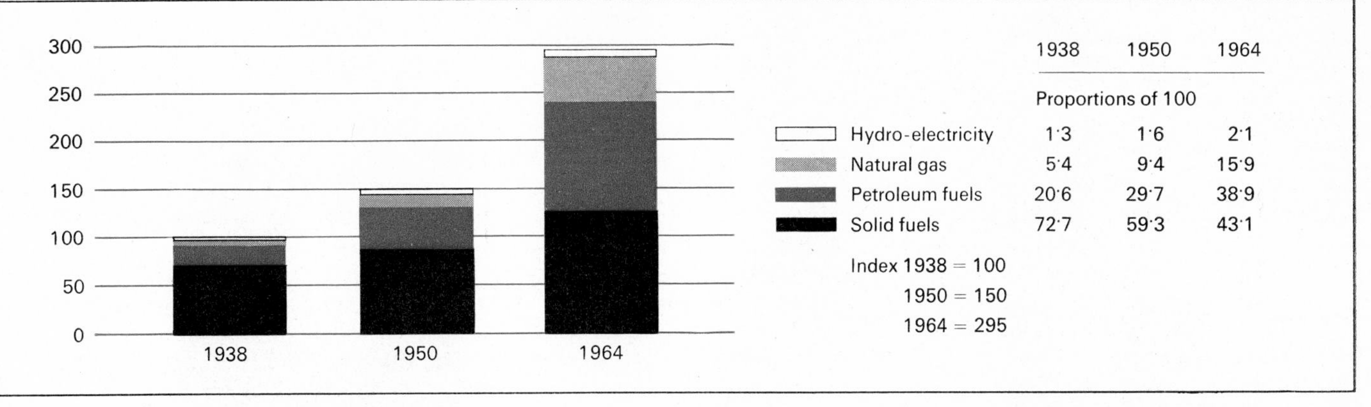

Fig. 7 Growth of total energy supplies

panies to devote much effort and money to research in many forms. Research is an important aspect of all the functions already mentioned, from exploration to marketing, which latter is associated very closely with technical applications.

Research is costly and research expenditure by the world petroleum industry outside the Sino-Soviet spheres has more than tripled during the last decade from an estimated £38 million in 1953 to approximately £125 million in 1963.

During recent years, major oil companies have spent, on average, about equal proportions, i.e. 25%, of their research funds on exploration and production, oil manufacturing methods, oil product development and chemicals. The research expenditure of the industry as a whole is of the order of 0·6% of its total expenditure, a figure in line with the average for other industries indulging in research.

Financial requirements

The international nature of the petroleum industry gives rise to many financial problems. Each of the many countries in which the industry operates has its own laws, institutions, tax systems, commercial codes and customs, all of which must be respected. With production in one country, manufacture in another and marketing in many, complex problems of banking, insurance, currency exchange and accounting are involved. These are matters of day-to-day routine beyond which is the problem of finding the funds to meet the heavy capital expenditure involved in the various operations of the industry.

In the post-war decade, the capital expenditure of the world petroleum industry was, on average, £2000 million a year, and over the fifteen years 1950–64 the total capital expenditure by the industry outside the Sino-Soviet spheres was about £55 000 million. During that period, world oil consumption increased 2½ times, and it is estimated that it will again double in the next fifteen years from 1965–80. Still greater capital expenditure will be required to meet this demand, probably exceeding £90 000 million. The annual capital expenditure is therefore likely to increase from something over £4000 million in 1964 to about £8000 million in 1980.

Fig. 8 shows how the capital expenditure of £4322 million in 1962 was divided among the various functions of the industry. The pattern differs considerably between the USA and the rest of the world outside the Sino-Soviet spheres, reflecting the different structural and fiscal circumstances in which the industry operates.

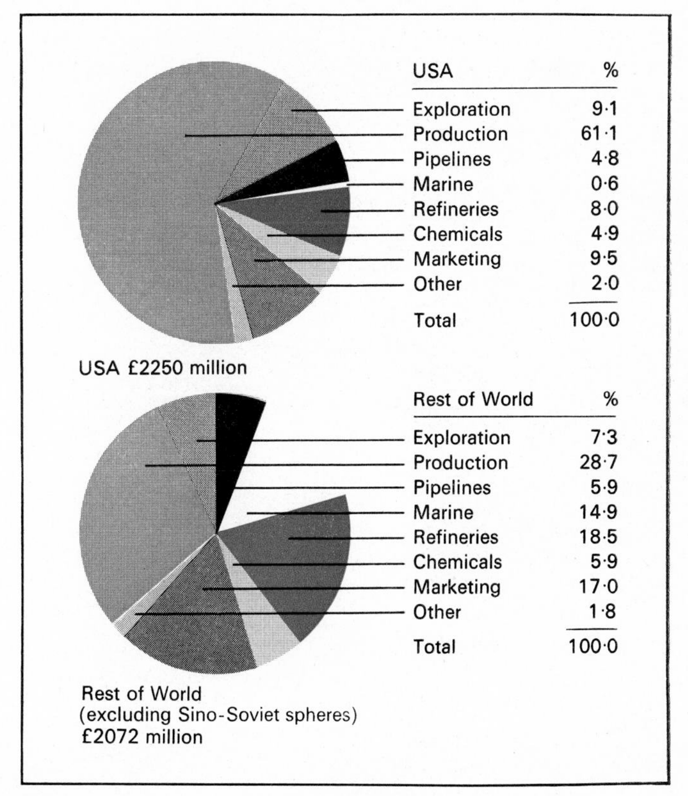

USA %
Exploration 9·1
Production 61·1
Pipelines 4·8
Marine 0·6
Refineries 8·0
Chemicals 4·9
Marketing 9·5
Other 2·0
Total 100·0
USA £2250 million
Rest of World %
Exploration 7·3
Production 28·7
Pipelines 5·9
Marine 14·9
Refineries 18·5
Chemicals 5·9
Marketing 17·0
Other 1·8
Total 100·0
Rest of World
(excluding Sino-Soviet spheres)
£2072 million

Fig. 8 Capital expenditure of the petroleum industry, 1962

In the USA the productivity of wells is low compared with that in the rest of the world, but crude oil is found close to the markets. Moreover, certain fiscal regulations strongly encourage exploration and production within the USA. Consequently, investment in exploration and production is high, that in transport low.

In the rest of the world, outside the Sino-Soviet spheres, crude oil tends to be located much further from the markets, but productivity of wells is greater. Investment in transport is therefore a much larger proportion of the total than in the USA.

Although investment in the chemical side of the industry has increased notably in recent years, it is still only a little over 5% of the industry's total capital expenditure.

Traditionally, the industry has generated most of its capital requirements from internal sources, and it may be expected to continue to do so in order to ensure the economic availability of funds at the time they are required. Despite the huge reserves of crude oil and natural gas now available throughout the world, it is expected that the continued demand for oil will necessitate the maintenance of a high level of capital investment.

Personnel requirements

An industry as large and varied in its operations as the international oil industry requires a correspondingly large and varied work force. Each year many thousands of qualified men and women, of many skills and of many nationalities, enter its ranks. It seldom happens, however, even in the more technically advanced areas, that the supply is as great as the demand, and in consequence the industry is continually looking to the size and quality – scientific, technical and human – of its reserves of trained men and women, in much the same way as it constantly looks to the size and quality of its reserves of crude oil.

Oil is an industry rooted in science and technology, with world-wide ramifications and vast marketing and distribution organizations, and with attendant financial problems. Geologists, physicists, chemists, metallurgists, engineers and specialized research workers in many fields are increasingly needed, as well as the commercial and financial brains; their recruitment in adequate numbers, and their development, present special problems to the industry. From their ranks come the co-ordinators, the forecasters, and formulators of policy. Without all of these an oil company would be unable to develop and apply the most modern techniques in exploration, production, transportation, refining, chemical manufacturing, research and marketing, which are essential if it is to retain its competitive position in the industry. Highly qualified men and women are scarce, however, and the oil industry must therefore play its own part in ensuring that adequate numbers of trained staff will be available for it.

By means of training schemes for its own personnel the industry can supply some of the skills it requires, but it may also be necessary to take wider action in the educational field. In production areas, such as the Middle East, it may be necessary to set up and staff schools to teach general and special subjects at various levels, in addition to providing instruction in oil technology. In other areas existing facilities may be supplemented by contributions to funds for increasing the numbers of science students at universities, by the institution of scholarships and apprenticeships, or by the support of advanced training and research.

Last, but by no means least, a very considerable supporting staff, on the technical as well as on the commercial and operations sides, is required. The need for sales forces, for accounting staff and for secretaries, typists and other clerical assistance is obvious. A less obvious but equally vital task which requires a large skilled staff is that of purchasing materials and ensuring their availability to the desired specifications at the right time. Within the industry a very diverse range of materials and equipment, which may at any one time include over 50 000 stock items, whose value is measured in millions of pounds, is continually being ordered and dispatched all over the world.

Without this staff the planned expansion of the oil industry would become an impossibility. Recruitment and training at all levels are therefore a constant preoccupation.

Oil companies

As already stated, the oil industry comprises a great number of companies differing enormously in size and scope of operations, ranging from a relatively few large companies, many operating internationally, to a large number of small concerns operating in one country in only one function. The inter-dependence of the various operations from exploration to marketing is such that many oil companies are active in all phases. These 'integrated' companies are an outstanding feature of the industry, but all companies, integrated or not, operate under highly competitive conditions. One major work of reference the *Oil and Petroleum Year Book* (Skinner's) lists more than 1100 oil companies of which the eight major international ones are as follows.

British Petroleum Company Limited (BP)

Originally the Anglo Persian, later the Anglo Iranian Oil Co; the British Government holds a majority interest (approximately 51%) in BP, although it does not directly participate in the management of the company. BP's operations in the western hemisphere are relatively small and its activities are based principally upon production in the Middle East (the company's main interests are a 50% holding in the Kuwait Oil Co, 40% in the Iranian Consortium, 23·75% in the IPC group of Companies and 66·7% in the Abu Dhabi Marine Areas) and its jointly owned operations with the Royal Dutch/Shell Group in Nigeria. BP markets in Europe, Africa, Australasia and Canada, with lesser interests in the Caribbean and South-East Asia; in the British Isles and South and East Africa, BP markets jointly with the Royal Dutch/Shell Group. BP is also a major seller of crude oil world-wide.

Compagnie Française des Pétroles (CFP/Total)

Formed originally to hold the French Government's interest in the Iraq Petroleum Company, IPC (the French Government has a 35% stock interest with 40% voting rights), CFP's major production area is still Iraq. The company has a 23·75% interest in all IPC group companies together with production in Iran (a 6% share in the Iranian Consortium), Abu Dhabi and Algeria. CFP markets products mainly in Europe, many African countries and in Australia under the 'Total' brand. Apart from minor production interests in Canada, CFP does not operate in the western hemisphere.

Gulf Oil Corporation

A major fully integrated company in both the USA and Canada, Gulf's main interests outside North America are in production. Its chief source is a 50% share in the Kuwait Oil Company but Gulf also has substantial production from Iran (a 7% share in the Iranian Consortium) and from Venezuela through Mene Grande. The company has small, but rapidly developing, marketing interests in the eastern hemisphere and is a major seller of crude oil throughout the world.

The Royal Dutch/Shell Group of Companies

The organization and activities of the Royal Dutch/Shell Group of companies are described in detail in the next chapter. The 'Group' is a fully integrated organization with widespread production and marketing interests. The principal producing area is Venezuela, but the Group also has production interests elsewhere in the western hemisphere, in the Middle East (23·75% share in the IPC group of companies and 14% in the Iranian Consortium), in Europe, in Algeria and Nigeria, and in the Far East. Group companies market in most countries throughout the world, in certain areas jointly with BP.

Socony Mobil Oil Company Inc

The company's sales are divided almost equally between the US, where it is a major fully integrated operator, and the rest of the world. Mobil has production in Venezuela and Colombia, Algeria and Libya, Europe and Indonesia and a small interest in the production areas of Iraq, Qatar, Abu Dhabi, Iran, and Saudi Arabia. Mobil markets in the western hemisphere, Europe, the Middle East, Africa and the Far East. Until 1962, operations in the east of Suez areas, except for the Middle East, were carried out in conjunction with Esso through the Standard Vacuum Oil Company.

Standard Oil Company of California

A major integrated company in the US and Canada, its principal source of production outside North America is in Saudi Arabia (a 30% interest is held in Aramco), with lesser interests in Iran and Venezuela. Standard California has minor marketing interests in Central and South America, but its main refining and marketing operations are through Caltex, jointly owned with Texaco. Caltex is an integrated company, with production interests in Indonesia, Bahrain and Libya, which markets throughout the eastern hemisphere, with the principal exception of West Africa.

Standard Oil Company, New Jersey (Esso)

The principal descendant of the Standard Oil interests, Esso is now the largest oil company in the world. It has fully integrated operations in the US and Canada, where it is the market leader, and is second only to the Royal Dutch/Shell Group in terms of sales outside North America. Esso has major production interests in Venezuela, Saudi Arabia (a 30% interest is held in Aramco) and Libya, with lesser, but still important holdings elsewhere in the Middle East (7% in the Iranian Consortium and 12% in the IPC group of companies), the western hemisphere, Europe and Indonesia. Esso markets world-wide, although is less well represented in the east of Suez area where, until 1962, refining and marketing operations were carried out jointly with Mobil through the Standard Vacuum Oil Company.

Texaco Inc

A fully integrated company in the US and Canada, Texaco has major production interests outside North America in the Middle East (a 30% holding in Aramco, 7% in the Iranian Consortium) and in the western hemisphere – Venezuela, Colombia and Trinidad. Texaco markets throughout the western hemisphere and West Africa, and jointly with Caltex in the UK. In the rest of the world, Texaco interests are carried out through the jointly owned Caltex organization whose activities are described under Standard Oil Company of California.

The Royal Dutch/Shell Group of Companies

The Royal Dutch/Shell Group of Companies is the name which, in the course of time, has been given to a complex of some five hundred companies whose shares are owned, directly or indirectly, wholly or in part, by N.V. Koninklijke Nederlandsche Petroleum Maatschappij (Royal Dutch) and The "Shell" Transport and Trading Company, Limited (Shell Transport).

These two companies are known as the parent companies of the Group; they are public companies with a widely distributed shareholding whose shares are bought and sold on the principal stock exchanges of the world. They hold the entire interest, 60% by Royal Dutch, 40% by Shell Transport, in Bataafse Petroleum Maatschappij N.V. (BPM) and The Shell Petroleum Company Limited (Shell Petroleum), which are holding companies holding the shares, wholly or in part, of the several hundred operating companies of the Group. These companies operate in all parts of the world outside the Sino-Soviet spheres, each carrying on one or more of the activities of the oil, natural gas and chemical sectors of the industry.

Origins

The parent companies began as rival organizations, one British, the other Dutch, towards the end of the last century. The Royal Dutch Petroleum Company was formed in 1890 in The Hague with the title Koninklijke Nederlandsche Maatschappij tot Exploitatie van Petroleumbronnen in Nederlandsch-Indië, N.V. (Royal Dutch Company for the Working of Petroleum Wells in the Netherlands Indies), with an initial capital of fl. 1 300 000, to operate an oil concession in north-eastern Sumatra obtained from the Sultan of Langkat. The title was later simplified to its present form, N.V. Koninklijke Nederlandsche Petroleum Maatschappij.

Under the management of J. B. Aug. Kessler (senior) the company's operations expanded considerably. When he died in 1900 its capital was fl. 5 000 000 in ordinary shares and fl. 1 500 000 in preference shares, and the company had weathered a stormy period of declining production and increasing foreign competition. H.W.A. (afterwards Sir Henri) Deterding, the succeeding manager, pursued a policy of seeking co-operation with other petroleum companies in the Netherlands East Indies (now Indonesia), and among the companies that responded was one whose share capital was held entirely by The "Shell" Transport and Trading Company, Limited. Thus were sown the seeds that, in 1907, resulted in the full association of the Royal Dutch with Shell Transport.

The "Shell" Transport and Trading Company, Limited was formed in 1897, with an initial capital of £1 800 000, to take over the oil interests of M. Samuel & Company, including a producing field in Dutch East Borneo, acquired in the previous year. These oil interests were becoming too important to remain part of the firm's general merchandising business. The firm had been founded by Samuel Samuel in the 1830s to carry on a general trade with the Far East, including ornamental shells which were popular in Victorian England. In 1890, Marcus Samuel, the son of the founder and later Lord Bearsted, first Chairman of Shell Transport, added kerosine to his wares, buying from Russian producers and shipping to the Far East. From this humble origin was derived the trade mark 'Shell' which was destined to become of such significance in the petroleum industry.

Integration

The first step in the integration of the parent companies was an Agreement in 1903 providing for the formation of the Asiatic Petroleum Company, Limited to act as joint marketing company in a defined area of the world for the Royal Dutch, Shell Transport and Rothschilds, who at that time controlled large supplies of oil. Rothschilds dropped out of the oil marketing business during the 1920s and subsequently disposed of their interest in Asiatic to a Group company.

The next step in the integration was in 1907 when the two parent companies transferred all the assets of their oil businesses to two new companies, The Anglo-Saxon Petroleum Company, Limited (Anglo-Saxon), in London and N.V. De Bataafsche Petroleum Maatschappij, later renamed Bataafse Petroleum Maatschappij, N.V., in the Hague. Royal Dutch took 60% and Shell Transport 40% of the shares in both companies and then withdrew from active operations, confining their business to the holding of these shares. As part of this operation Royal Dutch and Shell Transport transferred to Anglo-Saxon their share in the Asiatic Petroleum Company, Limited, which was renamed The Shell Petroleum Company Limited in 1946.

Development

Following the amalgamation in 1907, business expanded rapidly – in production, manufacturing, distribution and marketing. Between 1907 and 1914 oilfields were acquired in Romania, British Borneo, Russia, Egypt, Trinidad, Venezuela, Mexico and California, while those in the East Indies were extended.

During World War I the properties in Romania were destroyed and those in Russia confiscated. Between World Wars I and II there was further large expanion; new oilfields were developed in Mexico, Argentina, USA and British Borneo, and interests were acquired in the oilfields of Iraq.

In 1919 a minority interest was acquired in Compania Mexicana de Petroleo, 'El Aguila' S.A. (Mexican Eagle) which owned and operated the oilfields in Mexico, and BPM entered into a long-term arrangement with that company. In 1921 a joint marketing company for the UK, Shell-Mex Limited, was formed which was subsequently replaced by Shell-Mex and B.P. Limited in 1932. Another joint marketing company was also formed for operation in Latin America. These Eagle interests outside Mexico were transferred to a new company, Canadian Eagle Oil Company, Limited, in 1928. Mexican Eagle was taken over in 1938 by the Mexican Government against compensation, and Canadian Eagle, with its various assets, was absorbed into the Group in 1959.

After World War II there were large increases in oil production and refinery construction and by 1947 the war losses of the tanker fleet were made good. New oilfields were developed by Group companies in Canada, Colombia, the Netherlands, Nigeria, the Sahara and elsewhere, and new refineries were built, notably in the UK, the Netherlands, France, Venezuela, India and Australia. This expansion is reflected in Table 9.

Table 9 Production of crude oil and natural gasoline

	Production, millions of barrels	
Year	Royal Dutch/ Shell Group	World (excluding Sino-Soviet spheres)
1907	8	186
1914	33	323
1938	210	1 778
1956	631	5 719
1963	1 098	8 222

Group companies pioneered the new petroleum chemical industry which, from small beginnings in 1928, has become such an important part of their activities. Since World War II new chemical plants have been built in the USA, the Netherlands, France and Canada.

Post-war changes

In 1955, as a result of structural simplification, the business of Anglo-Saxon was vested in Shell Petroleum and the number of parent operating companies (as they were then known) was thus reduced to two, BPM and Shell Petroleum.

For many years these two companies formed the nucleus of the integrated enterprise carried on by Group companies. They combined the functions of shareholder and trader in their respective spheres and were the focus for the preparation of policies and programmes. In the years from 1951 onwards, however, each of these companies acquired an additional role – the provision of advice and service to operating companies. This role has assumed paramount importance in Group affairs and is now recognized as the appropriate method of conducting the business relationships between operating companies and the 'centre' in view of the greatly increased economic and political diversity of the post-war world.

Beginning in 1957, a thorough review was made of the arrangements at the centre between the companies in The Hague and in London and of the relationship of the companies at the centre with operating companies. The intention of this review was to ensure that all arrangements were in good order for the present conduct of business and sufficiently flexible to take account of likely developments.

As a result of the review, two radical changes were made in 1959. Firstly BPM and Shell Petroleum were divested of their mixed functions other than shareholding, their trading functions were transferred to operating companies, and they themselves became, and are now known as the 'holding companies'. Secondly, and more importantly, four 'service companies' were established, two for oil and two for chemicals, one for each in The Hague (subsidiaries of BPM) and one for each in London (subsidiaries of Shell Petroleum).

For Oil
In The Hague: Bataafse Internationale Petroleum Maatschappij N.V.
In London: Shell International Petroleum Company Limited.

For Chemicals
In The Hague: Bataafse Internationale Chemie Maatschappij N.V.
In London: Shell International Chemical Company Limited.

These companies, though separate and located in different countries, play complementary roles, providing economically and efficiently, without overlapping, the help and service required by the operating companies in the conduct of their business, and also the service of advising an operating company as to how its operations may be carried on within the context of the continued prosperity of all other Group companies. This latter service cannot readily be performed by any one operating company but can best be performed from the vantage point of the service companies. The service companies also carry out work for the holding companies when requested to do so and are also responsible for international supply and shipping activities which do not fall within the jurisdiction of any one operating company.

Shell Internationale Research Maatschappij N.V. is an additional service company providing facilities in the research field.

The services provided to operating companies are of two kinds, those relating to global affairs and those relating to local affairs.

Global affairs – The management of each operating company is responsible for achieving its short- and long-term aims. Some of the policies it wishes to establish may, however, require knowledge of affairs outside its jurisdiction, or they may prejudice the affairs of another Group operating company, for example matters of international supplies or of availability of international staff. On these matters managements of operating companies obtain advice from the servicing companies to ensure that the policies they wish to establish are in the best interests of their companies in both the short and the long terms.

Local affairs – The management of each operating company can establish most of its policies without in the process prejudicing the affairs of other Group operating companies, e.g. in matters concerning local transport, local employees or local investments. In these cases local managements alone can decide the extent of any outside assistance required and the service companies can provide it or advise where it may be best obtained. Such assistance is often derived from the experience and expertise developed by the operating companies themselves, collated and disseminated by the service companies.

Structure of the Group

The present structure of the group, resulting from these various organizational changes, is shown in Fig. 9.

The individuals who are generally known as the Managing Directors of the Royal Dutch/Shell Group of Companies are Managing Directors of Shell Petroleum and Members of The Presidium of The Board of Directors of BPM. They are also Directors of the service companies and are appointed by these companies to a joint committee, known as the Committee of Managing Directors, which considers, develops and decides on overall objectives and long-term plans to be recommended to the operating companies.

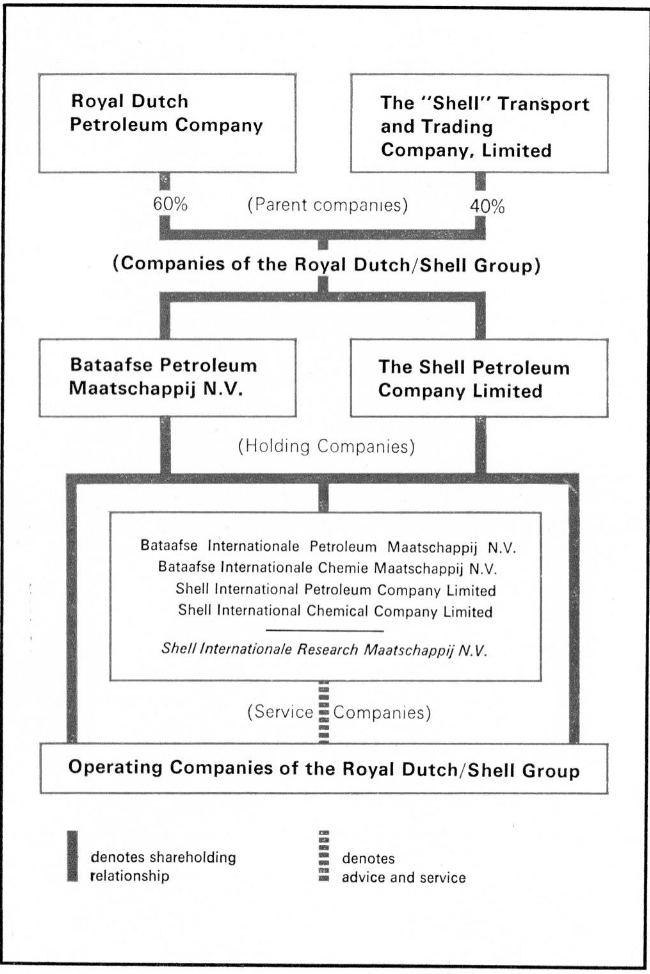

Fig. 9 Structure of the Royal Dutch/Shell Group of Companies

Operating companies

There are some five hundred operating companies all over the world doing a wide variety of jobs: holding, exploring, producing, manufacturing, transporting, marketing, researching. Some are concerned with only one main activity, whilst others are concerned with the whole gamut of oil industry activities. These latter are known as 'integrated' companies. Other companies undertake such auxiliary activities as the administration of pension funds or the ownership of real estate. In some of these companies Shell Petroleum and/or BPM own only part of the shares, the remainder being held by companies outside the Group or by public investors.

There are many reasons for the existence of such a large number of companies. Conditions vary from country to country and from one activity to another. In many countries it is necessary or desirable that companies operating there should be locally incorporated, and for legal and economic reasons it is generally desirable that a company should confine its business to a single country. Each company is a separate legal entity, controlled by its own board of directors.

It is impossible in this handbook to mention more than a few operating companies but the following are of particular interest.

Shell Oil Company (USA) is an integrated company in which Group companies own about 69% of the shares, the remaining 31% being owned by thousands of shareholders and the shares being quoted on the New York stock exchange. It engages in all phases of the oil business in North America; it owns and operates six refineries, and is one of the leading marketers of petroleum products in the USA. Its subsidiary, Shell Chemical Corporation, has eight chemical plants and markets a wide range of chemicals. Another subsidiary, Shell Development Company, is responsible for research and development. It also has a 50% interest in Shell Oil Company of Canada, Limited, which explores, produces, manufactures and markets oil products and chemicals in Canada.

Compania Shell de Venezuela Limited (CSV) is an integrated company in which Group companies own all the shares. It carries out all operations from exploration to marketing (oil products, chemicals, agricultural products) and is the largest oil-producing company in the Group. It produces principally from the area of Lake Maracaibo, where underwater drilling is now in progress, and operates two large refineries.

Through a 14% interest in Iranian Oil Participants Limited, and a 23·75% interest in Iraq Petroleum Company, Group Companies participate in oil production from Iraq, Iran and Qatar.

On the marketing side, Group companies are organized in several different ways. In most European countries Group companies market through wholly owned subsidiaries; the UK, Eire and France are, however, notable exceptions.

In the UK, Shell-Mex and B.P. Limited is a joint marketing organization for the distribution and sale in the UK of the petroleum products of Shell and British Petroleum. It has associated companies in Scotland (Shell and BP Scotland Limited) and in Eire (Irish Shell and BP Limited).

In France, Group companies own a majority of shares in Shell Française, the remainder being in outside hands, and the shares are quoted on the Paris stock exchange. Shell Française is a holding company holding shares in Shell Berre de Raffinage and Société des Pétroles Shell Berre.

Joint marketing organizations also exist in India and Pakistan where Burmah Oil Company and The Shell Petroleum Company have equal shareholdings in Burmah-Shell (India) and Burmah-Shell (Pakistan), which market petroleum products, and Burmah-Shell Refineries Limited, which operates a refinery at Bombay.

Yet another is the Consolidated Petroleum Company, owned 50% by Group companies and 50% by British Petroleum Company, whose many subsidiaries market petroleum products in South and East Africa, some Middle-East countries, Cyprus and Ceylon.

Activities of Group companies

In 1964 Group companies had interests in exploration, including offshore exploration, in twenty-eight countries, and interests in oilfields in twenty countries. Oil available from production and supply contracts totalled over 3 million barrels/day.

Nearly one-sixth of the world's tanker tonnage is managed or chartered by Group companies – the largest maritime enterprise in the world, comprising about 470 vessels totalling 13 million tons deadweight. Group companies also own or participate in 35 800 miles of pipelines handling crude oil, oil products or natural gas.

There are some seventy-seven refineries operated, under construction or projected by Group companies in forty-four countries and 3·4 million barrels/day of crude oil were refined by Group companies in 1964.

Group companies market in almost every country and supply nearly one seventh of the world's consumption of oil products outside the Sino-Soviet spheres. The USA is the largest single outlet for oil products although Group sales in Europe as a whole are higher than in the USA and Canada combined. In Europe, Group companies hold the largest share of the market – about 21 %. Group companies are the principal suppliers of aviation fuels to the world's airlines, and leading suppliers of fuels and lubricants for shipping.

Group companies have an important share of world gas reserves and have taken a prominent pioneering part in the growing natural gas business. BPM has a half share in the company that discovered in the Netherlands, one of the largest gas fields in the world and other Group companies are developing local markets for natural gas in Germany, Nigeria, East Pakistan and New Zealand. Group companies also have a 40 % interest in Conch International Methane Limited who hold valuable patents for transporting refrigerated natural gas by sea.

Group companies' interests in chemical manufacture taken together are larger than those of any other oil group and, on the basis of sales proceeds, they rank twelfth among the major chemical producers in the world. Manufacture of chemicals by Group companies is carried out in eleven countries.

Group companies carry out research in connection with all spheres of their activities, employing some 7000 people in twenty-seven research establishments.

The rapid expansion in world-wide consumption of oil products and chemicals calls for ever-increasing capital expenditure by Group companies to ensure that products are available when and where required in the quantities and qualities needed. It is expected that by 1970 the world will be consuming at least a further 11 million barrels/day of petroleum products in addition to the 29 million barrels a day consumed in 1964. Tables 9 and 10 give some idea of the expansion that has taken place within the Group to meet growing demands in the past. With their world-wide sources of supply, intensive and widespread search for new sources, and forward-looking programmes of research, Group companies are well equipped to continue to meet growing demands and to maintain their place in the forefront of the oil and chemical industries.

Table 10 Tanker tonnage

	Thousands dwt			
End of year	World	Group owned/ managed	Group chartered	Group total
1907	962	142	15	157
1914	2338	265	45	310
1938	16600	1410	529	1939
1956	44377	3021	5610	8631
1963	74982	4182	7517	11699

Production

Exploration

Drilling

Oilfield development and production

Exploration

Historical

In ancient times surface deposits or seepages of oil, bitumen and asphalt were used for a variety of purposes – medicinal, heating, building – and gas emanations were sometimes venerated as 'eternal fires'. There was probably no search or exploration for them, they were used as and when found.

From the drilling of Drake's well in Pennsylvania in 1859 until far into the twentieth century wells were sunk close to seepages – what is now known as 'seepage drilling' – but there was no exploration in the modern sense until geology was applied to the finding of oil in the late nineteenth century. In 1885 several new fields were discovered on the basis of the theory that oil accumulates in the crests of folded rock layers, known to geologists as anticlines.

The first employment of a geologist by an oil company appears to have been in 1897, but not until the discovery of the Cushing Field, Oklahoma, in 1912 as a result of geological survey did geologists enter the industry in any numbers. Soon afterwards, however, many hundreds were roaming all over the USA and other countries in search of anticlines. The period from 1912 to 1925, during which most of the principal anticlines in the USA were discovered, is known as the 'anticlinal period', the end of which marks the beginning of modern scientific exploration.

Origin, migration, accumulation of oil

If rocks in which oil might have formed in geological time are present in a given area, it may be possible that oil still exists in that area. The problem of the origin of crude oil in nature is therefore important for oil exploration.

It is now generally accepted that oil originated from the decomposition of aquatic, mainly marine, animals and plants buried under successive layers of mud and silt perhaps as much as 400–500 million years ago. An inorganic source of petroleum advocated by some US and Russian scientists remains an alternative though somewhat speculative hypothesis.

The primary requirement for the genesis of petroleum from organic material is an environment of shallow seas, such as the Gulf of Mexico, in which the water is rich in animal and vegetable life from microscopic to large. The second requirement is that organisms, on dying, should sink to the bottom of the sea and be buried by mud from rivers, in the way that mud from the Mississippi today buries millions of organisms daily as it settles on the bottom of the Gulf of Mexico. Conditions on the sea bottom must be such that no rapid decay of the dead organisms takes place by bacterial action; the oxygen content of the water must be small.

In the course of time mud and silt layers deposited on top of the potential source beds produce pressures and higher temperatures in these beds. At a burial depth of several thousand feet chemical processes, probably not dependent on bacterial activity, transform the soft parts of the organisms into oil and gas. Indications are that gas is preferentially generated at greater depths.

As the overburden pressure tends to compact the 'source rocks', oil and gas, probably together with some of the associated water, is squeezed out, provided adjoining formations are sufficiently permeable, that is, that they allow the passage of liquid and gas through the pores of the rock or through a system of fractures and cracks. So the rock fluids start to migrate, either upwards or sidewards or possibly downwards. There is evidence that oil has thus travelled over long distances, even dozens of miles.

In the past the path of migration must often have led to the surface, where the oil was washed away or its lighter components evaporated into the air. Seepages in all parts of the world, such as the Trinidad Pitch Lake and the perpetual fires of Baku, are evidence of oil and gas still escaping from the subsoil today.

Sometimes migration is halted, for instance by a layer impervious to the passage of fluids. If oil is thus trapped in a porous formation and is no longer able to move, an oil

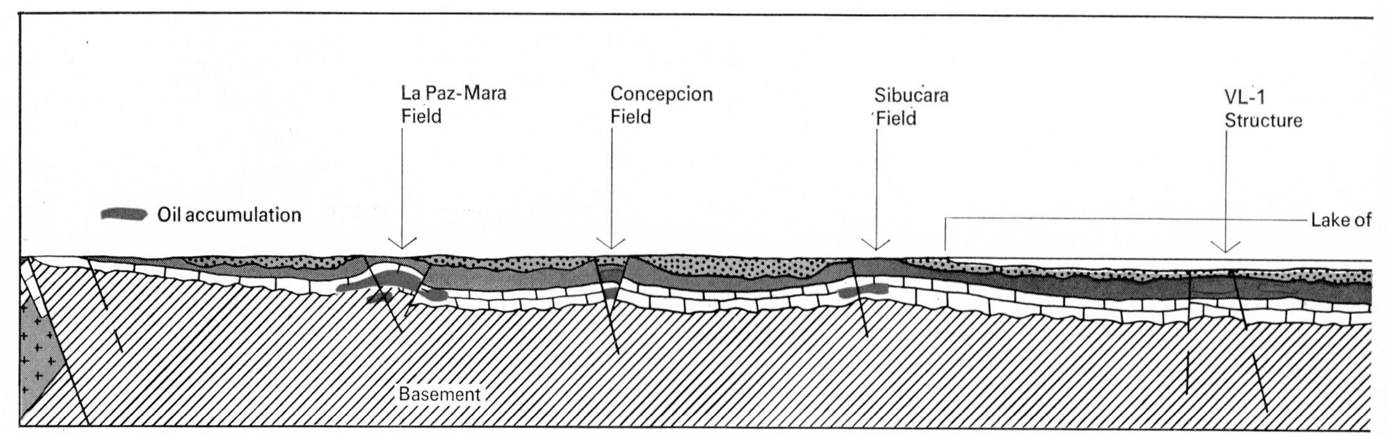

Fig. 10 Section through a typical oil basin: the Maracaibo basin of western Venezuela

accumulation forms. The porous formation provides storage capacity for the fluid in its pores or interstices, as a sponge holds water, and is called the 'reservoir rock'. The impervious layer that prevents further movement of fluid is the 'sealing formation', usually referred to as 'seal' or 'cap rock'. The seal must be shaped in such a way as to effectively trap the fluid in the reservoir. Various types of traps created by different geological phenomena are described below.

Geological features

Oil basins

Suitable conditions for the formation and accumulation of oil exist in the downwarped segments of the earth's crust where layers of sediment have accumulated to great thickness, thickest in the middle and thinner towards the edges. Such areas are called 'sedimentary basins', and are considered as potential 'oil basins' worth investigating for the presence of oil until its absence is definitely proved. Topographically they are generally low and many occur along the continental margins and in the foothills and lowlands bordering mountain chains.

Fig. 10 illustrates a typical section through an oil basin, the prolific Maracaibo basin in Venezuela, filled with sedimentary rocks and with a basement of much older rocks as its floor. Oil occurs in various formations, from the basement (La Paz–Mara field) up to the youngest or highest series, the Neogene (Pueblo Viejo and Mene Grande fields) although all the oil probably originated from only one formation, the Mesozoic, which covers the floor of the basin.

Fig. 11 shows the potential oil basins and the major producing areas throughout the world. Large oil accumulations are found in the large basins of the middle west of the USA, South America, the Middle East, North Africa and Nigeria, and around the Urals and the Caucasus. The basins of the Australian continent contain only a few known oilfields.

A thick basin does not necessarily contain more oil than a thinner one. The thinnest of the world's great oil basins, The Middle East basin, about 30 000 ft thick, is the most productive by far; the Californian basin, 60 000–70 000 ft thick, although very productive, is much less so than the Middle East and not more so than the US mid-western basins, 30 000–40 000 ft thick.

Several oil basins extend seaward as part of the continental shelf bordering the continents, the limit of which is roughly defined by the 200 metre (100 fathom) water depth contour. Exploration of continental shelves has progressed considerably since 1945. In the Gulf of Mexico oil has been found 60 miles off the US coast and the search now extends to about 100 miles. The entire North Sea has become an active exploration area. According to an internationally accepted Convention on the Continental Shelf, established by a United Nations conference on the Law of the Sea in 1958, a coastal state has sovereign rights outside its territorial waters for the exploitation of the natural resources of the continental shelf to the extent of the 200 metre contour or, beyond that limit, to where the depth of the water permits exploitation. Boundaries between states whose coasts are either adjacent or opposite to each other are generally agreed on to be the median line, i.e. a line formed by points equidistant from the nearest points of the coast line of either state.

Rock types

Rocks are divided into three main groups: igneous rocks, which include granite and volcanic rocks, consolidated from hot liquid material; sedimentary rocks, either fragments of other rocks deposited on land or under the sea by wind and water, or chemically deposited, for instance as evaporation products, or of organic origin; metamorphic rocks, igneous and sedimentary rocks whose composition and structure have been profoundly changed by heat and pressure.

Igneous and metamorphic rocks cover immense areas of the earth's crust, forming the central nuclei of the continents, called shields, or they occur as smaller masses (massifs) located all over the world. Many old shields and massifs were not submerged beneath the sea for considerable periods in their geological history and are therefore bare of sedimentary rocks and can bear no oil. In other regions, however, vast areas of igneous and metamorphic rocks subsided below sea level and became the floor of potential oil basins. Their nature normally prevents their bearing oil but if fractured they can act as reservoirs for oil that has migrated from overlying sedimentary rocks [Fig. 10, La Paz–Mara field].

The oil geologist is mainly concerned with the sedimentary deposits filling all the world's potential oil basins, which comprise about a tenth of the land area of the earth.

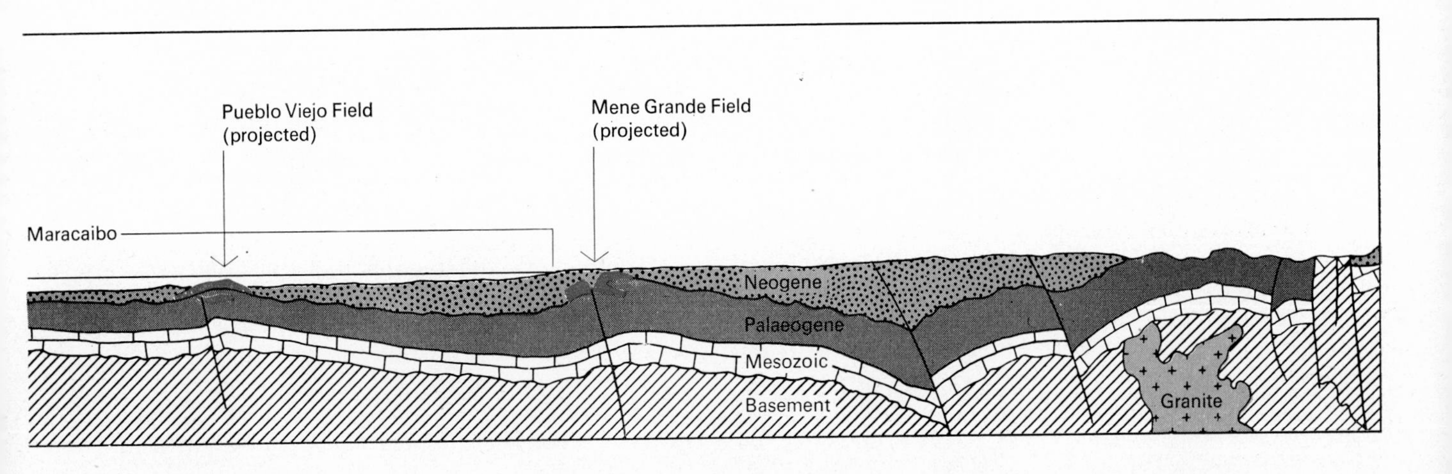

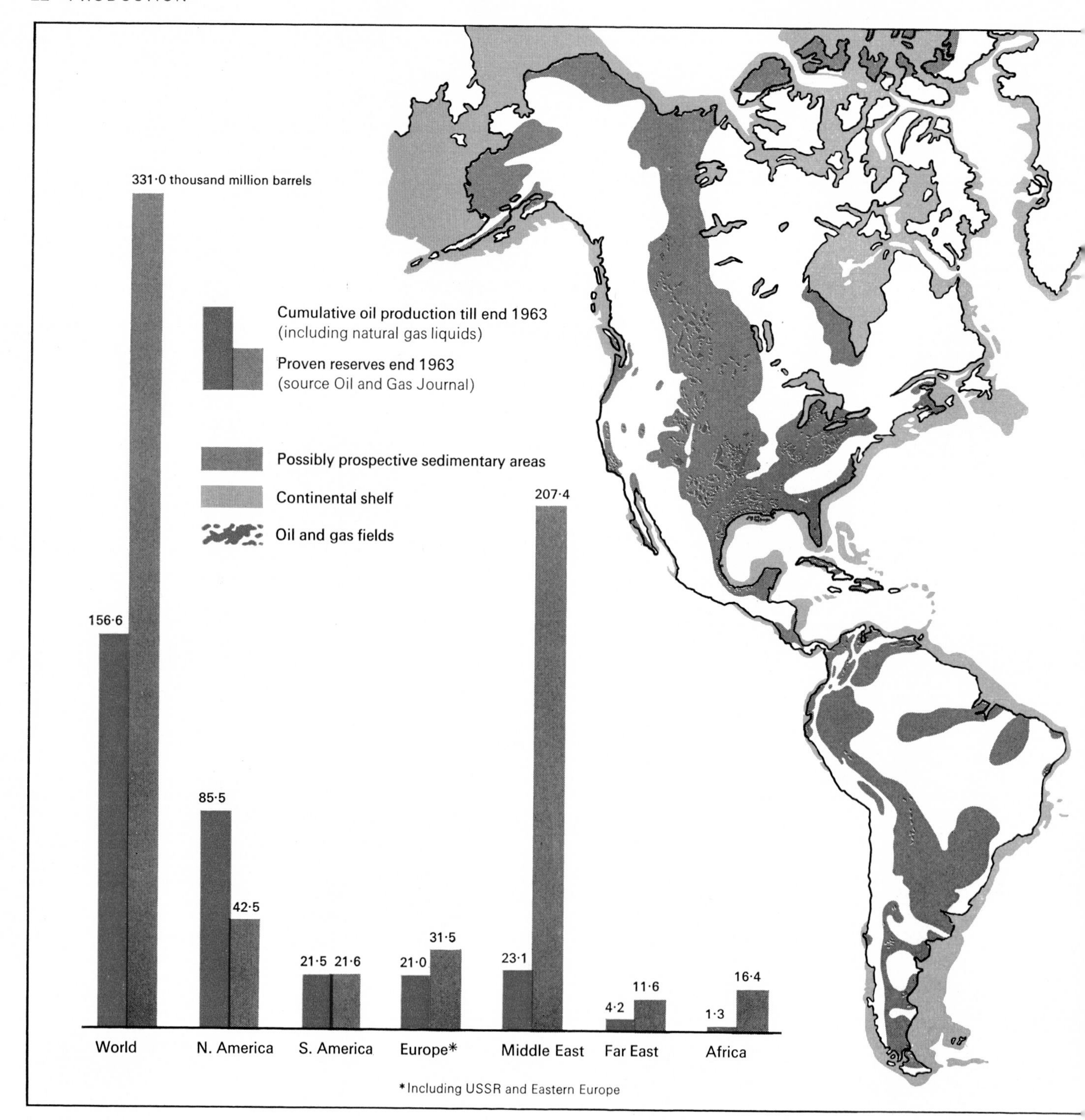

Fig. 11 Potential oil basins showing producing areas

Sedimentation

The products of denudation or erosion of the higher parts of the earth's surface are carried away by water, ice and wind in the form of pebbles, sand, silt, mud, etc, and are deposited as sediment in the valleys and plains and in the surrounding seas where they may attain thicknesses of many thousands of feet. Though slow, the action of running water and the like has brought about immense changes during the many millions of years of geological time. For example, the Alps and the Himalayas are gradually being lowered: the Grand Canyon is still being widened and deepened by the Colorado River: the Niagara Falls recede at the rate of a foot a year: the whole area of the Ganges basin is lowered by about a foot every thousand years. The eroded material is washed away by streams and rivers which carry it eventually into the sea where it may be distributed over enormous areas by ocean currents.

Under arid climatic conditions salt and anhydrite deposits called evaporites may form by evaporation of sea water, for instance in lagoons. Shallow seas of warm clear water favour the growth of corals and algae which are important contributors to the formation of carbonate rocks such as limestone and dolomite. Where vegetable matter accumulates, peat, lignite, and eventually coal beds may form.

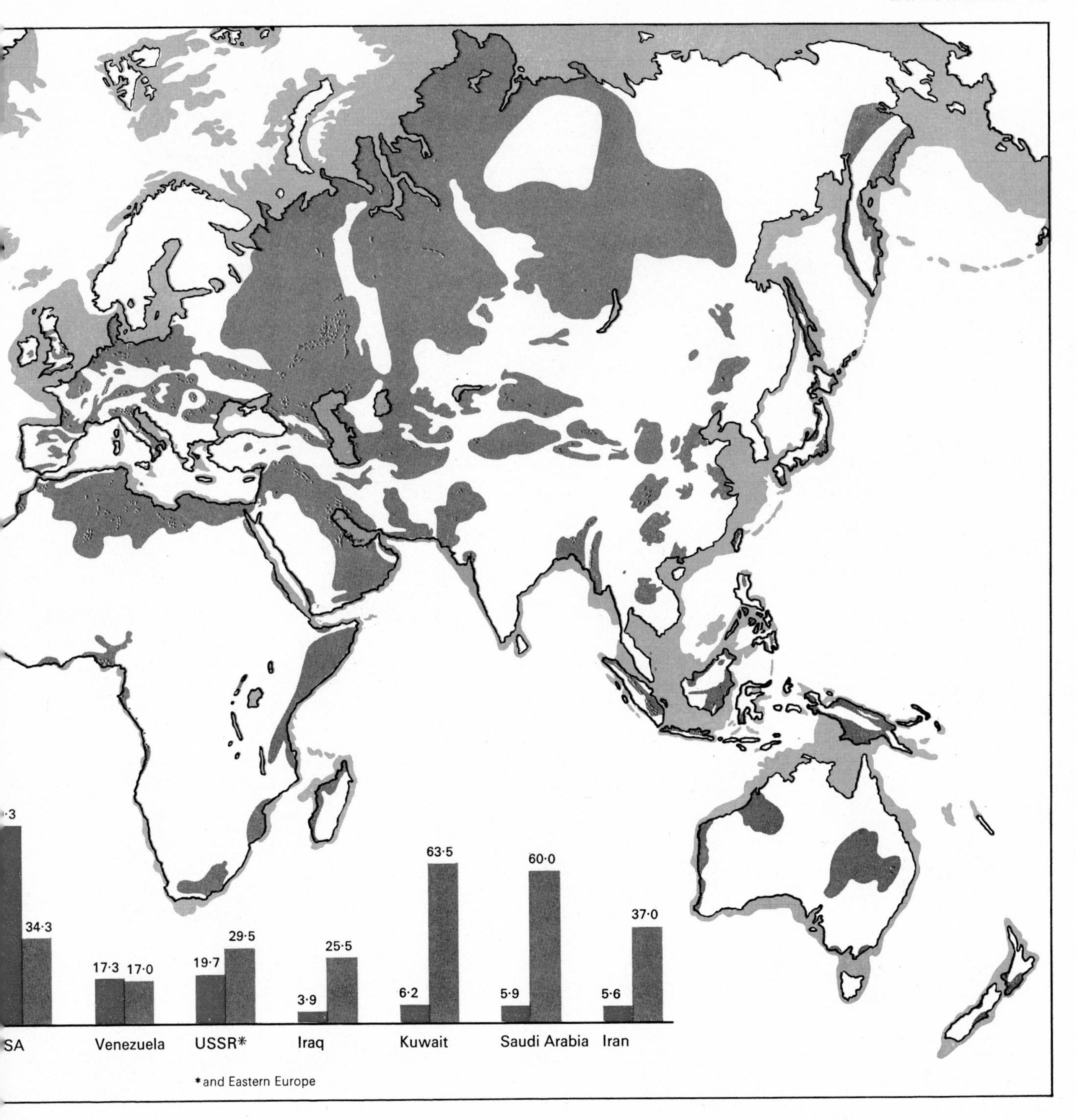

The beds of sedimentary rocks deposited in this way are seldom uniform in thickness, composition or texture. The variations may be small or large depending on many factors and a section through a series of sedimentary rocks usually shows lateral and vertical changes [Fig. 12].

Geological age and oil occurrence

By the study of fossils, both large and microscopic, the geologist is able to assign relative ages to sediments and so to determine the succession of beds one above the other. Since the distribution of some of the fossils of any one age is world-wide, the rocks of one continent or basin may be correlated with those of another. The absolute age of the rocks can be determined from a study of radioactive minerals and a geological time scale can be established as in Table 11 (p. 24).

Oil may be generated in sedimentary rocks of almost any age, but the older rocks will naturally have lost more of their oil than have the younger ones through seepages, cracks, erosion or heat from igneous or volcanic rocks. In the 236 major oilfields discovered up to 1956 having reserves of over 100 million barrels each and representing 83% of the world's known reserves, only about 10% of the oil occurs in the older rocks of the Palaeozoic era. This proportion has not significantly changed with more recent discoveries.

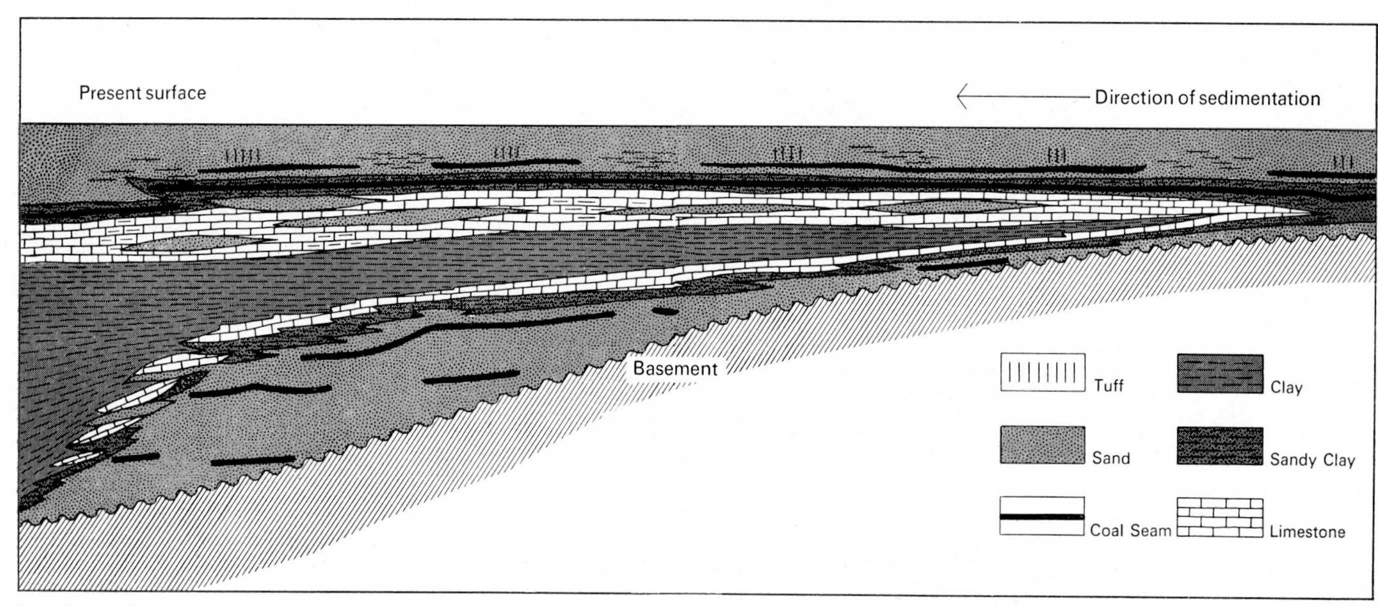

Fig. 12 Vertical and lateral changes in composition of sedimentary rocks. Section through the edge of the basin of southern Sumatra

Table 11 The geological time scale, based on *Principles of Physical Geology* by A. Holmes (Revised 1960)

Eras	Periods and epochs		Maximum known Thicknesses of strata in feet	Approximate Dates in years (according to radio-activity data)	Characteristic life
				Present day	
Cainozoic (Kainos or Cenos = recent; Zoe = life)	Quaternary	Recent or Holocene	6000	25000	Modern man
		Glacial or Pleistocene			Stone Age man
				1000000	
	Tertiary	Pliocene	13000	11000000	
		Miocene	21000	25000000	Mammals
		Oligocene	15000	40000000	
		Eocene	14000	70000000	
					Flowering plants
Mesozoic (Mesos = middle)	Cretaceous		64000	135000000	
	Jurassic		20000	180000000	Reptiles
	Triassic		25000	225000000	
Palaeozoic (Palaios = ancient)	Permian		13000	270000000	Amphibians and
	Carboniferous		40000	350000000	primitive plants
	Devonian		37000	400000000	
	Silurian or Gothlandian		15000	440000000	Fishes
	Ordovician		40000	500000000	Invertebrates
	Cambrian		40000	600000000	First appearance of abundant fossils
Pre-Cambrian eras sometimes described as:	Proterozoic		Unknown in detail		Scanty remains of
	Archaeozoic		but		sponges and seaweeds
	Eozoic		immensely great	at least 3000000000	No direct fossil evidence of life
Unrecorded interval (duration unknown)					
Origin of the Earth at least 4500000000 years ago					

Earth movements

More than once during geological history, the crust of the earth has been in movement. Sometimes lowlands and the adjoining sea bed were raised, so that areas where sediments had been deposited became land well above sea level, on the surface of which running water again sculptured the land into hills and valleys. Sometimes land was lowered and became submerged, and sedimentation began again on top of previously sculptured landscape.

Folds

If these movements had been uniformly vertical, uplifted sedimentary beds would generally be found lying more or less horizontally, as they often are. But in many places irregular movements corrugated and buckled the uplifted beds into folds. In their simplest form folds assume a symmetrical pattern of alternate upfolding anticlines and downfolding synclines [Fig. 13]. Under greater stresses an anticline may become asymmetrical or even overturned into a recumbent fold [Fig. 14]. Short anticlines, plunging on all sides, are known as 'domes'. Anticlines and synclines may vary in width from a few hundred yards to many miles [Fig. 15].

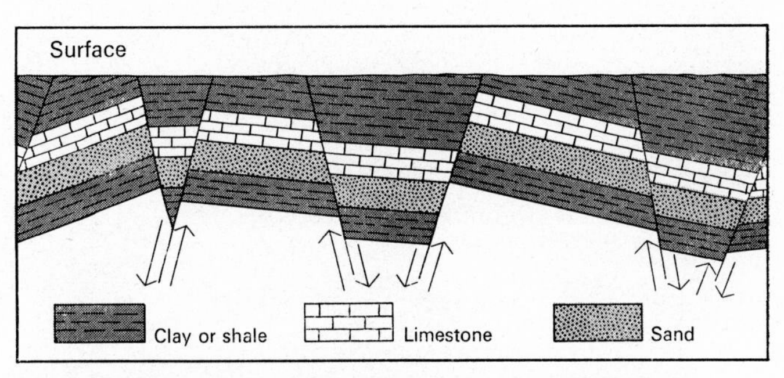

Fig. 16 Normal faults

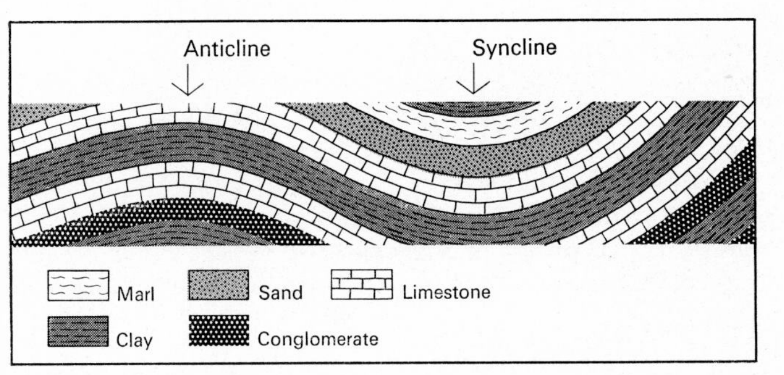

Fig. 13 Symmetrical anticline and syncline

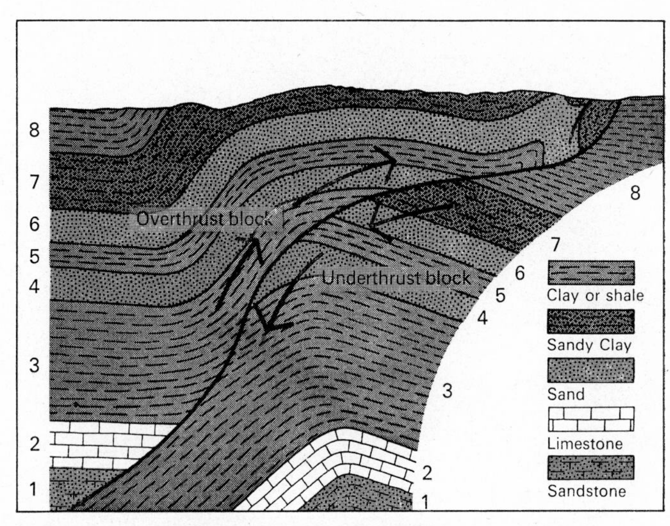

Fig. 17 Overthrust fault – Las Cruces, western Venezuela

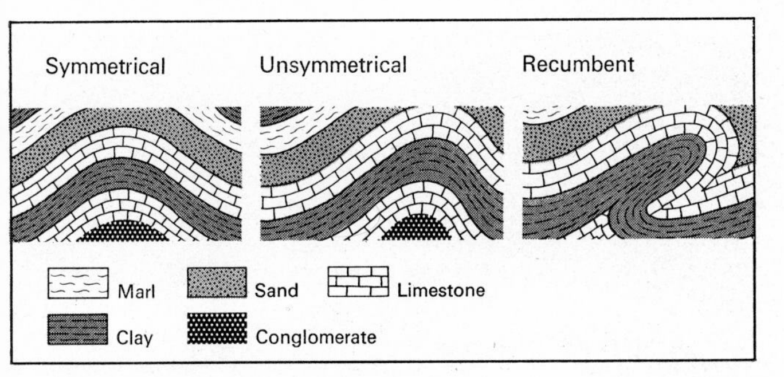

Fig. 14 Types of fold

Fig. 15 San Migueleto anticline, 60 miles north-west of Los Angeles, California

Faults

When the earth's crust is stressed beyond its folding resistance, breaks or 'faults' occur which may displace the beds on either side of the fault a few hundred or many thousands of feet. Displacement can occur either vertically or horizontally but is generally in both directions. If vertical displacement predominates, the fracture is a 'normal fault', with a rather steep fault plane [Fig. 16]; if horizontal displacement predominates, the inclination of the fracture is usually rather flat and the fault is an 'overthrust fault' [Fig. 17].

Unconformity

The cycle of sedimentation, uplifting and folding, and subsequent erosion has been often repeated during geological times, sometimes over a small area, sometimes on a continental scale. The deposits of each new cycle are laid down on the folded and eroded beds of the previous cycle until

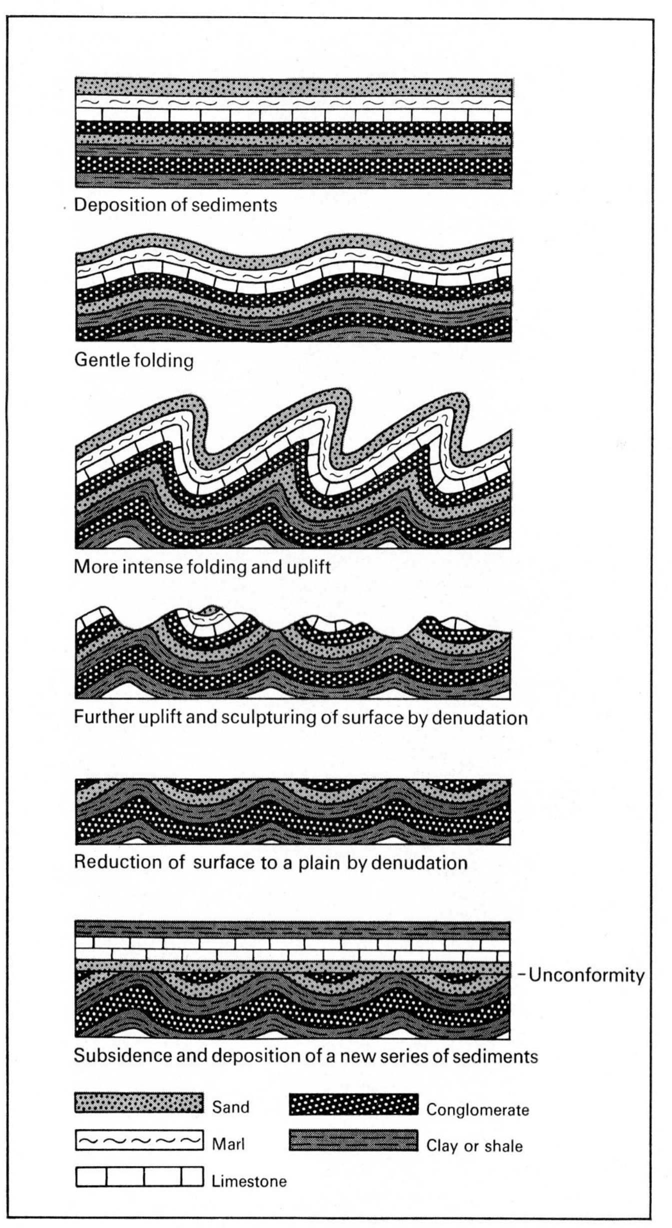

Fig. 18 Successive stages in the development of an unconformity

Fig. 19 Unconformity between the Eocene and Miocene – State of Lara, western Venezuela

they are involved in folding movements. The rocks of each new cycle are said to lie unconformably on the folds of the older cycle and the configuration is known as an 'unconformity' [Figs 18 and 19].

Oil accumulation

Oil and gas may have accumulated if the following essential geological conditions have been satisfied:

The presence of reservoir rock, i.e. formations containing interconnected pores (e.g. unconsolidated sands) or cracks and voids (e.g. some limestones).

The presence, at the top of the reservoir rock, of a formation (e.g. anhydrite or shale) impervious to the passage of fluids. When this lies directly over the reservoir rock, as in most oil traps, it is called a 'cap rock' or 'roof rock'.

The presence of 'closure', i.e. a geological configuration that prevents the lateral escape of fluids, as when the cap rock is concave as viewed from below.

These conditions define a potential oil trap in which oil, gas and water, migrating from the source rock, may accumulate. The oil and water will separate as a result of difference in density, and free gas, gas not dissolved in oil as a result of high pressure, if present, will collect in the highest part of the reservoir to form a 'gas cap' with the oil below it.

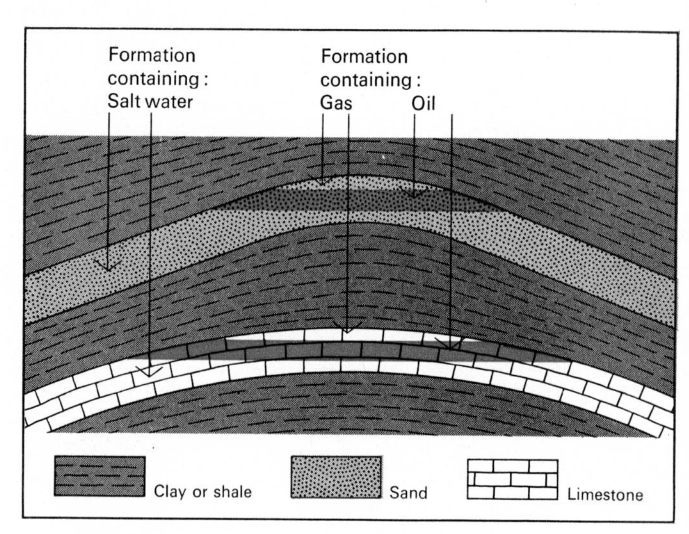

Fig. 20 Anticlinal traps

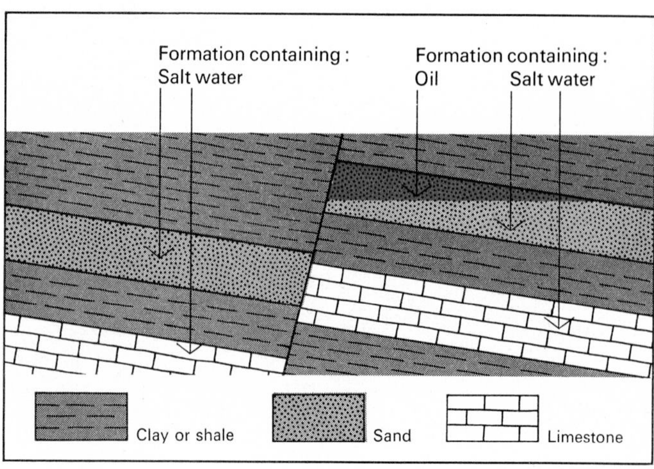

Fig. 21 Fault trap

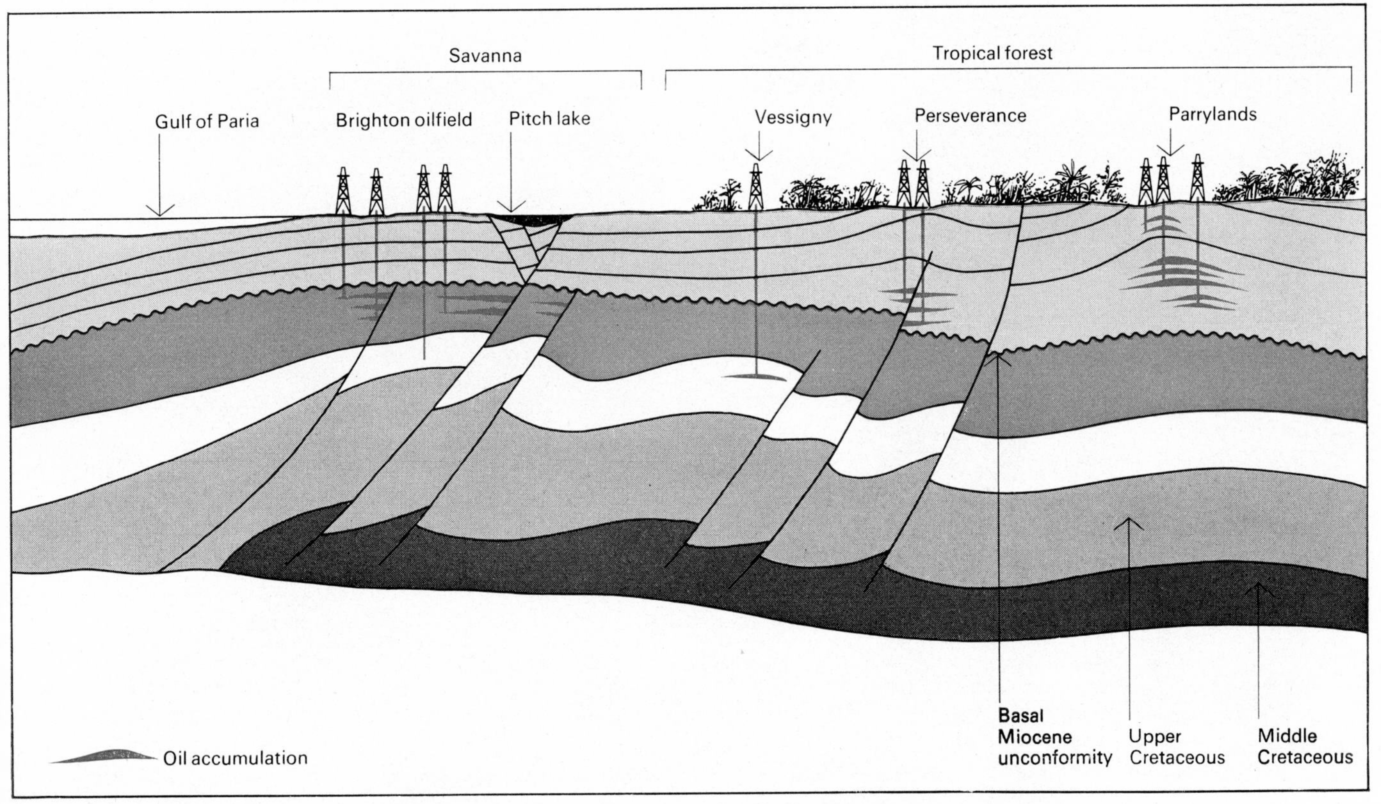

Fig. 22 Schematic geological section through the oilfields of south-western Trinidad (showing Trinidad Pitch Lake)

Fig. 23 Trinidad Pitch Lake

Below the oil the pores in the reservoir rock will remain full of usually saline formation water.

Oil traps

Oil traps are of many kinds divided broadly into 'structural' and 'stratigraphic' traps.

Structural traps

Structural traps result from some local deformation such as folding, faulting or both, of the reservoir rock and cap rock. Typical examples are anticlinal and fault traps and traps connected with salt domes.

Fig. 20 shows an anticlinal trap in which a reservoir sand and a reservoir limestone are capped by impervious beds which also cover the flanks of both reservoirs, providing closure and preventing the horizontal escape of oil and gas. The upper part of each reservoir contains gas underlain by oil-saturated rock; the pore space of the lower part is filled with salt water.

Fig. 21 shows a fault trap in which the fault provides closure for the sand reservoir by bringing an impervious layer alongside it on the updip side but not for the limestone reservoir in which oil and gas could not accumulate because they would escape updip through the sand.

Fig. 22 is a schematic section through the oilfields of south-western Trinidad in which both anticlinal and fault traps occur. Oil has escaped along a fault plane extending to the surface and giving rise to the well-known Trinidad Pitch Lake [Fig. 23].

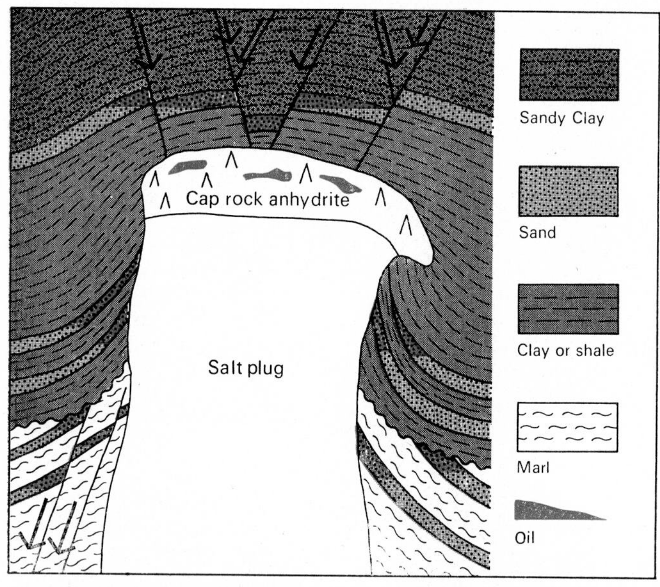

Fig. 24 Idealized section through a Gulf Coast salt-dome field, showing traps associated with salt intrusion

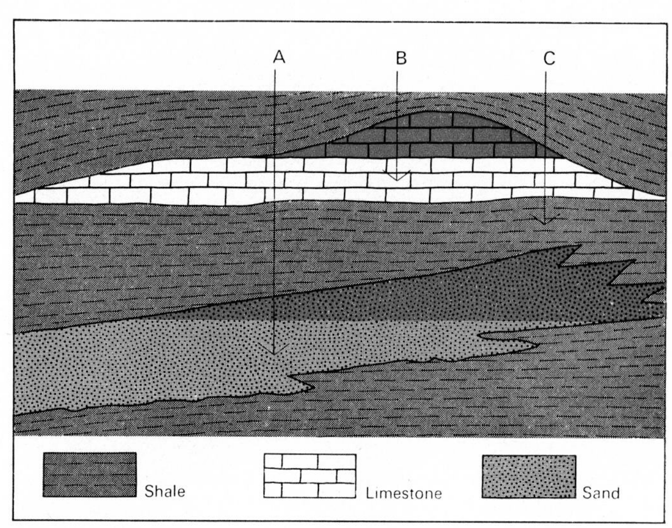

Fig. 25 Stratigraphic traps. Organic reef embedded in shale, and wedging-out sand

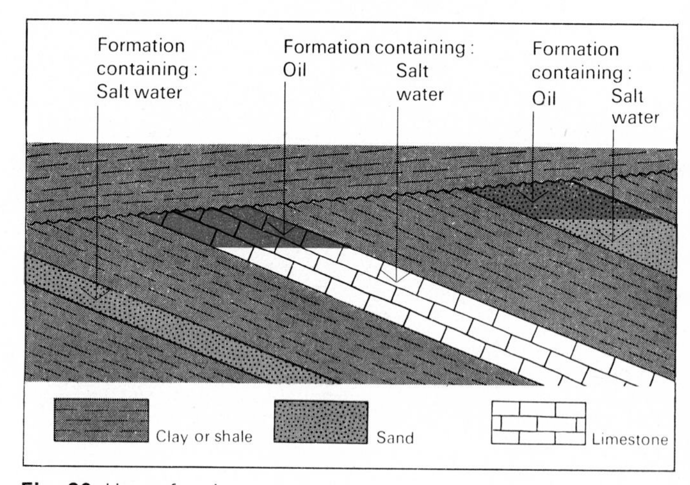

Fig. 26 Unconformity traps

Traps are sometimes formed by the local intrusion of deep-seated rocks into overlying sediment. Rock salt is a frequent intruder forming 'salt domes' – cylindrical, steeply conical or mushroom-shaped masses of rock salt, formed when salt was forced to flow plastically under very high pressure, punching its way up from deep-seated beds through the overlying layers. Porous formations, if present, have been truncated and effectively sealed by the salt plug [Fig. 24]. Oil may accumulate against the plug or above it in reservoir formations that have been folded by the rising plug, or in the porous remnant of older strata pushed up on top of the salt.

Stratigraphic traps

Sedimentary layers may change laterally in lithologic composition or may die out and reappear elsewhere as a different type of rock. Such changes often cause a lateral decrease in porosity and permeability, and the more porous section of the layer may form a 'stratigraphic' trap. Such a trap is often formed by the updip edge of a wedging-out sand layer [A in Fig. 25] that merges into an impermeable clay or shale [C in Fig. 25]. Oil accumulations also occur in traps formed by lenticular sand masses completely enclosed in tight sediments.

Limestone in itself is often impervious but may contain fissures and caverns that can form stratigraphic traps. The remains of an ancient coral reef buried by impervious sediments can also form a stratigraphic trap [B in Fig. 25].

A different kind of stratigraph trap may be formed by unconformities when a succession of layers, including a potential oil reservoir, have been uplifted, tilted, cut by erosion, and finally overlaid by impervious sediments that act as cap rock [Fig. 26].

Oil accumulations may result, not only from any one of the above-mentioned types of trap, but from a combination of two or more types. Some traps are not easy to recognize and it is not surprising, therefore, that even the most modern geophysical methods may fail to give an indication of their presence, in which case only exploration drilling can provide sufficient information, at a cost considerably higher than that of other exploration methods.

Even after the initial discovery of an exploitable oil accumulation, geological conditions may be so complicated that years may supervene and many development wells be drilled before the detailed pattern of oil occurrence in the area is fully understood.

Exploration methods

Oil exploration methods are the techniques employed in the search for oil. Their primary task is not directly to find oil but to provide physical evidence about the geological phenomena associated with oil accumulations and described in the preceding pages. Geological interpretation of the data thus provided may eventually lead to drilling and the discovery of oil.

Aerial surveying

Before commencing the exploration of new territory – even before surveyors or geologists go out – it is customary to photograph the whole area from the air. An aeroplane fitted with a wide-angled camera flies stripwise over the area taking photographs each of which overlaps those adjoining. By stereoscopic study of these photographs a fairly accurate topographical map, and a geological map showing the geological surface features observable from the air, are constructed [Figs 27 and 28]. These maps not only help in the planning of ground surveys but also enable geologists to be flown out by helicopter direct to the points of greatest interest. There is no longer any reason for surveyors or geologists to work 'blind' in the tropical rain forests or the arid deserts in which so much oil exploration has to be done. So great is the value of aerial surveys that it is usual nowadays to photograph even areas that have already been explored on the ground so that they can be reassessed. Large-scale aerial photographs are also invaluable in planning routes for roads and pipelines or sites for wells and camps.

Geological exploration

The outcrops of the rock layers in the potential oil-bearing area are mapped as accurately as possible as a result of geological observations on the ground. Wherever possible, observations are made, in the banks of rivers, on mountain slopes and cliffs, of the inclination of the strata (the dip) and of the horizontal direction (the strike) in which they extend. The physical characteristics and the fossil contents of the rocks are recorded, and samples are taken, to correlate with beds exposed elsewhere. The final detailed geological map may be built up from hundreds or thousands of observations made by one or more geologists over many years.

In areas of good rock exposure field work is comparatively straightforward but in regions covered by superficial deposits such as river sediments or in featureless areas where surface evidence is obscure or wanting, the work is more complex. Pits or trenches may have to be dug, auger holes drilled through the weathered soil layer, or a cored section of underlying rock obtained by the use of hand or light power driven drilling outfits. But where folds are hidden beneath sediments deposited since the deformation, they may not be revealed at all by geological methods and geophysical methods alone may be able to detect them.

Geophysical exploration

In the USA most of the oil-bearing structures visible at the surface had been mapped by the middle 1920s and new methods were needed to find structures that could not be detected by the surface geological methods then in use. Geophysical methods were tried and a gravimetric method, using the torsion balance developed in Europe, led to the discovery of the first 'gravity' oilfield in Texas, the Nash Salt Dome. So many salt domes were discovered along the Gulf of Mexico by this method in the next few years that it seemed probable that geophysics would take the place of geological surveys in oil exploration, a belief seemingly confirmed by the success of the seismic method which, by the early 1930s, had traced most of the salt domes along the Gulf missed by the gravimetric method.

Geophysical surveys are sometimes made in areas already explored geologically in order to obtain corroborative subsurface evidence, but they are chiefly applied where there is no surface evidence of structure, as in deserts, river delta, swamps and water-covered areas, or where possible oil-bearing structures are hidden by overlying deposits. The seismic and the gravimetric methods are most commonly employed but magnetic and electrical methods are also employed. The relative importance of these geophysical methods in 1960 for the world (excluding the Sino-Soviet spheres) was:

Seismic	8 913 crew-months
Gravimetric	1 371 crew-months
Magnetic	166 crew-months
Others	46 crew-months

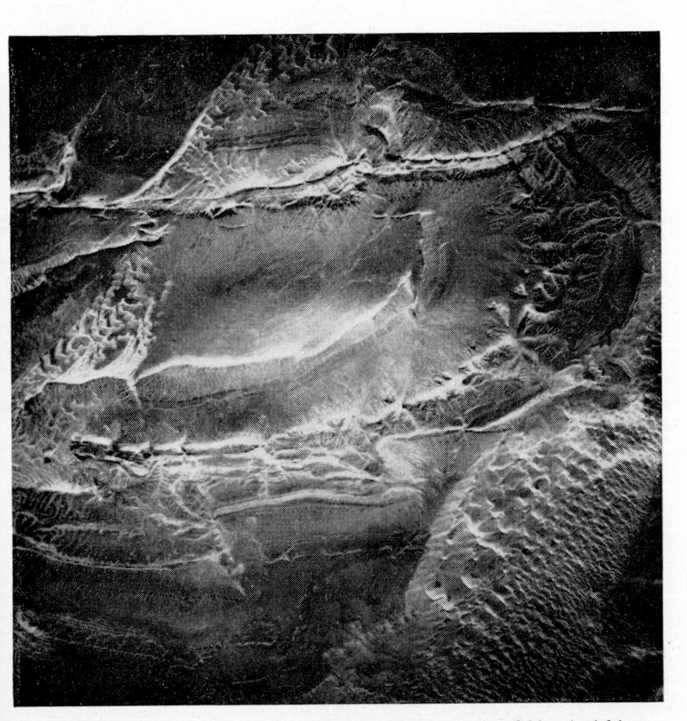

Fig. 27 Asymmetrical anticline. Aerial photograph of North African desert, Algeria

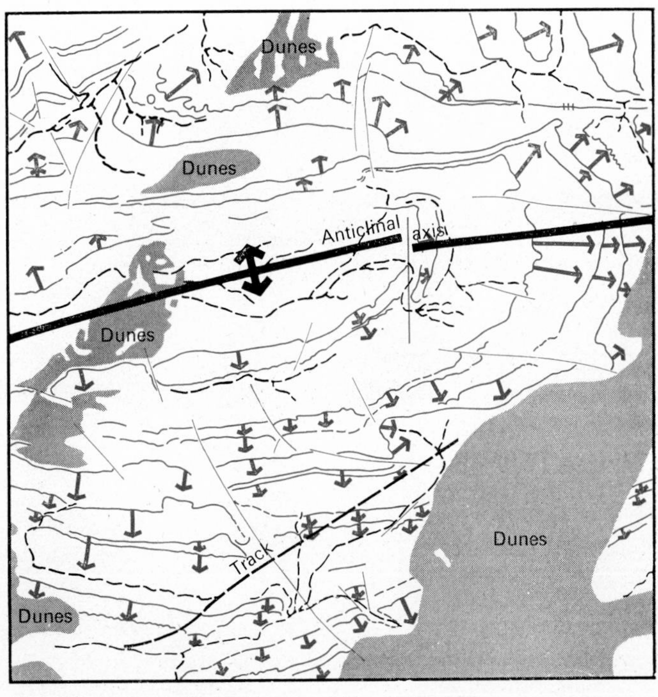

Fig. 28 Photogeological interpretation of Fig. 27

The seismic method

The seismic method provides the most direct evidence of geological subsurface structure at present obtainable. A charge or series of charges of explosive, detonated at or near the earth's surface, generates artificial earthquake waves which are relayed to a recording instrument by sensitive instruments known as seismometers or geophones, placed at varying known distances from the explosion. Of the two types of seismic survey, the most widely practised is 'reflection shooting', based on the principle that the vibrations caused by the explosion are partly reflected at the boundary between two strata of different density. The time taken by the waves to travel from the explosion down to the reflecting layer and back to the seismometer on the surface will indicate the depth of the reflecting layer provided the velocity of the waves in the successive rock layers is known. Fig. 29 shows equipment and procedure used in reflection shooting.

The second seismic method, 'refraction shooting', makes use of the fact that energy waves travel faster in more consolidated formations such as limestone and salt than in less dense ones. Vibrations change their direction (are refracted) at the boundary between two layers with different speeds of transmission of the waves. The waves may reach the seismometers at the surface if these speeds increase with depth, and the times required to reach the seismometers often make it possible to infer the character and depth of the rocks through which the waves have travelled.

At sea a survey boat in which the recording instrument is installed tows a cable 3000–10 000 ft long, to which a number of specially spaced hydrophones are attached. The shot is fired usually at the middle of the cable from a special shooting boat or from the survey boat itself.

The resulting waves are recorded by the hydrophones and a series of such 'spreads' are 'shot' as the boat proceeds on a set course, thus mapping the area.

Methods other than the 'explosive' method are also used to produce shockwaves. Examples at sea are the 'sparker', whereby an electric charge is discharged in the water as a spark which produces a shockwave, and the 'gas exploder', in which a mixture of gases is exploded in a closed container. On land a shockwave can be produced by dropping a heavy weight on to the surface or a series of waves by placing a vibrator on the surface.

In practice many geophones are generally used to record the waves emanating from one shockpoint, which gives better results with fewer explosions. This is called the 'stacking' or 'common depth point' method.

The field data are processed into seismic sections either on the spot or at a processing centre, optical and magnetic processing methods being widely used. A new processing method has been introduced recently whereby all data are

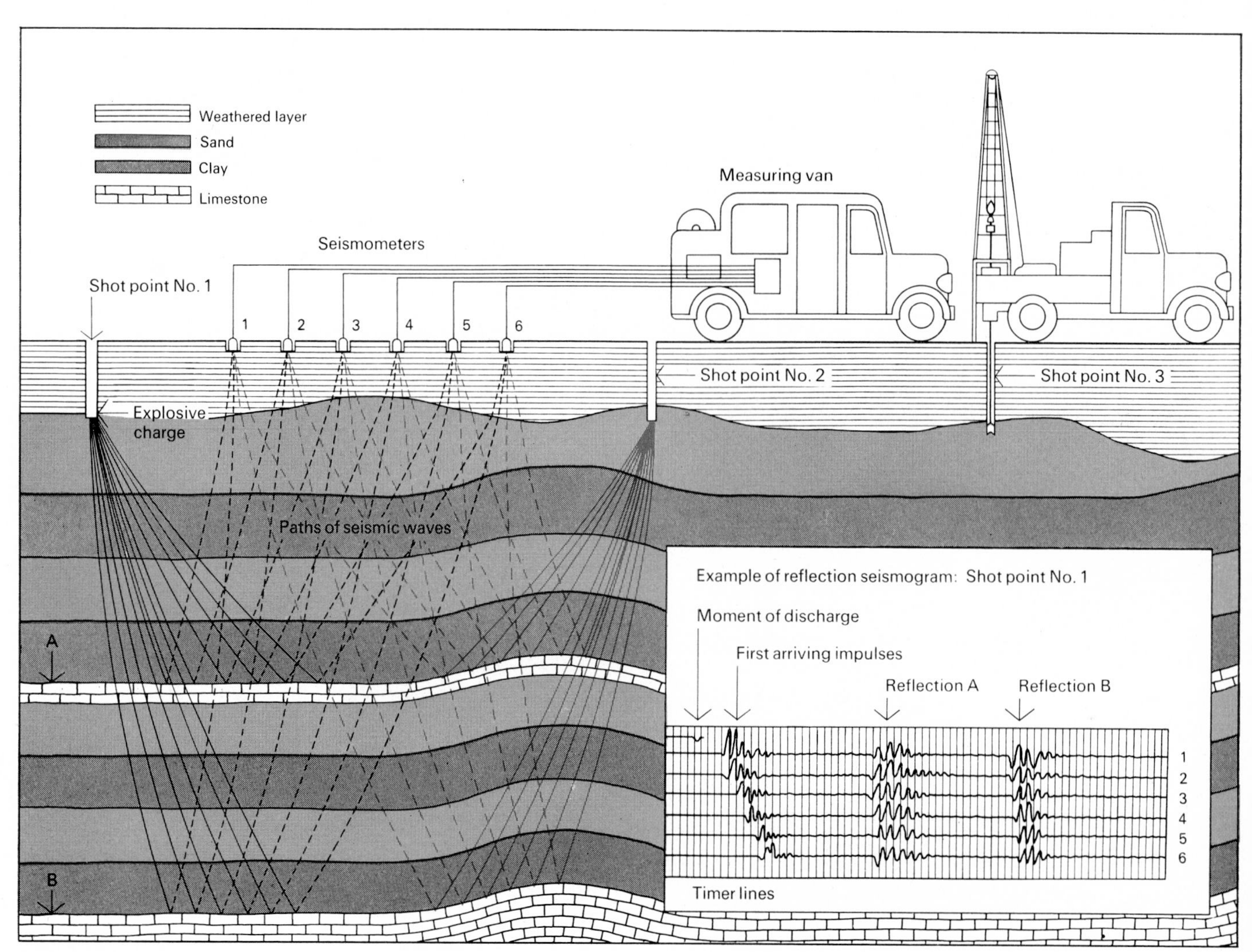

Fig. 29 Seismic survey

produced in or converted into digital form and dealt with by electronic computing machines.

The gravimetric method

The gravimetric method depends on measurements of the slight variations in the force of gravity at the surface of the earth, made with great precision by means of highly sensitive instruments known as gravimeters, torsion balances and pendulums.

At sea gravimetric instruments are lowered on a cable to the bottom of the sea where they are levelled and adjusted by remote control before readings are taken.

The force of gravity at any point on the earth's surface is influenced in magnitude and direction by the distribution of rocks of different densities underlying the area [Fig. 30]. Mathematical analysis of the variations may afford evidence of the presence of concealed geological structures and, under favourable conditions, can define them with considerable accuracy.

The magnetic method

The magnetic method depends on measuring the intensity and direction of the earth's magnetic field and inferring the underlying distribution of rocks possessing different properties from the local variations in this field. Magnetic surveys can now be made from low-flying aircraft, thus permitting rapid surveying and mapping.

Electrical methods

Electrical methods depend on the great differences in resistance to the passage of electric current offered by rocks of various types, and can disclose useful information about rocks buried beneath relatively thin mantles of surface soil or alluvium. Methods based on the same principle are used much more extensively in the course of drilling wells, to identify the formations drilled through and to assess their fluid content.

Geochemical exploration

Little use has been made of geochemical exploration outside the USSR and its practical value is yet uncertain.

One method depends on the inference that in areas overlying accumulations of oil and gas at high pressure, small quantities of gas may be expected to permeate to the surface and be detectable by chemical analysis. Other methods endeavour to detect the presence of bacteria that might indicate the presence of micro-seepages of hydrocarbon gas.

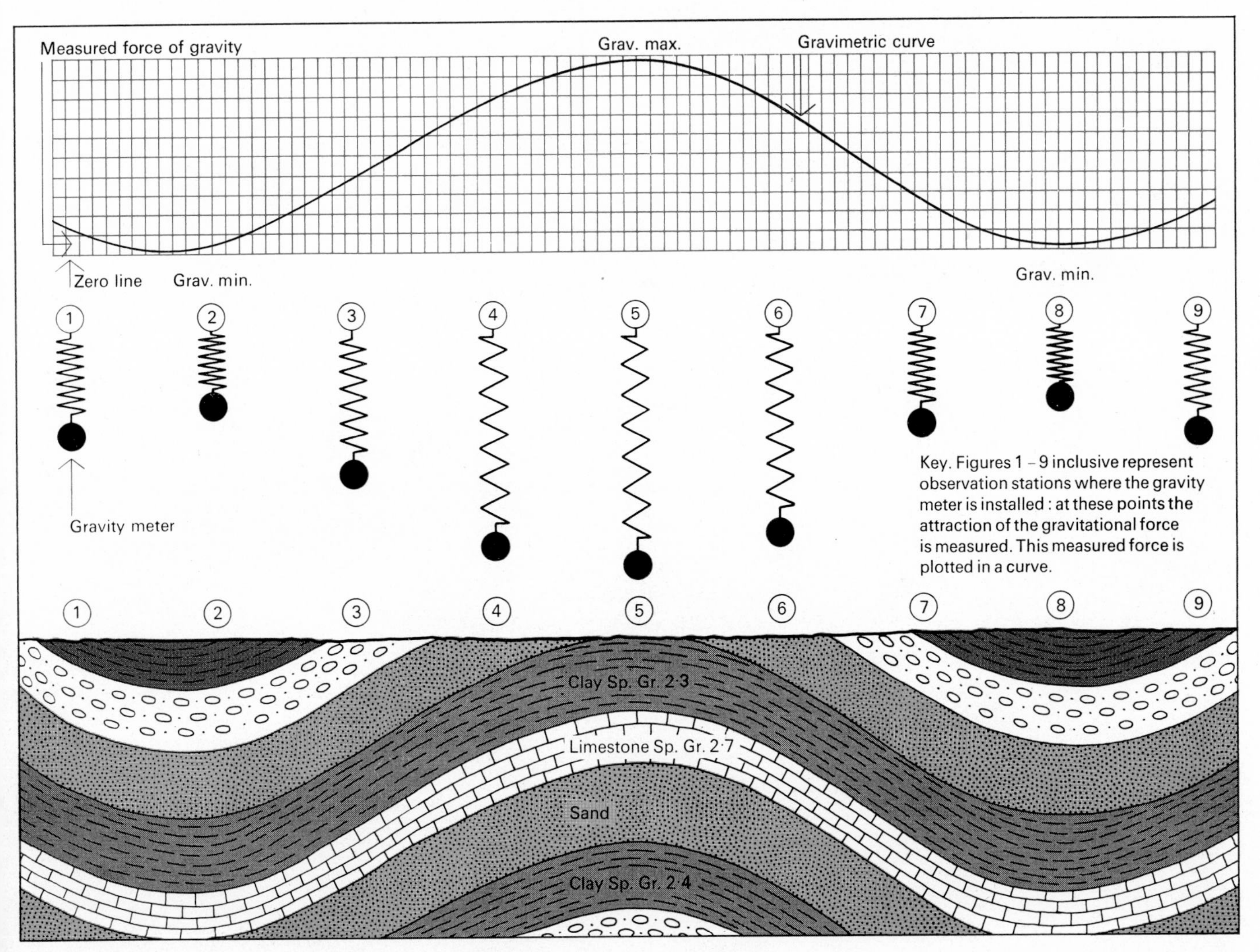

Fig. 30 Gravimetric survey

Exploration results

Geophysical and geological surveys can do no more than suggest underground conditions that may be favourable to oil accumulation; only the drill can prove the presence of oil. The enormous contribution made by geology and geophysics to modern exploration may be judged from what is called the 'success ratio', i.e. the ratio of the number of successful wells to the number of exploration wells associated with the various geological and geophysical methods. These ratios, based on USA data, are:

No scientific exploration success ratio 1 : 30
Geological exploration success ratio 1 : 10
Geophysical exploration success ratio 1 : 6
Geological and geophysical exploration success ratio 1 : 5

'Success' in these cases means merely that some oil or gas was found. If a quantitative standard of success were applied, the ratios would necessarily be less favourable. For example, in recent years in the USA only 1 in 219 exploration wells discovered an accumulation of more than 25 million barrels of oil reserves (a major field); for other countries, notably the Middle East and Venezuela, the results are more favourable.

Exploration drilling

In view of the great cost of a deep exploration well, exploration surveys by one or more of the above-mentioned methods, though costly, will save much money in the long run, particularly in inaccessible territory such as the dense jungles of Nigeria.

After the geologists and geophysicists have found what appears to be a favourable location for drilling, the prospect is sometimes further checked by drilling a number of small-diameter holes, several hundred feet deep, with a light portable drilling rig.

When all data have been assembled and a prognosis has been made of the layers to be expected at depth, a location is selected for an exploration well and deep drilling is started. The first well may reveal a commercial reservoir, but usually more than one well will be necessary, the first wells giving only geological information or sufficient shows of oil or gas to justify further drilling before a final judgement is passed on the value of the area.

All wells drilled to discover accumulations of oil are 'exploration wells', commonly known, especially by the drillers, as 'wildcats' – a designation at least half a century old emphasizing the hazards and the speculative nature of drilling in a new area. A successful wildcat is a 'discovery well'; an unsuccessful one is a 'dry hole'. After oil has been discovered, the first wells to be drilled to establish the limits of the field are 'outstep appraisal' wells, all subsequent wells being 'exploitation' wells or 'development' wells (p. 49).

If the first wells 'prove' an oilfield, the data from these and the appraisal wells are used in drawing up provisional plans for the development of the field and the plans are revised in the light of the further information obtained from the exploitation wells – and another oilfield will then have been added to the world's oil map.

Drilling

Historical

The technique of well drilling goes far back into history. It is first mentioned in ancient Chinese manuscripts, which describe wells drilled as early as the third century AD to tap underground strata for brine. About AD 1100, many centuries before the first well drilled in the western world, depths as great as 3500 ft were reached in China with very primitive equipment [Fig. 31]. The wells were drilled with a heavy bit, which hung from a rope and was jerked up and down by relays of men bouncing on a spring board. The weight of the periodically rising and falling bit drove it deeper and deeper into the ground. This method was the precursor of the 'cable tool' method, a percussion system used in oil well drilling in the nineteenth century and predominantly in the first two decades of the twentieth.

The petroleum industry is traditionally considered to have been born in 1859 near Titusville, Pennsylvania, where 'Colonel' Drake drilled the first well sunk with the express purpose of finding oil. Drake was an employee of a small company marketing lamp oil derived from surface seepages, and success in his well was achieved when the hole partly filled with oil at $69\frac{1}{2}$ ft.

At around the same time, oil wells were also being drilled in other places, notably at Oil Springs, Ontario, Canada, and at Wietze near Hanover, Germany, and there is some doubt as to which country should be credited with having drilled the first commercial oil well. There is no doubt, however, that the success of Drake's well was the incentive for the first oil boom in history. All these wells were drilled by the cable tool method.

The cable tool system was essentially a method of pounding out a hole by repeated blows with a bit attached to a 'drill stem', a heavy length of steel suspended from a wire rope. The drill stem provided the weight to force the bit into the ground, and the hole was kept empty except for a little water at the bottom. After drilling a few feet, the bit was pulled out and the cuttings removed with a 'bailer' – an open tube with a valve at the bottom. Steel pipes known as casing, of progressively smaller diameter, were run from time to time to prevent the hole from caving and to keep back any water flow.

Fig. 31 Early Chinese drilling rig

Cable tool drilling was cheap, simple and effective for shallow wells, but progress was slow, and no means was provided for stemming the flow of oil and gas where encountered under pressure. In such cases the wells blew out and spewed quantities of oil and gas over the countryside. The 'gushers' of these early days were spectacular but wasted a lot of oil and gas, and were a serious fire hazard.

The present-day method of drilling, known as the 'rotary method', was introduced at around the turn of the century. This method, which differs radically from the cable tool method, was first successful in the discovery well of the famous Spindletop field in the Gulf Coast region of Texas. With this method, the bit, instead of moving up and down, is attached to the bottom of a string of steel pipes and rotated by means of a rotary table which turns the uppermost pipe or 'kelly'. 'Drilling fluid' or 'drilling mud' is continuously circulated down through the hollow drilling string, through the bit and back up to the surface through the annular space between drilling string and borehole wall. The drilling fluid flushes the cuttings out of the hole, making removal of tools to clean the hole unnecessary and, by the weight of its column, holds in check fluids under pressure in formations penetrated by the bit, thus greatly reducing the risk of blowout.

In spite of these advantages, it was some little while before the rotary system replaced the cable tool method, which was still used for hard-rock drilling in parts of Pennsylvania as late as 1957. Such areas as retained this method, however, now use the rotary method with air as circulation medium, and employ special bits studded with ultra-hard tungsten carbide inserts.

Although the system employed in rotary drilling is still basically the same as that used in the Spindletop days, there is little resemblance between the old type rig, with its wooden derrick and primitive hoist driven by a small steam engine, and a modern installation with pneumatic controls and with diesel-electric drive sometimes capable of transmitting 3000 hp or more.

A variant of rotary drilling, often used in the USSR and Romania, is known as 'turbo-drilling'. With this method the pipe is not rotated but is kept stationary, and the bit is rotated on bottom by means of a fluid motor or turbine powered by the mud stream. Although the rate of penetration of the bit can be faster with this method than with conventional rotary drilling, pulling out of the hole is required much more frequently, as the bit wears out much faster, so that the overall efficiency is lower, especially in deeper wells and where heavy mud is used. However, the method has some application where high-grade steel is difficult to obtain, and for certain limited applications where rapid bit wear is unimportant.

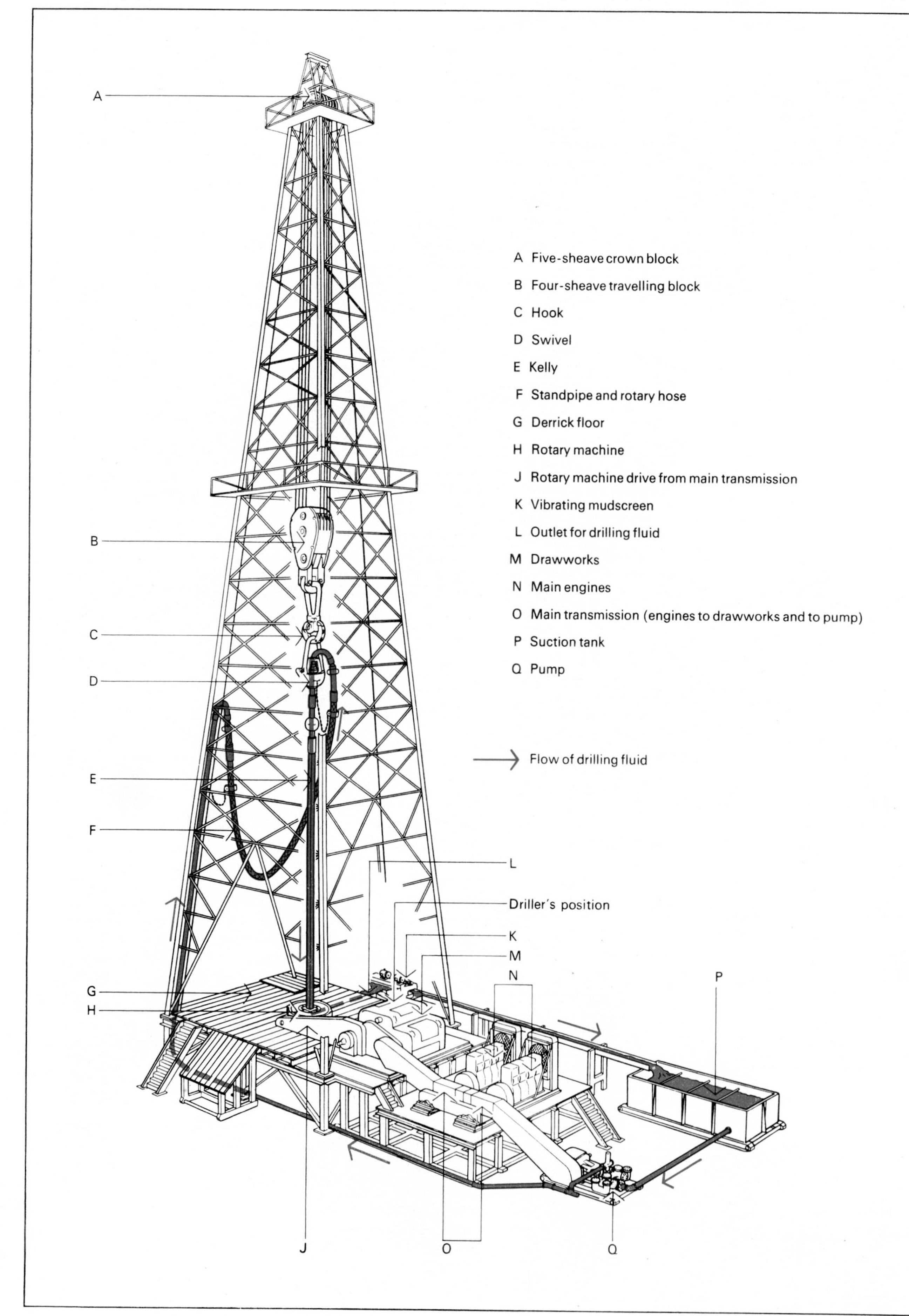

Fig. 32a Diagrammatic view of rotary drilling rig

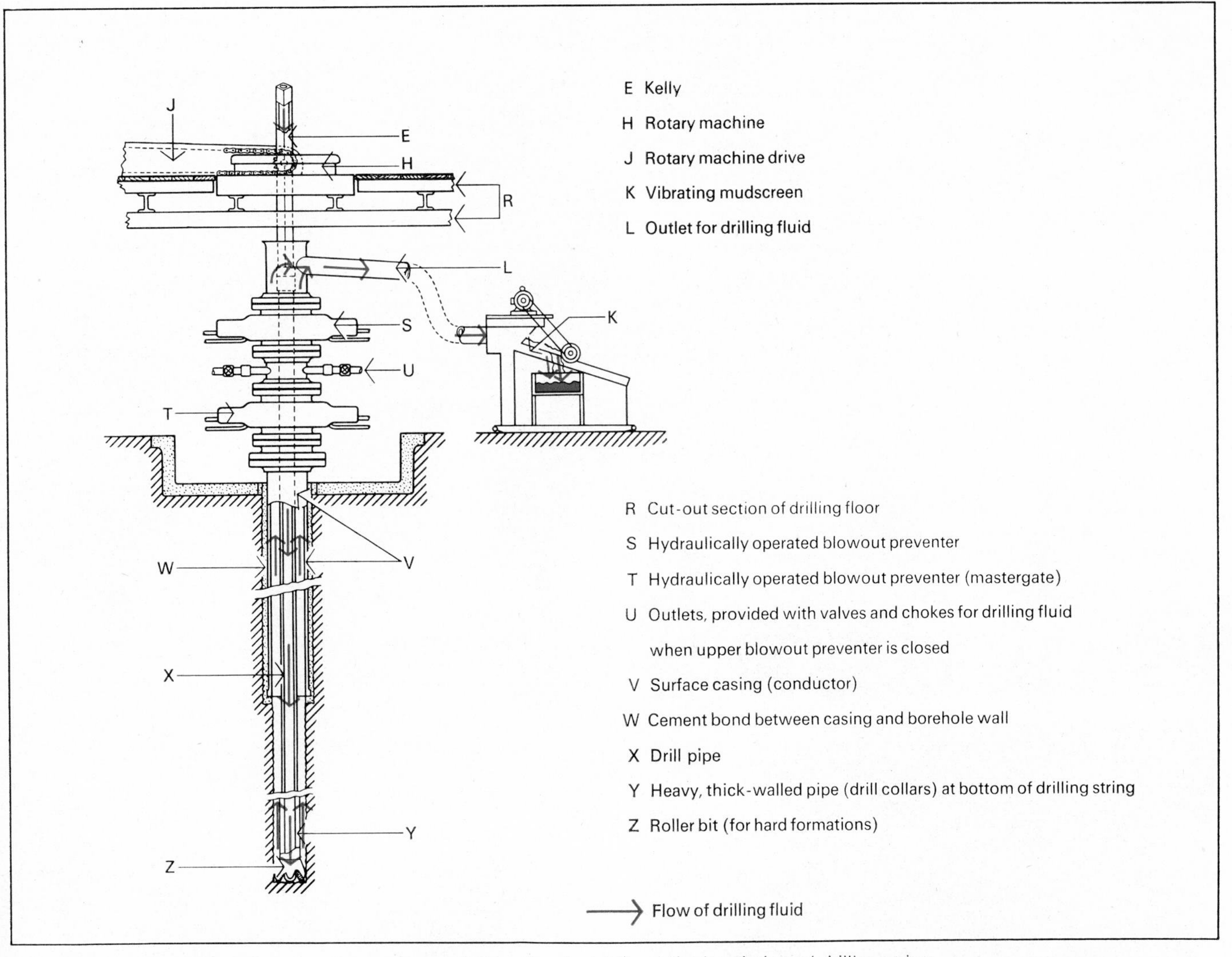

Fig. 32b Diagrammatic section showing equipment below the derrick floor, the borehole and drilling string

The modern rotary drilling installation

A rotary drilling installation consists essentially of bit, drilling string, rotating equipment, hoisting equipment, drilling fluid circulating equipment, prime movers and transmission, and an installation for pressure control [Figs 32a and 32b show the assembly].

Bit and drilling string

The spearhead of the drilling rig is the bit, which cuts its way far beneath the surface through formations sometimes harder than granite. The bit is screwed to the bottom of the drilling string, made up of lengths of special steel pipe (drill pipe), 30 ft long and usually 5 in. diameter but sometimes $4\frac{1}{2}$ in. or $3\frac{1}{2}$ in. or even smaller. Each length or joint is equipped with special steel couplings (tool joints) having a coarse tapered thread and square shoulder to ensure leak proof connections that can transmit torque and yet be made up and broken repeatedly, rapidly and safely.

The top joint, or kelly, passes through the rotary table and is used to transmit the torque or twisting moment from the rotary machinery to the drilling string and thus to the bit. This kelly is made square or hexagonal in cross section and sets of rollers are attached to the rotary table by means of a special housing known as the kelly bushing. The sets of rollers within this bushing form a square or hexagonal aperture through which the kelly passes and is driven by the table, thus giving an almost frictionless drive as the kelly is lowered and drilling proceeds.

Heavy, thick-walled tubes (drill collars) are used at the base of the drilling string, just above the bit. As the drilling string is lowered, the bit touches bottom and starts to take load, thus throwing the bottom of the string into compression. Ordinary drill pipe, which is designed only for tension loading, would soon fail under the buckling and fatigue stresses which occur at the bottom of the string.

In fact, all components of the drilling string must be of the highest quality and finish to withstand the high stresses imposed while drilling. Ordinarily several hundred horsepower may be transmitted mechanically to the bit by means of the drilling string while rotating. The high stresses are due partly to the extraordinary proportions of this string. If a scale model were made of a string 15 000 ft long and 5 in. diameter, and a knitting needle of normal cross section ($\frac{5}{64}$ in. or 2 mm) were used to represent the string, the length of the needle would be 234 ft.

The drilling string with bit attached is rotated at between 75 and 250 rev/min, with loads (on an $8\frac{3}{4}$ in. diameter bit) as high as 80 000 lb bearing down on the bit from the drill collars. The higher loads and slower rotating speeds are used for the harder rocks, and the higher speeds, often with lighter loads, for the softer formations, although recently higher loads have been used on occasions also for the softer rocks.

The ability to apply higher loads on fast-drilling formations depends on the flushing action at the bit, since drilling will slow down rapidly unless the hole bottom is properly scavenged. To achieve the proper scavenging action, the bit is provided with hardened steel nozzles through which the drilling fluid is ejected downwards at a high velocity (usually 300–400 ft/sec), just ahead of the rotating cones of the bit. Some 400 to 600 hydraulic horsepower may be used up in achieving this jetting action on bottom, in addition to the horsepower required to circulate to and from the bit.

The type of bit normally used is known as the three-cone rolling cutter bit, and is shown in Fig. 33. Fewer and longer teeth are used on the cones of bits intended for softer formations, while shorter teeth are used where formations are hard, the shorter teeth allowing for a larger and heavier bearing. For the softer formations it is also customary to set the cones with their axes to the left of centre, as shown in Fig. 34, which increases the scraping action on bottom. For very hard, abrasive formations, a special bit studded with inserts of tungsten carbide may be used [Fig. 35]. After about 10 to 12 hours use, the bits must be pulled out of the hole and replaced, because of either bearing or tooth wear [Fig. 36].

Hoisting equipment

When the bit is dull, the hoisting equipment is used to withdraw the pipe from the hole, and to run back again with the new bit on bottom. A 'derrick' or 'mast' is used to support the block and tackle system used for this purpose. After pulling the pipe upwards 90 ft (three joints of 30 ft each), the lowest drill pipe connexion (tool joint) is unscrewed, and the 'stand' of 90 ft of pipe is laid back on the side of the derrick and 'racked' in an approved manner, so as to remain safe and out of the way while pulling the next stand. Subsequent stands of pipe are then removed from the hole and racked in similar manner. When all stands of pipe and drill collars have been removed from the hole, a considerable weight of pipe is supported in the derrick and on the racking

Fig. 33 Three-cone rolling cutter bit for hard formations

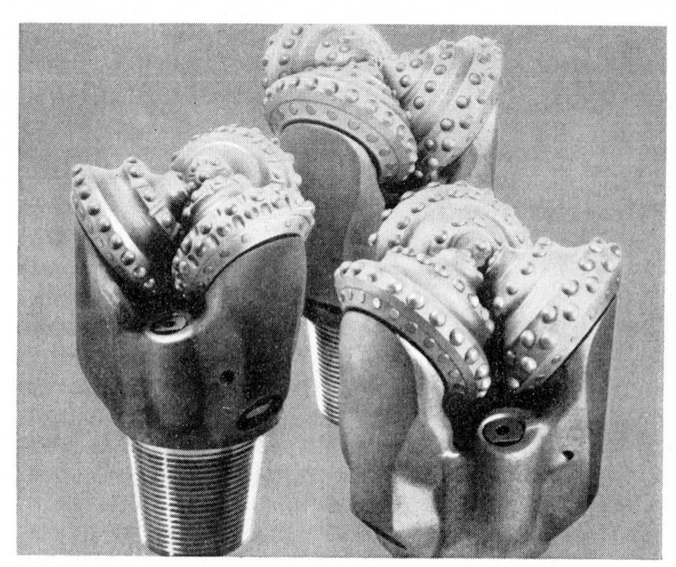

Fig. 35 Bit for hard formations showing tungsten carbide inserts

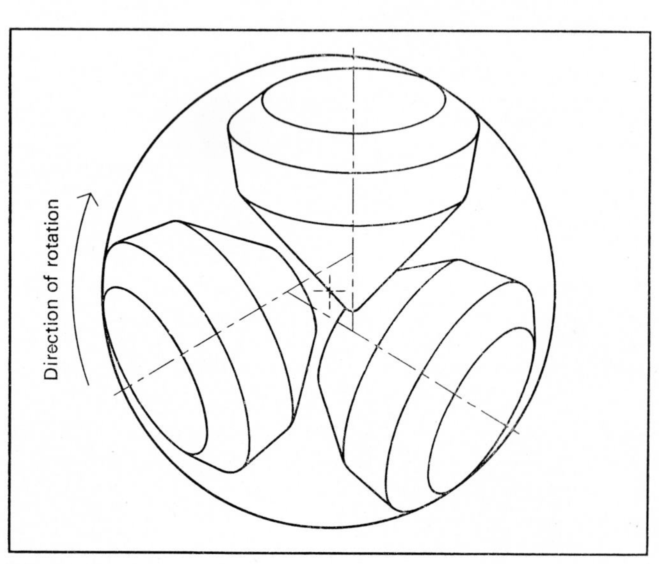

Fig. 34 Disposition of cones in bit for soft formations

Fig. 36 Three-cone rolling cutter bit, (left) new (right) worn

Fig. 37 Masts and derricks, Ventura field, California (mast *left*, derrick *right*). Note the stacked stands of drill pipe beside mast

platforms, and the entire structure must be designed to take these loads.

After the well is completed, the entire rig must be moved to the next drilling location, and while the conventional derrick and substructure are still used on deeper wells, they may be superseded in the case of shallower wells by a portable mast which can be lowered or telescoped to facilitate rapid moves between locations. Typical derricks and masts are shown close-by to one another in Fig. 37 taken in the Ventura field in California.

The powerful hoisting gear used to move pipe in and out of the hole may, on deep rigs, have a lifting capacity of 500 tons. The gear consists of a hoist (the drawworks), a fixed sheave assembly at the top of derrick or mast (the crown block) and a large tackle block (the travelling block) to which a hook is attached. Tough, flexible steel wire rope, $1-1\frac{1}{2}$ in. diameter, is wound round the drum of the hoist and reeved over the sheaves of crown and travelling blocks. The end opposite the hoist (the dead line) is attached to the base of the derrick and to it is clamped an apparatus that measures the tension on the line, which is recorded on the 'weight indicator' situated near the driller. The indicator shows the weight suspended from the hook and, during drilling, the weight resting on the bit. The instrument also makes a comprehensive record of drilling operations by continuously registering the loads on a moving chart.

The drawworks [Fig. 38] is mounted firmly at the level of the derrick floor, and consists of a steel drum and a system of shafts, chains, sprockets and clutches aimed at providing various alternative drive ratios, thus performing a function essentially similar to that of a gearbox on a motor car. The drawworks also contains a heavy duty braking mechanism for the drum with brake lever under the driller's manual control, catheads for operating pipe-handling tools, and a console equipped with instruments, control levers and handles for operating engines and drawworks manually, electrically, or pneumatically.

Rotating gear

The kelly and thus the drilling string are rotated by means of the rotary machine set in the centre of the derrick floor, through the kelly bushing.

The kelly in fact passes through and fits the aperture in the bushing so that it can be rotated while still free to move vertically throughout most of its length. The table is rotated through a 3:1 reduction gear driven by an electric motor or by chain drive through the drawworks from the diesel engines or other prime movers. The rotating kelly and drilling string are suspended from the hook by the swivel, their weight being taken up within the swivel by heavy roller thrust bearings which allow free rotation under heavy loads.

Drilling fluid circulation system

The drilling fluid is pumped under high pressure from a suction tank or pit outside the derrick, up a standpipe in the corner of the derrick, through the rotary hose and swivel to the hollow kelly and drilling string. After leaving the drilling bit, the fluid, carrying the drill cuttings, ascends to the surface through the annular space between drill string and wall of the borehole. At the well head it passes through a rapidly vibrating screen (the shale shaker) which retains most of the drill cuttings, and returns to the suction tank, often via an intermediate tank used for treating purposes.

The heart of the circulation system is the mud pump, a reciprocating, gear driven, dual piston type. As its breakdown during drilling might have serious consequences, including the loss of at least part of the hole, the pump must be of exceptionally sturdy construction, capable not only of sustained service under heavy loads, but also of handling

Fig. 38 Rotary drawworks for drilling at depths from 13 000–20 000 ft

abrasive, sand-laden fluids. Pumps with input rated capacity of 1000 hp or more are commonly used on the deeper wells, with working pressures in the range of 2500–3000 lb/in^2.

Prime movers and transmissions

Steam power, commonly used twenty years ago, has now been virtually completely superseded by the diesel engine as a source of motive power, although a number of gas engines are in use in the USA, and diesel-electric drives are also quite popular, especially on the more permanent installations such as those for offshore drilling.

The power plant of a typical heavy drilling installation using diesel engines may consist of three or four engines of 500 hp rating, each self-contained on its own skid for easy transport or removal. The engines may be coupled by a compound transmission system of clutches and chain drives, including drive to the mud pumps, or the pumps may be driven by one or more independent engine compounds. Often the diesel engines are equipped with torque converters or similar drives to achieve optimum performance and to improve smoothness of operation.

Pressure control equipment

Oil and gas occurring at shallow depth are usually associated with pressures at or about the equivalent of a column of salt water reaching from that depth to the surface. Gas, however, will tend to expand when being brought to the surface, and can easily eject some of the annular fluid column if not handled with dexterity. Furthermore a bit, when withdrawn rapidly from a hole containing viscous mud, can exert a powerful swabbing action causing gas or other fluid to enter the bore hole unless adequate care is taken during the early stages of pulling the pipe. At greater depths, oil, gas or salt water may be encountered unexpectedly at pressures in excess of that of the hydrostatic column, and allowance must be made for this in many of the areas where wells are now being drilled.

To handle these emergencies, a system of control equipment is usually installed at the well head after setting surface casing. This equipment, commonly termed the 'blowout preventer stack' can close off the annulus between drill pipe and casing within 15 seconds or less, and can hold pressure up to 5000 lb/in^2 or more depending on their size and rating. The preventers operate by hydraulic pressure which causes horizontally opposed pistons (rams) to close up and fit closely around the drill stem. Similar rams of different shape are used to close up against one another and thus shut off the entire opening at the well head should the pipe be already out of the hole. The arrangement is shown diagrammatically in Fig. 32b.

Drilling the well

The technique of drilling

The drilling of a well is a round-the-clock operation and usually continues uninterruptedly from the moment of drilling the first foot (spudding in) until completion. Under the supervision of a drilling foreman (toolpusher), three crews, each comprising a driller and four men, work three eight-hour shifts. A mechanic attends to the engines and other specialists are called in as required.

While the drillers are responsible for the mechanical operations of drilling, the engineer in charge has to see that the drilling programme is carried out to best advantage. He may examine drill cuttings and cores before sending them to the laboratory for more detailed examination; he may supervise production tests of potentially productive formations; he will repeatedly test the drilling fluid to ensure its proper consistency and performance, and will see that it receives any necessary chemical or mechanical treatment. This is most important, because neglected or improperly treated mud can seriously impede progress, or even lead to loss of well control, stuck pipe or equally serious hazards.

When the drilling string has been run to bottom and the kelly connected, the mud pumps are started and when normal circulation is achieved the rotary table is put into motion and drilling proceeds. The weight on the bit, as shown by the weight indicator, is kept at the required value by gradually lowering the string until the kelly has descended through most of its length and another joint has to be screwed on. The kelly is then raised until the first tool joint shows above the rotary machine when the weight of the string is taken up by inserting wedges (rotary slips) around the drill pipe. These slips fit into a recess in the rotary table, known as the table bushing. The kelly is then unscrewed by means of mechanically operated tongs and is placed to one side of the derrick. A 30 ft joint of drill pipe is screwed on [Fig. 39], the kelly is replaced and drilling is resumed.

At intervals, generally because a bit has to be replaced, the entire string is pulled and unscrewed in 90 ft stands which are stacked in a nearly upright position on one side of the derrick floor [Fig. 39] with the help of the derrick man. This man occupies a rather precarious position on a platform high up in the derrick, to which he is attached by a safety belt.

Pulling out and running in a long, heavy drilling string (the entire operation is a 'round trip') is a lengthy business in spite of efficient handling methods and powerful equipment. On a well organized rig drilling at 15 000 ft, it may take $5\frac{1}{2}$ hours to pull out and $3\frac{1}{2}$ hours to run back in again, the pulling out taking longer on account of the great weight (about 100 tons) to be lifted in the early stages.

Fig. 39 View on the derrick floor during the running in of the drilling string. A stand has been screwed on, the 'slips' have been pulled from their recess in the rotary machine, and the string is to be lowered

Casing the well

A well is started with a relatively large hole, $14\frac{3}{4}$–$17\frac{1}{2}$ in. or larger in diameter, which must be lined as soon as possible with steel pipes. In shallow development wells this surface casing may be run at a depth of only 150 ft or less, but deeper wells, especially exploration wells, may need to be cased to a depth of 1000 ft or more before drilling proceeds in the next section of the hole. This casing prevents the upper hole from caving and water from entering or mud from leaving the hole. It also provides a firm base and anchor for the blowout preventers and for the long strings of casings which may be run later to line the lower part of the hole. This casing is designated by its outside diameter, namely $13\frac{3}{8}$ in., $10\frac{3}{4}$ in. or $9\frac{5}{8}$ in., derived historically from 13 in., 10 in. and 9 in. nominal linepipe inside dimensions.

The surface casing is rigidly secured by filling the space between casing and wall with cement. Cement slurry is fed into the casing pipe, a rubber plug is placed on top of it, and drilling fluid then pumped in, so forcing the cement down inside the pipe and up again between pipe and wall. When the plug reaches bottom pumping is stopped and the well is left standing 12 hours or more for the cement to set. Drilling is then resumed using a smaller bit – $12\frac{1}{4}$ in. through $13\frac{3}{8}$ in. casing, $9\frac{5}{8}$ in. through $10\frac{3}{4}$ in. and $8\frac{1}{2}$ in. through $9\frac{5}{8}$ in. casing. If the well is successful and oil or gas is met, a further string of casing is cemented at or near the bottom.

Casing is expensive and its cost may be an appreciable proportion of the total cost of the well. For development wells, especially where conditions are already rather well known and where production rates do not call for large diameter completion strings, smaller clearances and reduced diameters may be warranted, as experience indicates, in the interest of reduced capital costs.

Drilling fluids (muds)

The progress and efficiency of drilling depend largely on the use of the right drilling fluid for the rock being drilled. Normal drilling fluids usually consist of colloidal suspensions of clays in water, with chemical additives to control viscosity and other properties. Under many conditions the use of an oil-in-water emulsion, rather than water alone, is advantageous. When drilling in low pressure oil-bearing formations, a non-aqueous oil-base mud may be preferable. Air, gas or aerated liquids can also be used in certain circumstances and result in very rapid drilling. In extremely deep wells the mud must remain fluid at temperatures of up to 400°F (205°C).

The main functions of the drilling fluid are as follows:

To assist in maintaining maximum drilling rate compatible with safety. To achieve this the drilling fluid must be of such a 'weight' (density) that it will only just prevent uncontrolled influx of gas, oil or water from the formations encountered. In addition, the solid content and viscosity of the fluid must be kept to a minimum and the 'filtrate loss' to a maximum for the formations drilled.

To remove drill cuttings from the bottom of the hole and the face of the drilling bit.

To carry the drill cuttings out of the borehole. The ability to do this increases with the velocity, viscosity and density of the ascending fluid. For efficient removal of the cuttings the velocity should not fall below a critical level (usually 120–180 ft/min).

C

To support and protect the wall of the hole. Caving or collapse of the hole may be prevented by the pressure of the fluid column against the wall of the hole. In addition a protective sheath (or mud cake) is deposited on porous formations by the ascending fluid. This mud cake must be thin and should restrict the entry of water (filtrate loss) from the drilling fluid into the formation.

To keep the drill cuttings in suspension when circulation is stopped, for instance when replacing a worn bit. To do this effectively the drilling fluid should stiffen or gel when at rest and become fluid again when put in motion.

To cool the bit. Considerable heat is generated by a bit drilling under heavy load.

To have such properties of electrical conductivity or resistivity as to assist in obtaining satisfactory electric logs.

When highly permeable formations are penetrated, drilling fluid may escape into them and either part or all of the fluid stream may be lost. To combat this, fibrous, flaky or granular 'lost circulation' materials (e.g. asbestos fibres, cellophane flakes or walnut shells) may be added to the drilling fluid. If losses cannot be stopped by this means, a slurry of cement, bentonite and water or diesel oil can be forced into the rock to plug the pores. For very large losses in vugular limestone a slurry of sand in water can be pumped down to fill the crevices. Alternatively in certain circumstances drilling can be continued without any return of the drilling fluid to the surface, allowing it all to disappear into the formation and maintaining a 'floating mudcap' above the loss of circulation zone to prevent the well from blowing out.

Directional drilling

Wells are normally drilled vertically, but sometimes it is necessary to drill a slanting hole, for example if the oil-bearing formation is beneath a built-up area. A further use for slanting holes (usually called 'directional' holes) is where a group of wells must be drilled from a single location (e.g. an offshore platform).

Generally speaking, the cost of drilling a directional well is greater than that of drilling a vertical well of the same hole depth. This is because of the slower drilling rate and the time required to make surveys of the course of the well, and to correct this course where necessary. About 30% additional time is required, on the average, for a directional hole.

Normally, the well is drilled vertically for a short distance, and cased, before deviation is begun. A steel wedge, or 'removable whipstock' is set on bottom to start the hole in the desired direction. The method of using the whipstock is shown in Fig. 40. A special bit is used inside this whipstock, and the whipstock forces this bit away from the vertical as the bit drills downwards and outwards while the whipstock remains stationary, and the pipe slides down within the upper sleeve built into the body of the whipstock as shown.

Special instruments based on the use of a magnetic compass are used to orientate the whipstock in the desired direction, and these instruments are used again from time to time to check the course of the hole. Various stiff or limber assemblies are used above the bit while drilling, to maintain hole direction or to allow the build-up of angle. Nowadays the engineer directing these operations is thoroughly familiar with the effect of various assemblies and drilling techniques on the probable course of the hole, and the whipstock, once used for the initial deflection may only be

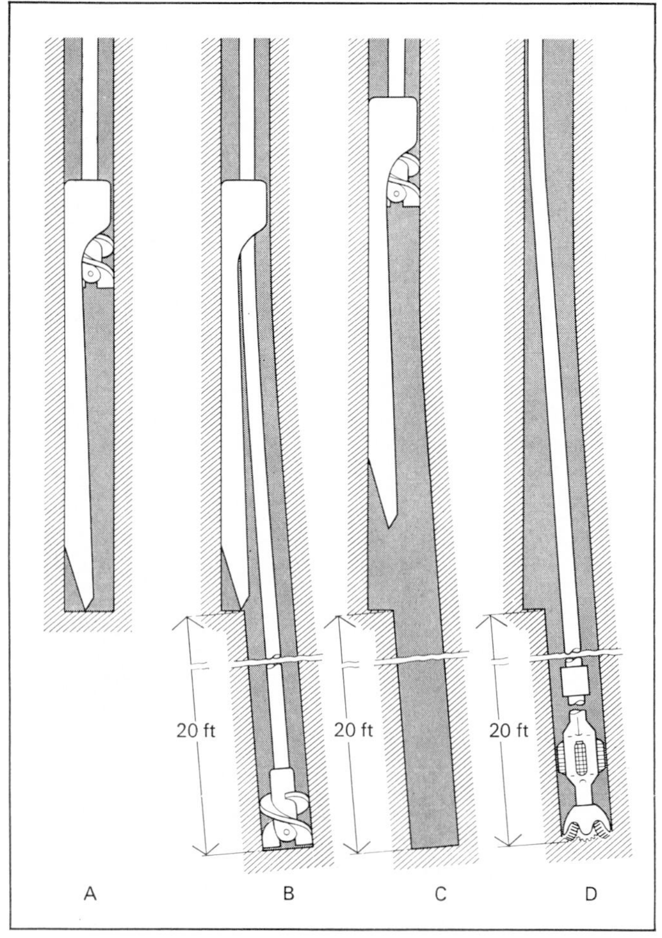

Fig. 40 Directional drilling: (a) The whipstock in position; (b) A short length of deviated hole is drilled; (c) The whipstock is pulled; (d) The deviated hole is reamed, and drilling is eventually continued

required occasionally to correct large deviations from the desired course of the well.

The build-up of angle proceeds until the desired maximum is reached. This may be 30°–40° or more, depending on the amount of sideways displacement required at the bottom of the hole. The rate of build-up of angle is about 2° or 2½° per 100 ft. Once the desired angle is obtained, it is usually maintained steady until the well is completed, since this allows a stiff assembly to be used, resulting in faster drilling.

The use of directional drilling has increased in recent years. Although the actual hole is more expensive, the overall cost of a group or 'cluster' of wells may be cheaper than that of the same number of vertical wells drilled each from its own surface location. In developing offshore fields in the Gulf of Mexico, twelve or more wells are sometimes drilled from one central platform.

A special use of directional drilling is to control a wild flowing well, by drilling a relief well from a point some distance (say 1200 ft) from the well blowing out. A directional hole is drilled to intersect the latter at approximately the depth of the producing layer. Large quantities of heavy drilling fluid are pumped down the relief well to 'kill' the flow in the main well. As may be imagined, great skill is required to reach the desired target sometimes many thousands of feet below the surface.

Drilling hazards

The drilling of a well is not always simple and one or othe of the following hazards may be encountered.

Blowouts

Blowouts are potentially the most dangerous and disastrou hazard, because of the risk of fire [Fig. 41]. The cost of re gaining control is often very high and much oil and gas ma be wasted. As a result of improved techniques and specia training of drilling crews, blowouts are now fortunatel rare.

However, although actual blowouts now seldom occur there is often a continual threat of a blowout occurring particularly where gas or oil is encountered at pressure higher than normally expected. The greatest diligence i required under such circumstances. The first sign is ofte an increase of drilling speed for no apparent reason othe than the fact that a higher pressure has been encountered This does not mean that control has been lost, but should ac as a warning to the driller. He must be constantly on th lookout for an increase in rate of return of drilling mu showing that foreign fluid is entering the well. He may sto the pump to see if the returns stop also. Later he may se gas bubbles in the mud, but here again this may not mear control has been lost, but only that gas-bearing formatio has been drilled up.

If indications show that formation fluid is entering or ha entered the hole, the blowout preventers must be close

Fig. 41 Blowout near Long Beach, California

and a check made to see what pressures if any build up at the surface in the closed-in well. The pressure reading serves as an indication of the amount of heavier mud required thereafter to keep the pressures under control, and this new mud must be pumped in immediately, while holding a back-pressure on the return line until the well has been circulated clean and drilling can resume in the normal manner.

The heavy mud must be kept available for any such eventuality, as without this the well cannot be kept under continuous control. Barytes (barium sulphate) or similar weighting material is added to the drilling fluid to give it this additional density.

Lost circulation

When a very porous formation or fissured rock, or rock containing cavities, such as limestone, is encountered, the mud seal on the borehole may be ineffective in preventing escape of the drilling fluid into the formation. Circulation will diminish or cease and drilling may then become impossible. Materials that plug the pores and fissures of the formation are added to the drilling fluid or, if this does not have the desired effect, cement or other means may be required. In extreme cases an extra string of casing may have to be set before drilling can be resumed.

Stuck drill pipe

The drilling string may become stuck in the hole as a result of mechanical obstruction such as a broken bit cone or excessive drill cuttings or caving formation, or through friction caused mainly hydraulically due to the overpressure of the fluid in the hole where pipe has been pressed into the mud cake, or through a combination of these causes.

The stuck pipe may sometimes be freed by 'spotting' a slug of oil as soon as possible opposite the stuck portion, and allowing this to soak while pulling and jarring on the string.

If the string cannot be freed in this way, the stuck point may be established by instruments, and a small explosive charge, lowered just above this point inside the drill string, is exploded to loosen the tool joint sufficiently to allow it to be unscrewed easily by rotation at the surface. The stuck portion must then be 'sidetracked', using a whipstock such as described under 'directional drilling' or other means.

Stuck pipe is not as common now as in the past, due to improvements in mud technique and to the use of 'stabilizers' in the drilling string which help prevent it from pressing into the mud cake. Special drill collars having a non-circular cross section also help in preventing this 'pressure differential' sticking.

Fishing

A part of the drilling string, bit cones or similar junk, left in the hole through mechanical failure, or by backing off as described above, are known as fishes.

Efforts may be made to remove such fishes, or the fish may be sidetracked as already described. Small parts may be fished with a magnet, or a 'junk basket', while the larger fishes involving pipe require an 'overshot' or 'tap'. The overshot is used to grip the pipe on the outside, while the tap screws into heavy-wall pipe such as drill collars and grips it with its tapered surface [Figs 42(a) and (b)].

Nowadays less time is spent attempting to recover a fish than formerly, especially in deep wells, because it is often more economical to back-off and sidetrack the fish than to spend time in arduous and often unsuccessful fishing operations.

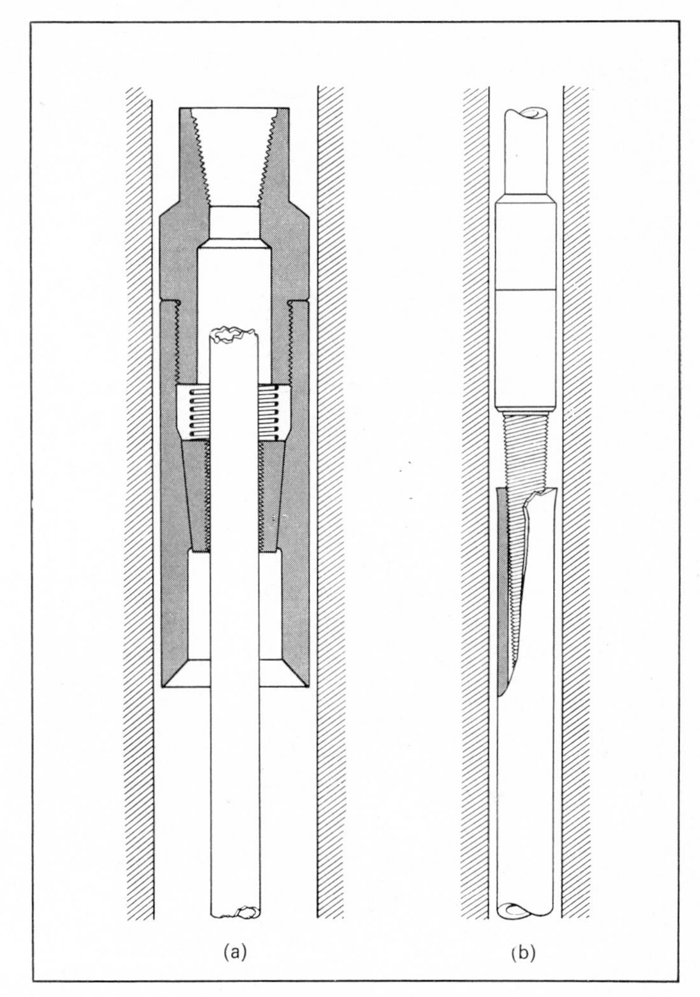

Fig. 42 Typical fishing tools: (a) Non-releasable overshot; (b) Fishing tap

Crooked holes

In the early days of drilling, wells were often considerably off vertical and followed a crooked and tortuous path. In an effort to correct some of the undesirable consequences, a concerted effort was later made to drill the wells as straight and as vertical as possible. These efforts were largely successful while low bit loads were practised, but the advent of higher bit loading, although improving drilling rates, sometimes resulted in increased hole angle, especially in steeply dipping formations.

To control deviation in the 'crooked-hole' formations, much money may be lost in holding up drilling weights to maintain a vertical or near-vertical hole, since normal penetration rates are seldom possible under such conditions. Moreover, the accidental build-up of hole angle followed by rapid corrective efforts often resulted in a 'dog leg' or rapid change of direction which was actually more hazardous than the angle it was intended to correct.

Modern practice is to allow reasonable natural deviation, say up to 10° or more, but to prevent the occurence of dog legs by suitable assemblies which stabilize the drill string and prevent a rapid change of angle. If the natural drift tendency is very pronounced, the surface location may be sited so as to allow the well to be completed at the desired point.

Marine drilling

Before World War II, little effort was made to drill for oil in the underwater regions of oil basins. In the 1880s, shallow wells were drilled from piers off the coast of southern California, near Rincon. In the late 1920s, immense developments started in Lake Maracaibo in Venezuela, and the sea extension of the Huntington Beach field (southern California) was tapped by means of directional wells drilled from beach locations. Drilling in the Caspian Sea, near Baku, was a still later development. But none of these wells can be said to have been drilled on the continental shelf.

After World War II, the search for oil was intensified, and the prospects revealed by geophysical surveys in the Gulf of Mexico soon led to the drilling of the first off-shore well in those waters. Since then, the technique of offshore drilling has developed rapidly, and many types of drilling platforms have been constructed suitable for operations far from shore in water as deep as 500 ft or more. With these platforms, wells are now being drilled in the Gulf of Mexico up to 100 miles off the coasts of Texas and Louisiana.

Offshore drilling is also in progress off the California coast, in Alaskan coastal waters, in the Gulf of Paria off Trinidad, off the coasts of Qatar and Iran, in the China Sea off Borneo, in African waters off Libya, off Australia, in the Gulf of Suez, and in the North Sea.

Marine drilling platforms must be sturdily constructed and capable of withstanding heavy seas, particularly in the Gulf of Mexico, where hurricanes commonly occur. To avoid damage by waves during stormy weather, the main deck may be 50–60 ft above sea level.

Drilling platforms fall into the following general categories.

Fig. 43 Offshore drilling platform and drilling barge (tender) in Lake Maracaibo, Venezuela. A helicopter is arriving on the landing platform

Fixed platform with floating tender

The platform, erected on piles driven into the sea bed, is just large enough to carry the derrick, drawworks, and engines. A drilling tender, moored to the platform, contains the power supply, circulating pumps (connected to the platform by hoses), mud storage tanks, drill pipe racks, casing, cement, cementing equipment, living quarters for the drilling crews, and generally a helicopter landing platform. This type of drilling platform is used in the Gulf of Mexico and, without living quarters, in Lake Maracaibo [Fig. 43]. Tender type platforms have the disadvantage that in bad weather the tender may have to be withdrawn from the platform with consequent interruption in drilling, although the frequency and length of these interruptions can be substantially reduced by slightly enlarging the fixed platform and installing on it some standby equipment such as a mud pump, some pipe storage space, etc.

Self-contained fixed platform

This is a greatly enlarged version of the small platform and does not require a tender. The unit is particularly suitable for drilling a cluster of as many as 18–24 or more directionally deviated development wells.

After the wells have been completed, the platform is sometimes used for the installation of production equipment, such as oil tanks and pumps for transferring oil production either into barges or to a shore installation through submarine pipelines.

Self-contained mobile platform

The cost of a self-contained fixed platform for deep water is high, amounting perhaps to as much as £500 000 to £1 000 000, exclusive of equipment, and less than half its cost can be recovered if the wells prove to be dry. In view of this high cost and the disadvantages of tender type operations, mobile platforms, which retain the entire drilling installation in place and can be towed from one location to another, are being used to an increasing extent for exploratory and development drilling in water up to 250 ft deep, in spite of their often greater cost (up to £2 500 000).

In the few years since the advent of marine drilling, designers have been very active, and numerous types of mobile platforms have been developed.

One of the most popular mobile units is the jack-up type.

Fig. 44 Self-contained mobile drilling platform (Transocean)

Fig. 45 Floating drilling platform in the Pacific Ocean north-west of San Francisco (Blue Water 2)

An example of this type is the Transocean rigs, one of which is being used in the North Sea. This unit consists of a floating hull 225 by 140 by 18 ft, which also serves as the working deck [Fig. 44]. The derrick and substructure, hoisting machinery, pipe racks, casing, crew quarters, and helicopter platform are installed on this deck. The main power plant, light plant, circulation pumps, and other equipment are installed in the deckhouse and inside the hull. Six large hollow steel columns fit into openings passing through the hull at the corners and along the sides. These columns are moved downward to penetrate the sea bottom and lift the hull above water into the drilling position by means of electrically driven pinions running on racks attached to the columns. The platform is lowered and removed by reversing this procedure. Mobile platforms of the jack-up type are now being constructed to operate in up to 300 ft of water.

Tender-assisted mobile derrick platform

A relatively recent development is the replacement of the small fixed platform, carrying the derrick and associated equipment only, by a small mobile derrick platform, which still needs to be assisted by a floating tender as described above.

Floating platforms

The development of floating drilling a few years ago was prompted by a desire for simplification and economy, as well as by the limitations of water depth capacity of the jack-up mobile units. Initial types were surface floating hulls, generally ship-shaped, and later developments included dual hulls and stabilizing outriggers. These were followed by the semi-submersible design developed from the column stabilized submersible mobile units discussed later. In the drilling position the hull of this type is submerged about 40–80 ft, and the balancing buoyancy is provided by large bottle-shaped corner columns which support the working deck above the hull. A recently built unit of this type is 204 ft square and 83 ft high to lower deck [Fig. 45].

Floating platforms are held on location by conventional anchors or by an automatically controlled propulsion system and have the advantage of being suitable for drilling even in thousands of feet of water.

Drilling from floating platforms requires the use of underwater well-heads which are normally installed on the sea floor and are operated either wholly from the surface or with the assistance of divers. Guidance systems must be provided so that drilling tools can be led into the well bore.

(a)

(b)

(c)

(d)

Fig. 46 Major components of underwater drilling equipment: (a) Guide structure that rests on sea bottom; (b) Low pressure blowout preventers used during shallow drilling; (c) High pressure blowout preventers for deeper drilling; (d) Underwater television to monitor remote sea-bed operations

Some of the special underwater equipment required in one typical system is illustrated above.

Submersible drilling barges

A strip of land along the Gulf Coast of Louisiana and Texas consists of deep swamps and marshes in which road-building and the preparation of well sites are very expensive undertakings. The many promising oil prospects in the area are reached by shallow canals about 10 feet deep which are dug in the soft, marshy soil by dredges. The drilling installation is mounted on the deck of a large flat-bottomed barge which has a narrow slit in the hull running longitudinally from one end through a point beyond the centre of the derrick. The drilling barge is towed to the site where the well is to be drilled and, when in position, is settled on bottom by flooding water-tight compartments. Once the well has been completed, the barge is raised by pumping the water out of the compartments. The barge is then floated off the well site, the slit in the hull allowing the barge to pull clear of the well-head protruding above the water.

Some drilling barges are very large and are used in drilling to great depths. In 1956, one was employed to drill the deepest well then in existence. The well, located near Lake Washington, southern Louisiana, reached a final depth of 22 570 ft.

When drilling moved to the deeper water of the river deltas and inland lakes the deck of the drilling barges was raised on stanchions or posts above the hull itself. For the still deeper waters offshore the deck had to be raised further and stabilizing agents had to be added in the form of large-diameter columns, or 'milk bottles', to provide the necessary stability when submerging the barge to the sea bottom. These units became known as 'submersible mobile units'; their hulls took the form of a pontoon or large-diameter pipe grid and the largest of these measures 200 ft from the bottom of the pontoons to the 'Texas Deck' on which the drilling rig and crew quarters are installed. This unit can 'sit-on-bottom' in water depths up to 170 ft.

Evaluation of formations

Drilling a well is an essential step in the location and efficient production of oil, but a lot of information has to be obtained from the operations in order to assess the prospects of the region or, if oil is struck, to plan the completion of the well and the development of the field (Oilfield development and production, p. 49). The formations penetrated must be identified, any oil or gas-bearing intervals located and as much information as possible gleaned about the nature of the reservoir in which they occur. The principal methods used to obtain this information are as follows.

Examination of drilling fluid

The presence of oil, gas or salt water in the formation may be revealed by traces in the mud flush returning to the surface. There may not be enough to be seen by visual inspection but certain tests will reveal even small traces of oil or gas. Oil is fluorescent so that when viewed under ultraviolet light even small traces emit a distinct glow. Gas may be detected by blowing air through the fluid and passing it through a 'gas detector' in which any inflammable gas is burnt over an electrically heated platinum filament and is detected by the resultant rise in temperature.

Examination of drill cuttings

Samples of drill cuttings are examined periodically. Although most of any oil they contained originally is flushed out by drilling fluid there often remains enough to give an oil stain or a discoloration of a colourless solvent such as carbon tetrachloride when the cuttings are shaken with it. Examination of the solvent under ultraviolet light is an even more delicate test.

The drill cuttings will reveal the nature of the formation being penetrated and enable them to be identified with formations known to exist in neighbouring wells. The fossil content, the mineralogical composition and the presence of ancient pollen may help to identify and correlate the formations.

Logging by examination of drilling fluid and drill cuttings involves no elaborate or expensive sampling and testing and gives quick results, but there is always an element of doubt whether the material examined has come from the bottom of the hole or has been sloughed off from higher formations. Supplementary logging techniques are therefore almost always used to confirm the information derived from fluid and cuttings. The following methods are used.

Electric logging

In practically every well one or more electric logs are taken at suitable intervals during drilling. An arrangement known as a 'sonde', equipped to measure some electrical, acoustical or radioactive property of the formations, is lowered into the hole on a multi-conductor cable. When the sonde is pulled up, a record of the measurements is produced at the surface [Fig. 47]. A simplified log is shown in Fig. 48.

The particular property recorded may not be of direct significance but can be related to properties such as the porosity or the fraction of the pore space which is saturated with hydrocarbons, and a knowledge of these is essential for the appraisal of a reservoir.

At the contact of impervious shales and permeable formations for example, variations in electrical potential may be observed in the borehole. A record of these potentials, the self potential log, will assist in delineating permeable formations. Moreover the magnitude of the potential variations will often allow the resistivity of the formation water to be estimated.

As a substitute for this log, or in addition to it, a gamma ray log may also be indicative of shales. It records the natural gamma radiation of the formations. Shales generally have a much higher level of gamma radiation than non-argillaceous formations.

The gamma ray log is an example of a nuclear log. It is often run in combination with a neutron log which serves to estimate the porosity of a formation. It contains a radio active source that emits fast neutrons which penetrate the formation and are there slowed down by collisions with atomic nuclei. At each collision they lose energy and are finally captured by the nuclei of formation atoms which thereupon emit gamma radiation. A detector mounted at a short distance above the source measures the intensity of this secondary gamma radiation or of the neutrons which have been slowed down to an intermediate energy level. Hydrogen is the most effective element in the slowing down process and as hydrogen is present in water and hydrocarbons saturating the formation pores, the porosity of the formation may be derived from the recorded signal. Gamma ray/neutron logs may also be run in cased holes. The cement and casing steel will attenuate the recorded

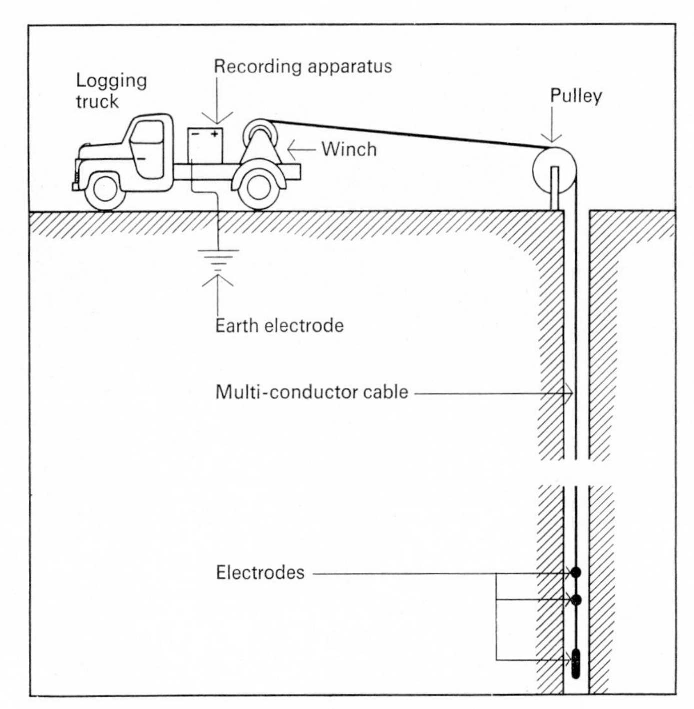

Fig. 47 Electric logging operations

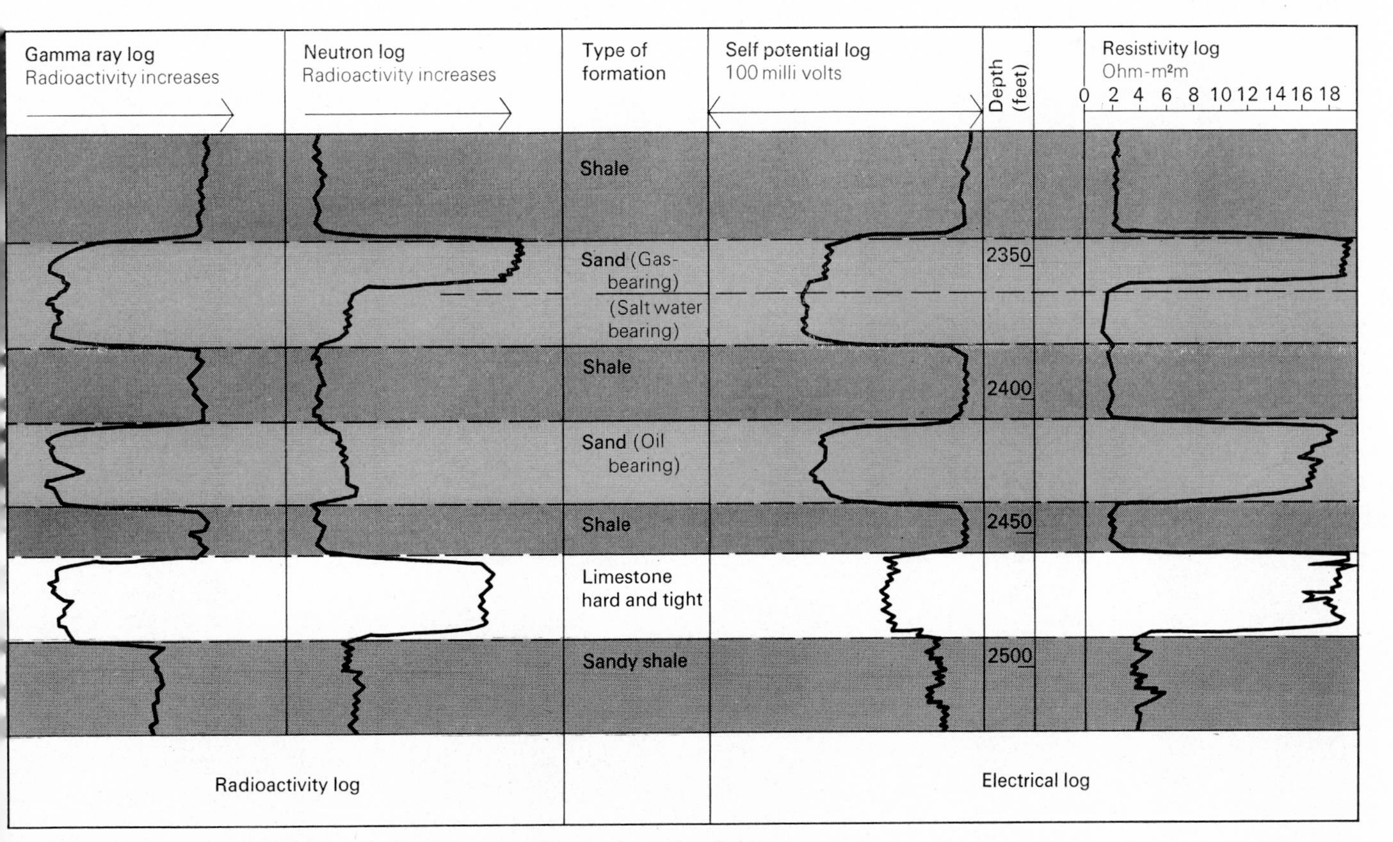

Fig. 48 Response of radioactivity and electric logs to different formation fluids

signals and for quantitative evaluation the log will not be of much use. It will still serve for correlations however (Oilfield development and production, p. 49).

A more recent development of a nuclear porosity log is the density log or gamma gamma log which contains a source emitting gamma radiation. A detector measures the gamma radiation scattered back to the sonde by the formations. The signal recorded reflects the density of the formations, from which the porosity may be deduced.

An 'acoustic' or 'sonic' log is another type of porosity log which is frequently run. It records the time that it takes an acoustic wave to travel over a certain distance through the formations. The speed of propagation of acoustic waves is much higher in solid rock than in fluids. Consequently the recorded travel time will reflect the porosity of the formations.

Although the above logs will assist in determining the quality of possible reservoir rock they do not reveal whether the porous formations contain any hydrocarbons. To obtain this information it is necessary to run resistivity logs which record the resistivity of the formations. The ability of a formation to conduct electric current varies inversely with the resistivity of the formation water and depends on the amount of water present in the pores, which is determined by the porosity and the fraction of the pore space occupied by non-conductive hydrocarbons. Provided that porosity and formation water resistivity are known, a resistivity log will enable the hydrocarbon content of a formation to be calculated. Although logging techniques are continuously improving, a single log generally does not allow determination of a property of interest with sufficient accuracy. By running a suitable combination of logs, disturbing factors may be eliminated or at least minimized.

Coring

When rock properties have been derived from logs, it is sometimes desirable to check the results against values accurately measured on actual formation samples from corresponding depths. Samples big enough for laboratory examination are obtained from known depths by 'coring'. The drilling bit is replaced by a 'core barrel' and a 'core head' by means of which a cylinder of the formation being drilled passes through the core head into the core barrel where it is retained and brought to the surface [Fig. 49]. In some formations the cores are badly broken and in

Fig. 49 Core samples

soft sandy formations they may be washed away by the drilling fluid. A representative sample cannot therefore always be obtained. Moreover progress is slower than when drilling normally, and the drilling string has to be pulled more frequently because of the limited length of core barrel. Coring is thus an expensive and uncertain process. In exploration wells it is seldom used for the added reason that the location of formations of interest is generally not known until these have been passed and when it is too late to core them.

These disadvantages can be overcome to some extent by 'side-wall' coring whereby small cores can be taken at any chosen depth in an uncased hole during periods when the drill pipe is out of the hole and in conjunction with a wireline log. Several hollow cylinders are shot into the wall by means of explosive charges from recesses in a steel cylinder, the 'carrier'. The charges are detonated by an electric current transmitted by a conductor cable on which the carrier is lowered. The cylinders are connected to the carrier by steel wires and are pulled out of the rock and to the surface with the carrier. Side-wall samples are, however, small and often badly contaminated by mud. Rock properties such as porosity and permeability will have changed due to the impact of the sampling bullet. Their use is therefore limited mainly to determining the lithology and age of formations and the presence or absence of oil, in particular to assist in evaluating logs.

The formation investigated in cuttings, cores or side-wall samples is not in its undisturbed state, and the samples rarely give a full picture of the formations penetrated. Much of the oil originally in the samples may be flushed out by the drilling fluid, making it difficult to distinguish between a sample thus denuded of oil and one from a formation that contains some oil but which would produce water only.

Formation tests

Although the above methods may give evidence of the presence of oil, or even indicate its amount, none will yield direct information about the rate at which a reservoir formation can produce fluids.

Prospective producing zones, particularly in an exploration well, may therefore be tested soon after being encountered by a method that reproduces to some extent conditions in a producing well. The principle of the method, 'drill-stem testing', is to isolate a part of the hole containing a possible oil or gas bearing formation and then to establish a direct connection between this part of the hole and the surface [Fig. 50].

A 'formation packer' and a 'drill-stem tester' are lowered on the drill pipe. The drill-stem tester contains valves that can be controlled from the surface so that no drilling fluid can enter the pipe while being lowered into the hole. The packer (a) is set first above the section to be tested, sealing off the space between wall and pipe, and by slightly lowering the drill string the main valve (b) in the tester is opened, thus bringing the isolated section of the hole into communication with the empty drilling pipe. Formation fluid then enters the pipe under the pressure in the formation, depending on which it will partly or completely fill the pipe. In the latter case the surface flow is controlled by valves.

After completing the test, which may last anything from a few minutes to 24 hours or more, the drill pipe is sealed at the bottom by closing the main valve, and drilling fluid from the annular space around the drill pipe is admitted

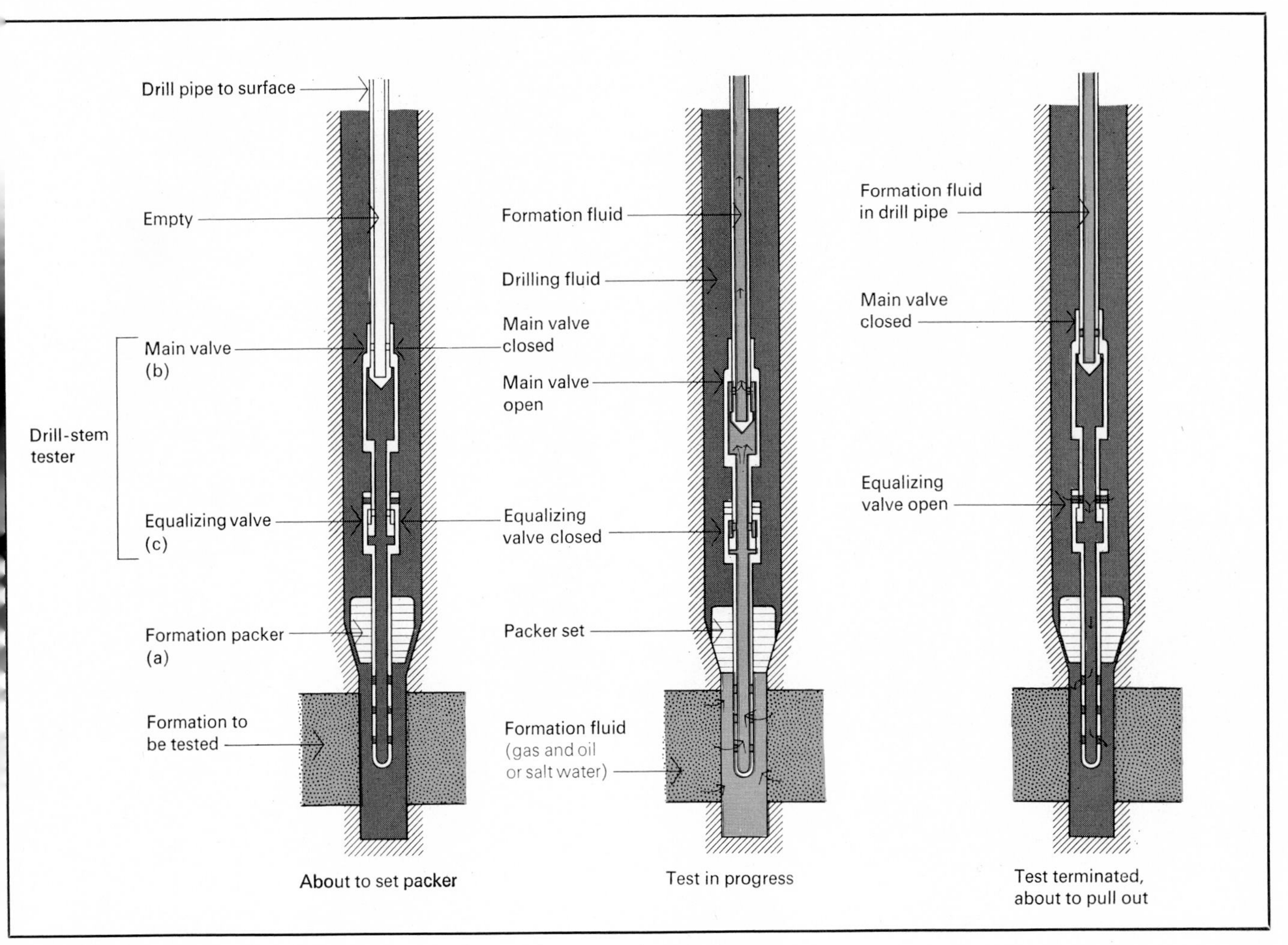

Fig. 50 The principles of drill-stem testing

below the packer through the equalizing valve (c). The packer can then be pulled loose and the whole assembly withdrawn from the hole.

Testing is not limited to formations close to the bottom of the hole or to uncased holes. It is possible to set packers both above and below a formation to be tested (straddle test) or to set them in the casing (hook wall packer) to test gun-perforated intervals at any time during the life of a well.

Completion methods

Should logging and testing indicate the presence of a potentially productive formation, the well must be completed in such a manner as to permit the production of oil. The walls of the hole above the producing layer (and if necessary within it) must be supported against collapse. The entry into the well of fluids from formations other than the producing layer, and the flow of the oil from the producing layer into other formations via the well, must be prevented.

According to the nature of the producing formation, and with possible major repair jobs in mind, different completion methods are used, but a string of casing is always run and cemented, at least to the top of the producing layer.

When the producing layer is firm and not liable to cave, the casing can be cemented immediately above it, leaving it unsupported. This method is often used in wells producing from limestone formations and is called a 'bare-foot completion' [Fig. 51]. If the producing layer is not firm, then it must be supported, which may be done in one of two ways.

Casing may be run through the producing layer to the bottom and cemented, after which holes are shot through the casing opposite the producing layer [Fig. 51b] by means of a 'gun perforator'. Perforators are of two types, both lowered into the hole on conductor cables and carrying explosive charges that are electrically detonated. In the 'bullet perforator' steel bullets are fired through the casing and cement; in the 'shaped charge perforator' small explosive charges are used, so shaped that the explosive force is focused and intensified into a small diameter jet which penetrates casing and cement.

Alternatively a smaller perforated or slotted pipe (liner) with holes or slots opposite the producing layer [Fig. 51c] may be hung from the bottom of the casing that has already been set.

In poorly consolidated sand formations, sand may be carried into the well with the oil and gas. This should be prevented, or at least kept to a minimum, to avoid plugging the well and to lessen wear of pumps, valves, liners, etc. The erosion of large quantities of sand can also cause caving of the overlying strata and damage to the casing. Various types of liner are used to prevent ingress of sand into the well–slotted pipe, wire-wrapped pipe and liners in which

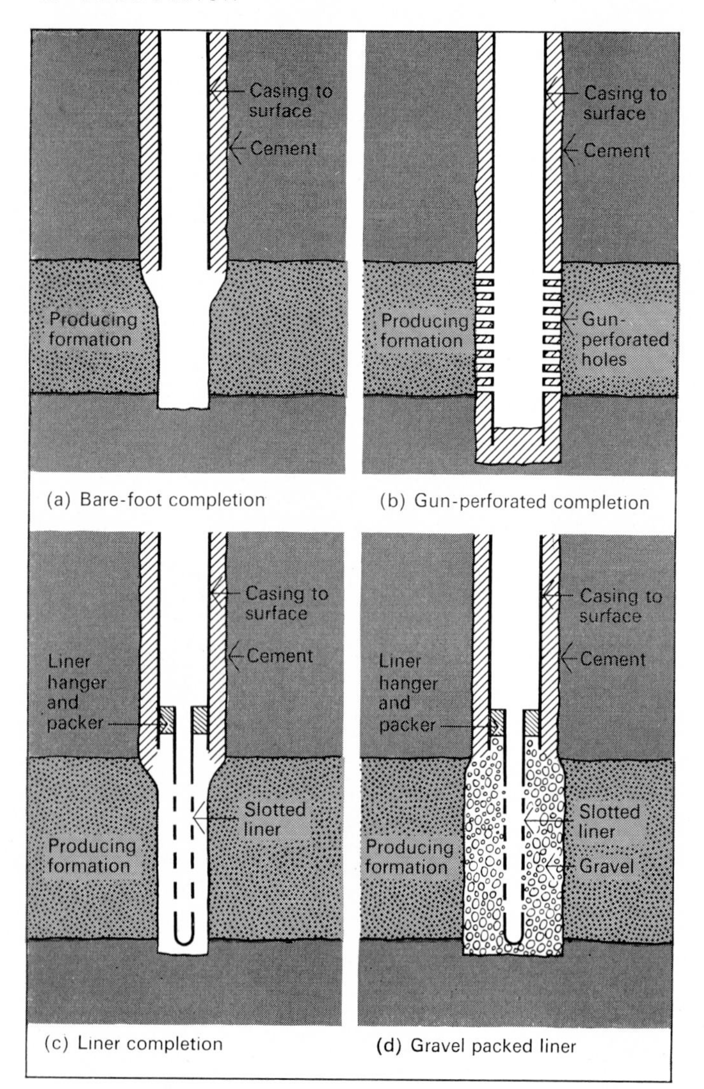

Fig. 51 Bottom hole arrangement of some types of completion

fine gravel is washed into place between the liner and the wall to form a sand-excluding screen [Fig. 51d].

The sand can also be consolidated by means of a special process using Epikote, an epon resin developed by Shell, to bind the sand grains without materially affecting the productivity of the well.

Fig. 52 Shell's undersea robot which swims with propellers, sees with television, hears with a hydrophone, and has an arm that can operate valves and turn lock screws

Marine completion and production

In general, the same methods used for completing and producing wells on land are used for wells in the open sea. This is particularly true for wells which can be completed with their well heads above the water surface, which is possible where operations are handled from fixed platforms. However, with floating platforms, where wells are completed with their well heads on the sea floor, the inaccessibility of the well control equipment in deep water beyond the reach of human divers requires the use of remote controls which can be operated either automatically or by surface-actuated underwater robots. One such robot is shown in Fig. 52 in conjunction with a typical underwater well head.

Oilfield development and production

The evaluation of a new oilfield

After oil has been discovered in an exploration well, efforts are made to evaluate the importance of the discovery. It is essential to determine at an early stage whether the newly discovered oil accumulation is large enough to permit profitable development, and this depends largely on its geographical location. A small accumulation in an accessible and established producing area might be profitably developed, while a considerably larger accumulation in a remote area, difficult of access, might be impossible to develop with a reasonable financial return.

A successful exploration well is followed by a number of 'outstep' or 'appraisal' wells, located with the object of determining the limits of the accumulation, variations in the nature of the reservoir rock, the depths of the gas/oil and oil/water contacts, etc. The directions of outstepping are based on the available geological information; if, for example, the discovery well were at or near the crest of an anticline, two rows of outstep wells would probably be drilled, one along the crest and the other at right angles to it, outstepping being continued until the limit of the field in each direction was found. On large structures and with a thick productive layer, outstep wells might be as much as a mile apart, but with smaller structures and thin reservoirs the distance might be less than half a mile.

During drilling of the outstep wells, data are obtained from electric logs, cores, etc. (p. 45) thereby continuously improving the interpretation of the geological structure of the field. The outstep drilling programme must consequently be continually reviewed, and revised if necessary, as new geological information becomes available. The electric logs, in conjunction with the formation samples, usually provide a means of tracing the rock layers from well to well and this 'correlation' is the basis from which the geological structure is deduced and mapped [Fig. 53]. At

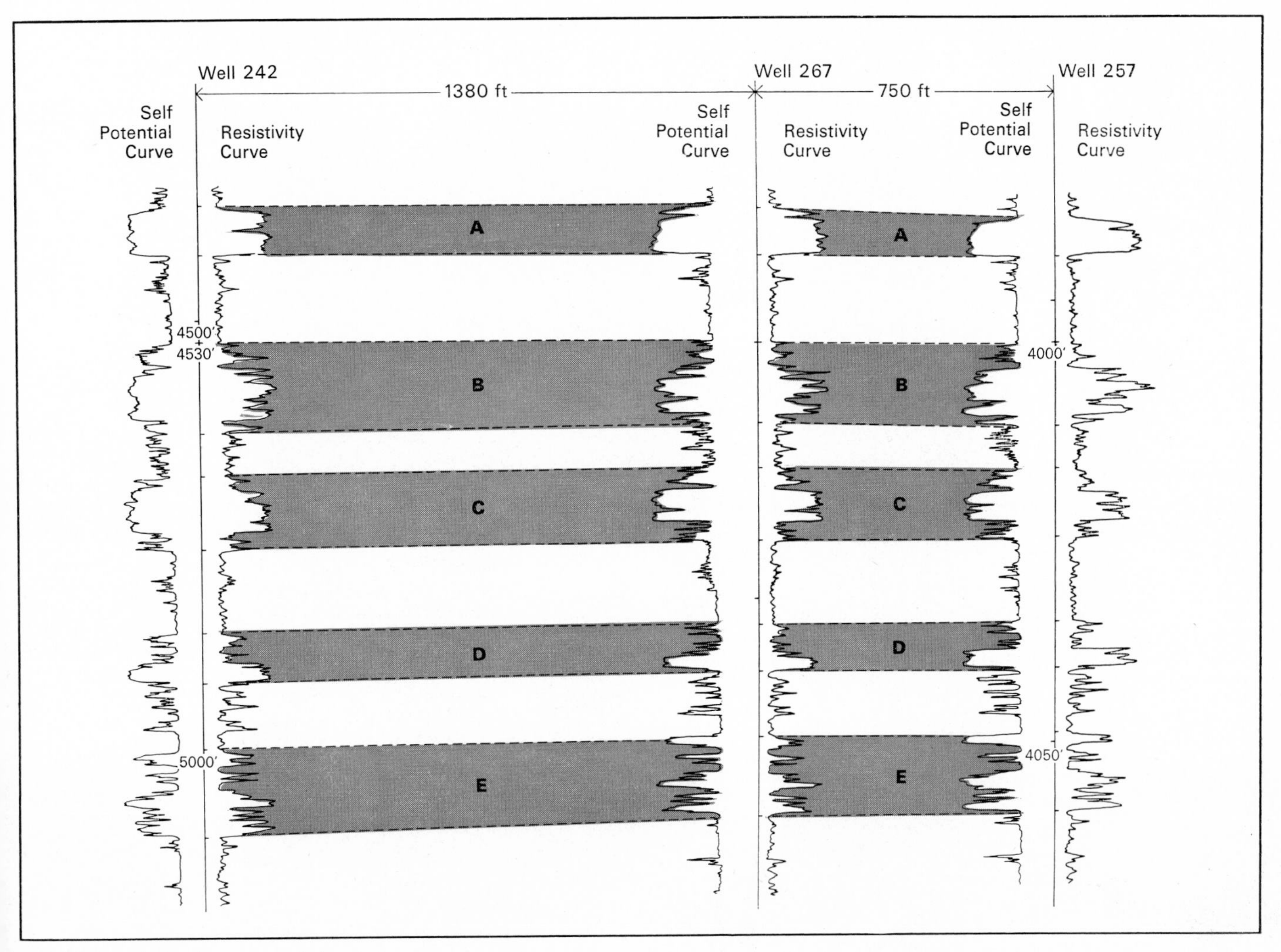

Fig. 53 Correlation by means of electric logs

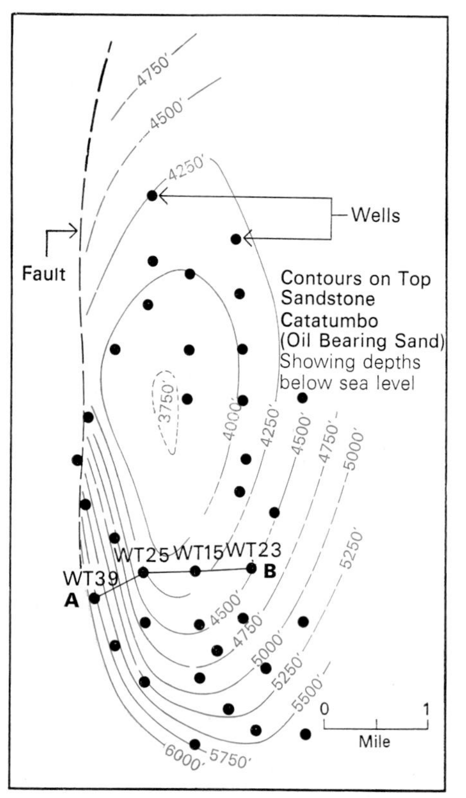

Fig. 54 Structural contour map, Tarra Field, Venezuela (simplified)

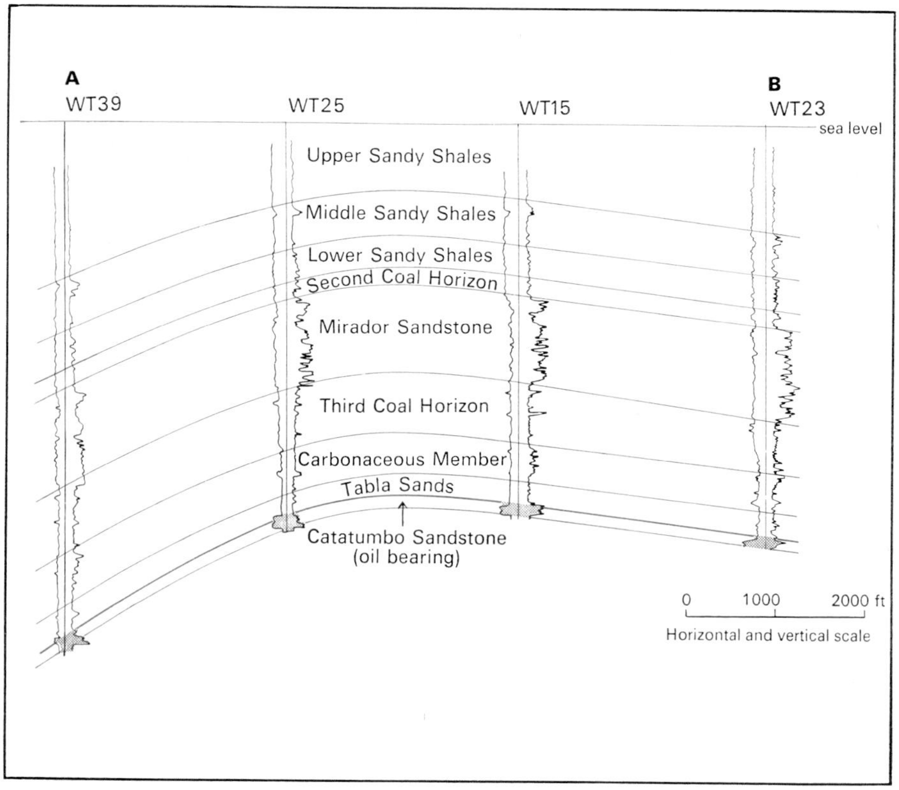

Fig. 55 The section through A-B shown in Fig. 54

each stage, however, the current interpretation of the geological structure must be regarded as a working hypothesis, subject to constant revision as new wells are drilled.

The structure is depicted in two forms: subsurface contour maps representing the shape of various rock layers in much the same way as a topographical contour map represents the shape of a hill [Fig. 54] and sections representing vertical planes through the field showing the position of the rock layers and the accumulations of oil and gas [Fig. 55]. These maps and sections are used in planning the position and depth of new wells. As soon as the outstep drilling has proved the field to be sufficiently large for profitable development, the drilling of development wells is commenced, but outstep drilling is continued until the limits of the field are defined.

Data obtained during the drilling of the initial wells and in their early production life are employed as a basis for a first estimate of the amount of recoverable oil and to predict future production behaviour. These are important factors in deciding the distance between the development wells, which are usually spaced regularly to fit a pattern or grid. The spacing of these wells is most important since the drilling costs are a major portion of the total capital outlay for development. If wells are too closely spaced capital expenditure will be greater than necessary; if they are spaced too widely, less oil may be ultimately recovered, it will take longer to produce it, and production facilities, staff, etc, will have to be maintained for a longer period. The expiry date of the concession must also be taken into account. A very careful study of all the factors involved must therefore be made in the initial stages of development and must be constantly reviewed while drilling proceeds.

The reservoir and its producing characteristics

In the first place a distinction should be made between oil and gas accumulations. The latter will be discussed in a later section.

An oil accumulation cannot be considered separately from the gas and salt water with which it is usually associated. Gas may exist in the free state in the higher part of the structure overlying the oil, but the oil, which is usually under considerable pressure, will in most cases contain much gas in solution. Water is usually present underlying the oil on the flanks of the structure (p. 26).

To produce oil from the reservoir it is necessary to maintain a reduced pressure at the bottom of the producing wells, by artificial means if necessary, so that the well pressure is lower than the reservoir pressure. Under this pressure difference oil with gas dissolved in it, and to a certain degree free gas and perhaps water, move towards and into the wells. The rate at which a well produces thus depends largely on the pressure at the bottom of the well, the reservoir pressure and the ease with which fluids can move through the reservoir towards the well. This latter depends on the viscosity of the fluid and the permeability of the formation.

As oil is withdrawn from the reservoir, the reservoir pressure usually decreases and the producing capacities of the wells consequently decline. The rate of decline in reservoir pressure, and hence of production and the amount of oil recoverable, is greatly influenced by the roles that gas and water play in the expulsion of oil from the reservoir, and consequently reservoirs may be divided into different types on this basis.

Ideally oil reservoirs may be classified into four types of reservoir drive mechanism: water drive, gas cap drive, depletion type (solution gas drive) and gravity drainage. A reservoir may often have features of two or more of these types but generally one or the other will predominate and it is convenient to consider each type separately.

Water drive

Fig. 56 is an idealized representation of water drive in which the reservoir formation is of indefinite extent and contains water underlying the oil on its flanks. The oil also contains dissolved gas.

The extent of the reservoir formation may be so great and the volume of water in it so large in comparison with that of the oil, that, with a very permeable formation, the extraction of oil may result in a replacement of the oil by water with little or no decrease in reservoir pressure, the water advancing up the flanks of the structure, sweeping the oil ahead of it. Under these conditions the wells will show practically no decline in rate of production until the water reaches them, and the flushing action of the water will result in the recovery of a high percentage of the oil originally present. In water drive reservoirs, development wells should not be sited too close to the original oil/water contact lest their producing life be uneconomically short.

If the permeability of the reservoir rock is low the production rates of the wells will also be relatively low. The water from the flanks will enter less easily and a decrease of reservoir pressure will be observed, resulting in declining well capacities. Due to decreasing reservoir pressure and to local drop in pressure around the well, gas may be liberated from solution, which also may adversely affect the productivity of the well. Although the water drive may still be quite effective in sweeping out the oil, it is not strong enough to maintain the pressure and the productive capacity of the field.

Since water, because of its lower viscosity, can flow through a formation much more easily than can most crude oils, too high a production rate can also result in water 'fingering' or 'coning' towards the well, especially in the case of a highly viscous oil. The well will then produce a far higher proportion of water than would normally be expected. When the formation is not homogeneous, but contains lenses and streaks of different permeabilities, water will advance more easily through the more permeable zones. It may break through to a producing well, the oil production of which may then decrease to a non-economic low level while the less permeable zones are still only partly depleted. As far as possible measures are taken to avoid this, but the recovery efficiency will inevitably be lower than when the formation is homogeneous.

Gas cap drive

Fig. 57 shows, in an idealized form, a gas cap drive reservoir. The main source of energy for moving the oil is the expansion of the gas cap resulting from the reduction in reservoir pressure as production proceeds from the underlying layer of oil. As the gas cap expands it pushes the oil ahead of it, the gas/oil contact moving down the structure.

To take full advantage of the gas expansion, no gas should be produced from the gas cap itself and the wells should therefore be located on the flanks of the structure and not at the crest. Even so, the gas/oil contact will in time reach down to the wells highest in the formation, and these wells will then have to be shut in to avoid waste of reservoir energy.

As the pressure falls, gas comes out of solution in the oil bearing zone of the reservoir. This gas will tend to migrate upwards to the gas cap and thus support the natural gas cap drive. However, due to the low pressure areas around the producing wells, this gas may also be drawn to these wells and produced with the oil. In that case restriction of the production rates of the wells may be advisable in order to promote the migration of the gas to the gas cap.

With the gas/oil contact close to a well, further opening up of the well can result in the gas coning down to the well in the same way as water cones upwards, resulting in a reduction of the rate of oil production.

Depletion type (solution gas drive)

A typical depletion type reservoir is often of limited extent, containing oil with its dissolved gas. The production of oil causes the reservoir pressure to decline below the 'saturation pressure', the pressure at which gas starts to come out of solution. The energy required to move the oil is obtained from the continued expansion of this evolved gas as pressures are reduced and the oil, together with an excess of gas, is thus forced towards the wells. It is good policy to produce as little gas as possible with the oil and to shut in any wells

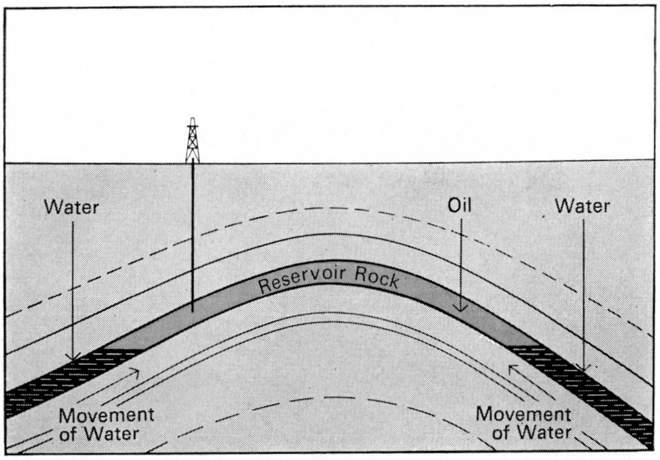

Fig. 56 Water drive field

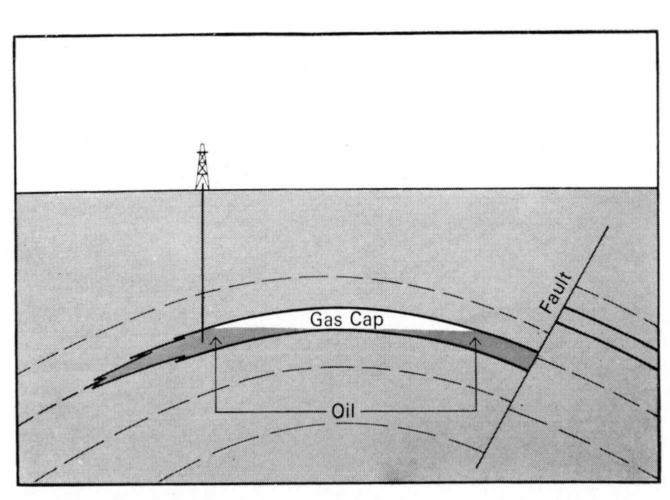

Fig. 57 Gas cap drive field

that may be producing an abnormal amount of gas. Even with the best practice, however, the depletion type of producing mechanism is relatively inefficient and generally a smaller fraction of the total oil content of the reservoir may be recoverable than under water drive or gas cap drive.

Gravity drainage

The effect of gravity will be the more pronounced, the more permeable are the oil-bearing zones and the more steeply they dip. For instance in a highly permeable and steeply dipping formation the gas coming out of solution will migrate upwards due to gravity much more easily than in a tight sandstone with only a few degrees of dip. In such a case of good gravity segregation of the gas, the oil should be withdrawn from wells situated on the flank of the structure.

Obviously there will always be a certain effect of gravity whether there is water drive, gas cap drive or depletion drive. In the final stage of the life of a depletion type reservoir, when practically all the gas has come out of solution and has been produced, the pressure has dropped to a very low level and the main cause of oil production left is the drainage of oil towards the wells under the action of gravity. The rate of flow towards the wells will then depend mainly on the dip of the formation, permeability and oil viscosity.

Gas and condensate reservoirs

In addition to occurring as a gas cap overlying an oil accumulation, gas may exist completely independent of oil. Where there is a ready market for it, these gas accumulations may be exploited commercially and with no artificial lifting methods necessary to bring the gas to the surface its production is simpler than that of oil.

The behaviour of a gas reservoir depends primarily on the degree of natural water drive. If there is a good natural water drive, the pressure in the reservoir will not decrease to an important extent. The well capacities will thus remain fairly constant, but any wells on the flanks of the reservoir will eventually be invaded by the advancing water front.

If there is no water drive, the pressure in the reservoir will decrease and also the well capacity will decline. For certain types of high pressure natural gas reservoirs, usually at great depth, this pressure drop may have additional consequences. Some such reservoirs produce considerable quantities of liquid hydrocarbons or condensate together with the gas as both condensate and gas exist as one homogeneous phase in the reservoir. If this is a liquid phase it is a volatile oil reservoir, if it is a gaseous phase it is a gas condensate reservoir.

When, because of fluid withdrawal, the pressure in a gas condensate reservoir decreases below a critical level, a liquid phase (condensate) makes its appearance in the reservoir. This phenomenon is known as 'retrograde condensation', indicating that the process involved is rather the opposite of the conventional condensation of liquid which occurs under less extreme conditions of temperature and pressure when a vapour is compressed. By this retrograde condensation much of the valuable condensate gets disseminated throughout the reservoir and becomes virtually irrecoverable. This may be counteracted by maintaining reservoir pressure through re-injection into the reservoir of the produced gas, after extraction of the condensate in a gas plant, the process being known as 'cycling' or 'recycling'.

Secondary recovery

The percentage of the oil that can be recovered from a reservoir by the energy originally available in that reservoir depends upon the characteristics of the reservoir rock and reservoir fluids and upon the type of recovery mechanism. If the recovery by these natural forces, the primary recovery, is relatively low, it may be economic to improve the recovery percentage by injection of fluids into the reservoir.

In the early days of secondary recovery, water or gas injection was not applied until a late stage of depletion had been reached.

In 'water flooding', water is injected under pressure into the formation via injection wells and the oil is displaced towards nearby producing wells. The operation has to be controlled, as in natural water drive operations, to ensure the regular advance of the water front. The injection water may have to be treated to prevent plugging of the formation by suspended matter or by chemical deposition.

In 'gas injection', gas is injected under pressure via the injection wells, which are generally located at relatively high positions, so that the oil is displaced downdip to the producing wells.

As the advantages of maintaining pressure in the oil reservoir, such as the higher well capacities, became more widely recognized the secondary recovery techniques were also applied earlier in the life of the field. The amount of water or gas injected and the oil and gas production are controlled in such a manner that the reservoir pressure is maintained at the desired level. This process is termed 'pressure maintenance'.

In recent years new recovery processes have found application. For the secondary recovery of very viscous heavy crudes 'thermal' methods have been developed. The viscosity of the oil in the reservoir is reduced by heating which can be effected by injection of steam or hot water or by partially burning the crude by means of air injection (*in situ* combustion processes). Also injection at an adequate pressure of a suitable mixture of natural gas and light petroleum products can result in better recovery from light oil reservoirs. This is the 'miscible fluid' injection processes.

Reserves

An important problem in the development of an oilfield is to get an efficient recovery of oil out of the reservoir rock. About 30% of the original oil content will ultimately be produced from the average reservoir; up to 80% may be recoverable from a highly permeable sand producing low viscosity oil under water drive, but only 10% or even less from a fine grained sandstone producing viscous oil under depletion conditions. This 'recovery factor', which can sometimes be improved by the secondary recovery methods described above, indicates the percentage of oil that can be ultimately withdrawn, and is an important factor for calculating 'oil reserves', i.e. the total volume of oil that should be recoverable. Reserves fall into three categories:

Proven reserves – those quantities of oil known with reasonable certainty to be present and to be commercially recoverable by today's techniques.

Probable reserves – reserves contained in probably oil-bearing parts adjacent to proven oil-bearing areas in an oilfield in development, or additional reserves that are likely to be obtained if secondary recovery is applied.

Possible reserves – the oil that may be expected from a field from areas outside the proven and probable areas or from more remote secondary recovery possibilities.

Thus in the early stage of development drilling the proven reserves of an oilfield will usually be relatively small and the probable and possible reserves will be relatively large. When development drilling has been completed the size of the oilfield and thus the amount of oil present underground are reasonably well defined. At that stage, however, the efficiency of the primary recovery and the possible additional recovery obtainable by secondary methods, if any, are often still rather uncertain so that even then recovery figures have a range of uncertainty and are subject to later revision.

The estimating of gas condensate reserves in principle follows the same lines as oil reserve estimating.

When the expectations from a general producing region, rather than from an individual oilfield, are considered, the total of the proven, probable and possible reserves, together with the past production of the oilfields at any given time, may not be a fair indication of the entire expectations of the region. New oil reservoirs may still be discovered as exploration progresses and the 'plausible expectations', (the oil expectable from future new discoveries) have therefore to be taken into account each time the total expectations from a region have to be estimated. These plausible expectations of prospective structures or basins can usually only be estimated on the basis of the geological knowledge of the areas concerned and by comparison with developed fields or intensively explored oil basins.

It will therefore be evident that these estimates are always speculative.

Production methods

After a producing well has been completed (p. 47) means must be provided to bring the oil to the surface. In most fields, the earlier wells will produce by natural flow, i.e. the oil will flow to the surface without assistance. At a later stage, as the reservoir pressure decreases, artificial lift like gas lifting and, later, pumping may have to be employed. Some fields, especially those producing very viscous crudes, will require artificial lift immediately after completion.

The three systems, natural flow, gas lifting and pumping, are described below. The oil is usually brought to the surface via a string of pipe up to 4 in. diameter, called the 'tubing'. This tubing is run into the well and hung from the well head with the bottom just above the producing formation. The function of the tubing varies with the type of production method. In general it forms a replaceable string that enables production methods or equipment to be changed at will, protects the casing from wear or corrosion, and enables the well to be filled with water or drilling fluid should it be necessary to 'kill' the well to effect repairs.

Natural flow

With natural flow the reservoir pressure forces the oil from the bottom of the well to the surface. The size of the tubing plays an important part in determining the pressure loss as the oil flows upwards through it, and consequently influences the producing rate. Gas coming out of solution in the oil helps it to rise up the tubing. Too large a tubing diameter would allow much of this gas to by-pass the oil without aiding its upward movement. Too small a diameter would result in too high a friction between fluid and tubing. There is thus an optimum size of tubing for any given conditions.

Offtake from the well is controlled at the surface by varying the size of a choke or 'bean' through which the fluid passes. The assembly of valves, and fittings at the well head whereby flow can be diverted through alternative chokes or the well can be closed in is known as the 'Christmas tree' [Fig. 58].

Many flowing wells, particularly gas wells, have very high pressures at the surface, 10 000 lb/in² or more, and adequate precautions must be taken against the well getting out of control. Equipment is provided that automatically shuts off production in the event of damage to or failure of the well head. Automatic surface safety valves close in the well at the well head while, particularly for offshore operations, special valves can be installed in the well itself to shut off flow below the surface.

An oilfield may contain more than one producing horizon, each with marked differences in pressure, specific gravity of oil, etc, and thus needing separate production. This may sometimes be done within the same well be means of a 'dual' or 'multiple' completion. A simple form of dual completion is shown in Fig. 59. This type of completion is frequently much cheaper than the alternative of drilling separate wells to each layer or exploiting the layers consecutively within each well. However flow rates are more limited, artificial lift is more complicated and costly, and repairs to any of the intervals are costlier and result in temporary loss of production from the other intervals. The overall economic picture is therefore not as favourable as that indicated by the savings during the completion stage.

Fig. 58 Christmas tree on a flowing well

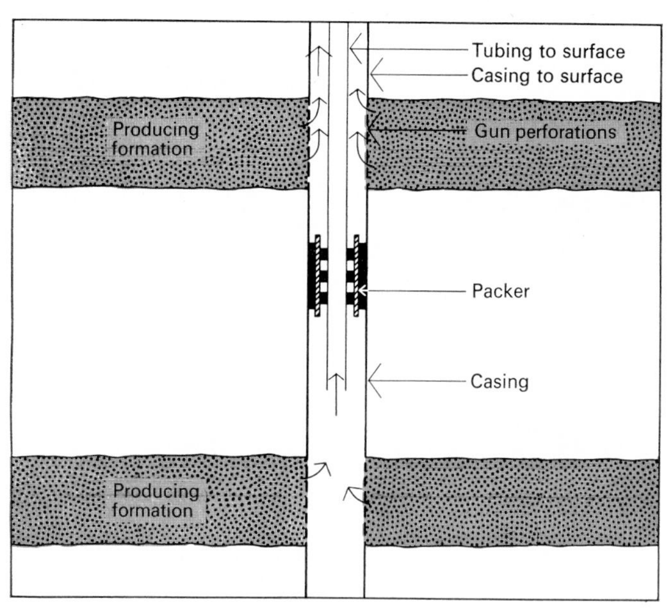

Fig. 59 Dual flowing completion

More oil is produced by natural flow than by all other methods combined; it is a high capacity method, simple and cheap. However, its efficiency diminishes as the reservoir pressure and flow rate decrease, and eventually a stage will usually be reached when production can be maintained only by installing gas lift or a pump.

Gas lift

Production by gas lift, is, in effect, an extension of natural flow. The amount of gas produced with the oil is artificially increased by injecting gas into the flowing column, usually by means of special valves set at various depths and controlling the amount of gas entering the flow stream through ports in the tubing. This increase in gas/oil ratio reduces the pressure needed to lift the oil to the surface, thus permitting higher production rates than would be possible by either natural flow or pumping and delaying the necessity for the installation of pumping equipment.

To commence injection at the foot of the tubing in a 'dead' well partially filled with 'dead' liquid containing little or no gas, an initial injection pressure would be required substantially higher than that subsequently needed to maintain production. To avoid the need for a high pressure gas supply solely for starting, gas lift valves are often installed in the tubing at predetermined points when the tubing is run into the well [Fig. 60]. These valves allow the gas to enter the tubing and to blow out the dead liquid at progressively lower points until the well starts to produce. Eventually all the gas enters the flowing column at or near the tubing shoe, where it is used with the greatest efficiency.

A gas lift installation often requires a large capital investment to provide a gas compression plant when high pressure gas is not available from the wells, but it is relatively easy to maintain and operates at low costs per unit of production. Its chief application is where large production rates have to be handled and may be the final lifting method in a well that produces large quantities of water in the later stages of its life.

Pumping

Although more oil is produced by flowing wells, most producing wells are operated by mechanical lifting methods using subsurface pumps. The simple reciprocating plunger

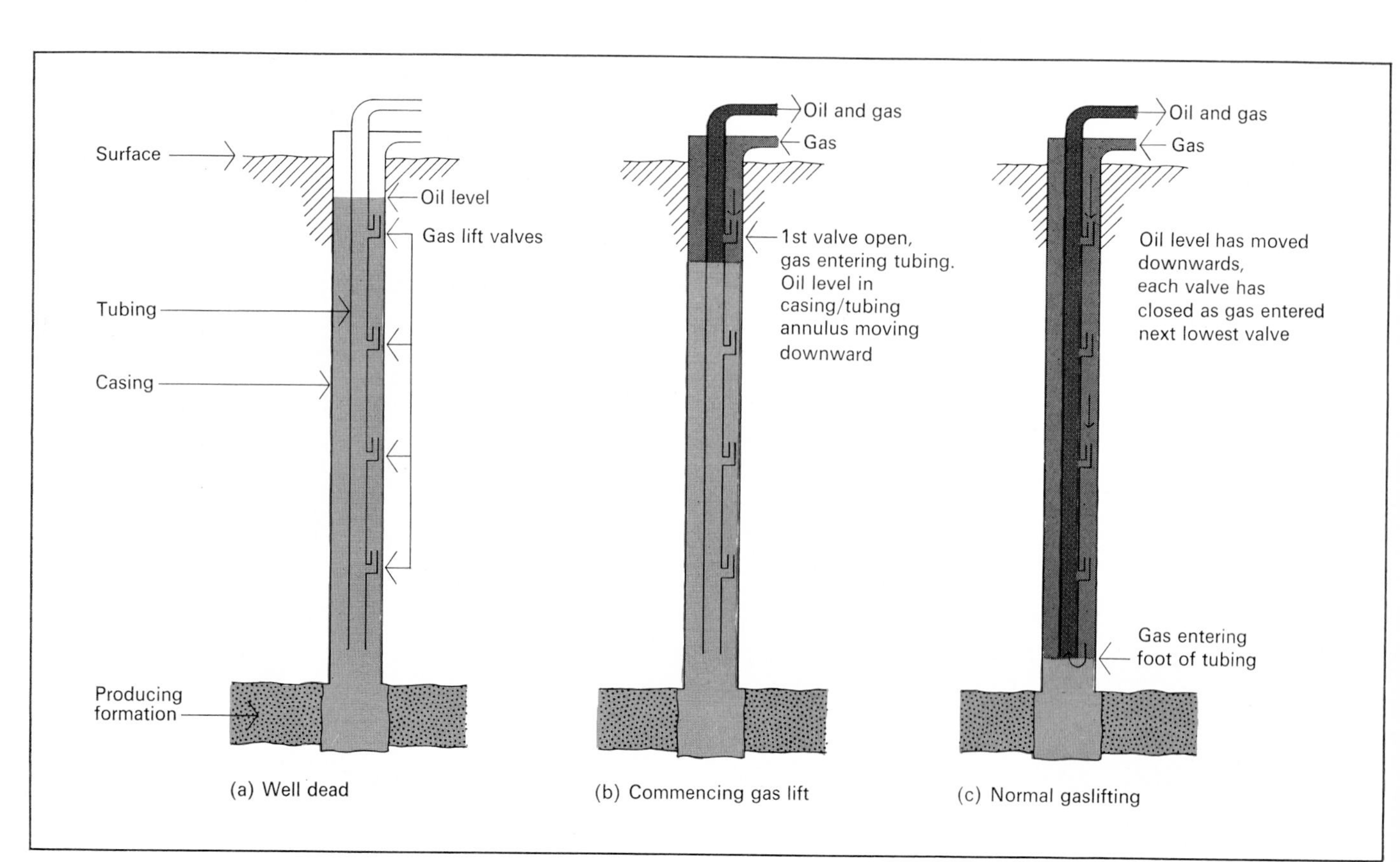

Fig. 60 Operation of gas lift valves

pump actuated by 'sucker rods' from a surface pumping unit is the most widely used [Fig. 61]. The pump is generally screwed on to or inserted into the foot of the tubing. The oil is then lifted up the tubing and the casing forms a passage for the gas, which would otherwise seriously interfere with the pumping of the oil.

The reciprocating motion for actuating subsurface pumps is usually provided by beam type surface units driven by gas, electric or diesel motors [Fig. 62]. The weight of the sucker rods and the fluid being lifted is counterbalanced by an adjustable weight or by a pneumatic cylinder.

Despite their superficial simplicity and wide acceptance, rod-operated plunger pumps are subject to certain disadvantages: alternate stretching and contracting of the sucker rods involves a loss of plunger stroke, a loss which increases with the depth of the pump: rods break as a result of cyclical stresses and of wear caused by friction between the rods and the tubing. Pumping systems have therefore been developed in which the pump is actuated by other means but they incorporate mechanisms requiring special facilities and factory maintenance and their use is therefore limited to countries where adequate services are available.

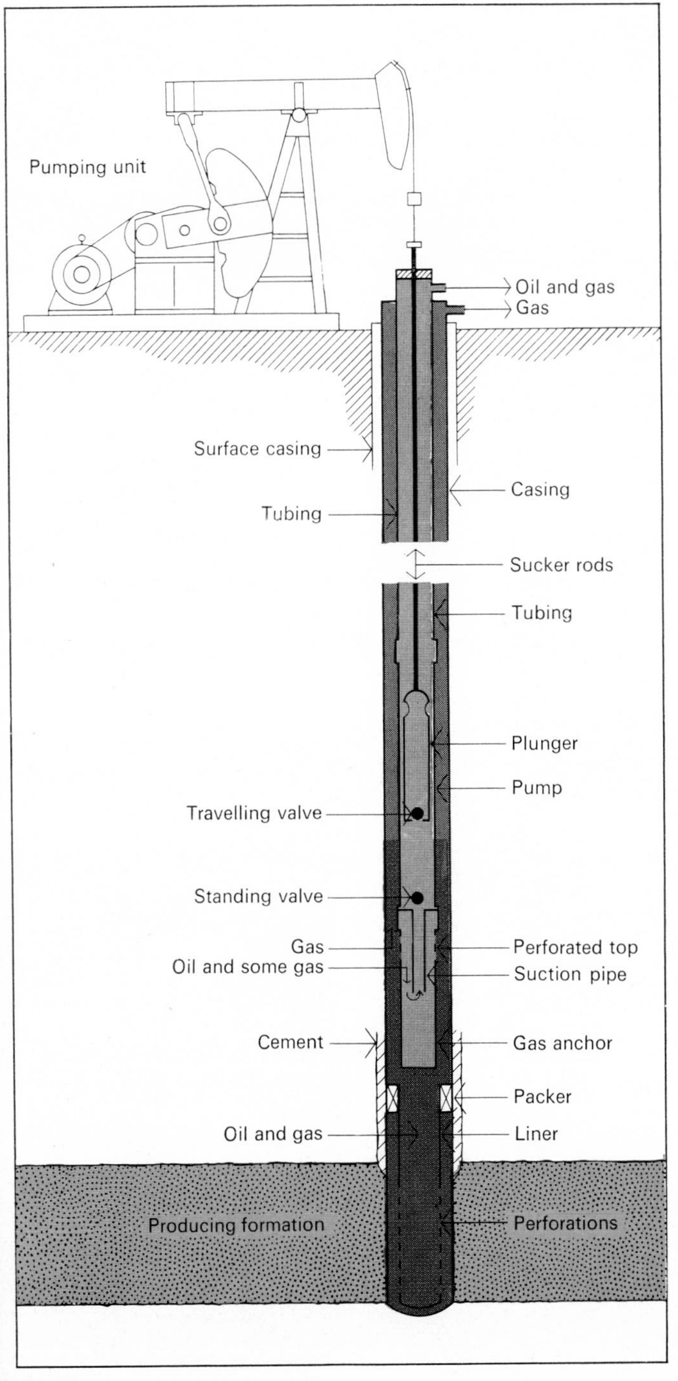

Fig. 61 Diagram of pumping well

Fig. 62 Typical pumping unit

Subsurface plunger pumps can be hydraulically operated by oil circulated by a pump at the surface – 'power fluid'. The pump plunger is reciprocated by a directly connected piston of a double-acting engine integral with the pump barrel and driven by the power fluid. Often a gas vent duct and a string of tubing to return the power fluid are also required. This reduces the pump capacities due to space considerations. At least two strings of tubing must be provided, one to carry the descending power fluid, the other to carry the ascending oil and spent power fluid. A variant of this type of hydraulically operated pump is the 'free-pump' which can be pumped into or out of the well through the tubing by means of the power fluid, at a small fraction of the cost of pulling sucker rods or tubing.

Subsurface centrifugal pumps are driven by electricity supplied from the surface by a cable clamped to the tubing. This method is applied in large capacity wells (up to 5000 barrels a day) and is well adapted for use in crooked holes. However, the cable is a disadvantage in running and pulling the pump and is a likely source of failure. Moreover, this type of pump is very sensitive to any solids in the produced fluid.

Well maintenance, repair and stimulation

Unfortunately, wells do not continue to produce without attention until the oil is exhausted. The amount of attention required can vary enormously and is influenced by both the reservoir characteristics (the type of formation, type of oil, etc.) and the production method. In general, pumping wells require the most attention.

Some of the more common mechanical troubles are: sand entry into the bottom of the well; deposits of wax in the tubing; breakage of sucker rods; wear of plungers and valves in subsurface pumps.

Sand may be brought into the well in spite of various types of liners or sand consolidation techniques. In addition to eroding pump parts in pumping wells and possibly well head fittings and surface equipment, it can fill the well bore to a considerable height. It is removed by means of an open ended tube with a valve at the bottom, lowered on a wire line (bailing), or by circulating oil or water, or by a combination of these methods. The well may then be out of production for several days.

Wax is deposited from some types of oil on the wall of the tubing in the upper, cooler part of the well. This wax can sometimes be removed by mechanical methods, but sometimes the tubing must be pulled and steamed out. To avoid this the temperature of the oil is sometimes raised by electrically heating the upper part of the tubing or by injecting hot oil into the well. Plastic coated tubing, which provides an especially smooth surface, minimizes the formation of wax deposits.

The pulling of sucker rods and tubing in order to replace broken rods or to change pumps, and the removal of sand by bailing, are usually carried out with a hoist and telescopic mast mounted on a truck [Fig. 63] though on older wells small production derricks may still be in existence.

In addition to routine maintenance, more radical repairs may be needed, varying considerably in nature and extent, from sealing a leaking well head to running a new liner. One of the commonest repairs is shutting off water that is entering the well from a section of the producing formation and this is usually effected by squeezing cement into the formation at the offending point. This may require very high pressures for which special pumps have to be provided, and packers set in the hole on the tubing to contain these pressures and to place the cement in the right place.

The more radical repairs and certain minor ones require heavy pulling equipment which is particularly expensive to operate in offshore activities. Under these conditions it is more economical to resort to a special technique called 'permanent type' well completion. The initial completion is more costly, since special equipment has to be incorporated for eventual use if certain types of repair have to be carried out, but such repairs can then be executed, using light-weight, less costly equipment without pulling tubing. The overall saving can be very considerable.

An important feature of production is the 'stimulation' of producing formations by well treatments in order to improve their rate of production. Acidization is an old established process used chiefly for limestone reservoirs. A solution of hydrochloric acid, often with other chemicals, is forced into the formation where it enlarges the flow channels by dissolving the limestone and thereby facilitates the movement of oil towards the well.

Another method is to cause fractures in the producing formation by pumping water or oil into it from the well at high rates and pressures. The fractures form flow channels for the oil, thus increasing the production rate. To prevent the closure of the channels when pressure is released, sand, glass beads, aluminium pellets, etc, are mixed with the fracturing liquid to prevent the crevices from closing.

Chemical treatment is also used to alleviate blocking of the formation near the well by drilling mud or oil/water sludge.

On the exhaustion of one particular producing horizon the well may be 're-completed' on a higher zone by setting a plug of cement against the former and gun perforating the casing (p. 47) opposite the latter.

Handling of oil, gas and water

Gathering systems

The oil produced at the well head is associated with a certain amount of gas and, possibly, water. Facilities have to be provided to separate the gas and water from the oil, to

Fig. 63 Well servicing hoist being raised before pulling sucker rods

Fig. 64 Marine gathering station on Lake Maracaibo

gauge the production of all three and to transport the oil to the main storage tanks, where it will await removal from the field by pipeline or tanker.

Commonly the production from each well is led through a 'flowline' from the well head to a gathering station [Fig. 64]. The gathering station, which handles production from several wells, is equipped with separators, in which gas is separated, and with tanks, in which the oil can be gauged and from which any water that settles can be drained off. The production of the wells is generally combined in the installation, but a separate set of test separators and tanks is usually provided through which the production of each individual well can be switched for gauging. The oil from the gathering station is usually pumped direct to the main storage tanks but should it still contain an appreciable amount of water it may first be passed through a chemical or electrical dehydration plant.

Local variations may be necessary in the system, e.g. heavy crude oils may require heating before being pumped or, in the case of high pressure wells, gas separation and pressure reduction may be carried out in several stages, perhaps at the well head.

Oil and gas separation

Oil and gas separators consist basically of vertical or horizontal cylindrical vessels containing baffles in which the oil and gas are separated. The detailed construction of separators varies widely according to the capacity required and the operating pressure, which may be from a few pounds to several thousand pounds per square inch.

The separated gas may be transported by pipeline and sold outside the field. However, this gas can also be a valuable source of energy on the oilfield, e.g. for use in heaters, gas engines, gas lift installations and injecting into the oil-bearing formation. The gas may also contain valuable liquid components which can be extracted in a gas plant. For the above reasons a pipeline system is usually required for the collection and distribution of gas.

Dehydration

(a) Oil

In most cases water is produced with the crude oil. The presence of this water is undesirable as it would occupy space in ships, pipelines and storage facilities which should economically be occupied by crude oil. Furthermore, to assist efficient processing at the refinery, crude oil should not contain more than 1% of water. Consequently most of the water produced with the oil is removed prior to shipment from the oilfield.

Water which separates freely from the crude is initially drained off at the gathering stations and subsequently at the main storage tanks. Unfortunately, water often occurs as microscopic droplets in a water-in-oil emulsion. These water droplets will not readily settle out and must be induced to coalesce into larger drops which will freely settle out. Special treatments are normally required to achieve this and in that event the 'wet production' will be pumped from the gathering station to a dehydrating plant. In order to promote coalescence of the water droplets, the emulsion may be heated and chemicals added or it may be passed between electrodes maintained at a high alternating potential of 15 000 volts or more.

Disposal of the large quantities of water that are often produced is sometimes a problem, as the water usually has a high salt content and would contaminate surface drainage systems. However, this water may, on occasions, be injected into the formation in a 'water flooding' secondary recovery project.

(b) Gas produced in association with oil

Usually the gas separated from the oil is saturated with water. If the gas has to be transported a long distance, most of the water may have to be removed in order to avoid corrosion in the pipeline. Gas dehydration can be achieved by either absorbing the water in a liquid solution or adsorbing it on a solid material called a dry desiccant.

(c) Gas from gas-condensate wells

The valves and chokes of high-pressure gas wells, and also gas transport lines, may become plugged owing to the formation of 'hydrates', which are crystalline compounds of water and certain components of the gas. They look like hard snow and are formed as a result of cooling, particularly when high-pressure gas containing water vapour is expanded

Fig. 65 Gas plant at Groningen, the Netherlands, showing separators, heat exchangers, glycol recovery and ancillary equipment

Fig. 66 Power station in Venezuela

to a lower pressure. To avoid this, a low-temperature separation process is often used by which most of the water in the gas, and also certain hydrocarbons, are separated as liquids. The pressure gas is expanded, and thus cooled, in a special type of separator installed near the well head. The resulting low temperature causes the formation of hydrates which collect in the bottom of the separator where they are melted by means of a heating coil through which the stream of high-pressure gas from the well is passed, if necessary after heating in a gas heater. The water and the hydrocarbon condensate are drawn off.

To prevent the formation of hydrates in the line between a gas well and the low temperature separators, glycol can be injected into the line at the well head and recovered from the separators for re-use.

Fig. 65 shows part of the processing facilities (separators, heat exchangers, glycol recovery and ancillary equipment) required for the production of gas from the large gas reserves in the northern part of the Netherlands (Groningen).

General facilities

In addition to the equipment and installations directly connected with the production or handling of oil and gas general facilities are also required. In remote areas their provision can constitute a very large part of the total development of an oilfield. For example, a large stores organization with well stocked warehouses may be required to ensure that essential projects are not held up by the lack of materials or equipment. Water supplies and all forms of communication have to be provided or developed. A power station, sometimes quite large in size [Fig. 66], may have to be erected to provide electricity. Fully equipped machine shops and vehicle repair depots are essential.

Housing, social, educational, hospital and recreational facilities have to be provided for the staff. In fact the development of an oilfield in remote areas requires, not merely the installation of oil production facilities, but the construction of a small town with all its requisite services.

The chemistry of petroleum

The chemistry of petroleum

The preceding chapters have explained how natural gas and crude oil are found and produced. Succeeding chapters will show how various oil products and chemicals are manufactured from these raw materials. This chapter gives a brief outline of the chemistry of petroleum which should help to explain how this is possible.

Matter is not infinitely divisible: there is a limit beyond which a substance no longer exists as such. The smallest possible unit of a pure substance like water still possessing its characteristic properties is a molecule. All water molecules are identical.

On further division, a molecule disintegrates into a characteristic number of atoms, the smallest possible units of a limited group of substances, the elements. All atoms of an element such as oxygen, carbon or hydrogen are identical and unite according to fixed rules. The disintegration of the atom is beyond the scope of this book.

The characteristic properties of a substance depend on the type, number and arrangement of the atoms composing its molecule. Water, for instance, is H_2O, H-O-H, the capitals H and O symbolizing atoms of hydrogen and oxygen respectively, the short lines representing the chemical 'forces' or 'bonds'.

Crude oils are mixtures of many substances, often difficult to separate, from which various oil products–petroleum gas, gasoline, kerosine, gas oil, fuel oil, lubricating oil, wax and asphaltic bitumen–have to be manufactured.

These substances are mainly compounds of only two elements, carbon (C) and hydrogen (H), and are therefore called hydrocarbons. Other elements may be ignored at this stage since they are present in only small quantities, although some of them, sulphur (S), have an important effect on product quality. Two kinds of processes for manufacturing oil products are used. By the physical methods the hydrocarbons in the raw materials are merely shuffled into technically useful groups without disruption. By the chemical or conversion methods the more complex hydrocarbons are broken down into simpler ones and rearranged in different patterns of technically useful groups.

Chemical products manufactured from petroleum cover a much more varied range of molecular types than merely hydrocarbons. They do not occur as such in crude oil or natural gas, but they are all compounds of carbon and hydrogen, most but not all of which are combined with other elements, such as oxygen (O), nitrogen (N), sulphur (S) or chlorine (Cl).

The manufacture of oil products is so different from that of chemicals, both in processes and equipment, that they will be described in separate chapters. But in broad outline the chemistry of petroleum is essentially the chemistry of hydrocarbons as given in this chapter.

Hydrocarbons

Hydrocarbons may be gaseous, liquid or solid at normal temperature and pressure, depending on the number and arrangement of the carbon atoms in their molecules. Those with up to four carbon atoms are gaseous; those with twenty or more are solid; those in between are liquid. Liquid mixtures, such as most crude oils, may contain either gaseous or solid compounds or both in solution. For example, oil from the Schoonebeek field in the Netherlands contains a high proportion of dissolved solid hydrocarbons; the crude oil is liquid as it flows from the well at some 70°C, but becomes almost solid on cooling, owing to crystallization of the solid compounds. Many crude oils from the USA, on the other hand, contain only a small proportion of solid hydrocarbons and remain liquid even at low temperature.

The simplest hydrocarbon is methane, a gas consisting of one carbon atom and four hydrogen atoms. The methane molecule can be represented as

```
   H
   |
H—C—H   or   CH4
   |
   H
```

The carbon atom has four bonds that can unite with either one or more other carbon atoms (a unique property) or with atoms of other elements. A hydrogen atom has only one bond and can never unite with more than one other atom. The larger hydrocarbon molecules have two or more carbon atoms joined to one another as well as to hydrogen atoms. The carbon atoms may link together in a straight chain, a branched chain or a ring.

```
   H  H  H  H  H
   |  |  |  |  |
H—C—C—C—C—C—H
   |  |  |  |  |
   H  H  H  H  H
```

or $CH_3—CH_2—CH_2—CH_2—CH_3$

straight-chain hydrocarbon or 'normal' compound

```
          H
          |
        H—C—H
          |
   H  H   |  H
   |  |   |  |
H—C—C—C—C—H
   |  |  |  |
   H  H  H  H
```

```
               CH3
                |
or CH3—CH2—CH—CH3
```

branched-chain hydrocarbon or 'iso' compound

```
      H     H
       \   /
H        C        H
  \    /   \    /
    C         C
  /  |        |  \
H    |        |    H
H    |        |    H
  \  |        |  /
    C         C
  /   \     /   \
H        C        H
       /   \
      H     H
```

or

```
     CH2
    /   \
 CH2     CH2
  |       |
 CH2     CH2
    \   /
     CH2
```

ring or 'cyclo' compound (rings of other sizes are possible)

From these three basic configurations a considerable number of hydrocarbons can be built up, especially since more complicated compounds may be formed by combinations of chains and rings, for example:

```
    CH2
   /   \
CH2     CH—CH2—CH—CH3
 |       |        |
 |       |       CH3
CH2     CH2
   \   /
    CH2
```

The number of hydrogen atoms associated with a given skeleton of carbon atoms may vary. When a chain or ring carries the full complement of hydrogen atoms, the hydrocarbon is said to be saturated, and such hydrocarbons are known as paraffins, paraffinic hydrocarbons or alkanes/cycloalkanes. Straight-chain structures are normal paraffins, branched-chain structures are isoparaffins, and ring-type structures are cycloparaffins or napthenes. Thus for three hydrocarbons with five carbon atoms, all pentanes, we have the following structures:

(a) $CH_3—CH_2—CH_2—CH_2—CH_3$ normal pentane, C_5H_{12}

(b) $CH_3—CH_2—CH—CH_3$ isopentane, C_5H_{12}
```
              |
             CH3
```

(c) cyclopentane, C_5H_{10}
```
CH2—CH2
 |    |
CH2  CH2
   \ /
   CH2
```

When less than the full complement of hydrogen atoms is present in a hydrocarbon chain or ring, the hydrocarbon is said to be unsaturated. Unsaturated hydrocarbons are characterized by having two adjacent carbon atoms linked by two or three bonds instead of only one. These links are known as double bonds and triple bonds; they are not stronger than the single bond, but on the contrary surprisingly vulnerable, with the result that the unsaturated compounds are chemically more reactive than the saturates.

Straight- or branched-chain hydrocarbons with one double bond are called mono-olefins or alkenes, hydrocarbons with a double bond in a ring are cyclo-olefins, or cycloalkenes, and those with two double bonds in the structure diolefins or dienes.

Hydrocarbons with a triple bond are called acetylenes or alkynes.

The simplest members of the olefin and acetylene series are ethylene and acetylene whilst butadiene is the simplest diolefin.

$CH_2{=}CH_2$	$CH{\equiv}CH$	$CH_2{=}CH—CH{=}CH_2$
ethylene	acetylene	butadiene

Neither olefins nor acetylenes occur in crude oil or natural gas, but are produced by conversion processes in the refinery and are important raw materials for chemical syntheses.

Ring compounds containing one or more six-membered rings with three alternate double bonds form an important group known as aromatics because most of them have a characteristic smell.

The simplest member is benzene, C_6H_6, in which each carbon atom carries only one hydrogen atom.

```
    CH
  //  \
HC     CH
 |     ||
HC     CH
  \\  /
    CH
```

benzene

More complex molecules of the aromatic series are obtained by replacing one or more hydrogen atoms by hydro carbon groups or by 'condensing' one or more rings.

```
    CH                 CH     CH
  //  \              //  \ C /  \\
HC     CH          HC     ||     CH
 |     ||           |     ||      |
HC     C—CH3       HC     ||     CH
  \\  /              \\  / C \  //
    CH                 CH     CH
```

$C_6H_5CH_3$ toluene

$C_{10}H_8$ naphthalene

Aromatic rings are customarily shown as simple hexagons (left), omitting the C and H symbols and the double bonds. When one or more hydrogen atoms are replaced by hydrocarbon groups the resulting compound is shown as in the example on the left. This procedure will be followed in succeeding chapters.

—CH_3

From these few examples it will be obvious that there is no end to the number and complexity of hydrocarbon structures. By introducing other elements, in particular oxygen, nitrogen and sulphur, the number of possibilities, and thus the number of possible organic chemicals, based on a carbon skeleton increases tremendously.

Non-hydrocarbons

A brief reference has already been made to the non-hydrocarbons that may occur in crude oils and oil products. Although small in quantity, some of them have a considerable influence on product quality. In many cases they have noxious or harmful effects and must be removed, or converted to less harmful compounds, by refining processes. In a few cases their presence is beneficial and they should not be removed or converted.

The most important elements occurring in non-hydrocarbons are sulphur (S), nitrogen (N) or oxygen (O); in some crude oils there are small amounts of metal compounds, of vanadium (V), nickel (Ni), sodium (Na) or potassium (K) for example. An account of these compounds will help to explain the background of some of the refining and treating processes described in succeeding chapters.

Sulphur compounds

Many types of sulphur compounds occur in crude oils in widely varying amounts from less than 0·2%w in some Pennsylvanian, Algerian and Russian crudes to over 6%w in some Mexican and Middle East crudes.

A distinction is often made between corrosive and non-corrosive sulphur compounds. The corrosive ones are free sulphur, hydrogen sulphide and mercaptans of low molecular weight. Moreover, they have an obnoxious smell.

Hydrogen sulphide, H_2S, has the structure H-S-H. If one of the hydrogen atoms is replaced by a hydrocarbon group, the compound is called a mercaptan, for example:

C_2H_5SH ethyl mercaptan

The compounds are formed during the distillation of crude oils; they may cause severe corrosion of the processing units, and addition of chemicals, proper temperature control and the application of special alloys in plant equipment are required to control them.

The non-corrosive sulphur compounds are sulphides (thio-ethers), disulphides and thiophenes. If the two hydrogen atoms in hydrogen sulphide are replaced by hydrocarbon groups, the compound is called a sulphide or thio-ether.

$C_2H_5—S—C_2H_5$ diethyl sulphide

The disulphides are formed either from mercaptans by oxidation or from sulphides and sulphur.

$C_2H_5—S—S—C_2H_5$ diethyl disulphide

Thiophenes are sulphur compounds with a 5-ring structure:

```
HC—CH   or  C4H4S   thiophene
||  ||
HC  CH
  \/
  S
```

The non-corrosive sulphur compounds, although not directly corrosive, may cause corrosion on decomposition at higher temperatures and therefore also require careful temperature control in processing units.

Apart from their unpleasant smell, both corrosive and non-corrosive sulphur compounds are undesirable in most products. In fuels the sulphur burns to sulphur dioxide and sulphur trioxide, which combine with the water formed by combustion to give sulphurous and sulphuric acids, which may cause serious corrosion in the colder parts of engines or furnaces. Furthermore, some sulphur compounds reduce the effect of anti-knock additives (tetraethyl lead and tetramethyl lead) on the ignition quality of gasolines. Sulphur compounds in illuminating kerosine promote charring of the wick and cause a bluish white deposit on the lamp glass. In dry cleaning solvents they may give a bad odour to cleaned goods and in paint thinners may affect the colour of the dried film.

Some natural gases have a high content of hydrogen sulphide; that from Lacq in France contains 15%v and in Canada there are wells producing natural gas with even 32%v.

The lower mercaptans are insoluble in water, but soluble in hydrocarbons, and have an intolerable odour. They react with sodium and copper to form sodium and copper mercaptides and with oxygen to form disulphides.

Thio-ethers or sulphides are also insoluble in water, but soluble in hydrocarbons, and have an offensive odour. Because of their relatively unreactive nature, however, drastic treatment is necessary for removal. Disulphides are more reactive than the thio-ethers on account of the S-S linkage and can readily be oxidized to water soluble compounds.

Thiophenes have a pleasant odour, comparable with that of benzene, and are relatively stable; they may even be beneficial.

Nitrogen compounds

Most crude oils contain less than 0·1%w of nitrogen, but some from California, Japan and South America contain as much as 2%w. The nitrogen compounds in the crude are complex and for the most part unidentified, but on distillation they give rise to nitrogen bases, compounds of pyridine, a six-membered nitrogen-containing ring, in the derived products.

Nitrogen bases often cause discoloration of heavy gasolines and kerosines, particularly when associated with phenols. In gasolines they may also cause engine fouling and in lubricating oils engine 'lacquer'. In heavy gas oil feedstocks for catalytic cracking they may reduce the activity of the catalyst by increasing coke deposits. Nitrogen bases can be removed by acid treament and recovered by neutralization of the acid extract.

Oxygen compounds

Some crude oils contain oxygen compounds. Their structure has not yet been established, but on distillation of the crudes the oxygen compounds decompose to form ring compounds with a carboxylic acid group (COOH), in the side chain.

```
    CH2
   /   \
CH2     CH2
 |       |
CH2     CH—CH2—COOH
   \   /
    CH2
```

These compounds are known as 'naphthenic acids', large quantities having been originally found in distillation products of Russian naphthenic crudes. The carboxylic acid group(s) may, however, be attached to hydrocarbon groups other than naphthenes, and 'petroleum acids' would be a more accurate term; 'naphthenic acids', however, is generally accepted. Some of these acids are highly corrosive and special alloys have to be used in processing equipment.

Naphthenic acids are extracted from distillates by alkali treatment, either during distillation or afterwards, and are recovered by acidifying the extract. They are valuable by-products used in the manufacture of paint-driers, emulsifiers and cheap soaps.

Phenolic compounds occur in some crudes and are formed during cracking. They are oxygen compounds containing one or more OH groups, derived from aromatic hydrocarbons. The simplest members are phenol, the cresols and the xylenols.

They are recovered during refining.

—OH

phenol

Other compounds

Several other elements occur in crude oils, either as inorganic or organic compounds, and remain in the ash on burning. They vary from crude to crude, but many crudes contain vanadium and nickel. Sodium and potassium are usually present, derived from saline water produced together with oil. Copper, zinc and iron are also found. These elements are generally of little account, but sometimes they are important e.g. vanadium is recovered as vanadium ashes from deposits on furnace walls, or from flue gases, when high vanadium fuels are burnt in refinery furnaces. Vanadium metal is an important component for the manufacture of special steels. Vanadium, iron and nickel in feed for catalytic cracking may spoil catalyst activity. Therefore the feedstocks have to be carefully distilled or redistilled to leave the metal compounds in the residue.

Hydrocarbon reactions

Of the four main groups of hydrocarbons (paraffins, olefins, naphthenes and aromatics), the olefins are the most reactive and the paraffins the least. In the refining of crude oil and in the manufacture of chemicals derived from petroleum, certain basic reactions play an important role. Some of them are also of interest in connexion with the performance properties of oil products, e.g. in the deterioration of gasoline and lubricating oils through oxidation and polymerization.

The following are the most important of these reactions:

Dehydrogenation – the elimination of hydrogen atoms from a molecule. A saturated hydrocarbon becomes unsaturated, and a chemical substance changes its type.

$$CH_3{-}CH_3 \longrightarrow CH_2{=}CH_2 + H_2$$

ethane — ethylene — hydrogen

$$CH_3{-}CHOH{-}CH_3 \longrightarrow (CH_3)_2C{=}O + H_2$$

isopropyl alcohol — acetone — hydrogen

Hydrogenation – the reverse process to dehydrogenation: the filling up of the 'free' places or double bonds in unsaturated structures by hydrogen atoms (addition).

$$CH_2{=}CH_2 + H_2 \longrightarrow CH_3{-}CH_3$$

ethylene — hydrogen — ethane

Cracking – disruption of the carbon-carbon bonds in large hydrocarbon molecules by heat, so that smaller molecules (both saturated and unsaturated) are obtained.

$$CH_3{-}CH_2{-}CH_2{-}CH_2{-}CH_2{-}CH_2{-}CH_2{-}CH_2{-}CH_2{-}CH_2{-}CH_2{-}CH_3 \longrightarrow$$

$C_{12}H_{26}$ dodecane

$$CH_3{-}CH_2{-}CH_2{-}CH_2{-}CH_3 + CH_2{=}CH{-}CH_3 + CH_2{=}CH{-}CH_2{-}CH_3$$

C_5H_{12} pentane — C_3H_6 propylene — C_4H_8 butylene

Pyrolysis – a severe form of thermal cracking; the disruption reaction is usually accompanied by a rearrangement of the fragments.

$$CH_3{-}CH_2{-}CH_3 \xrightarrow{800\,^\circ C} CH_2{=}CH{-}CH_3 + CH_3{-}CH_3 + CH_2{=}CH_2 + CH_4 + H_2$$

propane — propylene — ethane — ethylene — methane — hydrogen

$$CH_4 \xrightarrow{1200\,^\circ C} H_2 + C + CH{\equiv}CH$$

methane — hydrogen — carbon — acetylene

Isomerization – the rearrangement of the carbon skeleton of a molecule, conversion of a straight chain into a branched chain and the reverse.

$$CH_3{-}CH_2{-}CH_2{-}CH_3 \longrightarrow CH_3{-}CH(CH_3){-}CH_3$$

n–butane — isobutane

Cyclization – conversion of a chain into a ring molecule, hydrogen being lost.

$$CH_3{-}CH_2{-}CH_2{-}CH_2{-}CH_2{-}CH_3 \longrightarrow C_6H_{12}\ (\text{ring of six } CH_2) + H_2$$

n–hexane — cyclo-hexane — hydrogen

Alkylation – the introduction of a straight- or branched-chain hydrocarbon group, an alkyl group, into an aromatic or branched-chain hydrocarbon.

$$C_6H_6 + C_8H_{16} \longrightarrow C_6H_5{-}C_8H_{17}$$

benzene — octene — octyl benzene

$$CH_3-CH(CH_3)-CH_3 + CH(CH_3)=CH_2 \longrightarrow CH_3-C(CH_3)_2-CH(CH_3)_2$$

isobutane propylene isoheptane

Polymerization and Copolymerization – the combination of a number of unsaturated molecules of the same or different compounds to form a single large molecule, called a polymer when it is built up from a number of identical monomers, and a copolymer when it is a combination of two or more different types.

$$n\ CH_2{=}CH_2 \longrightarrow CH_3-CH_2-CH_2-CH_2-CH_2 - - - CH_3$$

ethylene polyethylene

Polymers are often solids (plastics), the properties of which depend largely on their molecular size.

Oxidation – the reaction of oxygen with a molecule that may or may not already contain oxygen. Oxidation may be partial, resulting in the incorporation of oxygen into the molecule or in the elimination of hydrogen from it, or it may be complete, forming carbon dioxide and water (combustion).

$$2\ CH_2{=}CH_2 + O_2 \longrightarrow 2\ CH_2-CH_2\ (\text{bridged by O})$$

ethylene oxygen ethylene oxide

(partial oxidation)

$$2\ CH_3CH_2OH + O_2 \longrightarrow 2\ CH_3-CHO + 2\ H_2O$$

ethyl alcohol oxygen acetaldehyde water

(partial oxidation)

$$CH_4 + 2\ O_2 \longrightarrow CO_2 + 2\ H_2O$$

methane oxygen carbon dioxide water

complete oxidation (combustion)

Reduction – the reverse of oxidation: the proportion of oxygen to hydrogen in the molecule is decreased.

$$CH_3-CHO + H_2 \longrightarrow CH_3CH_2OH$$

acetaldehyde hydrogen ethyl alcohol

Chlorination – in the reaction of a saturated hydrocarbon with chlorine one or more of the hydrogen atoms may be replaced by chlorine atoms with the formation of hydrochloric acid. The replacement of hydrogen by chlorine in this way is called substitution.

$$CH_4 + Cl_2 \longrightarrow CH_3Cl + HCl$$

methane chlorine methyl chloride hydrochloric acid

In the reaction of an unsaturated hydrocarbon with chlorine, two chlorine atoms are directly attached to the double bond. This is known as an addition reaction.

$$CH_2{=}CH_2 + Cl_2 \longrightarrow CH_2Cl-CH_2Cl$$

ethylene chlorine dichloroethane

Hydration – the addition of water to a double bond without breakdown of the molecular structure.

$$CH_2{=}CH_2 + H_2O \longrightarrow CH_3CH_2OH$$

ethylene water ethyl alcohol

Dehydration – the reverse process in the chemical field,

$$CH_3CH_2OH \longrightarrow CH_2{=}CH_2 + H_2O$$

ethyl alcohol ethylene water

but in oil manufacturing the term is also used for simple drying of a product (elimination of dissolved or emulsified water).

Esterification – the reaction of an alcohol with an organic or mineral acid with elimination of water to form an ester.

$$C_2H_3OH + CH_3COOH \longrightarrow CH_3COOC_2H_5 + H_2O$$

ethyl alcohol acetic acid ethyl acetate (ester) water

Hydrolysis – the decomposition of a molecular structure by the action of water. The hydrolysis of an ester results in the formation of an alcohol and an acid, and is the reverse of esterification.

$$CH_3COOC_2H_5 + H_2O \longrightarrow CH_3COOH + C_2H_5OH$$

ethyl acetate water acetic acid ethyl alcohol

Condensation – the coupling of organic molecules accompanied by the separation of water or some other simple substance, e.g. alcohol. A catalyst is usually required to promote the reaction.

$$2\ CH_3-CO-CH_3 \longrightarrow CH_3-CO-CH{=}C(CH_3)-CH_3 + H_2O$$

acetone mesityl oxide water

Sulphonation – the action of concentrated sulphuric acid on an aromatic hydrocarbon, e.g. benzene, to form a sulphonic acid. The hydrocarbon group in a sulphonic acid is directly linked to the sulphur atom.

$$C_6H_6 + H_2SO_4 \longrightarrow C_6H_5-S(=O)(=O)-OH + H_2O$$

benzene sulphuric acid benzene sulphonic acid water

Sulphation – the reaction of an olefin with sulphuric acid. An ester is produced by addition of the sulphuric acid to the double bond and the hydrocarbon group is linked to the sulphur atom through an oxygen atom.

$$C_6H_{13}—CH=CH_2 + H_2SO_4 \longrightarrow C_6H_{13}—CH(—O—SO_2—OH)—CH_3$$

octene + sulphuric acid → mono-octyl sulphuric acid ester

Hydrodesulphurization – the elimination of sulphur from sulphur-containing chain molecules in crudes or distillates by the action of hydrogen under pressure over a catalyst.

$$C_8H_{17}—S—C_6H_{13} + 2\,H_2 \longrightarrow C_8H_{18} + C_6H_{14} + H_2S$$

$$C_{16}H_{33}SH + H_2 \longrightarrow C_{16}H_{34} + H_2S$$

Catalysis – the alteration of the rate of a chemical reaction by the presence of a 'foreign' substance (catalyst) that remains unchanged at the end of the reaction, for instance hydrogenation using metallic platinum or nickel, and the cracking of a hydrocarbon using a silicate.

Types of crude oil

Crude oils vary widely in appearance and consistency from country to country and from field to field. They range from yellowish brown, mobile liquids to black, viscous semi-solids. But they all consist essentially of hydrocarbons. Their differences are due to the different proportions of the various molecular types and sizes of hydrocarbons previously described.

One crude oil may contain mostly paraffins, another mostly naphthenes. Whether paraffinic or naphthenic, one may contain a large quantity of lower hydrocarbons and be mobile or contain a lot of dissolved gas; another may consist mainly of higher hydrocarbons and be highly viscous, with little or no dissolved gas.

The nature of the crude governs to a certain extent the nature of the products that can be manufactured from it and their suitability for special applications. A naphthenic crude will be more suitable for the production of asphaltic bitumen, a paraffinic crude for wax. A naphthenic crude, and even more so an aromatic one, will yield lubricating oils that are rather viscosity sensitive to temperature. However, modern refining methods permit greater flexibility in their use of crudes to produce any desired type of product.

Crudes are usually classified into three groups, according to the nature of the hydrocarbons they contain.

Paraffin base crude oils

These contain paraffin wax, but little or no asphaltic matter. They consist mainly of paraffinic hydrocarbons and usually give good yields of paraffin wax and high-grade lubricating oils.

Asphaltic base crude oils

These contain little or no paraffin wax, but asphaltic matter is usually present in large proportions. They consist mainly of naphthenes and yield lubricating oils that are more viscosity sensitive to temperature than those from paraffin base crudes, but which can be made equivalent to the latter by special refining methods. These crudes are now often refered to as naphthene base crude oils.

Mixed base crude oils

These contain substantial amounts of both paraffin wax and asphaltic matter. Both paraffins and naphthenes are present together with a certain proportion of aromatic hydrocarbons.

This classification is a rough-and-ready division into types and should not be used too strictly. Most crudes exhibit considerable overlapping of the types described and by far the majority are of the mixed base type.

Natural gas

Natural gas

Outside North America, natural gas has been slow to attract commercial interest as compared with oil due simply to the absence of known sources of gas or, where they existed, to the lack of suitable markets within economic and physical supply range. When large supplies became available in Venezuela and in the Middle East in conjunction with crude oil, they were often too remote from consumer markets to be exploitable and, in many instances, had to be 'flared' in the process of crude oil production.

The post-war discoveries of natural gas in Austria, Czechoslovakia, France, Germany, Italy and the USSR, and the construction of adequate pipelines to distribute it, initiated a series of local commercial enterprises; more recent discoveries of very large deposits in the Netherlands and North Africa have enormously widened the prospects for gas development in Europe. Similar discoveries of natural gas in Argentina, India, New Zealand, Nigeria, Pakistan and other countries are also being commercially developed.

Great as is the present production of natural gas, total reserves are so vastly greater – estimated to be about 40% of all known petroleum reserves – that it is evident that natural gas is now an important world-wide source of energy, and for this reason the present chapter has been included to give a general account of natural gas as an increasingly important sector of the petroleum industry.

Nature and occurrence

The term 'natural gas' is applied to gas produced at the surface from underground accumulations of widely varying composition which may or may not be directly associated with accumulation of oil. With few exceptions the gas consists of at least 95%v hydrocarbons, the remainder being nitrogen and carbon dioxide with sometimes a small proportion of hydrogen sulphide. The principal hydrocarbon is methane, the lightest and lowest boiling member of the paraffin series of hydrocarbons. Heavier and higher boiling point members of this series, ethane, propane, butanes, pentanes, hexanes and heptanes, are present in decreasing proportions. While 70 to almost 100%v of the hydrocarbons in a natural gas may consist of methane, pentanes and heavier hydrocarbons rarely represent more than 1–2%v, and may be as little as 0·1–0·2%v. The chemical formulae and boiling points of the paraffin hydrocarbons found in natural gas are given in Table 12 below.

As shown in this table, methane, ethane, propane, and the butanes are gases at ordinary atmospheric temperatures and pressures while pentane, hexane, heptane and octane are liquids. However, just as air at atmospheric pressure can contain varying quantities of water vapour, depending on the temperature, so natural gas may contain amounts of these liquid hydrocarbons. It is then known as 'wet gas' as distinct from 'dry gas' containing none or only a small proportion of liquid hydrocarbons. These liquid hydrocarbons can be recovered from natural gas as 'natural gasoline'.

Of the gaseous hydrocarbons, methane, the main constituent, cannot be liquefied under pressure at atmospheric temperature but propane and the butanes can be liquefied under relatively low pressure at atmospheric temperature and are then known as 'liquefied petroleum gas', LPG. Natural gas can be liquefied at atmospheric pressure by cooling to about –160°C (–256°F) and is then known as 'liquefied natural gas', LNG.

Natural gasoline and LPG have a commercial value greater than that of natural gas and it may therefore be desirable to extract them before sale of the gas. The methods by which this is done are described under Oil products – manufacture (pp. 86 and 92).

Practically all oil accumulations have natural gas associated with them, the gas being dissolved in the oil under reservoir temperatures and pressures (solution gas) and often also forming a 'gas cap' of free gas above the oil (gas-cap gas). However, gas accumulations often exist independently of any oil accumulation and are then referred to as 'non-associated gas'. Such reservoirs are discussed under Oilfield development and production (p. 52).

Reserves of natural gas are always defined as being either associated or non-associated and this distinction is extremely important. In general, associated gas production is deter-

Table 12 Paraffin hydrocarbons in natural gas

Name	Chemical formula	Boiling point at atmospheric pressure °C	
methane	CH_4	–161·5	gaseous at atmospheric temperature and pressure
ethane	C_2H_6	–88·5	
propane	C_3H_8	–42·2	
isobutane	C_4H_{10}	–12·1	
normal butane	C_4H_{10}	–0·5	
isopentane	C_5H_{12}	27·9	liquid at ordinary atmospheric temperature and pressure
normal pentane	C_5H_{12}	36·1	
normal hexane	C_6H_{14}	69·0	
normal heptane	C_7H_{16}	98·4	
normal octane	C_8H_{18}	125·6	

Table 13 Total reserves (associated and non-associated) of natural gas

Area	Reserves ft³ x 10¹²
Middle East	181
USA	276
USSR and Eastern Europe	98
Africa	81
South and Central America	46
Western Europe	52
Canada	37
Asia/Far East	20

Fig. 67 General view, natural gas installation, Groningen, the Netherlands

mined by the accompanying production of crude oil; only solution gas is produced, it being generally undesirable in the interest of maximum crude oil recovery to produce 'gas-cap' gas, at least during a substantial part of the reservoir life. The 'solution gas' is frequently a major source of energy – sometimes the only one – in recovering the oil and the main problem is to minimize its production. In certain oil reservoirs it is advantageous to re-inject the gas to improve oilfield life and this is done where possible. Substantial quantities in excess of oilfield requirements may be produced, however, and in the absence of local markets or export possibilities, the excess gas has to be flared.

Non-associated gas, on the other hand, can be produced as and when markets develop.

Substantial reserves of natural gas exist in many areas as shown in Table 13. Fig. 67 shows a general view of the natural gas field installation at Groningen in the Netherlands.

Manufacture

Natural gas needs no elaborate refining such as is necessary with crude oil to prepare marketable products. It needs only relatively simple treatments to free it from undesirable constituents or to recover valuable non-gaseous constituents.

Dry gas requires relatively little treatment to remove undesirable material. Hydrogen sulphide and other sulphur compounds, if present, are removed by a 'sweetening' process as described for gasoline (p. 108); carbon dioxide, if present to excess, may be removed by absorption with alkali and any small quantity of condensable hydrocarbons are removed by cooling.

Wet gas requires more elaborate treatment to recover from it natural gasoline and liquefied gases. This is achieved by compression and cooling, absorption, adsorption, low temperature separation or a combination of these processes (p. 92).

Marketing

Natural gas is a very attractive fuel; it gives a clean burning flame, odourless combustion, easily controlled rate of heating and, if required, high heat intensity. Moreover, being piped direct to the point of application, it needs no customer storage or other handling equipment. It thus has many advantages over and above its inherent thermal efficiency and the potential market is extensive, limited only by availability which depends largely on the existence of adequate pipelines or other means of transport linking the gas source with the market. Due to the high cost of gas transport facilities, the market must be sufficiently large in volume and constant in offtake if unit transport costs are to be within reasonable limits. Where available, natural gas is therefore a fuel which can usually be expected to command a better price than that based on strict thermal parity with alternative fuels such as fuel oil or coal.

The specific applications of natural gas are dealt with in

some detail in the chapter, Fuels for domestic, industrial and agricultural use (p. 144). The marketing outlets for natural gas can be classified into domestic and commercial, industrial, and chemical industry.

The domestic market consists of a cooking and water-heating offtake that is low in volume and not sufficient on its own to provide a satisfactory base load, and a space heating offtake that is seasonal. In suitable climates a summer load may exist for swimming pool heating, air conditioning, etc. The domestic demand is, however, supplemented by what is known as 'commercial consumers', i.e. restaurants, hotels, stores, workshops, garages, etc, whose applications are similar to those of the domestic user.

The industrial market comprises industries such as metallurgical, ceramic, glass, and bread and biscuit baking, where natural gas can command a special price because of its special advantages in the processes they operate, and industries such as power stations and cement works, etc, which, although they gain no technical advantage from the use of gas, find it a convenient and economic fuel. In this category also are factory process steam boilers. Most heavy industry provides a fairly steady base load with limited seasonal and hourly variations but some light industries, e.g. bakeries, may have a more fluctuating demand.

The chemical industry uses natural gas as a feedstock for the manufacture of various chemicals. Being mainly methane, natural gas is relatively unreactive chemically; nevertheless it is used in the synthesis of plastics, weedkillers and so on. Its principal chemical use, however, is as a source of hydrogen, a basic raw material of the chemical industry (p. 196).

Natural gas can be supplied to these markets either direct from a trunk transmission grid, for example to large industrial consumers, or via the town mains of a local gas marketing company, the pattern depending on local agreements and arrangements amongst the suppliers.

Transmission

Pipelines

In most cases a pipeline is the only practical method of transporting gas and the pipeline has become the indispensible link between gas well and market.

Historically, pipelines have been known for centuries, the Chinese being the first to transport natural gas through bamboo pipes. Wooden pipes were used near New York in 1821 for transporting natural gas but were quickly followed by lead and cast iron pipes. None of these early systems, however, could be used at high pressure.

The first real forerunner of the modern steel high pressure transmission line was a 2 in. wrought iron line $5\frac{1}{2}$ miles long laid in 1872 in Pennsylvania. Two 8 in. wrought iron lines each 120 miles long with screwed couplings were laid soon afterwards to supply natural gas to Chicago but the laying of the Magnolia fourteen, sixteen and eighteen inch diameter 217 miles long acetylene welded line in 1925 marked the real beginning of a new era in pipeline development. With rapidly increasing knowledge of metallurgy and electric welding techniques since the 1930s, and steadily improving methods of corrosion prevention, construction of heavy duty lines up to or above 36 in. diameter is now quite commonplace. Whereas in the 1890s the operating pressures were of the order of 80 lb/in^2 (6 kg/cm^2) they are now 800–1000 lb/in^2 (55–70 kg/cm^2).

When gas flows in a pipeline there is a drop in pressure along the line, and to avoid uneconomically large pipe diameters and very high initial pressures, it is usually necessary to install compressor stations at intervals of 70–120 miles along the route. Each compressor station usually comprises two or more reciprocating or centrifugal compressor units, with a compression ratio of 1:4, driven by diesel, gas turbine or electric drives. Control is effected either by local staff or, on many modern lines, by remote control from a central control point which may be many miles away.

A pipeline requires relatively high capital expenditure but is comparatively low in operating cost, and in order to keep the unit cost of transport to a minimum, the line should be operated at the maximum possible loading. In designing a pipeline system therefore, due attention must be given to the possibility of either the provision of sufficient storage to meet peak demands, or some agreed method of planning the offtake to reduce variations to a minimum (peak shaving). This will be dealt with in more detail in a later section.

Good examples of large modern gas lines which have been built in the United States are:

The Tennessee Gas Transmission Company's two 30 in. lines, and a 24 in. line which extend from Houston (Texas) to West Virginia, a distance of nearly 1100 miles. South of Houston the system extends a further 270 miles, almost to the Mexican border.

The Panhandle Eastern Pipeline Company's triple line transmission system 1050 miles in length, running from Hugoton (Kansas) to Detroit, on which pipe sizes range from 20–30 in.

In Europe an outstanding example of a modern gas transmission system is the Netherlands Gasunie feeder system comprising 224 miles of 36 in. diameter and 70 miles of 24 in. diameter line which will be extended later. A further example is the 20 and 24 in. natural gas transmission line from Lacq to Paris.

A 40 in. line built in the USSR in 1963 runs from Gazli to Sverdlovsk, a distance of 1360 miles.

The cost of laying 100 miles of 26 in. line at the present time under average conditions in Europe is about £10 million without compressor stations.

Tankers

When it was apparent some years ago that vast reserves of natural gas were available thousands of miles and oceans away from the nearest consumers, it was obvious that a new technology needed to be born. Ocean transport of liquefied natural gas (LNG) has now been developed to the point where it is as feasible and free of hazards as the transport of conventional liquid petroleum.

The natural gas is liquefied by compressing, cooling, and expanding from a high pressure to produce a low viscosity liquid boiling at about −160°C at atmospheric pressure [Fig. 68]. The liquid may be stored in very well insulated above-ground tankage lined with aluminium or stainless steel, or in 'mud-pie' tanks made by simply digging a pit in the ground after installing a vertical ring of piping through which a cold liquid, for example liquid propane at atmospheric pressure, is circulated [Fig. 69]. The earth around the pit must be moist (wetted if necessary) so that a liquid-tight container is formed by the ice in the soil. A well-insulated roof is fitted, thus forming a permanent tank for the storage of LNG, which of course keeps it frozen. Heat equilibrium in

Fig. 68 Liquefaction plant with storage areas in background at Arzew, Algeria

the surrounding soil appears to be reached in about four years, and the facility is cheap to construct and safe in use since no spillage can occur.

Since LNG has a specific gravity about half that of crude oil and a calorific value per unit weight of not much more, a certain size of tanker can carry only about half the heating

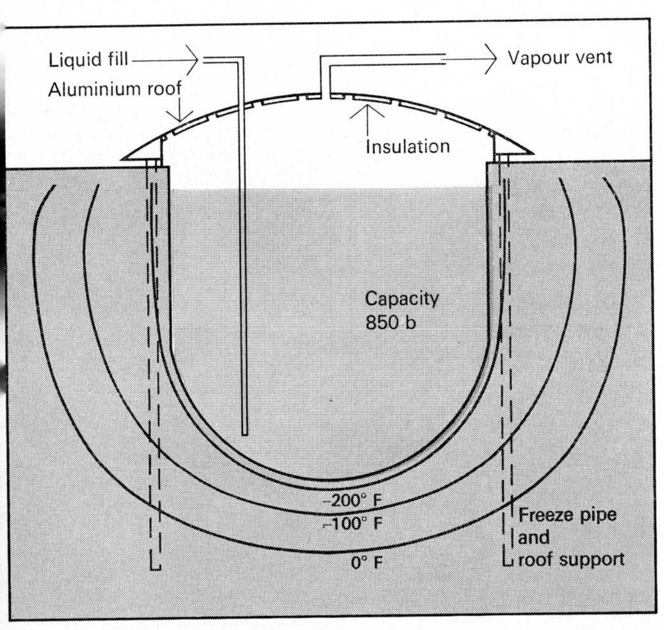

Fig. 69 Mud-pie storage of liquefied natural gas

value as LNG that it can carry as crude oil. The first attempt to carry LNG was by lining a barge with insulation and filling the LNG direct into it, but unfortunately it was found impossible to make the barge leak proof. Individual tanks fitted into insulated holds proved successful and have now been adopted for all LNG tankers afloat or building in 1964 [Fig. 70].

The individual tank system is costly and wasteful of space and a system is now being investigated, using a thick flexible skin or membrane that can be laid against an insulated hull, and which will therefore permit more complete filling of the ship. Several designs have been evaluated, all based on sheets of thin metal, corrugated in some fashion with repeating centres of symmetry, the positions of which remain unchanged when the sheet contracts at low temperature, thus allowing the membrane to be fastened to the insulation. It is not sufficient for the membrane to remain in position on the insulation, it also has to withstand repeated expansions and contractions due to temperature, to accept the hydrostatic load of the cargo – which may rise when the ship is in a seaway to as much as 21 lb/in^2 (1·5 kg/cm^2) and to give as necessary without rupture to accommodate the internal movements of the ship. A system of large stainless steel trays, welded on the edges of their upturned sides, has been evolved by Conch Methane Services Ltd, with smaller similar trays to offset the pattern and provide flexibility along the welds.

Conch Methane Services have played a large part in the promotion of the first commercial LNG ocean transport system which came into operation in 1964 transporting LNG from Arzew in Algeria to Canvey Island in England and the French partners in the Arzew consortium likewise initiated a service to Le Havre in 1965.

Two tankers, the *Methane Princess* and the *Methane Progress*, each capable of carrying 12 200 tons of LNG are in service between Algeria and the UK and are expected to deliver about 700 000 tons of LNG/year. A third tanker, the *Jules Verne*, will carry 235 000 tons/year to France, The LNG is regasified at the European terminals and fed into the methane grids now existing in the UK and France (Tankers p. 256).

Fig. 70 Aluminium cargo tank being lowered into *Methane Princess*

Peak shaving

The weather, gas users' domestic habits, industrial working hours, all influence the demand for gas to the extent that, in industrialized countries with cold or temperate climates, the winter time peak offtake may be four or more times greater than the summer holiday time offtake. Furthermore, daily peaks occur of even greater disparity between breakfast or midday cooking and heating periods and the small hours of the night [Figs 71 and 72].

Gas supply systems need to take measures to deal with these peaks as otherwise gas pressure would drop at the customers' appliances and dissatisfaction with gas as a reliable fuel would spread. But daily peaks and seasonal peaks present different problems.

Daily peaks are relatively easily dealt with by using low-pressure gas holders, where these exist, from a town's gas supply system, by the installation of high-pressure gas holders such as buried lengths of large diameter (42 in.) piping, or by line pack, i.e. by allowing all high-pressure pipelines to build up to maximum pressure during the hours of low offtake and to drop in pressure during the hours of high offtake. This latter method is safe since customer's gas supply pressure is always well below the high-pressure pipeline pressure and is kept constant by pressure regulators.

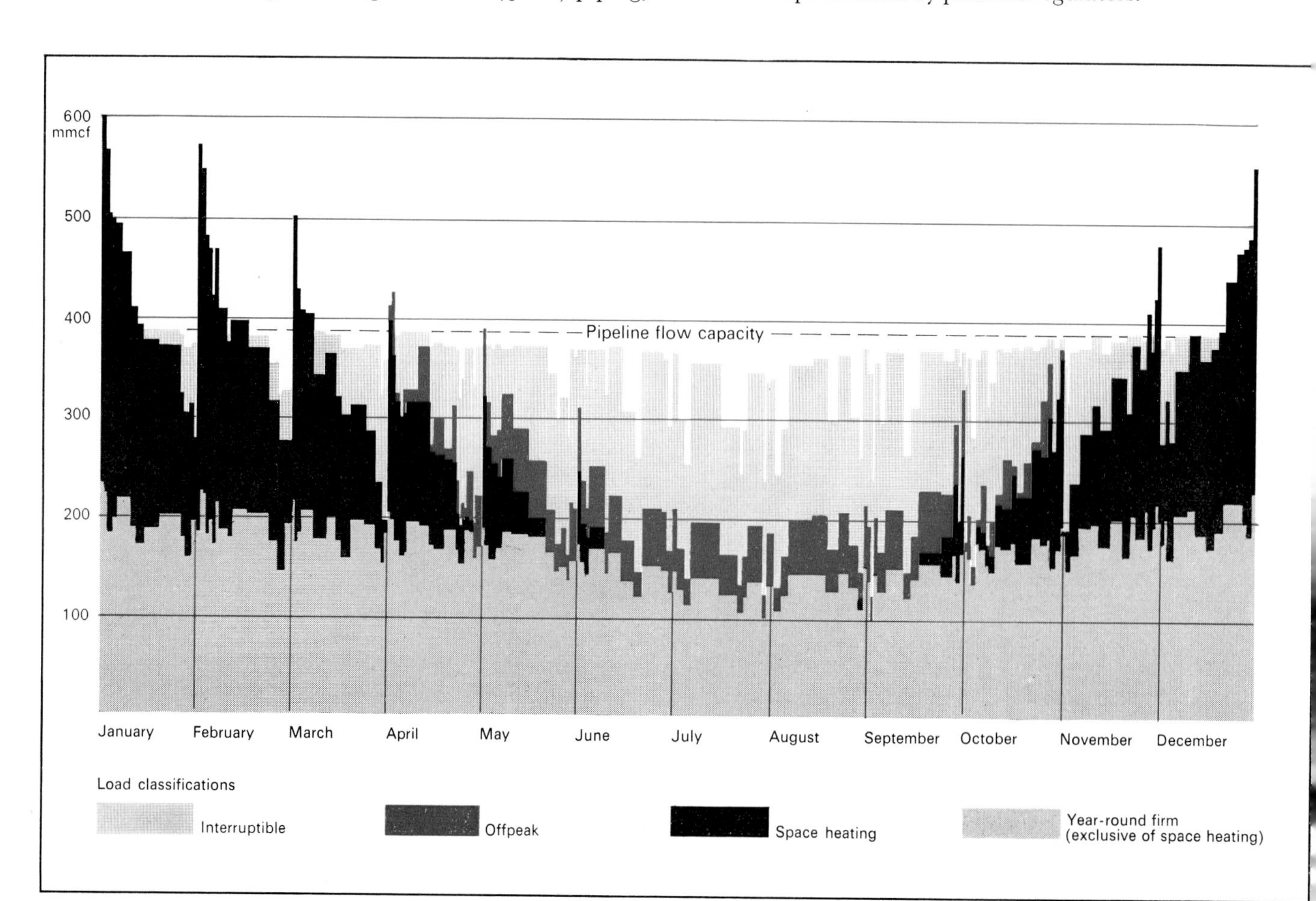

Fig. 71 Estimated daily gas loads for a year

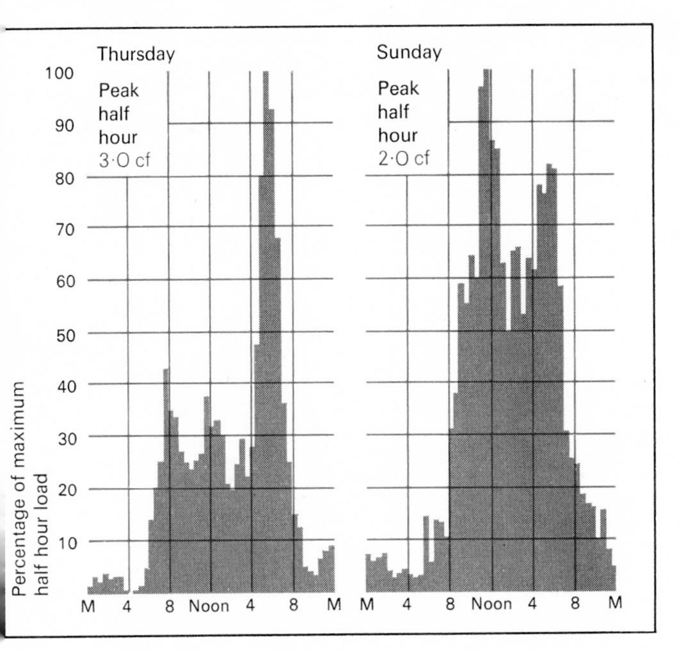

Fig. 72 Daily load curves for cooking

Seasonal peaks are much more difficult to deal with and costly measures have to be employed. If maximum offtakes were to be catered for by installing a trunk pipeline large enough to carry the maximum seasonal flow, the transmission company would be involved in undesirably high capital expenditure and be left with a pipeline that would be running at half capacity or less for most of the year.

A compromise in pipe sizing is usually arrived at by setting the pipe capacity at around two thirds of the maximum offtake and dealing with the peaks of offtake by 'peak-shaving' methods. The summer period of under-use of the line can be dealt with either by the time-honoured method of 'interruptible' contracts with industrialists who are able to use other fuels but who will take gas when it is offered at a lower price, or by promoting summer seasonal offtakes such as air-conditioning. In certain parts of the USA utilities have been so successful in this that they now have a summer seasonal high peak.

The peak-shaving method chosen depends on a number of circumstances. For small gas supply systems with only a short peak season, the cheapest in capital cost is to feed into the system a mixture of LPG and air carefully controlled to simulate the combustion characteristics of natural gas.

On a larger scale of capital and operating cost, but also based on liquid petroleum products, there is a choice of several thermal and catalytic reforming processes which will produce a gas sufficiently near to natural gas in combustion characteristics to be fed into the gas supply system.

Depleted oil or gas fields can be used for storage since it is possible to pump gas into a suitable geological formation and to retrieve it without any losses as and when it is required. Gas can also be pumped in and out of underground water pockets or 'aquifers', where these exist, though there may be some loss of gas. Aquifers can be located by geological surveys and by drilling wells similar to oilwells.

The mud-pie tanks already mentioned on p. 71, in which liquefied natural gas can be stored at about −160°C and at atmospheric pressure, offer an attractive method of peak shaving. During most of the year a small capacity liquefaction plant feeds LNG into storage and when gas is needed for peak-shaving purposes, the liquid is fed into a vaporizer.

Distribution

Town gas networks were initially developed to distribute manufactured gas from a small works to a comparatively compact area of supply. Even in large towns with more than one works, distribution was still a local matter with short distances and pressures limited to a few inches water gauge. Cast iron mains were used, jointed by means of compressed yarn and lead. The larger mains usually radiated rather like the spokes of a wheel from the central supply point and complex networks of smaller mains, usually linked into both adjacent feeders, supplied the areas between them.

As loads on the distribution system increased, these early mains have been superseded by either steel or mechanically jointed spun cast iron pipes operating initially at about 5 lb/in² (0·35 kg/cm²), but more recently at considerably higher pressures up to about 100 lb/in² (7 kg/cm²).

When a change over to natural gas is effected, if it is not reformed to a quality similar to that of town gas, the thermal carrying capacity of the system is considerably increased due to the higher calorific value, but loads usually increase so rapidly that substantial changes are required in the distribution system to increase its carrying capacity. Either the working pressure must be increased or a grid of high-pressure lines must be superimposed. Only small increases in the working pressure of the original system are usually possible and construction of a high-pressure grid is then essential. Such a grid also has the advantage that large industrial consumers can then usually be given a direct supply at the pressure most suited to their equipment.

When natural gas becomes available, the supply authority must decide whether it is to be distributed at around 1000 Btu/ft³ as received, or reformed to give a gas which is interchangeable with the town's gas of around 500 Btu/ft³ currently in use. The decision will depend primarily on whether the supply is sufficient to meet all present requirements with ample reserves for expected increases in offtake and on whether there is any political or other problem in continuity of supply.

If the supply is likely to be ample and continuous it is usually safe to proceed with distribution of straight natural gas. On the other hand, if supplies will not meet total requirements or there is some doubt about continuity of supply, the gas is usually reformed and mixed with manufactured gas before distribution. In this case, reforming plant capital and operating charges, and the thermal loss in the reforming process, will all increase the unit cost of the gas distributed.

The distribution of natural gas will entail the installation of suitable feeders and regulating stations and the testing of the existing distribution system. Consumers appliances are also generally designed to operate within a comparatively narrow range of gas characteristics and will need to be modified for use with natural gas or replaced.

Reformed natural gas, however, can usually be blended to give a gas interchangeable with manufactured gas and no change in appliances will be needed. If only relatively small quantities of natural gas are available and if the gas distribution system is for any reason wedded to low calorific value gas, the natural gas may be mixed in with the gas for enrichment purposes.

Research

The successful development of the marine transport of liquefied natural gas, described earlier in this chapter, has been for some time the major preoccupation of research in the field of natural gas. The system is still in its infancy and naturally presents various problems on which research is still needed. The regasification of the cold liquid (at about −160°C) absorbs a considerable amount of heat and research is being devoted to finding ways of doing this usefully – to make use of the 'cold'. Amongst the possible ways may be in the production of liquid oxygen or other gases, in the processing of food or, in the more distant future, in connection with solid state physics, computers and new methods of generating electricity.

Problems concerning the quality, use and transport of natural gas do not in the main involve research; they can mostly be solved by the application of existing technology. But research is involved in problems connected with the interchangeability of gases and the conversion of gas appliances. Natural gas has a much higher heat content per unit volume than has town gas and the burners of cookers, water heaters and other domestic or industrial appliances need adjustment or conversion. Appliances are now available that are adjustable for use with all gases but most existing appliances in Europe were designed for town gas only. Conversion of one appliance may cost £10–£15 and a large sum of money has to be expended by a gas distribution authority when it changes the quality of its gas. Research has assisted in the development of a simple cheap conversion burner that will substantially reduce this expenditure.

Heat can be transferred from a flame to boiler tubes or to a workpiece in a furnace either by radiation by virtue of the brightness of the flame or by convection by the sweeping action of hot gases over a surface. Natural gas burns with a flame of little radiance whereas coal and oil burn with radiant flames. An industrial furnace designed to operate with a radiant flame from oil will not work so efficiently with the non-radiant flame of natural gas. Research is being undertaken to solve this problem so that natural gas may be sold at no disadvantage to competitive fuels.

Natural gas in the USA

The natural gas industry in the United States was born over 140 years ago when gas was used in small quantities for street lighting and home heating in Fredonia, New York. The industry can really be dated, however, from 1883 when a low-pressure natural gas pipeline was built into the city of Pittsburgh, Pennsylvania. During the next fifty years, growth was slow and gas use was limited to localities close to where it was produced. By 1900, natural gas was being produced in seventeen states, primarily in connection with oil production, and most of it was being flared. In 1901, the fabulous Spindletop Field was discovered near Beaumont, Texas, with large quantities of gas as well as oil. Next came the Texas Panhandle field in the Texas and Oklahoma Panhandles in 1918 and the Hugoton field, Kansas, in 1920, the largest dry gas reserve in the world.

In the late 1920s, the development of high-strength steel pipe, economical ditch digging equipment, and other equipment and techniques permitted the movement of higher pressure gas to more distant markets. Use of manufactured gas in the late nineteenth and early twentieth centuries resulted in development of gas distribution grids in most of the cities in other parts of the United States.

Although natural gas was used in sizeable quantities in those parts of the nation where it was being produced particularly in the south-west, still today the heart of the natural gas production and pipeline business, it was not until after World War II and further technological advances in pipeline transport that the gas pipeline industry came into its own and thus began the massive task of moving natural gas from the places where it was produced to the places where the markets existed. Today the natural gas pipelines in the United States comprise some 270 000 miles of gathering and transmission lines, serving over 36 000 000 customers. Since 1945, natural gas has become available to every part of the United States and the distribution grid systems in every large city and practically every small city or town have been converted to use natural gas. Today, 98% of all gas used in the United States is natural gas, with only a trace of manufactured gas still available, and this primarily for peaking service.

In 1945, natural gas supplied 13% of the $31\,500 \times 10^{12}$ Btu total energy requirements of the United States, whereas today it supplies over 30% of the approximately $50\,000 \times 10^{12}$ Btu total energy requirements.

Natural gas is by far the leading supplier of energy to the home, where it is used mainly for space heating, cooking, hot water, clothes drying, refrigeration, and more and more for air conditioning. It is enjoying fast growth in the commercial segment, where it is used for similar purposes and for steam generation, both for general purposes and for generation of electricity. The great bulk of all natural gas consumed in the United States is used by industry.

The three segments of the natural gas business – the producer, the pipeliner, the distributor – developed essentially as separate corporate entities. The producer was primarily orientated toward the oil business prior to 1945 and found gas a rather bothersome product for which there was very little demand. The distributor built his system on gas manufactured mostly from coal and later oil, but had no direct relationship with the natural gas producing industry. By 1945, the interstate pipeline industry was already under Federal regulation with profits limited to a level below that enjoyed by the non-Federal-regulated oil producing industry. Both producers and distributors, however, assisted, encouraged, and sometimes participated in the development of the pipeline industry which was necessary to bring together the source of supply and the distant markets.

The producer sells his gas to the pipeline companies and also probably directly to adjacent industry; the pipeline company sells the gas to the gas distribution companies, to other pipeline companies, and for direct consumption by industries located along its system; the gas distribution company is the ultimate marketer, selling directly to the householder and to industries and commercial establishments in its area. No longer is natural gas an unwanted by-product of oil production; today it occupies a strong position in the economy of all natural gas producers and its consumption is growing at an annual rate of 3·5%.

Natural gas in the world energy picture

The USA and the USSR are the world's two largest users of natural gas. In 1962 the natural gas contribution to total energy requirements was about 32% in the USA, 14% in the USSR and 2·8% in the rest of the world. The estimated consumption of natural gas in the more important consuming areas is shown in Table 14.

Table 14 Estimated consumption of natural gas, 1963

Area	Consumption ft³ x 10^{12}
Middle East	0·04
USA	15
USSR and Eastern Europe	3
Africa	0·01
South and Central America	0·31
Western Europe	0·55
Canada	0·75
Asia/Far East	0·11

It is difficult to forecast future developments as much will depend on the discovery of new sources of gas which lend themselves to economic development, but even with the known reserves, it is expected that natural gas will take an increasing share of total energy consumed.

Where gas sources are abundant and readily exploitable in an industrial community, a pattern of energy consumption similar to that of the USA may be expected; thus it is estimated that in the Netherlands gas will in due course account for more than one third of all energy used.

At the present time, Western Europe may well be standing on the threshold of important changes in the energy pattern if the intense exploration effort in NW Europe, and the North Sea, should disclose further large reserves of natural gas.

Glossary of natural gas measurement

Natural gas is usually measured in cubic feet or cubic metres and quantities are given in thousands (10^3), millions (10^6), or milliards (10^9). The terms billion and trillion are best avoided on account of the different meanings in different countries. They are sometimes used, however, and have the national meanings shown in Table 15.

Table 15 National terms; million-trillion

Units	British	USA	French	German	Dutch
10^6	Million	Million	Million	Million	Miljoen
10^9	Milliard	Billion	Milliard or Billion	Milliarde	Miljard
10^{12}	Billion	Trillion	Trillion	Billion	Biljoen
10^{18}	Trillion	—	—	Trillion	Triljoen

Volumetric measurement of natural gas is made to the standards shown in Table 16, where 1 cubic metre (m³) = 35·3147 cubic feet (ft³).

Table 16 Volumetric standards for natural gas

Country	Standard unit volume of gas	Abbreviation	Conditions
USA, UK	Standard Cubic Foot	Scf	60°F: 30 in. (762 mm) Hg Wet
Metric, other than the Netherlands	Normal Cubic Metre	Nm³	0°C: 760 mmHg Dry
The Netherlands	Normal Cubic Metre	m_n^3	15°C: 760 mmHg Dry

Table 17 Conversion factors; natural gas

Pressure

Bar	Standard Atmosphere	Kilogram per square centimetre kg/cm²	Pound per square inch lb/in²	Millimetres column of mercury mmHg
1	0·987	1·020	14·50	750·0
1·013	1	1·033	14·70	760·0
0·981	0·968	1	14·22	735·54
0·0689	0·0680	0·0703	1	51·713

Heat quantity

Megajoule MJ	Megacalorie Mc	Kilowatt hour kWh	Therm 100000 Btu
1	0·2388	0·2778	0·00948
4·186	1	1·163	0·03968
105·5	25·20	29·31	1
3·6	0·860	1	0·03412

Calorific value

Megajoule per normal cubic metre MJ/Nm³	Kilocalorie per normal cubic metre kcal/Nm³	Megajoule per normal cubic metre (Dutch) MJ/m_n^3	Megacalorie per normal cubic metre (Dutch) Mc/m_n^3	British thermal unit per standard cubic feet Btu/Scf
1	238·8	0·948	0·2263	25·02
1·055	252	1	0·2388	26·39
4·417	1055	4·186	1	110·5
0·004186	1	0·00397	0·000948	0·1047
0·03997	9·55	0·03790	0·00905	1

Oil products – manufacture

Manufacturing processes
Distillation
Crystallization
Solvent extraction
Adsorption and absorption
Cracking
Reforming
Polymerization, alkylation, isomerization and cyclization
Asphalt blowing
Treating processes
Subsidiary processes

Manufacturing processes

No one crude oil can provide a full range of finished oil products in the proportions and qualities that the market requires. The essential function of an oil refinery is to manufacture, as economically as possible, the necessary quantities of gas, gasoline, kerosine, gas oil, lubricating oil, fuel oil, wax and asphaltic bitumen from the crude oil or oils supplied to it. To do this, appropriate processes must be applied and the necessary plant and equipment must be available.

The processes may be grouped as follows.

Physical separation processes

The hydrocarbon molecules are not changed in structure during the operations and no new compounds are formed.

Distillation – separation according to molecular size, making use of the difference in boiling point.

Crystallization – separation according to size and type, making use of the difference in melting point and solubility, as in oil dewaxing, combined with filtration or centrifuging.

Solvent extraction – separation according to type, for example, paraffins from aromatics, making use of the difference in miscibility with a third component.

Adsorption – separation according to size or type, making use of the difference in adhesion to porous materials (gas/solid and liquid/solid systems).

Absorption – separation according to size or type, making use of difference in solubility in a liquid, for example, light gases from heavier ones (gas/liquid systems).

Chemical conversion processes

If crude oil were subjected to physical processes alone, the ratio in which various products became available would be entirely out of balance with market demands. Conversion processes, which involve a change in size and structure of the hydrocarbon molecules, are a necessary part of modern refinery operation since they convert products surplus to requirements into others in greater demand. The main processes are:

Break-down processes – cracking (thermal and catalytic)

Build-up processes – polymerization, alkylation

Type-change processes – dehydrogenation, isomerization, cyclization, reforming (thermal and catalytic) and asphalt blowing.

These processes are not strictly separated in practice, for example break-down, build-up and type-change processes occur simultaneously in cracking and reforming.

Treating processes

By these the products obtained by separation and conversion processes are purified by physical and chemical means and brought up to marketing specification as to odour, colour,

Fig. 73 General view of a large refinery, Pernis, the Netherlands

stability, etc. Treating of intermediate products is sometimes necessary to remove compounds or impurities which may interfere with subsequent processing steps.

Subsidiary processes

By the application of the above-mentioned processes to crude oil and its fractions, a limited number of refined oil products are produced. Some of these may be suitable for marketing as such but more often than not they have to be blended together in suitable proportions, with or without additives, to produce products meeting marketing specifications and suitable for various applications. For example, gasolines of the desired ignition quality are produced by blending various gasoline fractions and by adding lead compounds and other chemicals; lubricants for various automotive, marine and industrial applications are prepared by blending to the required viscosity characteristics, with or without additives; bitumen is blended with kerosine to form 'cutbacks'.

More elaborate processes are applied in some instances, as in the manufacture of emulsions of wax or bitumen in water, or of water in lubricating oils (marine lubricants), and in the manufacture of lubricating greases.

These blending and manufacturing processes are not normally regarded as 'refining' processes and are usually carried out in separate 'blending plants' or 'installations', which may be situated on the same site as a refinery or at some distant location where refinery grades are received in bulk and finished products are despatched to the market as required.

Integration of refinery processes

The selection and arrangement of refinery processes and the optimum use of the various plant streams are called 'process integration'. Wide variation in output of products can be achieved by proper choice and design of the processing units, based on the available feedstock and the quantity and quality of the market requirements. Allowance may have to be made for importation of additional products or the export of surplus material. Crude oil evaluation and market evaluation determine the planning of the primary processing facilities, crude oil distillation, vacuum distillation and cracking units.

The crude oil distillation unit separates the crude into distillates and a residue, often called 'long residue'. After further treatment the distillates are used for the conventional products. The long residue may be redistilled at reduced pressure in a vacuum distillation unit, the distillates from which may be used as feedstock for catalytic cracking, as base material for lubricating oil manufacture or as a component for fuel oil. The residue, called 'short residue', may be used either for fuel oil blending or, when produced from suitable crudes, as a base material for the manufacture of asphaltic bitumen or of certain grades of viscous lubricating oils known as 'bright stocks'.

Once the primary processing units have been planned, the properties of each product to be manufactured must be studied in order to determine what secondary processing units will be required to make the products meet the marketing specifications. For example, it may be necessary to improve the ignition quality (octane rating) of the 'straight-run' gasoline fraction from primary distillation. This can be done by either thermal or catalytic reforming. In addition to this quality improvement, thermal reforming produces olefins which can be converted by alkylation and polymerization processes into valuable gasoline blending components of good ignition quality. The catalytic reforming processes yield appreciable quantities of fairly pure hydrogen, which may be used for hydrodesulphurization.

If first-quality illuminating kerosine is required, it may be necessary to install a sulphur dioxide or sulfolane extraction unit to improve the burning properties. Similarly, the manufacture of lubricating oils may require the installation of units for solvent extraction, dewaxing and clay treatment, depending on the nature of the distillate and the marketing specifications. The above examples show how, by the selection of appropriate processing units, a refinery is planned to meet a marketing programme. It will also be

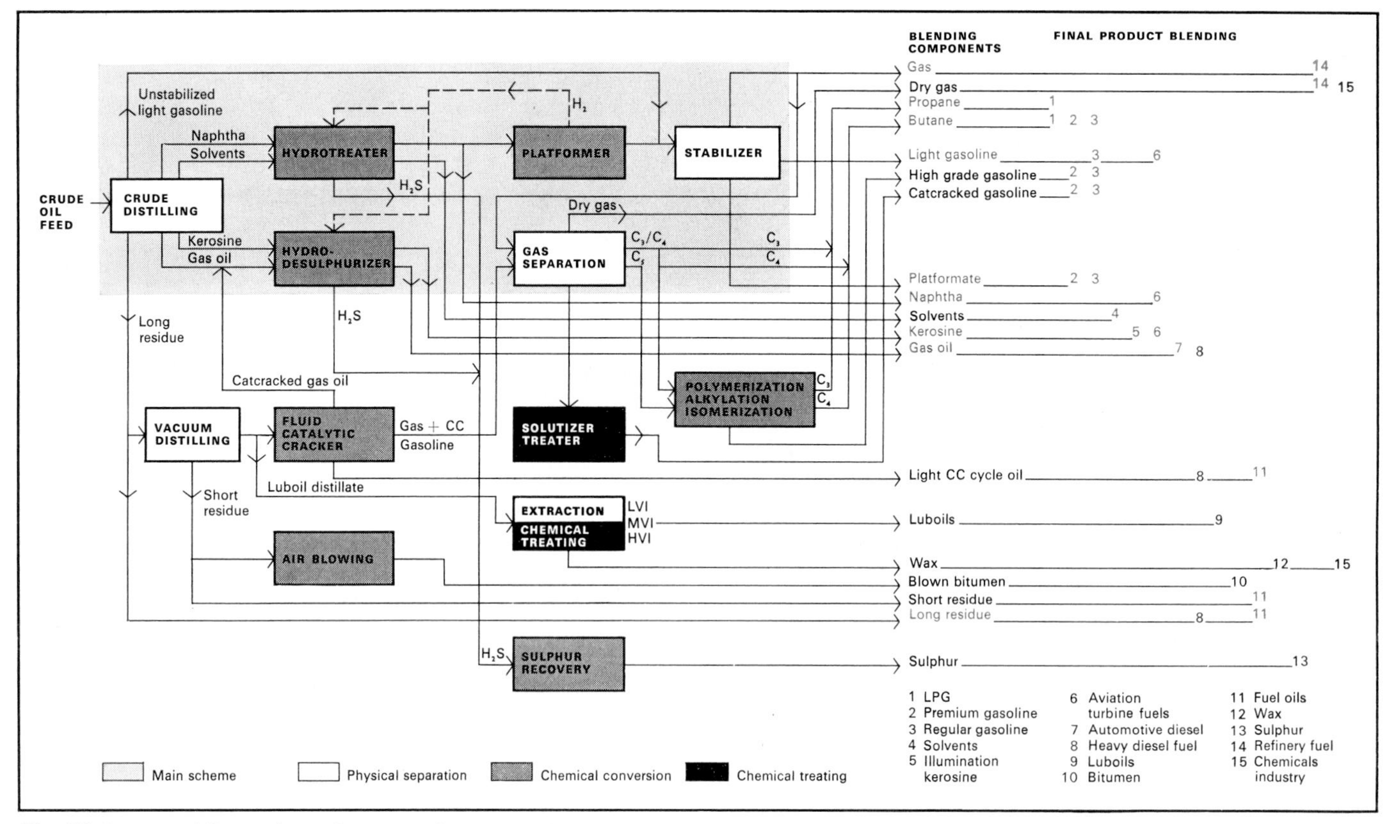

Fig. 74 Integrated flow scheme for processing crude oil

appreciated that, in order to deal with future changes in crude oil supply or marketing requirements, these units must be so designed as to be capable of operating under different conditions. Manufacture of the main products can thus be varied between wide limits, although product quantity and quality are necessarily interdependent. Fig. 74 shows a typical integrated flow scheme for processing crude oil.

Utilities and other requirements

When the principal processing units have been agreed upon, estimates must be prepared for the overall consumption of high- and low-pressure steam, electricity, cooling water, processing water, fuel and compressed air. These are collectively referred to as utilities. Subsequently, these utilities must be planned, taking into account the possibility of purchasing one or more of these items locally. Distribution systems for the various utilities must then be devised.

Fuel, both liquid and gaseous, is consumed in the refinery plant furnaces and boiler houses. Integrated fuel burning systems are designed to consume preferentially the gases produced in distilling, cracking and refining operations, which cannot otherwise be used. Since the quantity of gas available for fuel is generally less than the overall fuel requirements of the refinery, flexibility is ensured by installing both gas and liquid fuel burning systems.

Finally, on the process side, integrated safety systems must be developed to release pressure and to permit the rapid removal from the plants of inflammable, toxic or hazardous material in cases of emergency. Provision must be made for handling spent chemicals, catalysts and other waste materials, for the prevention of air and water pollution by smoke and oily material, and also for the reprocessing or economic disposal of off-grade products, resulting for instance from a changeover of feedstock or from other operating disturbances.

A refinery must also be equipped with the necessary tanks for the storage of crude oil and intermediate and finished products, with the necessary lines, pump houses and jetties, and also with road and rail tank racks and facilities for the receipt of crude oil and the dispatch of finished products.

Good provision must be made for the prevention of fires and for fire-fighting equipment in the event of an outbreak.

Laboratories are required for continuous control of the products and the efficient running of all processes and services.

Automatic instrumentation plays an increasingly important role in refinery plants and processes. Fig. 75 shows a typical control room in a modern refinery.

Fig. 75 Control room in a refinery

Distillation

The first step in the manufacture of petroleum products is the separation of crude oil into the main conventional fractions by distillation. This is the most important process in the refinery, because, in addition to its use for separation, it plays an important part in refining the products to marketing specifications.

A main distinguishing feature of the various products is their volatility or ability to vaporize. This is associated with the size of the molecule; in compounds of a similar type, the larger the molecule, the lower the volatility. At ambient temperature and pressure, gasoline is a liquid that vaporizes readily, while kerosine and fuel oils are liquids requiring higher temperatures to vaporize them. Products like paraffin wax, solid under normal conditions, require heating to a relatively high temperature before they liquefy and to still higher temperatures before they vaporize.

Volatility is related to the boiling point; a liquid with a low boiling point is more volatile than one with a higher boiling point. When a liquid, say water, is heated, the energy of its molecules increases and more molecules are able to pass through the surface of the liquid into the space above, i.e. more molecules pass into the vapour state. The pressure in the space above the surface, normally atmospheric pressure, tends to restrict the formation of vapour, but the temperature of the liquid determines the number of molecules leaving the surface of the liquid, and this in turn determines the vapour pressure of the liquid at that temperature.

When the vapour pressure is equal to or slightly higher than atmospheric pressure, vapour forms freely throughout the whole liquid, as is shown by the disturbance of the liquid surface and the formation of vapour bubbles in the liquid: the liquid is said to boil. The temperature at which a pure liquid boils is its boiling point and remains constant until all the liquid has evaporated, an important characteristic of a pure substance. The boiling point varies with pressure. At normal atmospheric pressure pure water boils at 100°C (212°F), ethyl alcohol at 78°C (172°F). Similarly, each of the individual hydrocarbons present in crude oil has its own characteristic boiling point. The boiling point is lowered by reducing the pressure in the space above the liquid (by creating a vacuum) and raised by increasing the pressure.

The heat imparted to the liquid in the process of boiling is retained in the vapour (latent heat of evaporation) and if this heat is removed, the vapour condenses back into the liquid state, giving off the heat of condensation. This is seen when steam (water vapour) from a kettle of boiling water strikes a cold surface.

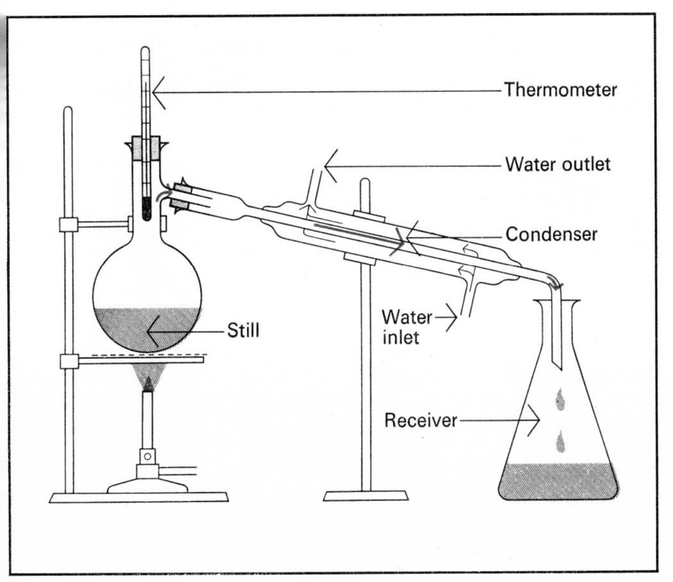

Fig. 76 Simple laboratory distillation apparatus

Simple distillation

The series of operations comprising boiling and condensation is known as distillation. A simple laboratory distillation apparatus is shown in Fig. 76.

The liquid is boiled in a flask or 'still', the vapour is condensed in a tube or 'condenser' surrounded by cold running water, and the distillate collected in a receiver.

In a mixture of several liquids of different boiling points, each component has its own characteristic vapour pressure, and the total vapour pressure above the liquid is the sum of the partial vapour pressures of the components. The mixture boils when the total vapour pressure is equal to the (external) pressure above the liquid.

When such a mixture is distilled, molecules of each component will vaporize, and the composition of the vapour phase will depend on the vapour pressures and the concentrations of the components in the liquid phase. Since the lower-boiling-point components have the higher vapour pressures, the distillate will at first be richer in these than in the higher-boiling-point components, whereas the liquid in the still will have a higher concentration of high-boiling-point components. As distillation proceeds, the composition of both distillate and residue will change progressively until all the liquid has been distilled into the receiver.

Boiling starts at a temperature which lies somewhere in the range of the boiling points of the components, and depends on their ratio in the mixture. The initial boiling point (IBP) is defined as the temperature at which the first drop distills over. The temperature gradually increases during distillation, and the more volatile components distil over. The liquid becomes richer in higher boiling components until the last drop of liquid evaporates at the highest temperature, the final boiling point (FBP).

Fractional distillation

Using a simple distilling apparatus as described above, it is not possible to effect sharp separation between the components of a mixture in one distillation. By redistilling the

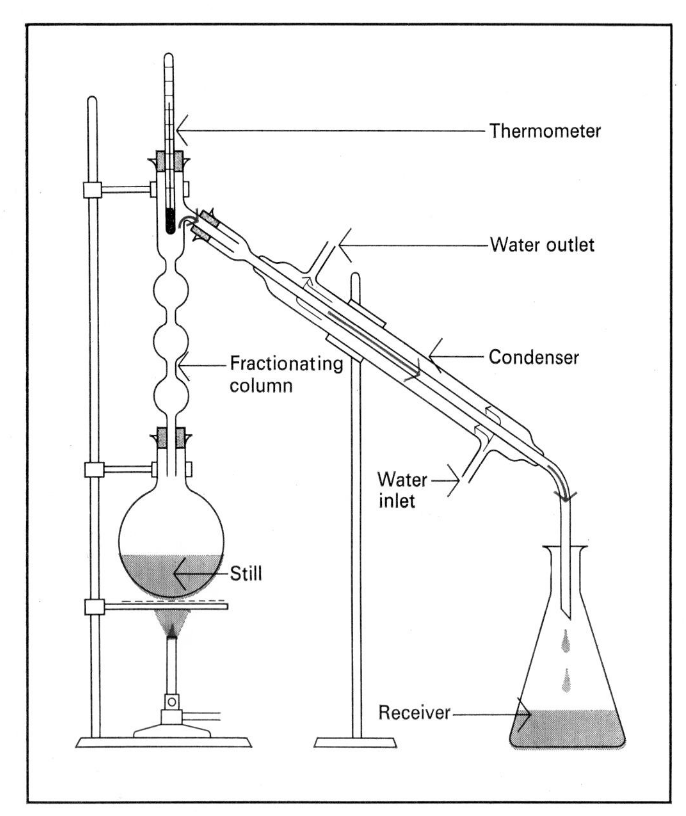

Fig. 77 Laboratory fractional distillation apparatus

first portion, a distillate richer in the more volatile components will be obtained, but the yield will be low, since part of the components always remains in the still. To effect a good separation it is necessary to modify the apparatus for continuous condensation and redistillation by inserting a still-head or 'fractionating' column between still and condenser, as shown in Fig. 77. Some of the vapour from the boiling liquid condenses as a liquid fraction in each bulb of the column. The condensation of further vapour from the still supplies heat, which re-evaporates the lighter or lower-boiling-point components from the liquid in the bulbs. These components condense in the next higher bulb, and so on up the column. As it becomes richer in the heavier, less volatile and higher-boiling-point components, the liquid in the bulbs flows back to the still. Thus there is a countercurrent flow of vapour and liquid, the vapour ascending the column and becoming lighter as the heavier components condense, and the liquid descending and becoming heavier as the lighter components re-evaporate. The vapour passing over the top into the condenser consists at first of the low-boiling components, and as these are removed the temperature of the liquid in the still increases steadily and higher-boiling components distil over. By changing the receiver at intervals, several different fractions are obtained. A fraction separated in this manner may consist of a relatively pure component from a simple mixture or a number of components from a complex mixture, depending on the composition of the mixture distilled and the type of apparatus. This process is called 'fractional distillation'.

Distillation of crude oil

The products obtained from crude oil do not consist of single hydrocarbons, except in the case of simple gases such as propane and butane. Each fraction contains many compounds and boils within a certain range. Crude oil is separated into a number of distillate fractions and a residue consisting of the higher-boiling-point components.

The boiling range of a particular fraction may be that required for a specific product, for example gasoline. Alternatively, the product may be prepared by blending a number of fractions, so that the blend has the required boiling range.

Good fractionation is important if overlapping between one fraction and the next one is to be avoided. For example the fraction or fractions intended for use as kerosine should not include the more volatile components of the gasoline range, which would lower the IBP and the flash point (the lowest temperature at which the vapours of the product forms an inflammable mixture with air, under standardized conditions). On the other hand, the gasoline fraction should not contain kerosine components, which would raise the FBP and adversely affect its performance as an engine fuel.

In the early days of refining, stills consisted of cylindrical tanks into which the crude oil was charged. The oil was heated and the vapour condensed, no fractionating equipment being used. Illuminating oil (kerosine) was the main product. The process was intermittent, the residue being removed from the still and a new batch introduced. Following the development of the internal combustion engine, the need for improved fractionation led to the use of simple fractionating columns, corresponding, in principle, to the still-head in the laboratory apparatus. This simple intermittent fractionation process is no longer used in petroleum refineries, except for the manufacture of relatively small quantities of special products with narrow boiling ranges, for example 60–80°C (140–175°F) or 100–120°C (212–248°F). These products, mainly used as solvents and obtained from a gasoline fraction, are known as SBP (special boiling point spirits).

Present-day demands for large throughputs and high-quality products require units capable of continuous operation and efficient fractionation. In a laboratory fractional distillation apparatus the temperature of the still is continuously raised, and the fractions of increasing boiling ranges are intermittently removed. In a refinery distillation unit, however, the oil is heated to the highest temperature required to vaporize all the volatile products, which, together with the unvaporized components, enter the fractionating column. Here, as in the laboratory apparatus, condensation and re-evaporation take place as the vapour ascends the column.

Fractions with the required boiling range are continuously withdrawn from appropriate points along the column, the lightest (most volatile) from the top and progressively heavier or less volatile fractions at lower levels. The portion of crude oil that is not evaporated in the still, is removed from the bottom of the column. The separation of the volatile components is assisted by the use of steam. When steam is continuously blown into hot oil, it contributes its own partial pressure, thus depressing the partial pressure of the oil, so that it boils at a lower temperature.

Steam distillation is used in the distillation of higher boiling components to avoid the chemical decomposition that would take place at high distillation temperatures. Distillation under reduced pressure (vacuum distillation) is used for the same reason.

The very light products, such as propane and butane,

cannot conveniently be condensed at atmospheric pressure and normal temperature because of their low boiling points, propane −42°C (−44°F), butane −0·5°C (31°F). Therefore, to separate them from other gases and from each other, distillation is carried out under pressure, which increases the boiling point and therefore the temperature of condensation.

Simple distilling unit

The principle of a simple distilling unit is shown in Fig. 78. The crude oil first passes through a heat exchanger in countercurrent with the outgoing hot residual product (fuel oil) which itself must be cooled before running to storage. Preheated crude oil then enters the furnace, where it flows continuously through a series of pipes heated by flames. The temperature is raised to that required to vaporize all the volatile components and the hot vapour/liquid mixture enters the fractionating column in the form of a mist, the vapour passing upwards and the liquid downwards. The process of condensation and re-evaporation takes place in the 'rectifying' section. The hot oil passes downwards into the 'stripping' section, where any light products are removed by the action of steam.

The most volatile components, gas and gasoline, are removed from the top of the column. The gasoline vapour is condensed in the condenser by cooling water: the uncondensable gaseous hydrocarbons remain in the vapour phase and are thus separated from the condensate. By returning part of the condensate, called the 'reflux', to the upper part of the column, a downward stream of liquid is maintained and the temperature at the top is controlled by varying the amount returned.

Other distillate products are removed from the column as side-streams, the point of removal being chosen to give a product of the appropriate boiling range. In the diagram, two such streams are shown, representing a kerosine and a gas oil fraction. In order to improve the fractionation, and to avoid using a much taller and therefore more expensive main column, each side-stream is further fractionated in a 'side stripper'. These are, in effect, small fractionating columns in which all components more volatile than those required in the product are evaporated with the aid of steam injected into the bottom of the side stripper; the vapour stripped off is returned to the main column and bottom products from the side strippers are cooled before storage.

The proper temperature at the bottom of the column (and thereby all temperatures throughout the column) is maintained by circulating part of the residue through a heater called a 'reboiler', and back into the column; this is in addition to the use of reflux to control the temperature at the top of the column.

Heaters

Heaters must be designed in such a way that the oil is brought to the required temperature with the minimum consumption of fuel and without chemical decomposition of the hydrocarbons, which can result from either prolonged

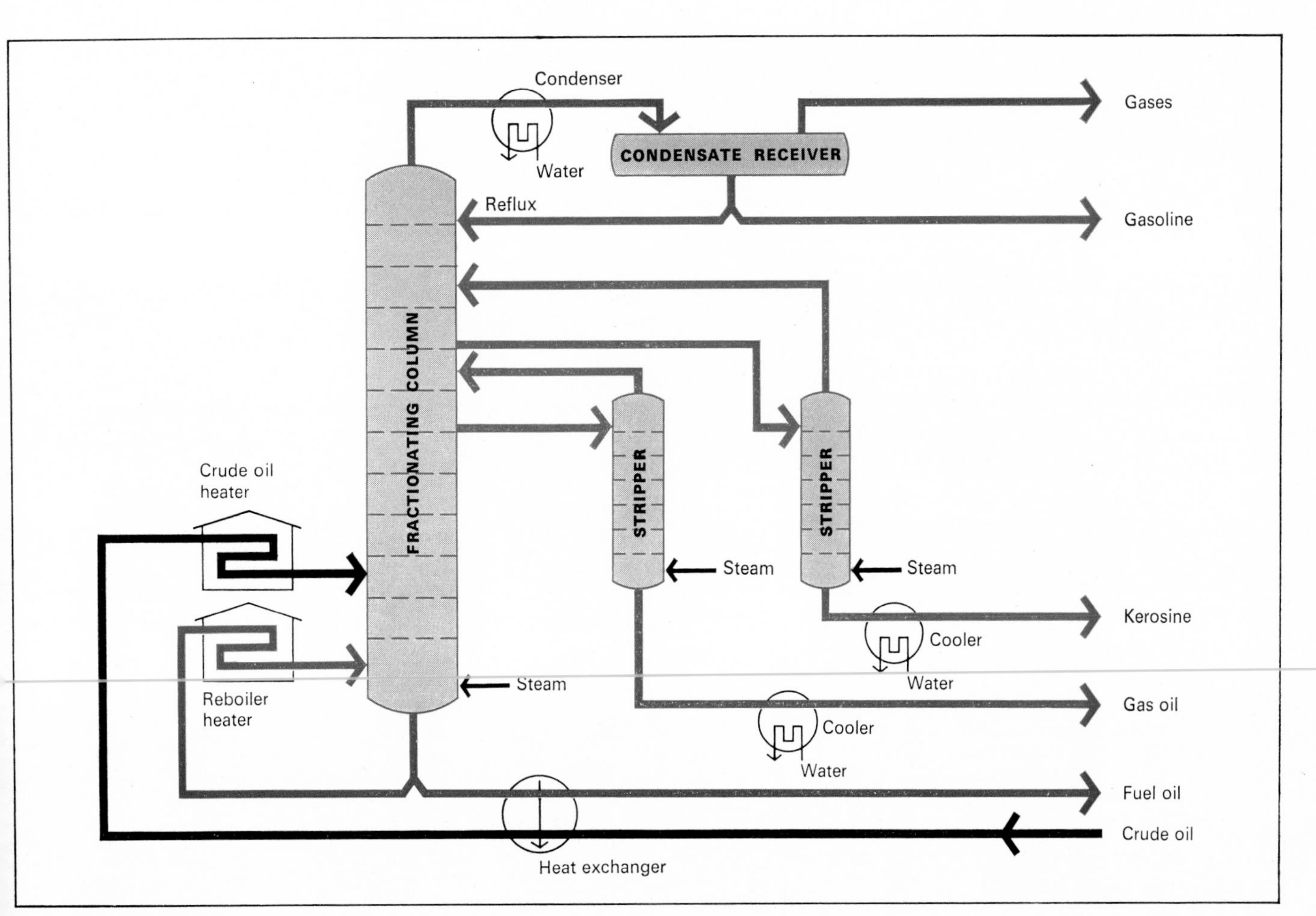

Fig. 78 Simple distillation process

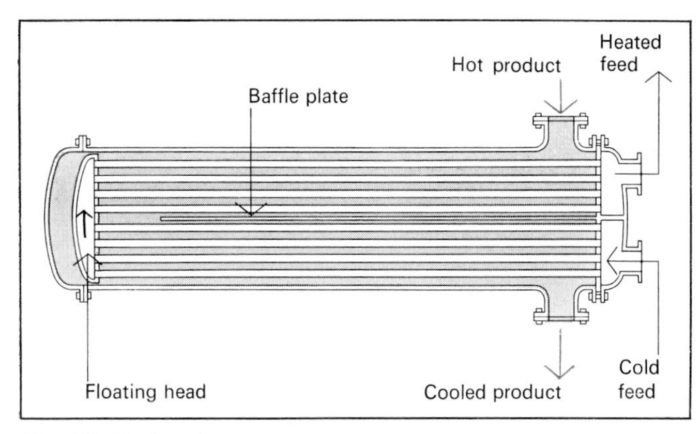

Fig. 79 Heat exchanger

heating or from high temperature. The oil is heated in two stages, first in a heat exchanger, then in a furnace.

A heat exchanger [Fig. 79] consists of a cylindrical vessel inside which a nest of tubes is fitted. A hot product passes through the vessel and around the tubes through which the liquid to be heated is flowing. For maximum efficiency, the flow of the two streams is arranged in countercurrent. The tubes are fixed at one end, but in order to allow for expansion and contraction, the other end may be attached to a 'floating head' so that movement can take place.

In a modern furnace the oil flows continuously through a series of tubes about four inches in diameter, joined together so that the oil passes backwards and forwards through the furnace. The tubes are mounted in a steel furnace lined with firebrick, heat being supplied by oil or gas burners. A tubular heater of this type is shown in Fig. 80.

The incoming oil passes through a bank of tubes heated only by the hot gases passing up to the flue and shielded from the direct radiant heat of the furnace, the flow of oil

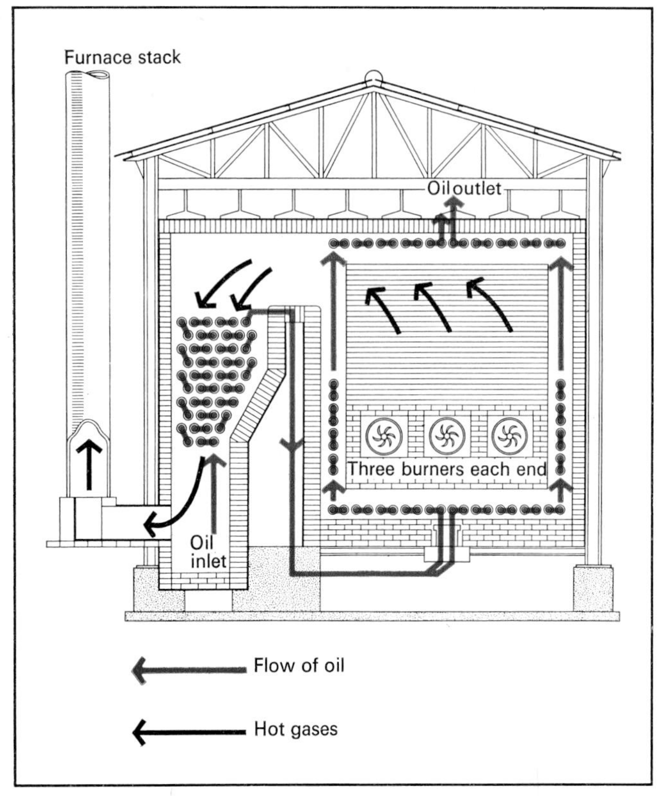

Fig. 80 Tubular heater

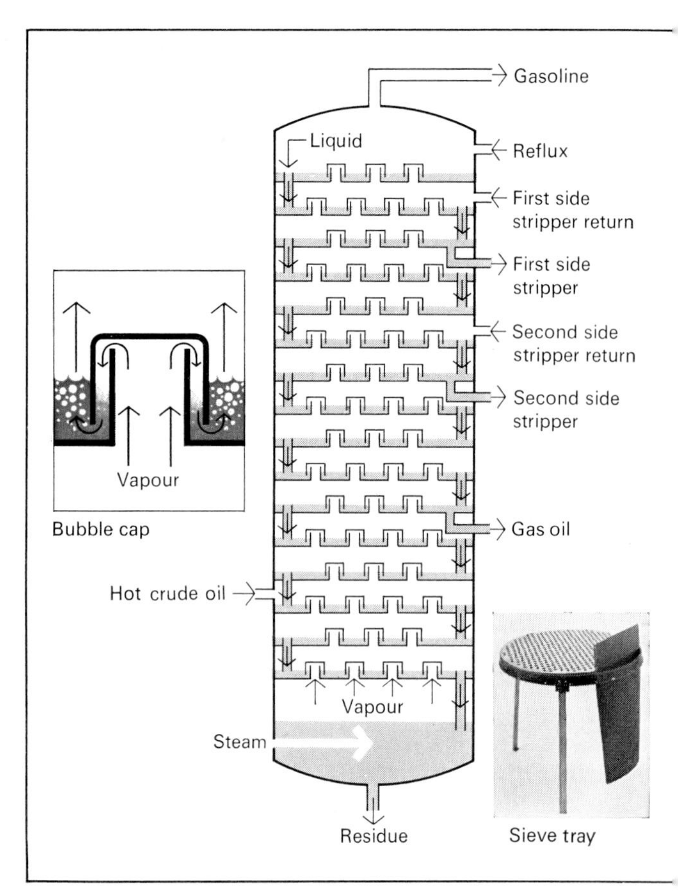

Fig. 81 Fractionating column showing trays and caps

being countercurrent to the flow of hot gases. The oil then passes through a further bank of tubes mounted on the walls of the combustion chamber and is raised to distillation temperature by radiant heat. By supplying the heat in this manner, in convection and radiant sections respectively, consumption of fuel in the furnace is reduced because of the recovery of heat from the flue gases, and chemical decomposition is reduced by subjecting the oil to the high radiant temperature of the furnace for as short a time as possible.

Fractionating columns

A fractionating column consists of a vertical steel cylinder divided by horizontal plates into a number of sections. These plates are called trays. A section of a column and details of the trays are shown in Fig. 81.

The condensed liquid collects on the trays up to the level of the overflow pipe, which rises a few inches above the level of the tray, and flows down through the overflow pipe onto the next lower tray. The trays have a large number of perforations through which vapour passes upwards from the lower tray. Each perforation is surmounted by a short pipe or 'riser', over which a cap is fitted, so that the vapour is forced to pass through slots or serrations in the perimeter of the cap and through the liquid held on the tray. These caps are called 'bubble caps'. As the vapour bubbles through the liquid, reasonably good contact between vapour and liquid is obtained, causing any low boiling components in the liquid to vaporize and any high boiling compounds in the vapour to condense. There is thus a process of condensation and re-evaporation on each tray, the vapours ascending the column, the liquids descending. Each tray will contain a lower boiling fraction than the one below, and fractions with different boiling ranges can be continuously withdrawn from different levels in the column.

The size of the columns, the number of trays and the number and type of bubble caps vary with the function of the column, each column designed according to its purpose. For special purposes grid trays or sieve trays [Fig. 81] are used instead of bubble cap trays, but the general principle remains the same.

Modern crude oil distilling units

The products separated in the crude oil distilling unit of a modern refinery may be broadly classified, in order of decreasing volatility, into gases, light distillates, middle distillates and residue. The gases consist chiefly of methane, ethane, propane and butane. The first two are used as refinery fuel or may be supplied, together with other refinery gases, for making town gas. Propane and butane may be liquefied by compression and marketed as liquefied petroleum gas (LPG). Butane may to some extent be added to motor gasoline.

The light distillates comprise fractions which may be used directly in the production of motor and aviation gasolines. The heavier, higher-boiling-point fractions in this range are the lighting, heating and jet engine kerosines and the feedstocks for reforming processes described in the chapter on Reforming (page 100). The special boiling point spirits and white spirits are obtained by further distillation of an appropriate gasoline fraction in a special plant designed to give a high degree of fractionation, so as to produce the narrow boiling point ranges required. The heavier

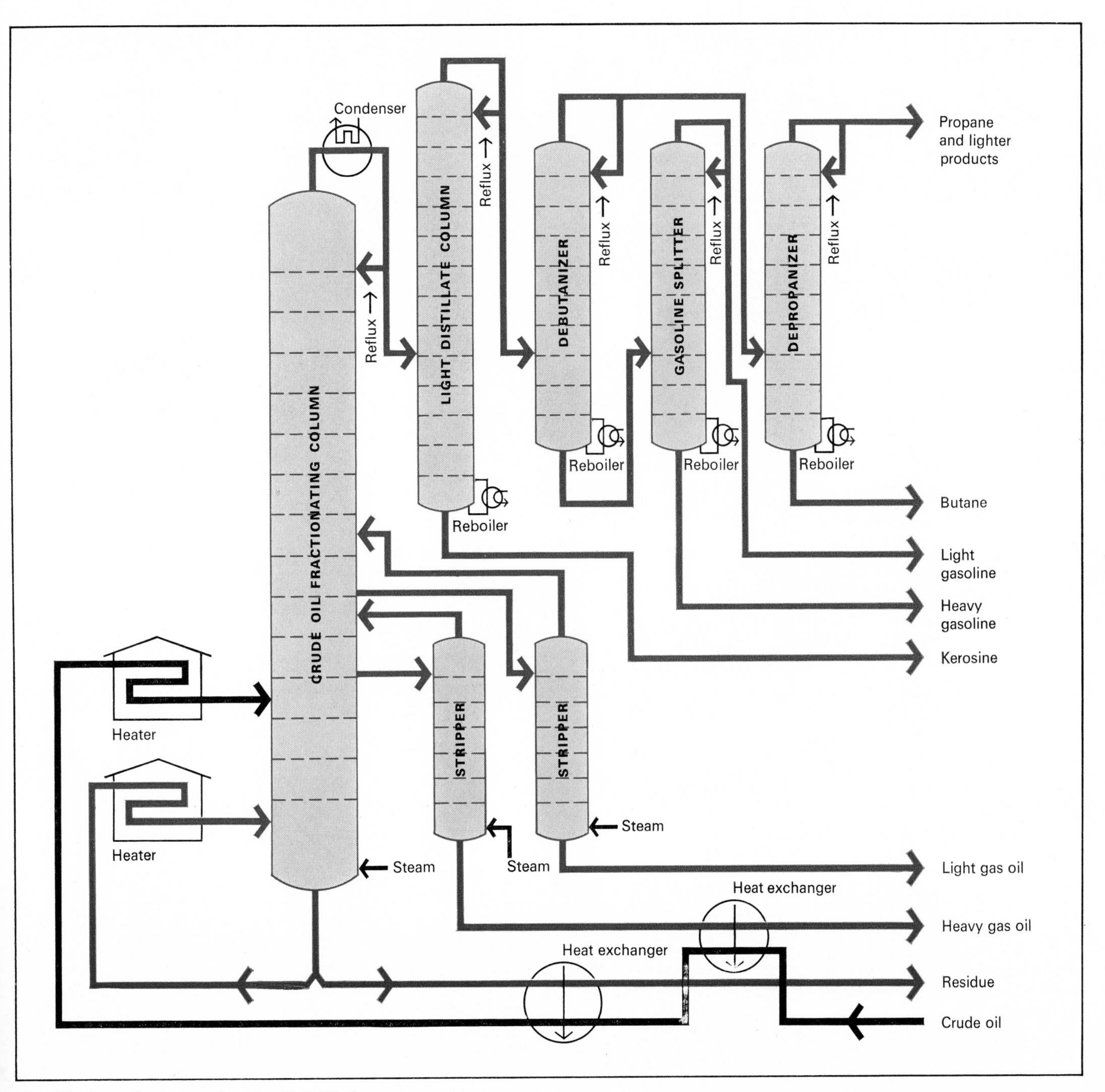

Fig. 82 General scheme of crude oil distillation

fractions falling within the gasoline range are sometimes referred to as naphthas.

The middle distillates are used as gas oil and diesel fuel and also for blending with residual products in the preparation of furnace fuels. The distillates used as feedstocks for cracking purposes may be obtained from the middle distillate range.

The residue, consisting of the components that are not removed as distillates, is used as fuel oil or for the manufacture of lubricating oils, wax and bitumen.

In order to obtain the most effective and economical separation of the fractions, a modern distilling unit consists of a number of fractionating columns and side-strippers, in place of the single column described above. Fig. 82 shows the general scheme of crude oil distillation and a crude oil distilling unit is shown in Fig. 84.

The crude oil passes through heat exchangers to the furnace, where it is raised to the distillation temperature, approximately 300–350°C (570–660°F), depending upon the feedstock and the products to be made. The hot oil and vapours then enter the first fractionating column.

Part of the top product from the column, after condensation, is used as reflux; the remainder is transferred to the second or light distillate column. Heat is supplied to this column by a reboiler. The top fractions comprise gasoline and lighter products, and the bottom product is kerosine.

Butane, propane and lighter products are separated under pressure in the debutanizer and depropanizer, heat again being supplied by reboilers. The removal of the very volatile products from gasoline fractions in this manner is

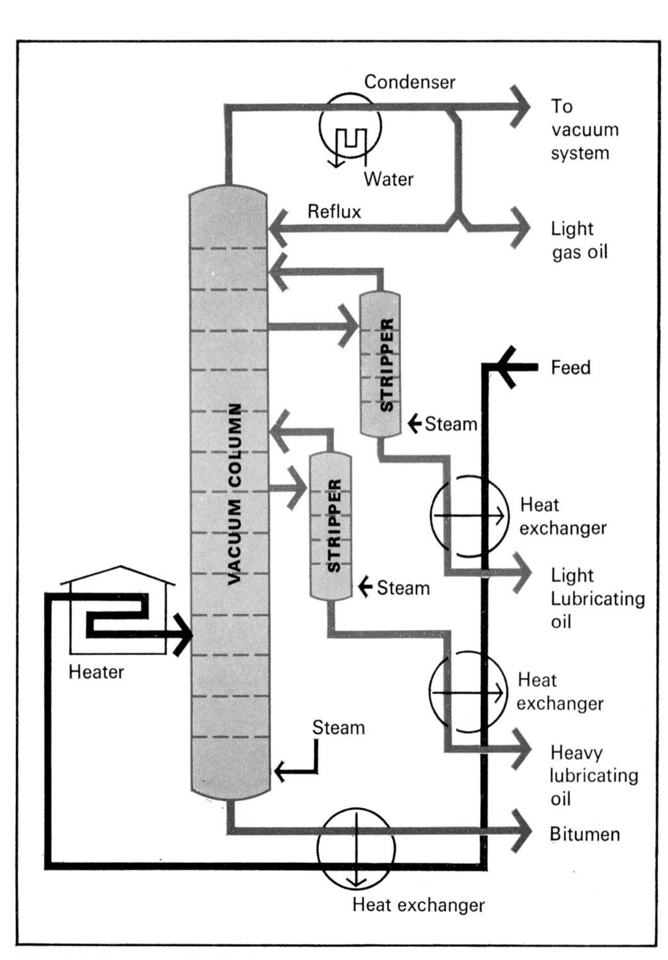

Fig. 83 Vacuum distillation process

Fig. 84 Crude oil distilling unit

referred to as stabilization, and the process is used not only in crude oil distillation, but also in the recovery of liquid products from natural gas, and in the fractionation of the gases and volatile liquids from cracking units.

The gasoline from the bottom of the debutanizer is further fractionated into light and heavy gasoline, the latter being used, if necessary, for the manufacture of white spirit or special boiling point spirits or subjected to thermal or catalytic reforming.

Side-streams are taken from intermediate points in the first column and stripped in small stripping columns to produce light and heavy gas oil. The residue from the bottom of the crude oil column may be used as fuel oil; or it may be redistilled in a vacuum distilling unit to produce, as distillates, gas oil, lubricating oils or catalytic cracking feedstock. The residue from this vacuum distillation may be used as fuel oil or for bitumen manufacture, or may be suitable for the manufacture of 'bright stock' or as a feedstock for thermal cracking.

A diagram of the vacuum distillation process is shown in Fig. 83. Vacuum is obtained by means of a device known as a steam ejector, or vacuum pumps may be used. In all units efficient heat exchangers are incorporated to transfer heat from outgoing vapour and liquid streams to the incoming crude oil, thereby reducing the fuel consumption in the furnaces and of cooling water in the condensers.

Extensive use is made of automatic control instruments, which not only record temperatures, pressures, levels, and rates of flow, but also automatically operate the control valves. By the use of instruments in this way, steady operating conditions and product quality are maintained. Automatic instrumentation also results in the virtual elimination of intermediate product storage tanks which were previously required for the adjustment of properties of products before they were passed to finished product storage. This 'in-line blending' (p. 111) means considerable reduction in the number of expensive tanks, as well as substantial economies in pumping costs, manpower and supervision.

Crystallization

Paraffin wax consists essentially of paraffin hydrocarbons of high molecular weight, which readily separate by crystallization when an oil fraction containing them is cooled. Paraffin wax occurs in lubricating oils made from paraffinic crude oils and must be removed in order to avoid poor performance and congealing of the oils at low temperatures. The process is essentially cooling of the oil to cause the wax to crystallize and then separation of the solid from the liquid by filtration or centrifuging. In older type plants the oil is cooled in chillers, consisting of two concentric tubes. The waxy oil flows through the inner tube and is cooled by brine flowing through the annular space between the tubes. The viscous chilled mixture of oil and wax is kept moving through the chiller by a worm conveyor and pumped through large filter presses in which the wax crystals are retained, allowing the wax-free oil to pass through. When full, the presses are opened and the cake of crude wax is removed. This type of process has three disadvantages. Firstly, it is discontinuous and a number of operators are required to handle the presses. Secondly, the high viscosity of the oil renders filtration difficult, especially with heavy oils. Thirdly, it cannot be used for residual oils on account of the presence of microcrystalline waxes, consisting of crystals of microscopic size. In order to overcome these difficulties, a diluent was used (a heavy gasoline or gas oil) to maintain fluidity. Wax, however, is appreciably soluble in such diluents and lower dewaxing temperatures were required.

Solvent dewaxing

Modern solvent dewaxing processes were introduced to overcome these difficulties. By using a mixture of solvents it is possible to obtain a filtrate of low viscosity at chilling temperature and a good crystallization of all types of wax in a form suitable for efficient filtration. The low viscosity makes it possible to replace discontinuous filters by more economic continuous rotary vacuum filters. The use of a combination of solvents, adjusted to different feedstocks, increases the flexibility of the process.

A diagram of the solvent dewaxing process is shown in Fig. 85. Usually two solvents are used: toluene, which dissolves the oil and maintains fluidity at low temperatures, and methyl ethyl ketone (MEK), which dissolves little wax at low temperatures and acts as a wax precipitating agent. Propane and a chlorinated hydrocarbon such as dichloromethane are sometimes used.

The process has three stages: mixing the oil with the solvents and chilling; filtration of the chilled oil to separate the wax; recovery of the solvents and their recycling.

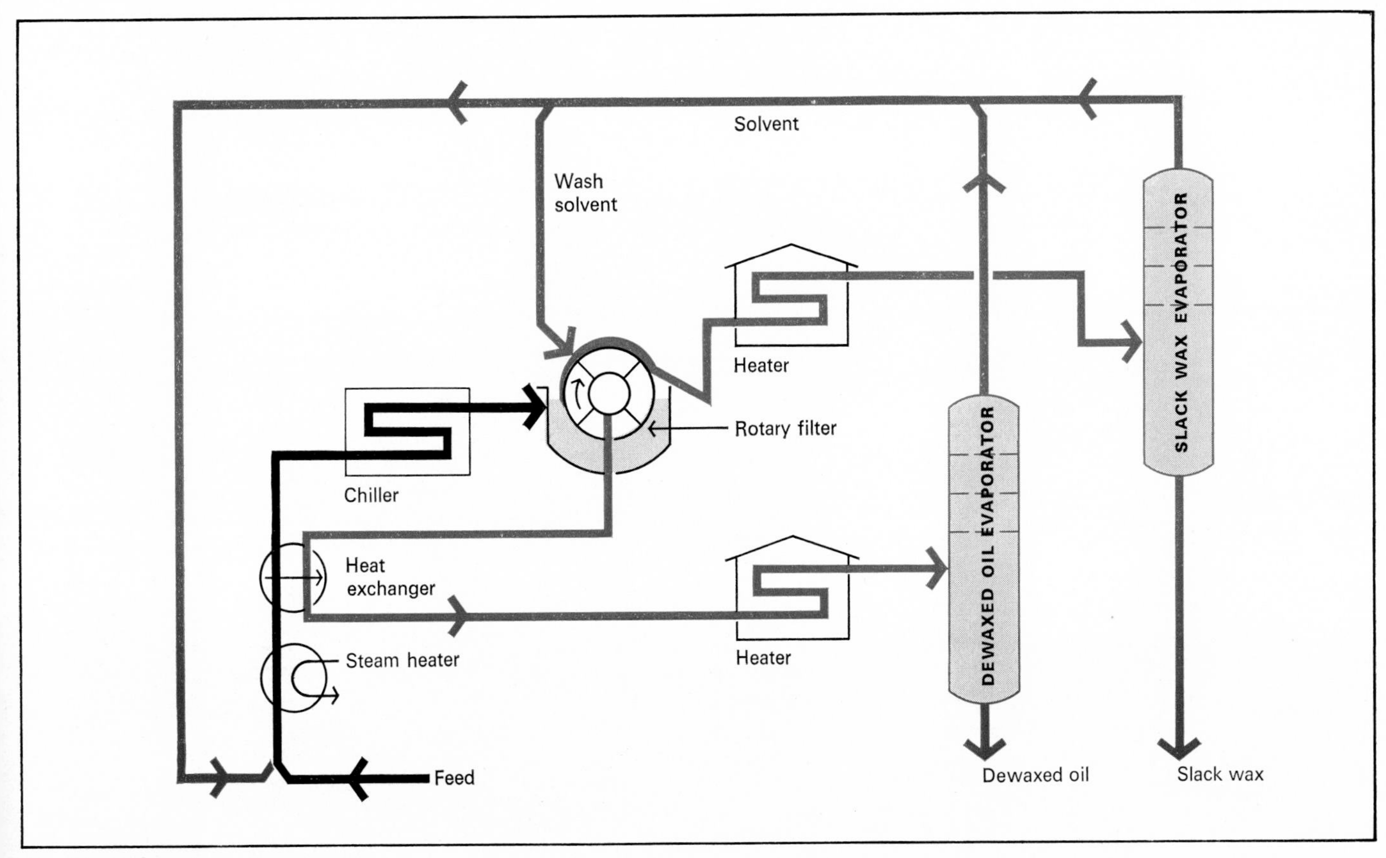

Fig. 85 Solvent dewaxing process

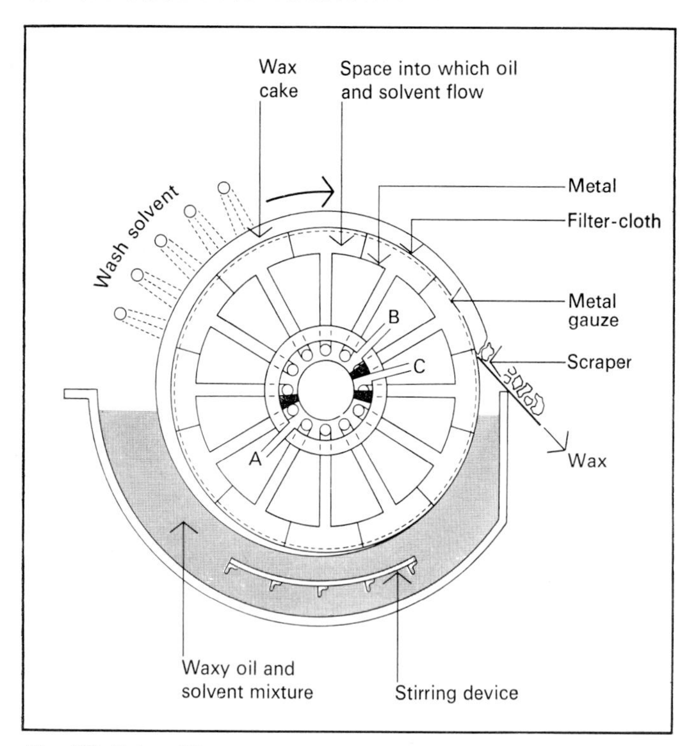

Fig. 86 Rotary filter

The waxy feed is mixed with the solvents and heated to ensure complete solution. The mixture is cooled down to filtration temperature (usually −20°C (−4°F), first by heat exchange with cold, outgoing filtrate, followed by refrigeration with liquid ammonia or propane. The cooling is carried out in concentric pipes as previously described, and the chilled mixture flows to the rotary filter [Fig. 86]. This is a cylindrical drum covered by cloth mounted on coarse mesh metal gauze. The drum rotates slowly on a horizontal axis, the lower portion passing through a cylindrical tank into which the oil and wax slurry is fed. The drum is divided into a number of segments by radial partitions from the centre to the circumference, and each segment is connected by a pipe to the end of the drum. As the drum rotates, these pipes make contact with stationary ports on the filter casing. As each segment passes through the wax, oil and solvent mixture, vacuum is applied to the interior of the segment through the appropriate port on the casing [A on Fig. 86] and the solution of oil in the solvent is drawn through the filter cloth into the drum, whilst the wax forms a cake on the surface and is carried round by rotation of the drum. Cold solvent is sprayed over the wax layer to wash the adhering oil from the wax cake on the filter. Oil and solvent leave the drum through the appropriate port [B] as the rotation continues. The wax cake is loosened from the filter surface by a slight pressure of inert gas, which is applied to the segment as it comes opposite the next port [C]. The wax is removed by a scraper to a trough, along which it is moved by a worm conveyor. Finally, the solvents are separated from both wax and oil fractions by distillation and recycled to the process, while the 'slack wax' and lubricating oil are run to storage.

Sweating processes

Another physical separation process where use is made of the difference in melting point is the 'sweating process' for removing the lower melting point components and most of the oil from slack wax. This process consists in gradually increasing the temperature of the solid slack wax so that at first the oil, together with the lowest melting point waxes, drains away from the cake. As the temperature is increased, waxes with still higher melting points become liquid and drain away. By control of the temperature of sweating, oil and lower melting point waxes, referred to as 'foots' oil, are removed, leaving a cake of paraffin wax with the required melting point.

In this way fully refined paraffin waxes with less than 0·5 %w oil are obtained. Sweating may be stopped at an earlier stage to produce 'scale wax', with an oil content up to 2 %w.

The 'sweating chamber' contains a number of flat trays [Fig. 87], fitted with a metal gauze, 10 cm from the bottom. Before the charge is poured on to the trays, the bottom section is filled with water until the water layer is level with the gauze. Then the molten wax is charged on to the trays and floats on the water layer. The charge is allowed to solidify, after which the water is drained off, leaving the solid wax cake resting on the gauze. On raising the temperature of the chamber, the sweat oil drips through the gauze, whereas the solid wax remains on it. After sweating, the wax is melted by steam.

The 'sweating tunnel' can be considered as a continuously operating version of the sweating chamber. The trays, constructed similarly to those already mentioned, are mounted on a trolley, which is mechanically propelled through a heated tunnel where the temperature is controlled to give the required amount of sweating. The heat economy of the tunnel is much better than that of the chamber, and the tunnel is very suitable for the production of high-quality waxes.

The best sweating equipment for the manufacture of high quality waxes is the 'vertical tube sweating stove'. It consists of a cylindrical vessel containing a bundle of vertical tubes one inch in diameter and a horizontal perforated plate in the bottom. The operation of the stove is similar to that of a sweating tray, except that both cooling and heating are achieved by water circulation through the tubes. The advantages of the vertical tube stove are its low price, simple construction, easy operation, high capacity owing to the large surface, and good temperature control.

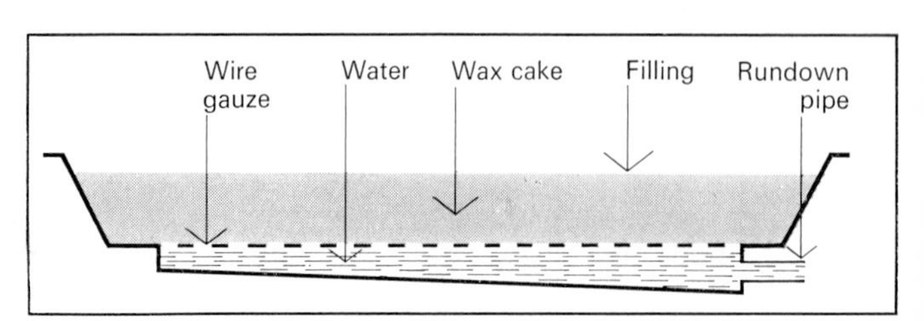

Fig. 87 Wax sweating tray

Solvent extraction

Separation by means of distillation is based on differences in boiling points and does not differentiate between chemical types, such as paraffins, aromatics and naphthenes. A fraction separated by distillation contains more or less of each type, depending on its boiling range and the crude oil used. However, the performance of a product in service depends on the chemical nature of the components as well as on their physical properties.

The presence of aromatic hydrocarbons in kerosine produces a smoky flame when burnt in a wick-type lamp and a more or less luminous flame in a jet engine. Formerly sulphuric acid treatment was used to remove aromatic components and so improve the burning qualities. The treatment was expensive and the disposal of the spent acid and the constituents so removed presented a difficult problem. About 1907 a process was developed for the removal of aromatic hydrocarbons from kerosine with the aid of a solvent, liquid sulphur dioxide, which has advantages over acid treatment in that the undesired aromatic hydrocarbons can be recovered unchanged and the refining agent can be recovered and used again. The process, known as the Edeleanu process after the inventor, opened the field for the development of other solvent extraction processes, which are now used not only for the refining of kerosine, but also for the manufacture of high-grade lubricating oils and high-octane gasoline fractions.

Principle of solvent extraction

The process is based on the use of a solvent in which one group of oil components, usually the aromatics, is preferentially dissolved. If the unrefined oil is thoroughly mixed with the solvent and then allowed to settle, two layers or phases are formed. The lower or extract phase will contain the dissolved components (for example, the aromatics) and the upper or raffinate phase will consist of the undissolved components (for example, the paraffins). The unrefined oil is thus separated into a raffinate containing the less soluble components and an extract containing the more soluble components. Both raffinate and extract are chemically unchanged, since the process involves only physical separation. After separation of the phases the solvent is recovered by distillation from both phases and re-used in the process.

The choice of solvent depends primarily on its selectivity for the type of component to be removed. It must be cheap and readily available, resistant to chemical change during use, and safe to handle. Each of the phases obtained in a simple one-stage process, as described above, contains some of the components of the other phase. The quality of the raffinate could be improved by repeated extraction with fresh solvent, but large amounts of solvent would be required, making the process expensive on account of the high cost of solvent recovery. In practice, therefore, the extraction

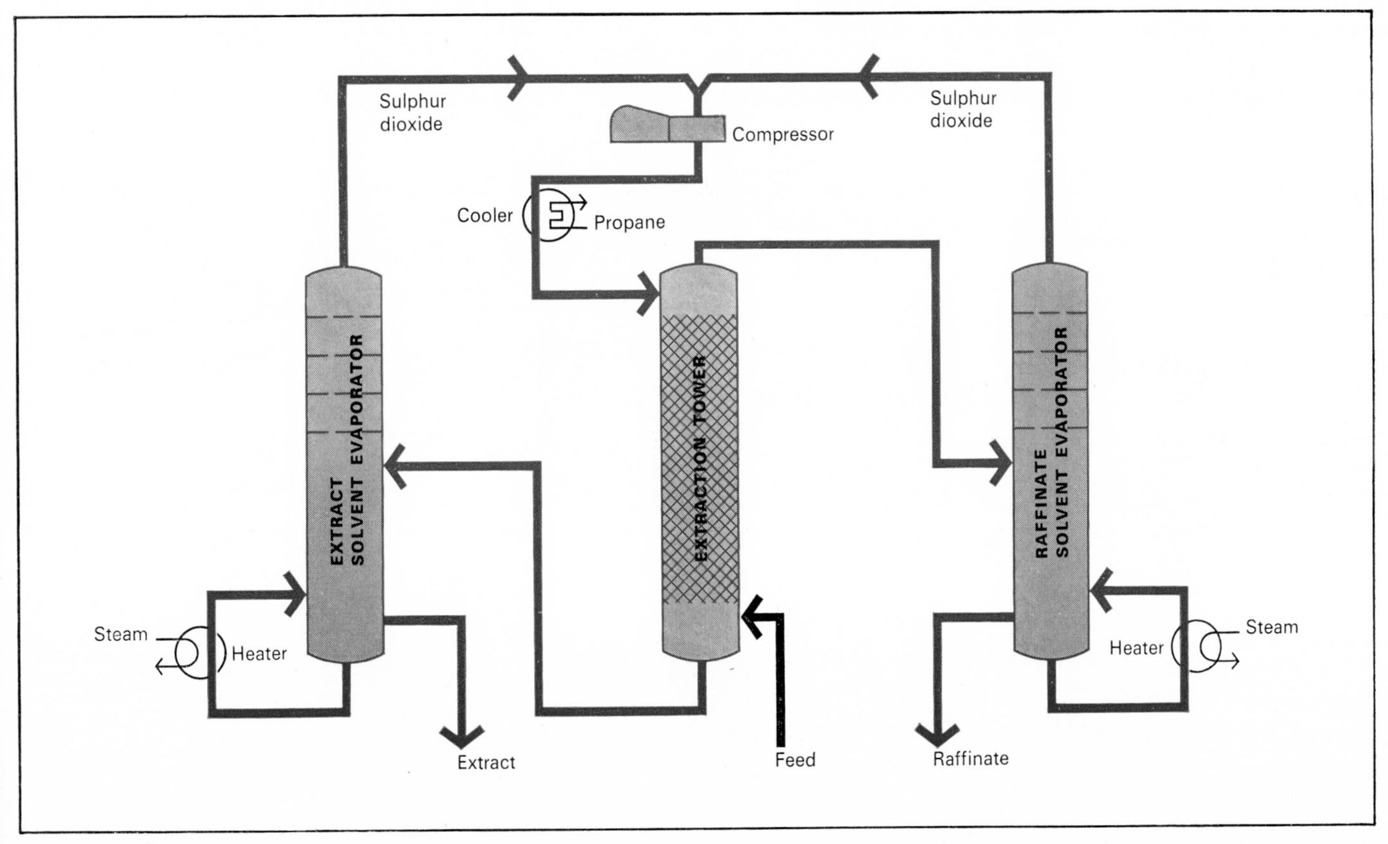

Fig. 88 Edeleanu extraction process

is always performed in a number of stages, but instead of the addition of fresh solvent at each stage, the flow of oil and solvent is arranged in countercurrent, so that the outgoing raffinate is finally extracted with pure solvent to remove the last traces of impurities. The solvent is used successively in other stages of the process and finally meets the fresh oil as it enters the extractor.

The mixing and separating can be performed in a series of mixing and settling tanks, but this method involves high capital and operating costs. Mixing and settling can be combined in practice by using a 'packed' column, i.e. one filled with suitably shaped packing material, such as small open-ended ceramic cylinders or saddles, to break up the flow of liquid. In such a column the oil and solvent enter near the bottom and top respectively, and are intimately mixed as the liquid flows through the packing. Raffinate is withdrawn from the top and extract from the bottom of the column. The separation of raffinate and extract is influenced by temperature and each process is operated at the most suitable extraction temperature, the temperature range throughout the extracting system being carefully controlled.

Solvent extraction of kerosine

In the Edeleanu process, a simplified flow diagram of which is shown in Fig. 88, kerosine is treated with liquid sulphur dioxide in a packed column. The kerosine, by virtue of its lower specific gravity, passes up the column and meets the heavier liquid sulphur dioxide coming down. The sulphur dioxide dissolves the aromatic components from the kerosine, the raffinate is removed from the top of the column, together with some solvent, whilst the bulk of the solvent containing the aromatics is removed from the bottom. The remainder of the plant consists of evaporators, compressors and coolers required to recover the sulphur dioxide from the two phases and return it for re-use.

The raffinate, now essentially paraffinic hydrocarbons, is a good quality kerosine for lamps, stoves and jet engines. The extract, because of its high aromatic content, has good anti-knock properties, and is suitable as a tractor fuel or as base material for chemical products.

Solvent extraction of lubricating oil

The lubricating oil fractions obtained from crude oils by vacuum distillation contain aromatic components, which are undesirable since they oxidize in engines to sludge-forming compounds, and moreover have poor viscosity/temperature properties. In the manufacture of high-grade lubricating oils, therefore, it is necessary to remove these aromatic compounds, which can be done by solvent extraction. Insulating oils, white oils and medicinal oils made from lubricating oil distillates require a severe sulphuric acid treatment, but it is more economical to remove the aromatics by solvent extraction prior to acid treatment.

The Edeleanu process was first applied to lubricating oils in 1926, but sulphur dioxide has certain limitations as a solvent in lubricating oil extraction on account of low solubility of higher-boiling aromatics. Although, by using a blend of sulphur dioxide and benzene, some improvement can be effected, more suitable solvents such as furfural and phenol are now used. Furfural has a boiling point of 162°C (324°F) and is made from waste materials of the cereal processing industries. Phenol is a product of coal tar distillation, boiling at 181°C (358°F). Both compounds have a cyclic structure and are therefore good solvents for aromatics and other cyclic compounds.

Furfural extraction is the most widely used extraction process for lubricating oils and is applied in many Shell refineries; solvent recovery is a relatively easy matter, although precautions must be taken to avoid oxidation and decomposition of the solvent.

In view of the high cost of solvent recovery and the low value of lubricating oil extract it is essential that the maximum amount of refined oil should be produced with the minimum use of solvent. The ready separation of the phases is considerably influenced by the temperature at each stage throughout the system. An improved device for treating

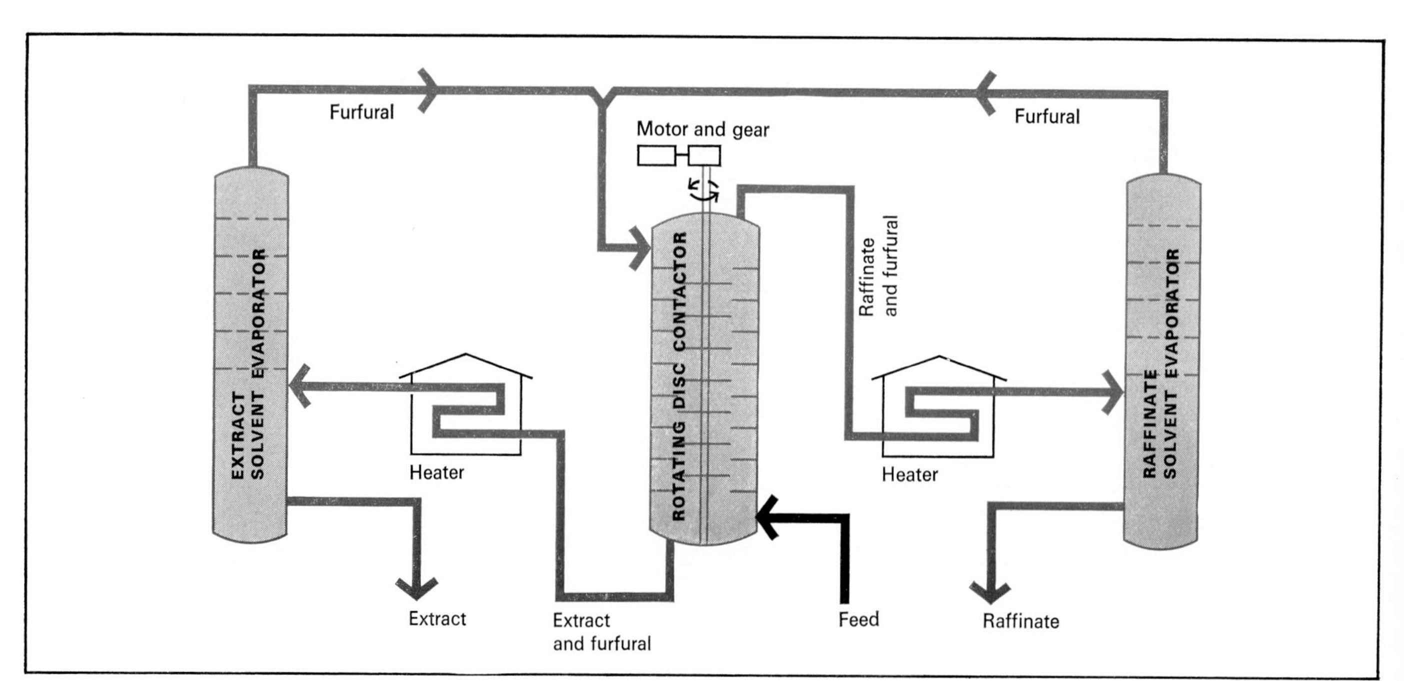

Fig. 89 Furfural extraction process

Fig. 90 A rotating disc contactor

lubricating oil with a solvent and separating the phases, developed within the Group, is the rotating disc contactor (RDC), consisting of a vertical cylinder divided into a number of compartments by means of horizontal diaphragms, called 'stator rings', each with a central hole. A disc, attached to a central shaft passing through the holes in the diaphragms, rotates in each compartment; these discs are called 'rotor discs'.

The flow of oil and solvent is similar to that in the packed column. Mixing of solvent and oil is enhanced by the rotation of the discs; the raffinate phase passes upward through the space between the discs and the stator rings, while the extract phase flows downwards. By adjusting the speed of rotation of the discs, the degree of mixing can be controlled satisfactorily. A diagram of a furfural rotating disc extraction unit and a photograph of such a unit are shown in Figs 89 and 90.

Propane deasphalting

Bitumen is separated from lubricating oils by vacuum distillation, by which bitumen-free distillates are obtained. This process, however, cannot be applied to the heaviest oil fractions, in view of their chemical decomposition at the high temperatures which are required. High-quality residual lubricating oils (bright stocks) are manufactured by 'deasphalting' such fractions by means of propane. In this process, which is a single solvent extraction process, the feed is treated with liquid propane under pressure by countercurrent flow through a packed column, the oil entering at the top and the propane at the bottom. The paraffinic components are preferentially dissolved in the propane and are withdrawn from the top, whilst the bitumen is withdrawn from the bottom. After distillation and recovery of the propane, a lubricating oil stock, which is free from bituminous components, is obtained. Propane deasphalting is followed by furfural extraction.

Solvent extraction of gasoline fractions

In the manufacture of high-quality motor and aviation gasolines, solvent extraction can be applied to straight run, thermally or catalytically cracked and reformed gasoline fractions. Sulphur dioxide and sulfolane (a cyclic derivative of butadiene and sulphur dioxide) are used as solvents.

Extractive distillation of gasoline fractions

A combination of two physical separation methods, distillation and solvent extraction, is used in the recovery of pure aromatics (benzene, toluene and the xylenes, important base materials for the chemical industry) from straight run, thermally and catalytically cracked or reformed gasoline fractions. In this process, developed by the Group, a fraction containing aromatics is heated to the necessary temperature and fed into a distillation column. A selective solvent, in which the aromatics are more soluble than the other components, is introduced close to the top of the column [Fig. 91]. The solvent extracts the aromatics and passes from the bottom of the column to a second column, where the aromatics are separated from the solvent as a distillate. The solvent recovered from the bottom of the second column is recycled into the process. The most commonly used solvents are phenol, sulfolane and acetonitrile.

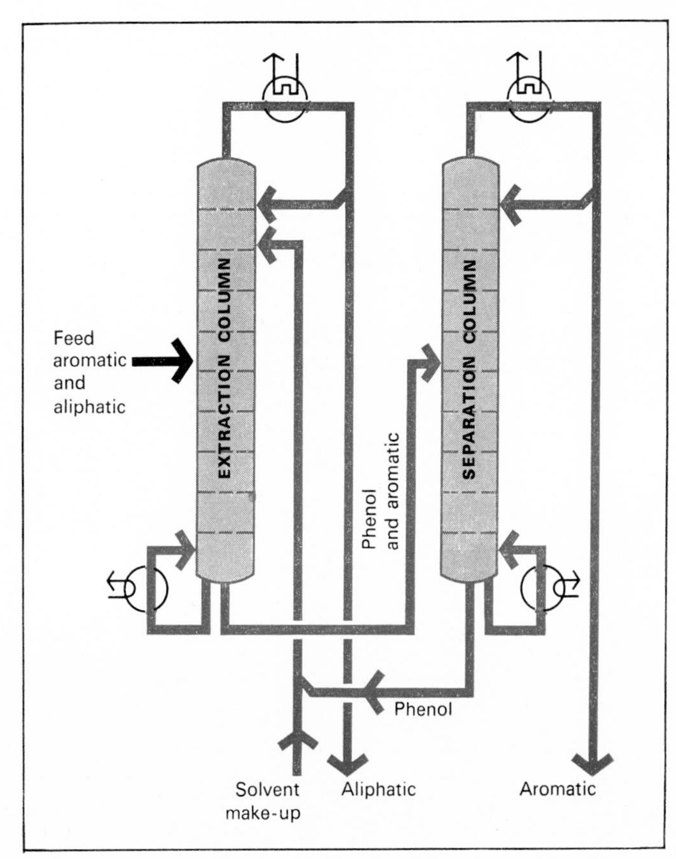

Fig. 91 Extractive distillation process

Adsorption and absorption

Adsorption

Certain highly porous materials, like activated charcoal, silica gel and alumina, have the power of condensing on their surfaces large amounts of vapour, preferentially the heavier and unsaturated hydrocarbons, from a gas mixture.

An adsorption unit processing natural gas or refinery gas may consist of a battery of large vessels containing the activated adsorbent. The gas is passed through one vessel until the adsorbent is saturated and then switched to another vessel. The saturated adsorbent is steamed to drive out the adsorbed components, which are again collected and condensed. After drying with hot gas and cooling, the adsorbent is ready for a new adsorption cycle. The process cannot be used for all gases. If hydrogen sulphide is present, it is strongly adsorbed by the active material which then loses its capacity to adsorb hydrocarbons.

Absorption

This is essentially a solution process. Gases and low-boiling-point volatile hydrocarbons occur in natural gas and are produced in many processes for the manufacture of petroleum products. Of the gases, hydrogen, methane and ethane can be liquefied only under high pressure and at low temperatures but propane and butane can be liquefied under moderate pressures at atmospheric temperature. The olefins, ethylene and propylene, are produced in cracking units and can also be readily liquefied. These light hydrocarbons are increasingly valuable as LPG or as base material for the chemical industry. Efficient gas recovery units are therefore necessary in modern refineries. The separation of the light hydrocarbons from the gases cannot economically be carried out in a normal fractionating column because of the high pressures and low temperatures that would be involved for the production of the required reflux.

The operation of an absorption process is similar to that of a distillation process. The 'wet gas', i.e. the gas which still contains valuable heavy components, is introduced into the bottom of the absorption column and lean absorption oil towards the top [Fig. 92]. The unabsorbed gas (dry gas) leaves the top of the absorber, whilst the 'fat' absorption oil leaves the bottom. This fat oil may be fed into a second column (debutanizer), where the C_3 (propane/propylene) and the C_4 (butanes/butylenes) are recovered. They can be separated further into C_3 and C_4 hydrocarbon fractions. The absorption oil (debutanized gasoline) circulates continuously between absorber and debutanizer, losses being made up as required.

The temperatures in the absorption column are controlled by the amount and temperature of the lean oil (much in

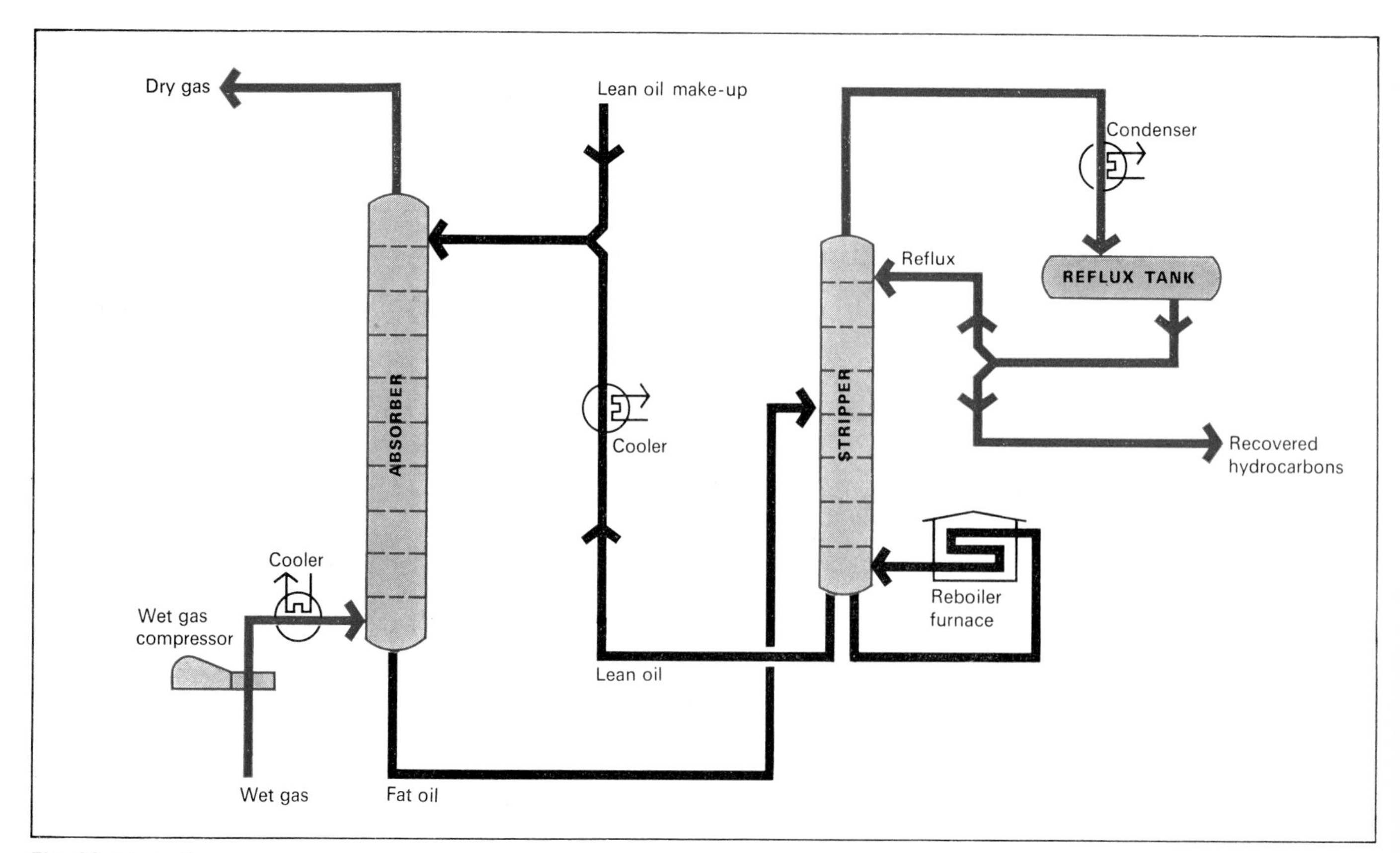

Fig. 92 Absorption process

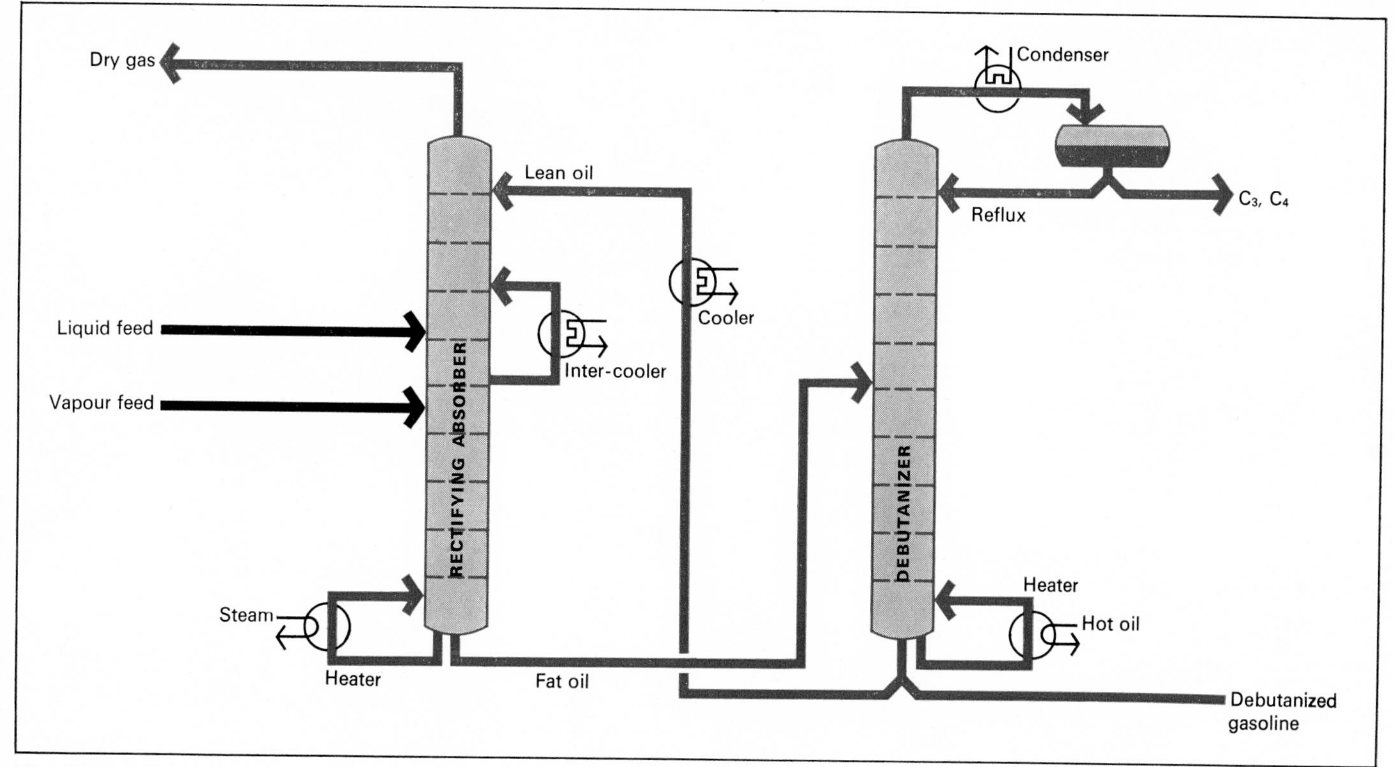

Fig. 93 Rectifying absorption process

the way in which reflux controls the temperature in a fractionating column) and by the use of intermediate coolers. The stripping column temperatures are controlled by the reboiler heat input.

Greater flexibility in operation and better control of product quality are achieved by combining the absorption process with a stripping process in the same column. This process is called 'rectifying absorption' and is generally used for further processing of refinery products [Fig. 93].

The unit processes two feed streams, wet gas and unstabilized gasoline containing propane and butane. The lean oil inlet is near the top of the column and the feed inlets are near the middle. In the upper section of the column, lean oil flowing down absorbs the less volatile components from the rising vapour. By introducing the liquid feed above the vapour feed an additional absorbing effect is obtained. The heat released by the condensation of the vapour is removed by one or more intercoolers so as to keep the temperature in the absorption section (the section above the feed entry) sufficiently low.

The dry gas from the top of the absorber consists of hydrogen, methane, ethane and ethylene. The last two may be separated as base materials for chemical manufacture. Otherwise they are used as refinery fuel or sold for town gas manufacture. The liquid flowing down the absorption section contains more absorbed components than it is desired to recover. In the section below the feed inlet this excess is removed by heat supplied by a reboiler and sometimes by interheaters. This section is called the 'stripping section'.

The 'fat' oil from the bottom of the rectifying absorber, containing C_3 and C_4 hydrocarbons and gasoline, passes to a debutanizer column. Here C_3 and C_4 are removed by distillation under pressure as top product and the gasoline is recovered as bottom product. Part of the gasoline is used as lean oil in the rectifying absorber, the remainder for gasoline blending.

Cracking

The development of the internal combustion engine made it necessary to produce more light fractions than are present naturally in crude oil. Moreover, the ignition quality of these fractions, which is of paramount importance, depends on the molecular configuration of the fuel hydrocarbons. For spark-ignition engines, branched-chain and ring compounds (both naphthenes and aromatics) are better than straight-chain compounds, and unsaturates (olefins) are in general better than the corresponding saturates. In diesel (compression-ignition) engines the reverse is the case, straight-chain compounds having the better ignition properties.

Thermal cracking

When hydrocarbons are subjected to relatively high temperatures over a period of time, the large molecules of heavier oils are broken down into smaller ones such as those of the gasoline and gas oil type. Heavy petroleum distillates and residues are subjected to temperatures from 425–500°C (800–900°F) at pressures between 2–25 kg/cm² (28–355 lb/in²). The composition of high molecular weight fractions is very complex and much research has been carried out on their behaviour under cracking conditions.

Long-chain paraffinic hydrocarbon molecules break down into a number of smaller ones by rupture of a carbon-to-carbon bond. The smaller molecules so formed may break down still further. When this occurs, the number of hydrogen atoms present in the parent molecule is insufficient to provide the full complement for each carbon atom, so that 'unsaturated' compounds are formed.

$$CH_3—CH_2—CH_2—CH_2—CH_2—CH_2—CH_2—CH_3 \longrightarrow$$
$$CH_2=CH—CH_3 + CH_3—CH_2—CH_2—CH_2—CH_3$$

The rupturing can take place in a variety of ways and secondary reactions can occur between the molecules formed. In cyclic compounds, rupture normally takes place in the paraffinic side chain and not in the ring.

The final products consist of gases, light hydrocarbons in the gasoline and gas oil range and heavier products. By selection of the type of unit, feedstock and operating conditions, the yields and quality of the various products can, within limits, be controlled to meet market requirements.

As a result of the introduction of thermal cracking, the production of gasoline from a given quantity of crude oil was practically doubled during the period 1919–35. Moreover, the ignition quality of the cracked gasoline was superior to that of most gasolines produced from crude by straight distillation (straight-run gasolines). Thus both quantity and quality of available gasoline increased and so it was possible to meet the anti-knock requirements of engines of increasing compression ratio developed by the automobile and aircraft industries.

Thermal cracking processes can be classified into three groups according to the purpose for which they are used.

Conversion of oils into materials of a different boiling range – for example, thermal cracking for the production of gasoline and gas oil from heavy oils, gas, residual fuel oil components and coke also being produced.

Improvement of certain properties – for example 'visbreaking' and thermal reforming. Visbreaking is the lowering of the viscosity of very viscous oils by mild thermal treatment, thus making them suitable for further handling and increasing their value as fuel oil components.

Production of feedstocks for special purposes – for example, cracking of paraffin wax with long-chain molecules to produce a distillate with a lower molecular weight and a high olefin content. Such a distillate is used as a raw material for the production of synthetic detergents, lubricating oil additives, OXO alcohols and high molecular weight carboxylic acids.

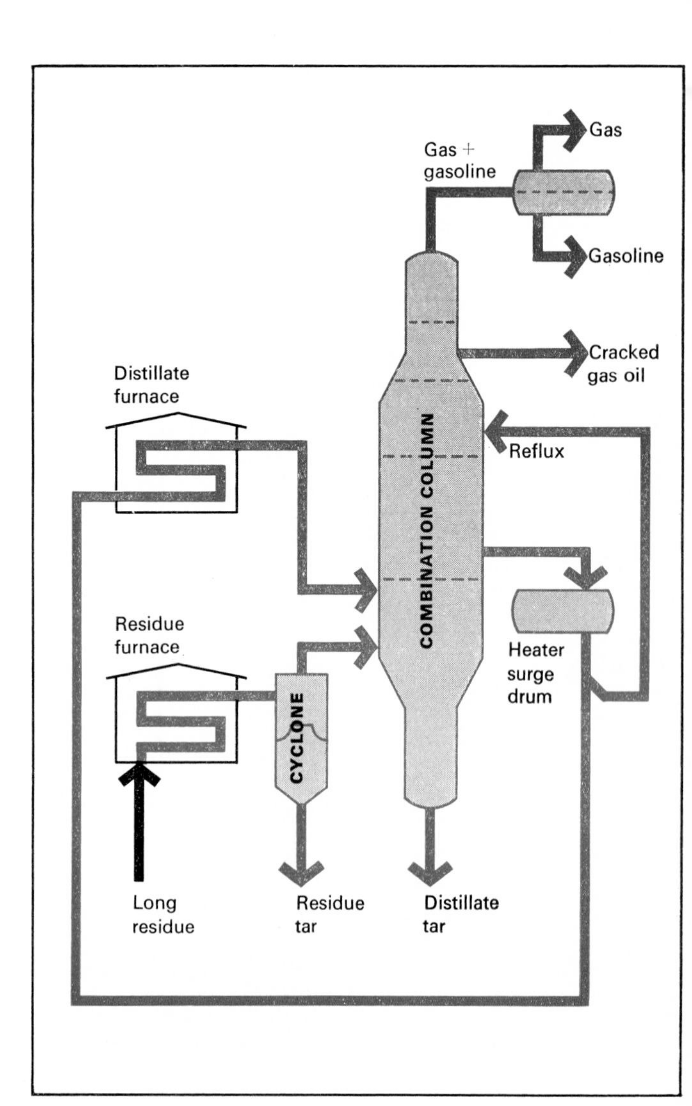

Fig. 94 Thermal gas oil unit

Thermal cracking is little used nowadays for the production of gasoline, having been superseded by catalytic cracking, which produces gasoline of higher octane number. It is still used extensively, however, and to a growing extent, for other purposes: cracking long residue to middle distillates (gas oil), short residue for viscosity reduction (visbreaking), long or short residue to produce bitumen for briquetting, wax to olefins for the manufacture of chemicals, naphtha to ethylene and synthesis gas (also for the manufacture of chemicals), selected feedstocks to coke for use as a moderator in atomic piles and for the manufacture of electrodes.

The nature of the end product depends on the severity of the cracking process in temperature and duration, mild conditions result in visbreaking, very severe conditions in coking. Middle distillates are produced according to the scheme illustrated in Fig. 94. Long residue is fed to the residue furnace where it is cracked under relatively mild conditions into a distillate and a tarry residue. The distillate is fractioned in the 'combination column' into gas, gasoline, cracked gas oil (middle distillate), a heavier fraction and a tarry residue. The heavier fraction is fed to a distillation furnace where it is subjected to a second cracking operation, the products of which are also fed to the combination column for fractionation.

Visbreaking

Visbreaking is an important application of thermal cracking to produce fuel oil components of reduced viscosity. The unit consists in principle of a furnace and a distillation column, and operates at 480°C (895°F) and atmospheric pressure [Fig. 95]. The viscosity of a (naphthenic) heavy fuel is reduced from 15 000 cS/50°C to 600 cS/50°C.

About 2 %w gas and 4 %w gasoline are produced as by-products. Gasoline fractions must be eliminated in view of flash point specifications of the fuel.

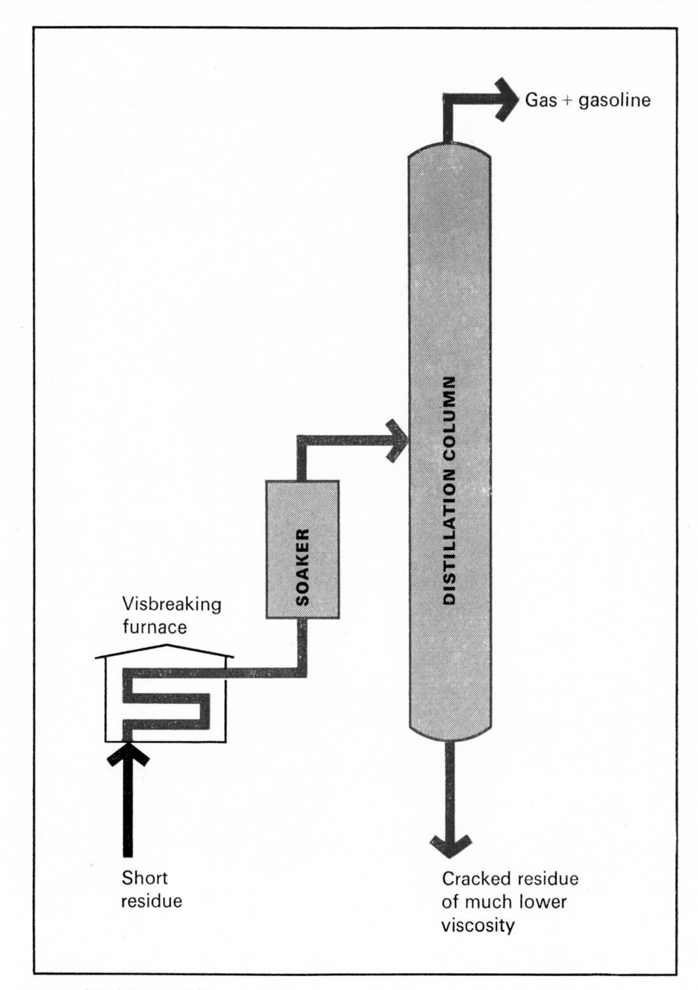

Fig. 95 Visbreaking process

Dubbs process

The Dubbs process, once extensively used by the Group, is now applied only on a limited scale for the manufacture of petroleum coke, but the following description is given for the sake of completeness and because various current terms originated from the Dubbs operation [Fig. 96].

The cracking is carried out in stages, so that the optimum conditions are applied at each stage. The heavier fractions of the fresh feed and the recycle oil are subjected to relatively mild conditions so as to produce maximum gasoline and a minimum amount of coke and heavy products. The medium sized molecules in the gas oil, which need more intense cracking, are subjected to a more severe treatment. The process is therefore referred to as a two-coil selective process. Nowadays, with the growing interest in the production of middle distillates, this stage may be considerably modified or even omitted.

The feed, the residue from a previous distillation, is introduced into the fractionating column, where it meets the hot cracked vapour from the 'flash chamber' [Fig. 96]. The vapour is cooled and the heavier components condensed, while any light material present in the feed is vaporized. The cracked vapour is thus separated into gasoline and gas as top products, a gas oil fraction as a side stream and a heavier product (cracked and non-cracked) as a bottom product.

The hot bottom product is pumped into a heavy oil heater, where, together with the heavy cracked products condensed from the cracked products from the flash chamber, it is partially cracked at a temperature of 465–490°C (870–915°F). The mixture of cracked liquid and vapour coming from the furnace enters the 'reaction chamber' at the top. The lighter gas oil fraction, drawn off as a side stream from the column, is concurrently subjected to more severe cracking conditions in the light oil heater at temperatures between 510–550°C (950–1020°F). The cracked products leaving the light oil heater enter the reaction chamber together with the stream from the heavy oil furnace.

The cracked mixture, at a pressure of about 24 kg/cm^2 (340 lb/in^2) in the reaction chamber, flows from the bottom into a second chamber, called the flash chamber. A stream of relatively cold gas oil, the 'quench oil', is introduced into the bottom line to slow down the cracking reaction and prevent excessive coke formation. The pressure in the flash chamber is reduced to about 10 kg/cm^2 (140 lb/in^2) with the result that some of the products evaporate. By this means, vapours of the lower-boiling cracked products are separated from the residue of liquid cracked products.

Volatile fractions are further removed from the residue in a 'stripping' column, operating at low pressure. The top product from the stripper is recycled to the process as quench oil.

The hot vapour from the top of the flash chamber is introduced into the bottom section of the main fractionating column. The cracked, unstabilized gasoline passes overhead

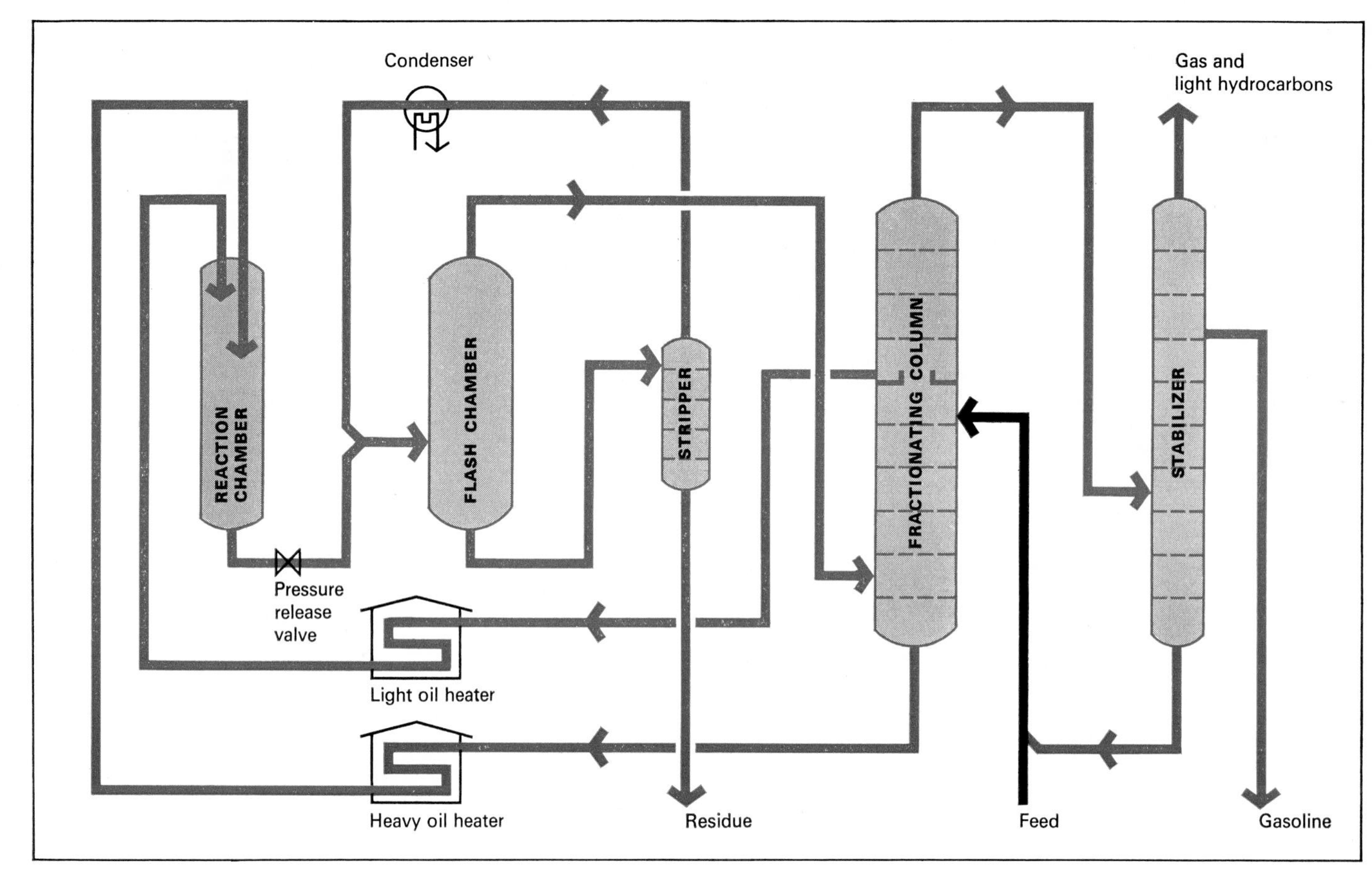

Fig. 96 Dubbs cracking process

to the stabilizer, where gases and light hydrocarbons are removed. The gas oil and heavier products are recycled to the process together with fresh feed.

The Dubbs process can be operated in two ways, according to the products required. For maximum gasoline production, the process is operated in such a way as to produce gasoline and coke with no cracked residual fuel. This is the 'non-residue method'.

Alternatively, under less severe conditions, a fuel residue can be made without coking. This is the 'residue method'.

When it is desired to produce coke, the residue from the bottom of the reaction chamber is run into a separate 'coking chamber', either direct or through a special furnace, where the cracking reactions are allowed to proceed until the residue is further cracked to coke. During the removal of the coke from the chamber, the flow of residue is directed to a second coke chamber, so that continuous operation is maintained.

The coke is removed from the chamber in one of the following ways. In the first and older method a steel cable is suspended in spiral windings from the top to the bottom of the chamber. The coke is removed through the bottom by winching out the cable. This involves high operating costs. The hydraulic method, introduced by the Group, consists in cutting the coke into lumps by high-pressure water jets. The higher initial cost of this method is offset by lower operating costs.

Petroleum coke was a valuable solid fuel; at present it is a starting material for making carbon electrodes for the electrochemical industry and for pure graphite as a moderator for atomic power stations.

Present-day thermal cracking units operate like Dubbs units without coking to produce maximum middle distillates (165–350°C; 330–660°F) instead of maximum gasoline (221°C; 430°F). These units also have two furnaces, a heavy-oil and a light-oil furnace.

Catalytic cracking

Concurrently with the development of thermal cracking processes, attempts were made to develop processes for producing better quality gasoline by cracking oils in the presence of a catalyst (aluminium chloride as early as 1916).

A catalyst (p. 65) changes the rate of a chemical reaction without being itself changed chemically. If a complicated series of simultaneous reactions takes place, one may be more accelerated than another by a certain catalyst, so that it seems that the catalyst makes a selection.

In the early years catalytic cracking was not very successful, but in 1936 the Houdry fixed bed catalytic cracking unit came into successful operation and other types of units followed.

The catalytic cracker is still the most important source of high-grade gasoline and also provides raw material for the vast and rapidly growing petroleum-chemical industry. The world's catalytic cracking capacity amounts to approximately 500 000 tons intake per day.

Many substances can act as conversion catalysts, but considerable research was necessary to develop a catalyst that would promote selectively the reactions by which desirable products are obtained, and that was easily regenerative and economically attractive. Some natural clays

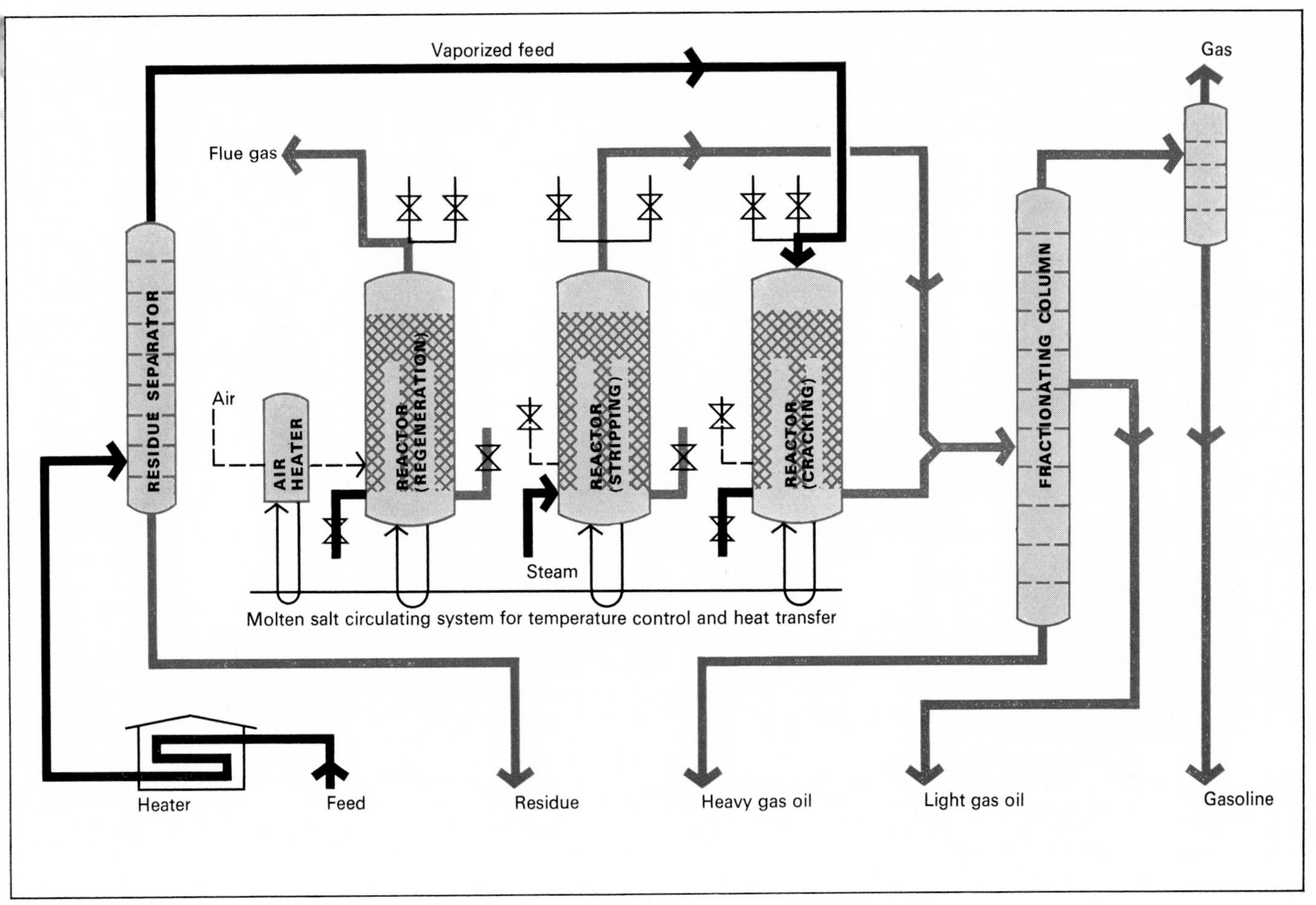

Fig. 97 The Houdry fixed bed process

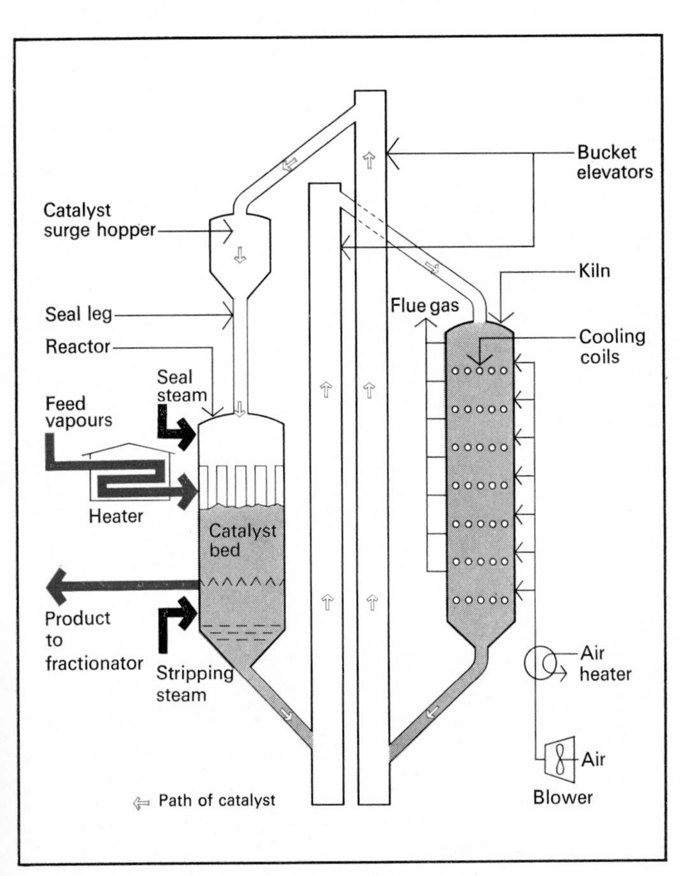

Fig. 98 The Thermofor catalytic cracking process

were found to be suitable catalysts and at the same time synthetic materials based on silica and alumina were developed. Synthetic catalysts containing either 12·5%w alumina and 87·5%w silica or 25% and 75%w respectively are in general use.

Both the specific surface area (total surface of the pores per gramme) and the particle size of a catalyst have a major effect on its behaviour and suitability. Catalysts are used either as pellets or as a fine powder. The catalysts not only increase the rate of cracking reactions, but improve the anti-knock quality of the gasoline. At the same time relatively small amounts of light gases (C_1, C_2) and large amounts of C_3 and C_4 olefins are formed.

The improved gasoline quality is due to the formation of isoparaffins and aromatics. At the same time the quantity of unsaturates (olefins and especially diolefins) produced is lower than in thermal cracking on account of hydrogen transfer from naphthenes to diolefins, which improves the stability of the gasoline by reducing the tendency towards gum formation.

The octane number, a measure of anti-knock value (F1 – method, p. 181) of unleaded catalytically cracked gasoline ranges from 80–84, depending upon feedstock and operating conditions, compared with 60–70 for thermally cracked gasoline.

The carbonaceous material formed during cracking, usually referred to as 'coke', is deposited on the catalyst surface, thus reducing its activity. It is therefore necessary to regenerate the catalyst, so that it may be used repeatedly, and this is accomplished by burning off the coke. In the

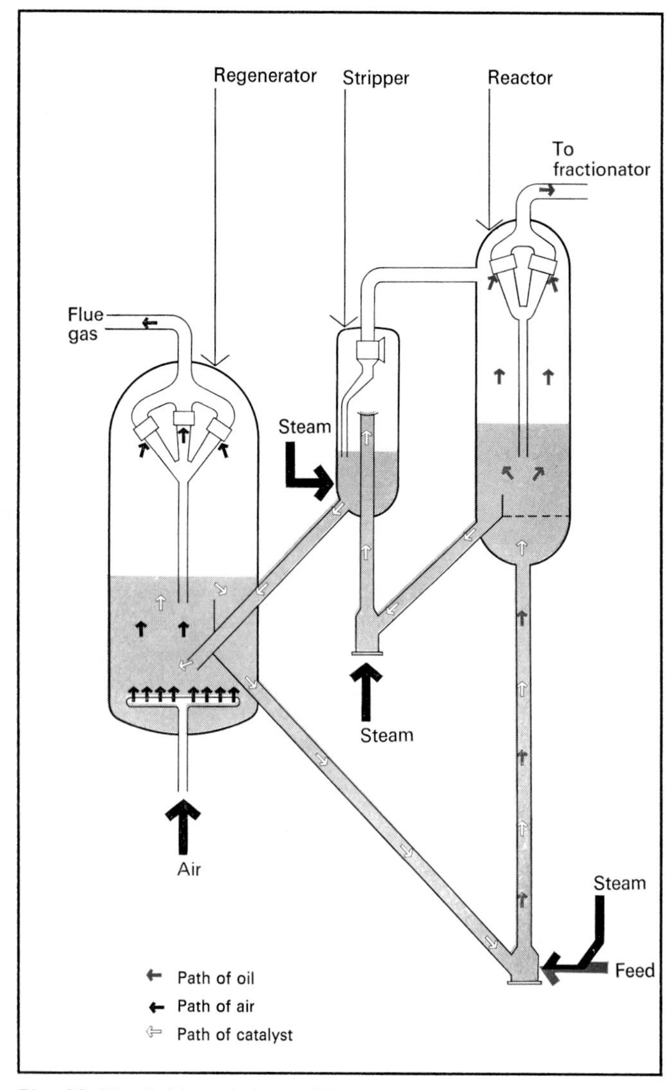

Fig. 99 The fluid catalytic cracking process

course of time, however, the catalyst gradually loses its high specific surface area and hence its activity, and must be replaced by fresh material. As was mentioned above, the feedstock for thermal cracking can be either distillate or residue. For catalytic cracking, however, a distillate should be used, as a residual feedstock would deposit trace metal components on the catalyst leading to rapid decline of selectivity.

In catalytic cracking operations there are three steps in the cycle, the cracking step in which the reaction takes place, the stripping step to eliminate adsorbed hydrocarbons, and the regeneration step in which coke is burned off the catalyst. These are followed in all types of catalytic cracking processes, the Houdry fixed bed process, the Thermofor moving bed process and the fluidized bed process.

Houdry and Thermofor processes

In the Houdry process the pellets stayed in the reactors and after the cracking step were steam stripped and regenerated by burning the coke with air *in situ* [Fig. 97]. In the Thermofor process the catalyst pellets were removed from the reactor by a bucket elevator, stripped, regenerated in a regenerator kiln and returned to the reactor by another elevator [Fig. 98]. The Houdry process was intermittent and very difficult to control even by means of instruments; the Thermofor process was mechanically complicated, allowing only a limited ratio of catalyst circulation rate to oil feed rate. Both are now obsolete or in only very limited application.

Fluid bed process

The quick transport of catalyst between reactor and regenerator is an essential feature of a continuous catalytic cracking process. Therefore, further development was based on the use of a catalyst in the form of a very fine powder. Whirled up with a gas or vapour, the powder behaves very much as a liquid and can therefore be readily and continuously moved from one vessel to another. This catalyst state is known as the fluidized state and the process as the 'fluid catalytic cracking process'. The Group has expended much effort in the development of this process since 1942. In the modern process [Fig. 99] the feed enters the bottom of the straight vertical reaction riser, where it meets a stream of hot regenerated catalyst flowing down the inclined regenerator standpipe from the regenerator.

The oil is vaporized by the hot catalyst and the vapour carries the powdered catalyst in a 'dilute phase' up the riser into the reactor vessel. The catalyst settles out in the reactor to form a 'dense' bed of whirled-up catalyst powder. This is fairly stable depending on the size and density of the particles and on the density and velocity of the vapour. The cracking reactions start in the reactor riser and continue throughout the reactor bed. Hot cracked-oil vapour from

Fig. 100 Fluid catalytic cracking unit

the top of the reactor passes to the fractionator. Spent catalyst is continuously drawn off from the reactor and is carried up a second riser into a stripper vessel by steam injected at the bottom. Oil products entrained in the spent catalyst are removed by steam in the stripper and pass into the top of the reactor, where they join the main stream of cracked vapour passing to the product recovery system. The steam also maintains the fluidized state of the catalyst.

The stripped spent catalyst, on which coke is deposited during cracking, passes to the regenerator, being delivered direct into the (fluidized) regenerator bed by gravity flow and pressure difference. Air is supplied to the regenerator by an air blower and distributed throughout the (spent) catalyst bed. The coke deposit is burnt off, the flue gases leaving from the top. The regenerated catalyst is drawn off from the bottom of the regenerator and passes down the regenerator standpipe to the bottom of the reactor riser, where it joins the fresh feed. Here the cycle recommences.

During operation the catalyst particles are reduced in size by mechanical rubbing and the finer particles tend to escape from the system in the overhead product stream. To catch these fines, dust separators or 'cyclones' are built into the top of both reactor and regenerator to separate the fine catalyst particles from the gas and vapour streams. Such fine particles as are carried over into the product fractionating system are removed with the bottom product as slurry oil.

The reactor products are fractionated: gases, cracked gasoline, light and heavy gas oils are produced in proportions depending on feedstock and operating conditions. The gases pass to the gas plant, where the light gases, mainly methane, ethane and ethylene are removed and go to the refinery fuel gas system. The heavier gases are further separated by distillation under pressure into propane/propylene, butane/butylene and gasoline. The gas oil side streams from the fractionator are called light and heavy cycle oils. The former may be hydrodesulphurized (p. 65) and used as a gas oil component. Otherwise the cycle oils are used as fuel components or recycled to the feed.

The heavy cycle oil, which is rich in aromatic hydrocarbons, is also used for the manufacture of carbon black or for making weedkiller. Fig. 100 depicts a fluid catalytic cracking unit.

Two-stage catalytic cracking

A further development in fluid catalytic cracking is to carry out the cracking reactions in two stages. After the feedstock has been brought into contact with the catalyst in the first-stage reactor, the products are separated in the first-stage fractionator into gas, gasoline and 'unconverted' material. This is then fed into the second-stage reactor, where further cracking takes place. By this means only a short contact time is given in the first-stage reactor, thereby reducing the formation of gases and heavy products, including coke. The overall result is that more gasoline and less coke and gas are formed than from single-stage operation under similar conditions. The higher capital cost of a two-stage plant can be offset under certain conditions by the increased value of the products.

Hydrocracking

In order to meet the requirements for still higher quality gasolines, hydrocracking was developed as early as 1930. This is catalytic cracking in the presence of a small amount of hydrogen, introduced from outside. The process was applied on a limited scale in Germany and the UK during the war, but after the war it was stopped as being too expensive.

Renewed interest is now being shown in the process and extensive research is being done to find catalysts that will enable economic operation. A few units are in operation in the United States. The original working pressure of 100 kg/cm^2 (1420 lb/in^2), has been increased to 150 kg/cm^2 (2130 lb/in^2). The hydrogen required is prepared by methane/steam or naphtha/steam reforming.

There are now under development two hydrocracking processes, a one stage process, producing gas oil as a main product, and a two stage process, making gasoline as platformer feed (Catalytic reforming, p. 100).

The advantages of this very promising process are high yields of high-grade gasoline or gas oil, and the possibility of 'cracking to extinction' of a feed without coke formation, but capital and operating expenses are high.

Reforming

Cracking of straight-run gasoline under strictly controlled conditions so that conversion is limited will improve ignition quality. This is called 'reforming'. Partly it is a break-down process, partly a build-up process in which smaller molecules are combined to larger ones (polymerization, p. 64), partly a type-changing process, by which normal paraffins are converted to isoparaffins (isomerization, p. 63) or to ring components (cyclization, p. 63).

It can be achieved thermally (thermal reforming) or by the aid of a catalyst (catalytic reforming).

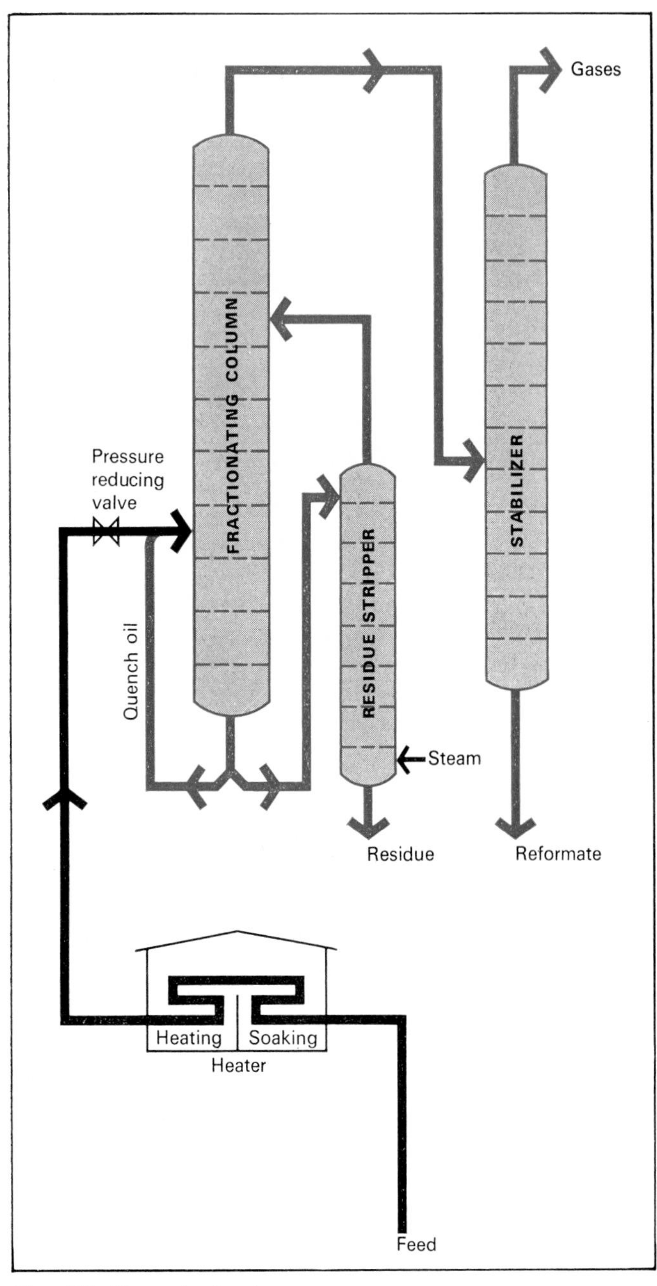

Fig. 101 Thermal reforming process

Thermal reforming

The chemical reactions in thermal reforming are similar to those in thermal cracking, i.e. long-chain paraffins yield olefins and paraffins of lower boiling points. Naphthenes are dehydrogenated or may lose their side chains, just as aromatics do. The products formed may combine to a certain extent with each other, resulting in a gasoline of much wider boiling range and better ignition quality than those of the feedstock. In addition, gas and gas oil are obtained.

Since the smaller hydrocarbon molecules of all types in reformer feedstock are thermally more stable than the larger molecules in cracking feedstocks, thermal reforming requires higher temperatures and longer reaction times than thermal cracking. In order to prevent the reactions from proceeding too far, resulting in excessive gas formation and lower gasoline yield, the hot products leaving the furnace are immediately cooled by quenching with cold oil. The whole unit consists essentially of a heater, in which the reforming reactions take place, and a fractionating column for separation of the products [Fig. 101]. The heater has two sections. In the first the feed is brought to the required reaction temperature and in the second (soaking) section it is maintained at about the same level to allow time for the reaction to proceed to the desired extent. Reforming is usually carried out at temperatures around 550°C (1020°F) and at pressures from 85 to over 100 kg/cm² (1200 to over 1400 lb/in²) and then reduced to 7–14 kg/cm² (100–200 lb/in²) by means of a pressure-reducing valve in the transfer line from furnace to fractionating column. As the products leave the furnace, they are cooled by injection of quench oil. The remainder of the unit consists of the usual equipment for gas recovery, stabilization of reformed gasoline and stripping of reformed residue.

Thermal reforming is less important nowadays than formerly.

Catalytic reforming

The yield of gasoline of good ignition quality obtainable economically by thermal reforming of heavy gasoline is rather low. Just as catalytic cracking was a tremendous improvement in thermal cracking, catalytic reforming has also increased both yield and quality of reformed gasoline.

Several reforming processes use a platinum containing catalyst and the 'platforming' process introduced by the Universal Oil Products Company (UOP) in 1949 is extensively used by the Group.

The catalyst consists of an alumina carrier containing between 0·4 and 0·75%w platinum, the proportion depending on the type of product required. Small amounts of chlorine and/or fluorine are also present as activators. The feed, straight-run gasoline, is introduced with a surplus of hydrogen. The normal reactions as in thermal cracking occur, but under the influence of the catalyst, type-changing reactions (isomerization and cyclization) also occur. More-

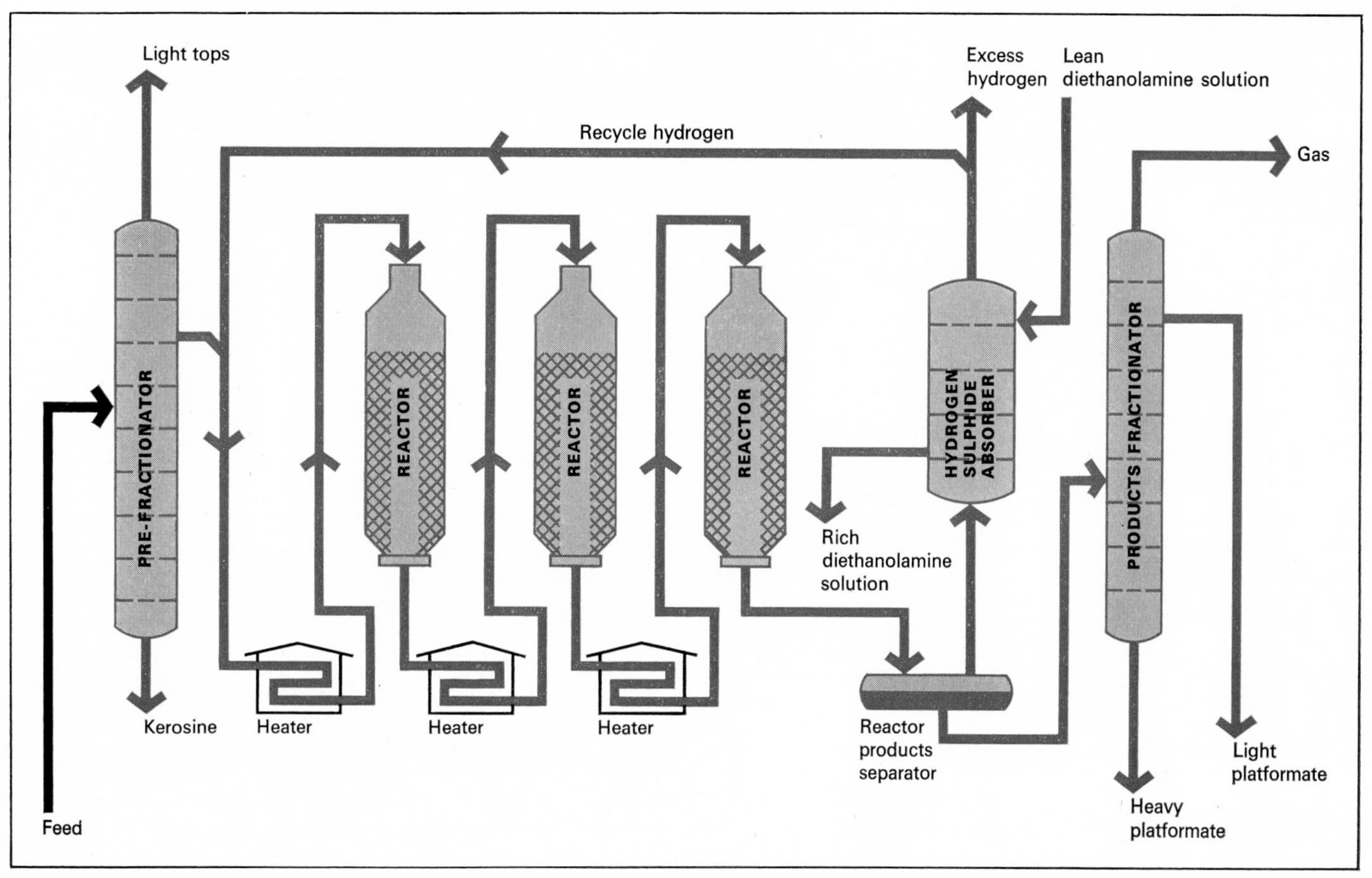

Fig. 102 Catalytic reforming process (platforming)

over, hydrogen converts the olefins into fully saturated compounds. The result is that catalytic reforming of straight-run heavy gasoline yields a product richer in aromatics and isoparaffins and poorer in naphthenes and straight-chain paraffins. Components of low ignition quality are converted into components of high ignition properties with a minimum formation of undesirable unsaturated products. A diagram of the process is shown in Fig. 102. The straight-run gasoline is first distilled in the feed preparation section. This is necessary to adjust the initial and final boiling points and to remove dissolved oxygen and water. A fraction boiling between 40–180°C (100–360°F) is removed from the column, mixed with hydrogen (recycle gas) and passed through heat exchangers in countercurrent with the hot product from the reactors. It is then raised to reactor temperature in a heater. The vaporized feed now passes in succession through a series of three reactors consisting of cylindrical steel vessels, filled with the pelleted catalyst, through which a centrally placed perforated pipe runs. The oil vapour enters at the top of the reactor casing and so passes into the annular space between the reactor wall and the catalyst. It then flows through the bed of catalyst towards the centre pipe, passing through the perforations and out at the bottom. Heat is absorbed during the reactions, so that the vapour has to be reheated. This is done by passing it through heaters between the reactors, in order to maintain the correct temperature in each reactor.

The effluent from the last reactor passes to a gas separator and thence to the product fractionating section. Here the lighter hydrocarbons are removed and the reformed product, called 'platformate', can be split into a light and heavy grade, if so desired. Platformate is used as a component in regular, premium and aviation gasoline blends.

The gas from the reactor effluent contains the hydrogen set free by the reforming reactions; it is recycled after the removal of hydrogen sulphide. The process in the reactor is carried out in an atmosphere of hydrogen, which suppresses coke formation on the catalyst and hence keeps it active. The temperatures in the reactors are about 500°C (930°F) and pressures between 10–50 kg/cm^2 (140–710 lb/in^2) are used, depending on feedstock and quality of product required.

The catalyst can be regenerated *in situ* until its activity falls below the economic minimum, when it is removed and replaced. Platinum can be recovered from the spent catalyst.

This process may be used either for making premium motor gasoline components or for the production of platformate rich in aromatics, which can be used for aviation gasoline or as a source of aromatics for the chemical industry. More hydrogen is produced than is required in the process and is available for hydrodesulphurization (p. 108) or other hydrogenation processes.

Polymerization, alkylation, isomerization and cyclization

As the demand for motor gasoline increased, attention was directed to the possibility of manufacturing gasoline components from the gases produced simultaneously with the liquid products in cracking operations and which had hitherto been used only as refinery fuel.

The cracking gases contain unsaturated hydrocarbons of low molecular weight, but of high reactivity, and so can be made to combine to form larger molecules with boiling points within the gasoline range. By selection of feedstock and processes, products of high anti-knock value can be produced. These processes, known as 'polymerization' and 'alklyation' processes, are of great value to increase quantity and quality of gasoline from the available feedstocks and for producing valuable base material for the chemical industry.

Polymerization

In polymerization (p. 64) the atomic arrangement of the original molecules is maintained but the molecules are linked together. For example, two molecules of the unsaturated hydrocarbon isobutylene can combine to form a new molecule, diisobutylene.

$$\underset{\text{isobutylene}}{CH_2{=}\overset{\displaystyle CH_3}{\underset{\displaystyle CH_3}{C}}} + \underset{\text{isobutylene}}{CH_2{=}\overset{\displaystyle CH_3}{\underset{\displaystyle CH_3}{C}}} \longrightarrow \underset{\text{diisobutylene}}{CH_3{-}\overset{\displaystyle CH_3}{\underset{\displaystyle CH_3}{C}}{-}CH_2{-}\overset{\displaystyle CH_3}{\underset{\displaystyle \| \atop CH_2}{C}}}$$

The product obtained by polymerization from the basic molecule, the monomer, is called a polymer. Products formed by combination of two, three or four of the same monomer are called dimer, trimer and tetramer respectively. The interest of polymerization processes in the oil industry is declining, but they find an increasing application in the chemical industry for the manufacture of synthetic plastics, resins and rubbers. Special, often highly purified base materials, highly active and sensitive catalyst and well-controlled reaction conditions are applied to produce high molecular polymers.

The lower molecular products, formerly of interest as gasolines, were unsaturated products formed by polymerization of two or three low molecular weight olefins (C_3, C_4) that were converted by hydrogenation into isoparaffins with high anti-knock value and used as blending components of premium or aviation gasolines.

Around 1930, attention was paid to purely thermal polymerization, but soon the advantage of using catalysts led to catalytic polymerization and around 1935 polymerization plants came into commercial operation. Shell Development's sulphuric acid and Universal Oil Products' phosphoric acid processes were used for the polymerization of propylene in propane/propylene feedstock and of butylenes in butane/butylene feedstock. Both processes are now practically obsolete for the manufacture of gasoline components, but the phosphoric acid process was used for a long time, and is still used for the manufacture of products such as propylene tetramers, base material for various chemical products. Therefore, a short description of the phosphoric acid polymerization process will be given.

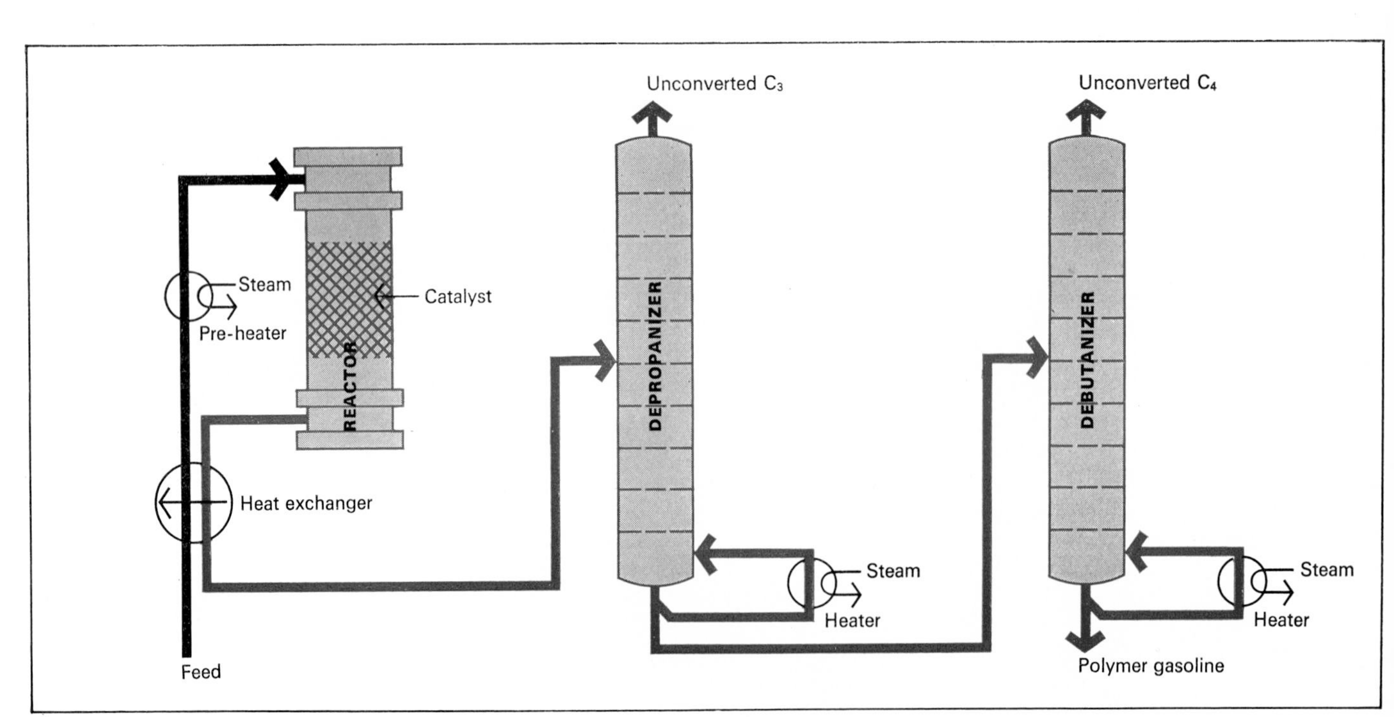

Fig. 103 Phosphoric acid polymerization process

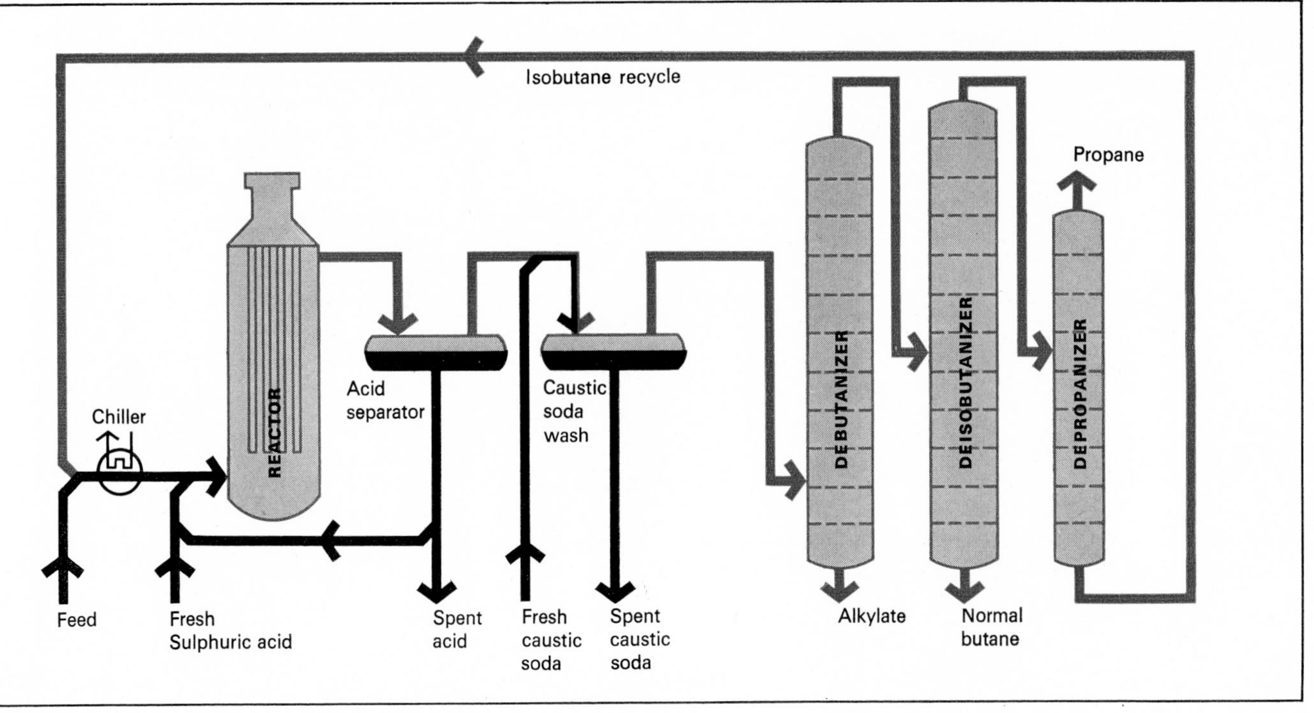

Fig. 104 Sulphuric acid alkylation process

The catalyst is phosphoric acid on pellets of kieselguhr as a carrier. The flow scheme is shown in Fig. 103. The feedstock, a propane/propylene fraction, passes through a heat exchanger where it is heated by the effluent of the reactor. The temperature is raised to the desired level in a preheater, either by steam or by hot oil and the feedstock then passes over the catalyst in the reactor. The heat generated during polymerization must be removed and is used to raise steam. The effluent from the reactor, is fractionated into polymer product and unchanged feedstock. Residual propane/propylene may be used as LPG. Temperatures and pressures vary between 190–230°C (375–445°F) and 64–82 kg/cm² (910–1165 lb/in²), depending on the type of product required, and a conversion of 85–95% is achieved.

Alkylation

The term has already been explained on page 63. The alkylation reaction most commonly used in the petroleum industry is that of a saturated branched-chain hydrocarbon, generally isobutane, with an olefin.

$$CH_3-\underset{CH_3}{\overset{CH_3}{\underset{|}{\overset{|}{C}}}} + CH_2{=}CH-CH_2-CH_3 \longrightarrow$$

isobutane α-butylene

$$\longrightarrow CH_3-\underset{CH_3}{\overset{CH_3}{\underset{|}{\overset{|}{C}}}}-CH_2-CH_2-CH_2-CH_3$$

iso-octane

Alkylation can be effected by heat alone, but extremely high pressures and rather high temperatures are required and, consequently, expensive equipment. Catalytic processes allowing mild reaction conditions, applicable to a wide variety of olefins, have therefore been developed. Sulphuric acid and hydrofluoric acid are employed as catalysts.

Alkylation with sulphuric acid catalyst

The feed is a butane/butylene fraction rich in isobutane, the alkylate (product) contains large amounts of iso-octanes. In order to suppress side reactions, the ratio of isobutane to olefins in the feedstock should be at least 4 to 1. Recycling of isobutane serves to maintain the required ratio. A diagram of the process is shown in Fig. 104. The feed is first chilled to about 5°C (40°F) and mixed with the catalyst, 98% sulphuric acid. After passing through a reactor at about 7°C (45°F) the acid is separated from the oil layer containing the alkylate and unreacted hydrocarbons. The acid is recirculated to the reactor, the hydrocarbon phase is neutralized with caustic soda and then fractionated to remove light gases and unreacted isobutane, which is recycled to the feed. The alkylate may be further fractionated into light and heavy alkylate for use in premium motor and aviation gasoline blending. With the development of jet fuels the latter product is of decreasing importance.

Alkylation with hydrofluoric acid (HF) catalyst

The fundamental reactions taking place are similar to those when using the sulphuric acid catalyst. There are, however, certain differences in handling the catalyst, anhydrous hydrofluoric acid, which is a gas used in liquefied form. Recovery of spent sulphuric acid is difficult, but spent hydrofluoric acid can be readily and continuously regenerated by simple distillation. Consumption of catalyst is

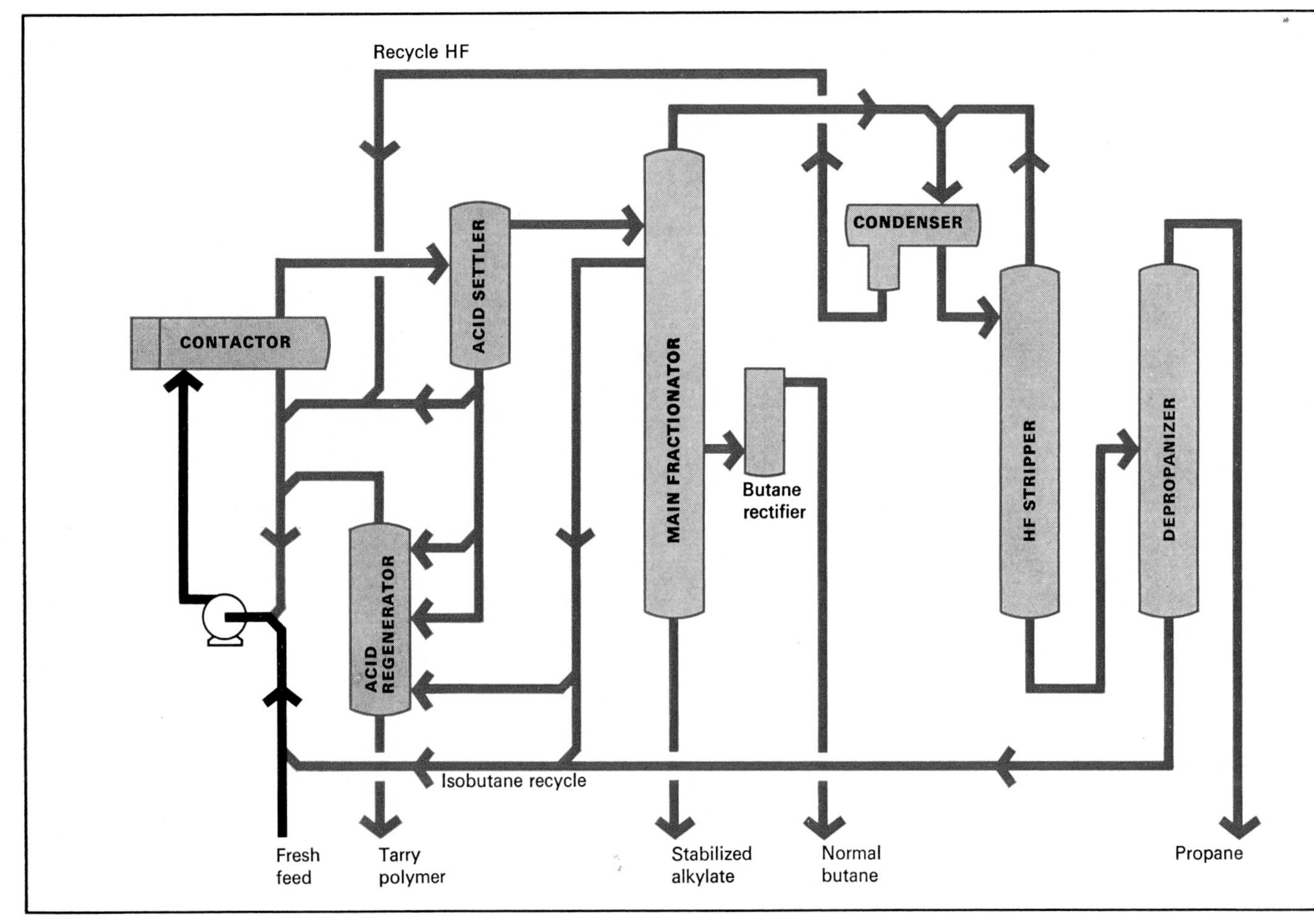

Fig. 105 Hydrofluoric acid alkylation process

therefore low. But it is a highly toxic and very corrosive material, and special precautions have to be taken in handling it, and special materials used in the construction of the plant.

Higher reaction temperatures can be used than with sulphuric acid, 25–45°C (75–115°F). Costly refrigeration facilities are not required [Fig. 105]. The properties of the alkylates depend on the type of feedstock used.

Fresh feed containing olefins and isobutane in the required ratio, together with an isobutane recycle stream, is circulated as an emulsion in liquid hydrofluoric acid (HF) through a contactor, which is essentially a cooler, removing the heat of the exothermic reaction.

A slip stream of emulsion leaves the contactor and passes into a settler, where it separates into an upper hydrocarbon layer (containing some HF in solution) and a lower HF layer (containing some hydrocarbons). The hydrofluoric acid layer is recycled to the circulation system while the hydrocarbon layer is pumped to the main fractionator from which stabilized full-range alkylate is obtained as bottom product, suitable for use as a premium motor gasoline component without further treating. Normal butane is obtained as top product from a side rectifier column fed from the vapour space of one of the lower trays of the main fractionator. After condensation this butane is led over solid caustic potash (KOH) to remove any traces of HF and can then be used as LPG or as a motor gasoline component. Recycle isobutane is drawn from the vapour space of one of the higher trays of the main fractionator and after condensation joins the fresh feed to the unit.

The vapours leaving the top of the main fractionator consist of HF, propane and isobutane. After condensation most of the HF separates from the hydrocarbons and is returned to the circulation system. The hydrocarbon is pumped to an HF stripper, where HF dissolved in the hydrocarbon is removed as vapour over the top of the column. These top vapours are condensed in the same condenser as used for the top vapours from the main fractionator.

The bottom product of the HF stripper is passed to a depropanizer, where propane is obtained as the top product. After passing through a vessel containing solid KOH it can be used as LPG. The bottom product, mainly isobutane, is recycled.

The HF catalyst has to be purified (regenerated) by distillation in order to remove small amounts of tarry higher polymers and water that may enter with the feed and, if present in larger quantities, would make the acid highly corrosive.

This regeneration is carried out by distilling a slip stream of the acid returning from the large acid settler. Superheated isobutane vapours serve as stripping medium. The tarry polymers leave the bottom of the column and are disposed of as fuel in the refinery.

Regenerated HF is obtained as top product and, after condensing, is returned to the reaction system.

Isomerization

In the alkylation process isobutane was mentioned as one of the base materials. Since the gases from cracking opera-ions do not contain enough isobutane in proportion to the butylene and propylene required for a properly balanced olefin/isobutane alkylation feed, a process was developed to convert butane into isobutane by isomerization (p. 63).

Aluminium chloride ($AlCl_3$) was used as a catalyst in all early isomerization processes, but the activity was increased later by the use of hydrogen chloride as a 'promoter'. Commercial processes are either 'vapour phase' or 'liquid phase', but liquid phase processes are now preferred for isomerization of normal butane, normal pentane and normal hexane into isobutane, isopentane and isohexane respectively.

The feedstock, after drying, is mixed with hydrogen chloride and passes through the reactors containing aluminium chloride catalyst supported on alumina as a carrier. Traces of catalyst are removed in an absorber containing activated alumina. The hydrocarbons pass to a stripping column in which hydrogen chloride is removed and recycled to the feed. Isoparaffins and unconverted normal paraffins are separated in a fractionating column, the normal paraffin being recycled to increase the overall yield. In the conversion normal butane $\rightleftarrows$ isobutane, the composition of the equilibrium mixture is 65% isobutane at the prevailing reaction temperature. As this composition is reached only after a long time, the reaction mixture is worked up before equilibrium is reached.

A second example of isomerization is the conversion of 5-ring naphthenes with one or more side chains into 6-ring naphthenes which can be further isomerized to aromatics and hydrogen, using platinum as the catalyst.

Platinum as an isomerization catalyst is further applied in the Penex process of UOP developed for the isomerization of pentane and hexane.

$$\underset{\text{methylcyclopentane}}{C_5H_9CH_3} \longrightarrow \underset{\text{cyclohexane}}{C_6H_{12}} \longrightarrow \underset{\text{benzene}}{C_6H_6} + \underset{\text{hydrogen}}{3\,H_2}$$

Cyclization

A similar platinum-catalyzed reaction is the conversion of a straight-chain paraffin hydrocarbon into a naphthene and then into an aromatic. This is called cyclization (p. 63).

$$\underset{\text{n-heptane}}{CH_3{-}CH_2{-}CH_2{-}CH_2{-}CH_2{-}CH_2{-}CH_3} \longrightarrow$$

$$\underset{\text{methylcyclohexane}}{C_6H_{11}CH_3} + \underset{\text{hydrogen}}{H_2} \longrightarrow \underset{\text{toluene}}{C_6H_5CH_3} + \underset{\text{hydrogen}}{3\,H_2}$$

Both cyclization and isomerization produce hydrogen and play an important role in platforming.

Asphalt blowing

Asphaltic bitumen is the residue obtained by distillation of asphaltic base crude oil, sometimes in a combined atmospheric and vacuum distilling unit, but usually in a separate vacuum unit (p. 86). This is 'straight-run' bitumen, the properties of which are described on page 119. Bitumen is also obtained by precipitation from residual fractions by propane (propane deasphalting, p. 91). 'Propane' bitumen is not used as such, but is blended with other grades (cutterstock).

Bitumen is manufactured in various grades from soft to hard and brittle materials. The grade of the bitumen depends on the amount of volatile material removed during distillation, the greater the amount removed, the harder the residual bitumen.

For its various applications bitumen is characterized by softening point (p. 185) and penetration (p. 182). For many industrial applications bitumen with properties differing from those associated with straight-run bitumen are required. To meet these requirements, special grades are manufactured by blowing air through hot liquid bitumen. These 'blown' bitumens differ from straight-run bitumen, chiefly in respect of the relationships between softening point and penetration.

By means of blowing, more bitumen of a certain penetration can be produced in comparison with the distillation process. Blown bitumen is also produced by blowing heavy oil fractions at a stage earlier than their distillation to a residual bitumen.

Bitumen can be considered as a colloidal system of highly condensed aromatic particles in an oil with ring-type molecules, and its rheological properties depend on the concentration of the particles in the oil phase and the character of the oil.

The blowing is a dehydrogenation process followed by polymerization of the unsaturated hydrocarbon molecules formed. The side chains of the highly aromatic molecules are also partly dehydrogenated, and polymerization and condensation with the aromatic nuclei form larger condensed aromatic nuclei. This produces a change in the rheological and mechanical properties of the colloidal system.

The blowing process is now carried out by feeding a heated charge stock continuously into liquid bitumen in a column provided with an inner tube. The bitumen flows downward in the column and then upward through the inner tube, leaving it via a level pot. Air is blown through the molten mass by means of a number of jets arranged in the bottom of the column. The air stream is directed downward, but the air bubbles rise through the down-flowing molten mass in countercurrent, so that air low in oxygen meets the fresh feed first. The oxidation reactions are exothermic, much heat is produced and the reaction temperature has to be carefully controlled. With the countercurrent flow arrangement there is less chance of overheating than in the formerly used blowing systems in which overheating could lead to cracking (spoilage of quality) or to afterburning of the vapour at the outlet of the column and even to explosions.

The blown bitumen is withdrawn continuously from the column and pumped to storage through heat exchangers in which the incoming feed is warmed.

Treating processes

'rom the primary operations described in previous chapers, a wide range of product streams are obtained. In most ases the properties of these streams, either as final products or as feedstocks for further processing (for example catalytic racking or reforming) are adversely affected by certain omponents and these must be removed or converted into ess harmful compounds by further refining processes (treatng). The undesirable constituents are mainly olefinic and oxygen-, nitrogen- and sulphur-containing compounds.

Colour and odour of lubricating oil and paraffin wax and tability during storage and distribution of gasoline are imortant marketing factors, and treatment with hydrogen hydrotreating) and chemicals (chemical treating) may be ecessary to remove noxious and unstable compounds from hese products.

Chemical treating involves the use of chemicals such as ulphuric acid, and further treatment is necessary to remove ll traces of these and of undesirable compounds formed and lissolved in the oil.

Wherever possible, the substances removed are recovered nd sold, or are used for the manufacture of other products. 'or example, naphthenic acids, recovered from kerosine, gas oil and lubricating oil distillates are sold, whereas hydrogen ulphide, produced in sulphur-removing processes, is used for he manufacture of sulphur and sulphuric acid.

Treating of light products

Removal of hydrogen sulphide

Gases and the lighter hydrocarbon products (LPG, gasoline, SBP, white spirit and kerosine) may contain hydrogen sulphide, either originally present in the crude oil or formed luring refining by the decomposition of other sulphur compounds. This is an extremely undesirable contaminant, not only on account of its bad odour, but also because its easy convertibility to sulphur makes the product corrosive. If its concentration is low, hydrogen sulphide is usually removed by washing with a strong alkali (10% NaOH) until all the alkali has been consumed. The spent alkali is rejected and fresh alkali taken. If the concentration is high, it is more economical to use a regenerative process in which the hydrogen sulphide is absorbed in a liquid that is practically immiscible with the product. The liquid is then separated from the product, stripped of hydrogen sulphide, and reused. The Girbotol and the Shell Adip Amine washing processes are typical regenerative processes. The Girbotol process, shown diagramatically in Fig. 106, usually employs mono- and diethanolamine.

The process consists of two sections: absorption and regeneration. The absorption solution at about 40°C (105°F) enters the top of the absorber, which consists of a tray column for gas or a packed column (p. 90) for liquid treatment, and flows down the column in opposite direction to the hydrocarbon stream, which enters at the bottom. The purified product leaves the absorber at the top.

The solution containing the hydrogen sulphide, after passing through a heat exchanger, enters the regenerator column, which is similar to a fractionating column, at about 90–95°C (195–205°F). As it flows down the column, the solution is heated to 105–110°C (220–230°F) by steam rising from a reboiler at the base of the column, and hydrogen sulphide is expelled from the top of the column. Hot absorbent solution, now free from hydrogen sulphide, flows from the base of the regenerator through the heat exchanger and is pumped back via a cooler to the top of the absorber and used again.

As in most regenerative absorption processes, removal of H_2S from the hydrocarbons is not complete, but residual H_2S can be removed by a caustic soda after-wash.

In a recently developed Shell process, the 'sulfinol' process, a mixture of diisopropyl amine, sulfolane and water is used for the removal of carbon dioxide and hydrogen sulphide from synthesis gas hydrogen.

Removal and conversion of mercaptans

The mercaptans occurring in liquefied petroleum gases,

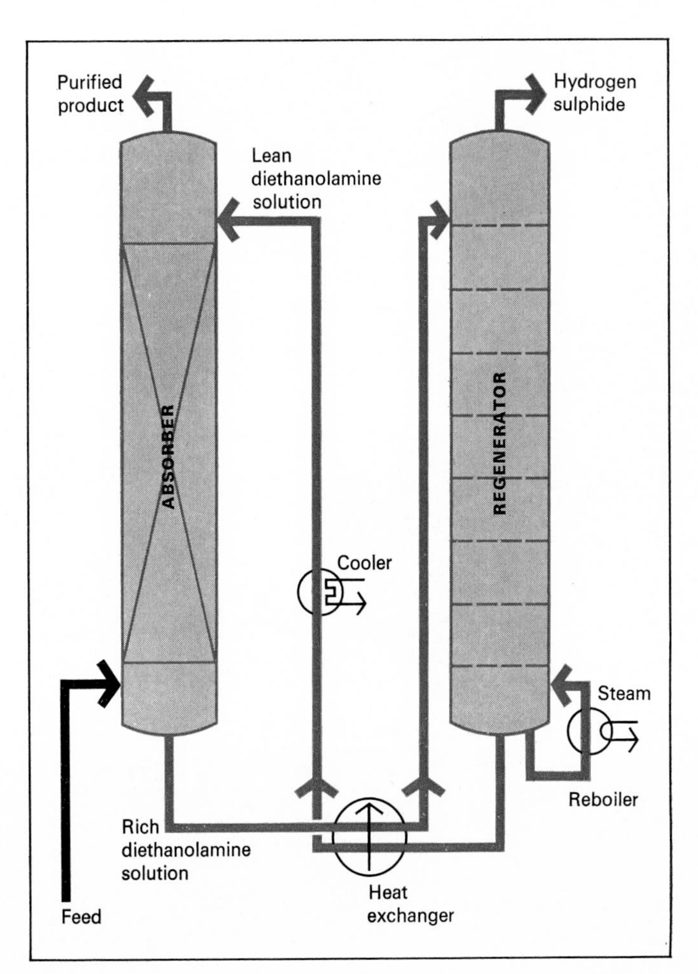

Fig. 106 Girbotol process

gasolines and kerosines are particularly undesirable because of their bad odour, and are normally removed or made less harmful by some form of treatment. Those present in the C_5 and lower fractions can be removed by treatment with a strong alkali, normally caustic soda, which forms soluble compounds with the mercaptans. The spent alkali, together with the sulphur compounds, is either regenerated or re-used elsewhere as semi-spent caustic. The alkali solution is regenerated by distilling off or oxidizing the mercaptans and recycling the alkali to the process.

Heavier mercaptans present in fractions higher than C_5 are not readily soluble in caustic soda, but its solvent power may be increased by the addition of certain organic compounds called 'solutizers'. A regenerative process for removing mercaptans in this way, known as the solutizer process, developed by the Group, is still in use in some refineries for treating gasoline of high mercaptan content.

Caustic potash may be used in preference to caustic soda. Cresylic acids are most commonly used as solutizers, although many other compounds, for instance isobutyric acid, are also suitable. The spent solutizer solution is regenerated by air blowing, which converts the dissolved mercaptans to disulphides, which are then extracted with a suitable solvent. Alternatively, the spent solution may be steam stripped where cheap fuel is available.

Sweetening

There may be economic justification for removing the mercaptans from gasoline of high mercaptan content, e.g. by the solutizer process, since their presence makes it necessary to add rather more TEL (tetraethyl lead) to the finished gasoline blend in order to obtain the required octane number. In most cases, however, it is sufficient to convert the mercaptans into disulphides by means of a 'sweetening' process since disulphides do not have a strong objectionable smell or affect the lead requirement, and can be allowed to remain in the product; thus, although no sulphur is removed, the gasoline is sweetened by the conversion of mercaptans to disulphides.

Many sweetening processes are available. One of the oldest, the 'doctor' treatment, employs a solution of lead oxide (litharge) in caustic soda together with sulphur. Sodium hypochlorite solutions and copper chloride are also used for the conversion of mercaptans to disulphides.

A modification of the solutizer process is nowadays extensively used by the Group, the gasoline being treated simultaneously with solutizer solution and air. The mercaptans dissolved in the solutizer solution are converted to disulphides, which then redissolve in the gasoline. Gasoline and solutizer solution are separated, and the latter is recycled and used again.

Another process is the 'Merox' (mercaptan oxidation) process, devised by Universal Oil Products, in which a catalyst dissolved in the caustic soda phase considerably enhances the sweetening reaction.

The sweetening processes described above are not entirely satisfactory for the treatment of kerosines and jet fuels. A satisfactory process has been developed within the Group in which raw fuel and a small quantity of sulphuric acid are intimately mixed. The acid sludge is then separated and recycled, a very small percentage of fresh acid being injected into the recycle acid stream to maintain the desired acid strength. In addition to the sweetening effect, the sulphuric acid treatment has a beneficial effect on other properties, such as colour and gum-forming characteristics.

Hydrogen treatment

The increased production of crude oils containing relatively high proportions of sulphur compounds has led to a steady increase in the sulphur content of various refinery streams. On the other hand, the trend of market demand for certain products, for example diesel fuels, is for oils of lower sulphur content. It has therefore become necessary to develop methods for the removal of sulphur compounds from these products. Processes using concentrated sulphuric acid for sulphur removal are sometimes employed, particularly for the treatment of kerosines, but these have limited application and with the availability of cheap hydrogen as a by-product from catalytic reforming it has been possible to apply hydrogen treatment on a commercial scale.

In this treatment the sulphur compounds are removed by converting them into hydrogen sulphide by reaction with hydrogen in the presence of a catalyst.

In the previously mentioned processes, hydrogen sulphide and mercaptans are affected, while alkylsulphides and thiophenes are hardly touched. In hydrotreating processes practically all sulphur compounds are converted to hydrogen sulphide.

It is essential to choose such a catalyst that only the sulphur removing reaction is carried out and no hydrogenation of hydrocarbons (e.g. aromatics $\rightarrow$ cycloparaffins) occurs. Olefins are, however, converted into paraffins. The usual catalyst is a mixture of cobalt and molybdenum oxides supported on an alumina carrier.

The hydrogen sulphide formed may be removed by scrubbing the hydrogen-rich gas, separated from the plant product, with an amine or other alkaline absorber liquid (p. 107) and may then be recovered for the manufacture of sulphur and sulphuric acid.

Hydrogen treatment is usually applied to distillates boiling below about 350°C (660°F), i.e. gas oils and lighter products. However, the process can be adapted to heavier oils (with the exception of residues) and also to cracked products. In certain circumstances it may be preferable to remove the sulphur at an earlier stage than the final product. Hydrodesulphurization is therefore sometimes applied to the feedstocks for catalytic reforming and cracking plants and even to a whole crude oil distillate before working up the distillate into the separate products. In this case not enough hydrogen from catalytic reforming may be available, so that an additional hydrogen producing unit has to be installed, for instance the steam reforming of naphtha.

The Shell hydrodesulphurization process

Fig. 107 is a diagram of the Shell hydrodesulphurization process, which is typical of hydrotreating processes and Fig. 108 shows the processing unit. The feedstock is mixed with hydrogen from the platformer (or other source) and also with the hydrogen-rich recycle gas recovered from the desulphurized product. The mixture is heated in a furnace to a temperature between 300–380°C (570–715°F) and then passed through the reactor, which is charged with pelleted catalyst, the pressure in the reactor being between 40–60 kg/cm² (570–855 lb/in²). Under these conditions the feedstock remains partly in the liquid phase and the system is referred to as the 'trickle flow' process.

The reactor effluent, consisting of desulphurized oil,

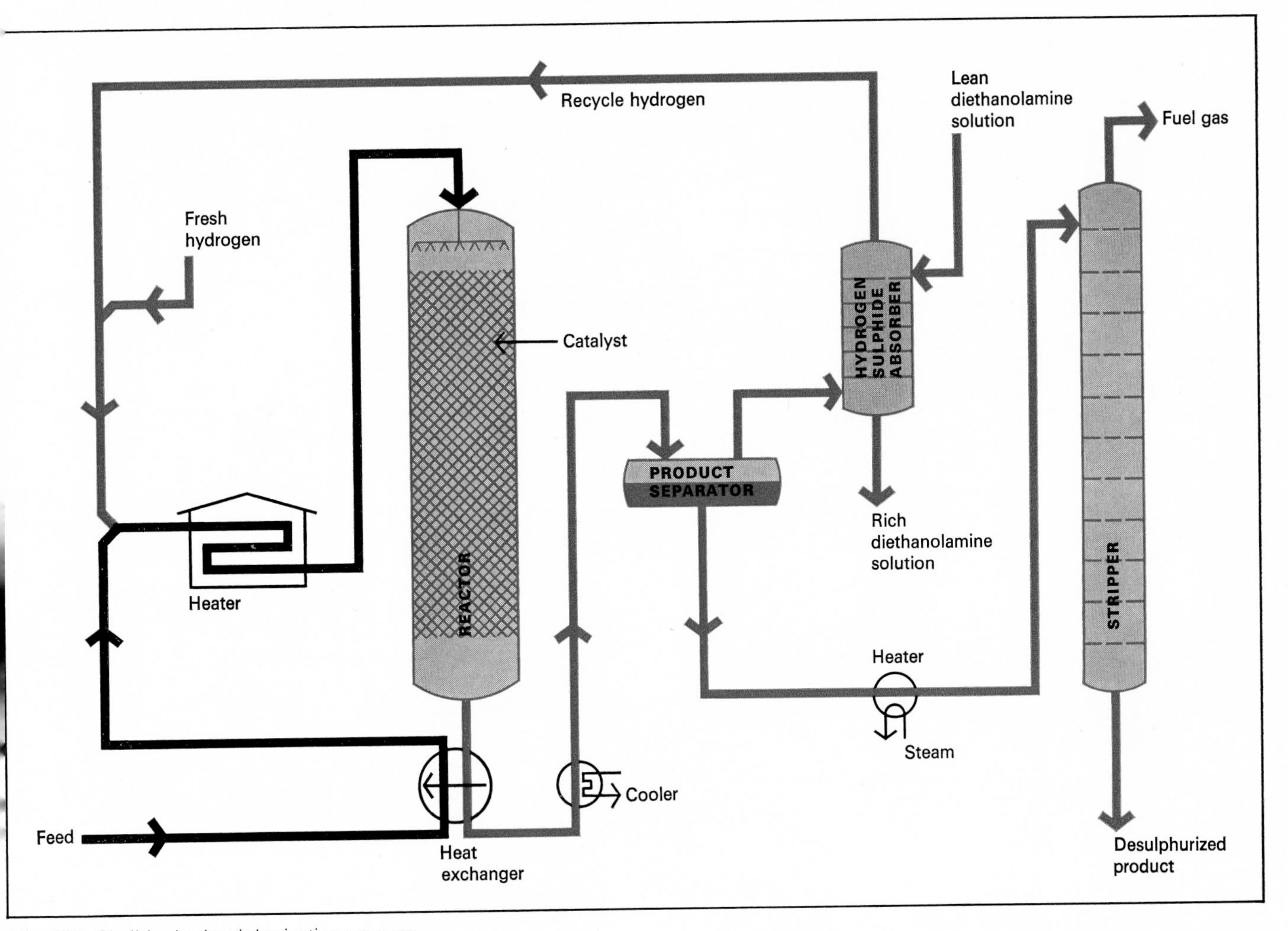

Fig. 107 Shell hydrodesulphurization process

hydrogen and hydrogen sulphide, is cooled and the products are separated in the high-pressure product separator. The hydrogen-rich gas, from which hydrogen sulphide is removed, is recycled to the feed inlet and the liquid product passes to a stripping column, where dissolved hydrogen sulphide and light hydrocarbons are removed. The catalyst has a long life and is regenerated, when necessary, without removal from the plant, by passing over it a mixture of steam and air to remove carbonaceous products. The trickle flow process is very flexible and can be used for treating a variety of refinery streams.

Removal of water

It is often necessary to remove suspended or dissolved water. Cooling can assist in decreasing the amount of dissolved water and the suspended water is removed by settling and coalescing. Dissolved water can be reduced by passing the hydrocarbon stream through a suitable hygroscopic absorbent, which can be regenerated; either a solid absorbent such as activated alumina, or a liquid absorbent such as diethylene glycol may be used. In the latter case a 'water dew point' is replaced by a 'glycol dew point'.

The cheapest way is to pass the products through a bed of calcium chloride or a similar drying agent, which is replaced when no more water can be absorbed. Disposal of the spent agent may create a problem. The dew point reduction attainable with calcium chloride is rather small.

Fig. 108 Hydrodesulphurizing unit

Removal of carbonyl sulphide

Carbonyl sulphide, COS, a compound of carbon, oxygen and sulphur, is a frequent contaminant of the C_3 fraction and to some extent of refinery gases. It is removed by treatment with a diamine solution or with warm dilute alkali solutions.

Stability of gasoline

With the introduction of the cracking processes it became necessary to treat the gasoline in order to remove unstable hydrocarbons which, on storage, give rise to the formation of resinous substances, generally referred to as 'gum', and to improve the colour.

In the early days of cracking, the gasolines were treated with sulphuric acid, followed by redistillation. Losses were rather high, and furthermore, some of the desirable hydrocarbons were removed by the treatment. Nowadays, cracked gasolines are given a multi-stage washing with caustic soda, followed by a sweetening step, before the gasoline is blended. This treatment also removes any acidic constituents.

The use of 'inhibitors' greatly improves the stability. Inhibitors are chemical compounds that prevent or retard the gum-forming reactions and are added in small quantities to the gasoline.

Clay treatment

Trace contaminants are sometimes removed by treatment with an adsorbent clay. Substances that promote colour and gum instability in gasolines, produced by severe cracking, are removed in this way.

Treating of lubricating oils

Lubricating oils are sometimes finished by acid, clay, or acid and clay treatment, or more recently by hydrogen treatment.

Acid treatment

For the acid treatment, sulphuric acid of 98% strength is normally used. To avoid undesirable reactions, a temperature between 35–65°C (95–105°F) is maintained and about 2–5%w of acid used. Contact time is also kept short. In older plants the process is carried out in a series of 'agitators' and settling tanks. Agitators are cylindrical vessels with conical bottoms and fitted with steam coils. Oil and acid are pumped in and the mixture is agitated by air blowing; the oil and acid mixture is transferred to a settling tank, where the acid sludge separates by gravity.

In more modern units, air mixing has been replaced by pump mixing, and the acid sludge is separated from the refined oil by centrifuging instead of settling. Acid treating is normally followed by lime and clay treating, so that generally no special provision has to be made for neutralization of the treated oil.

For manufacture of special oils, such as transformer oils and medicinal oils, a treatment with oleum (strong sulphuric acid containing free sulphur trioxide) is necessary, followed by alkali washing.

Clay treatment

The acid treated oils are given a final treatment with clay (sometimes referred to as 'earth') to improve the colour and stability by removing traces of unstable and coloured products from the previous acid treatment. The process consists of contacting the oil with the clay, either batchwise or continuously, and then filtering the mixture to free the oil from the clay. Two types of clay are used, non-activated and activated clays.

Non-activated clay is naturally occurring clay, such as Fuller's earth, normally used below 100°C (212°F) for the finishing of the cheaper industrial oils.

Activated clay (also called acid clay) is clay which has undergone a special acid treatment to increase its activity as an adsorbent. Acid treated clay is often used at a higher temperature, between 150–300°C (300–570°F).

The oil is heated to about 80°C (175°F) and mixed with the clay in a 'slurry' tank by stirring. The mixture is heated to the treating temperature, according to grade, and then intimately mixed by stirring by steam agitation in a contact tank.

The spent clay is separated from the refined oil by means of a filter. The oil is then dried in a vacuum column and subsequently filtered in a 'blotter' press to remove any fine clay particles which may have passed the main filter.

The activated clay used in the above process cannot be regenerated.

Hydrofinishing of lubricating oils

For various reasons acid and clay treating is not attractive. It is expensive, due to high chemical consumption and labour requirements, and the disposal of acid sludge and spent clay causes serious problems. They usually cannot be dumped freely and burning of acid sludge to recover sulphur dioxide for sulphuric acid manufacture causes considerable air pollution. Hydrofinishing can overcome these disadvantages. It involves a catalytic hydrogen treatment at elevated temperature and high pressure in order to convert unstable compounds, thus improving colour and colour stability in a manner superior to acid and clay treating.

The process applied is basically the Shell trickle hydrodesulphurization process, already described for gas oil treating (p. 108).

A special feature of hydrofinishing lubricating oils is the application of a two-stage procedure, the oil being treated at two different temperatures. This can be achieved either by using two separate reactors or by maintaining two different temperature zones in one reactor by recycling part of the cooled product to the middle of the reactor. Catalysts are the same as used in the Shell trickle process. Co/Mo or Ni/Mo on alumina at 100 kg/cm^2 (1420 lb/in^2) hydrogen pressure and 350°C (660°F). Mild conditions are preferred in order not to remove all sulphur compounds, some of which play a certain role in the oxidation inhibition of the oil.

Subsidiary processes

Various subsidiary processes are employed to manufacture products meeting marketing specifications from the refinery grades produced by the processes described in previous chapters. The most important of these are blending, emulsifying, and grease making.

Blending

Blending is a physical process in which accurately measured or weighed quantities of two or more components are mixed together to form a homogeneous blend. The components may all be petroleum fractions or may include other materials, for example fatty oils, dyes, functional additives, referred to collectively as 'additives', in proportions from a few parts per million to 10 or 20 %w. The blends will be formulated to have the required properties for particular applications and will usually be required to meet appropriate marketing specifications.

Blending is required for oil products of all kinds. Gasoline as marketed is usually a blend of several refinery grades derived from different processes, generally contains lead anti-knock compounds, and may contain other additives, e.g. to prevent spark-plug fouling, carburettor icing, etc. Kerosine may be a blend of two or more refinery grades. Most lubricating oils are blends of two or more base oils with or without additives, ranging from the simplest two-oil blends to quite complex formulations containing several non-petroleum ingredients. Fuel oils are frequently blends, either of distillates or of distillates and residuals. Petroleum waxes are blended together and with natural waxes or polyolefins. Bitumens are blended together, or with volatile solvents to form cutbacks.

In principle the process of blending is the same in all these instances but the details will vary according to the nature of the components and the complexity of the mixture, for example gasoline components can be blended readily by very simple mixing, lubricating oils may require moderate heating (60–80°C; 140–180°F), waxes and bitumen require more heating and the mixing of hot bitumen with cold volatile solvent obviously requires more care than the cold mixing of lubricating oils.

Blending can be carried out either intermittently by 'batch blending' or continuously by 'in-line blending'.

Batch blending

In batch blending the components are transferred in weighed or measured quantity from their individual storage to blending tanks in which they are mixed by paddles and baffles, by air blowing, by pump circulation or by a combination of these methods. Various circulating systems are employed to ensure rapid and efficient mixing. In suction mixing a vertical perforated pipe in the tank draws approximately equal quantities of liquid from several levels of the tank into the suction side of the pump and the resulting mixture is discharged back into the tank. In jet mixing in-

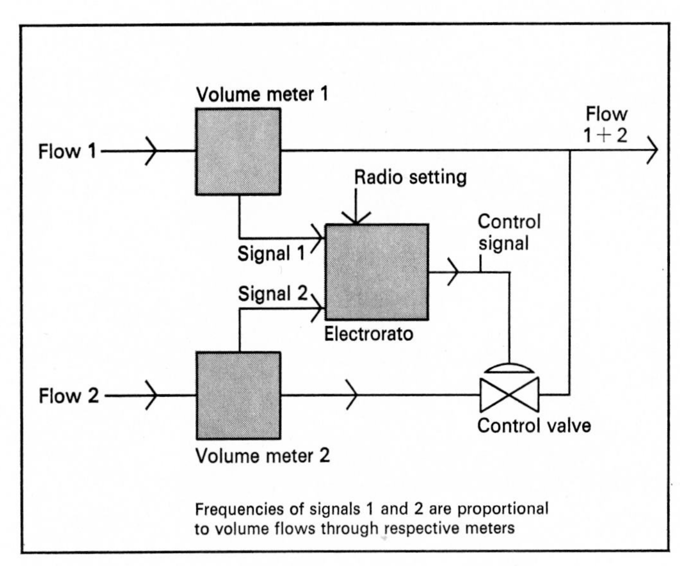

Fig. 109 Electrorato in-line blending

clined nozzles connected to the discharge side of the pump are installed in the tank and the jets of liquid ejected from them cause a swirling of the contents of the tank. The blending tank may be heated by steam or hot oil coils or jackets according to the type of material being blended.

In-line blending

In-line blending is now widely used not only in blending plants but in the main refineries (p. 86). All components are pumped simultaneously into a common discharge pipe or header at rates of flow corresponding with the required proportions, the rates of flow being accurately controlled by automatic metering devices. Blending takes place in the lines between the header and the storage tank into which the blend is discharged. Fig. 109 shows the Electrorato control of in-line blending and Fig. 110 shows the blending lines.

Special blending

The blending of TEL/TML with gasoline requires special precautions in view of their toxicity. Care must be taken that operatives do not come into contact with the fluids or inhale their vapours; they must wear protective clothing and undergo regular medical examination. TEL/TML is continuously sucked into a portion of the gasoline passing through an ejector and the resulting mixture is then injected into the main gasoline stream in the blending line.

Emulsifying

Some oil products are marketed as emulsions with water. An emulsion is a dispersion of fine droplets of a liquid (the

Fig. 110 In-line blending lines

disperse phase) in the bulk of another liquid (the continuous phase) with which it is immiscible. A third substance, the emulsifier, is necessary to keep the droplets dispersed in a stable emulsion. The oil product may be dispersed in the water (oil in water, o/w, emulsion) or the water may be dispersed in the oil product (water in oil, w/o, emulsion).

Bitumen emulsions (p. 120) and marine lubricant emulsions (p. 141) are the best known examples respectively of o/w and w/o emulsions but both types are made with petroleum waxes (p. 119), the former for impregnating and waterproofing, and both for polishes. Both bitumen and wax emulsions are truly emulsions (liquid-liquid systems) as made hot, but they may not strictly conform to the definition when cold. However, they behave like emulsions in practice, i.e. the deposited bitumen or wax particles fuse together to form continuous films, and they are generally accepted as emulsions.

Emulsions are made either by adding the disperse phase slowly to the continuous phase with continuous agitation in a paddle mixer, or by feeding the two phases simultaneously to a colloid mill or homogenizer. The simplest form of colloid mill consists of a metal rotor rotating at high speed in a housing with a narrow gap between them, the two liquids being fed into the gap and emulsified as they pass through it. In either process the emulsifier may be dissolved in the continuous phase or may be formed *in situ* by interaction between constituent parts dissolved one in each phase, e.g. acid in the oil, alkali in the water, forming soap when they come together. Oil and water can be emulsified at ambient temperature, but wax and bitumen must be heated to render them liquid and the water phase has also to be heated to maintain fluidity during the process.

Grease making

Greases usually consist of solid or semi-solid dispersions of metallic soaps or other thickeners in a mineral or synthetic lubricating oil.

In the conventional method of making soap base greases, all or part of the oil is charged into an autoclave together with fatty material and alkali. The mixture is heated to a controlled temperature and stirred until soap formation (saponification) is complete. The mixture is then transferred to a kettle equipped with heavy duty stirring gear and scrapers, and the balance of the oil (if any) is added. Cooling at a controlled rate with continuous stirring results in the formation of the grease structure. Pre-made soap may be used instead of fatty matter and alkali, especially for lithium greases. Temperatures, rates of heating and cooling, and intensity and duration of stirring are all critical factors in the process and must be rigorously selected and controlled, according to the type of grease being made.

The manufacture of greases with inorganic thickeners is the same in principle as with soaps, i.e. the thorough dispersion of the thickener in the oil and suitable control of thermal and mechanical conditions to permit a structure to form. The details of the process will vary according to the type of thickener used.

Various continuous processes for the manufacture of grease have been devised, especially for lithium greases. The soap is mixed with the oil and the mixture passed through a series of heating, mixing and cooling tubes or vessels so adjusted to permit the formation of a grease structure, the resulting grease being finally passed through a high-pressure mill to homogenize it.

Oil products–applications

Introduction

The manufacture of oil products from crude oil is dealt with under Oil products – manufacture (p. 77). This section of the book will describe the principal applications of these products. This introduction gives some idea of what they are and what properties they must have to be satisfactory in use, the following chapters describe how and where oil products are used, and the final chapter deals briefly with some of the tests that are used to control their quality and assess their performance.

Oil products fall into four main categories, fuels, lubricants, waxes and bitumens, in each of which there are a number of types with well-defined characteristics, and within these types again there may be a number of grades each designed to meet the requirements of a particular application. Of the fractions produced from crude oil about 85 %w is used as fuel of one sort or another, about 12 %w for applications in which it is not burnt, e.g. hydrocarbon solvents, lubricants, wax (other than for candles) and bitumen, and about 3 %w as feedstock for chemical manufacture.

In dealing with the applications of these products, it is convenient to consider jointly the fuel and lubricant requirements of internal combustion engines according to the use of the engine (automotive, aviation, marine and industrial) and all other applications of fuels and lubricants under the two headings: 'Fuels for domestic, industrial and agricultural use' and 'Lubricants for industry'. Again it is convenient to include under the latter heading certain automotive, aviation and marine uses of lubricants such as gear oils and greases, because they are essentially the same as their industrial uses. Also under Lubricants for industry are included oil products that are not lubricants, but which are customarily associated with lubricants in their development and marketing, such as electrical oils and protectives.

Fuels

Most of the world's oil supply is used as fuel, either in engines to produce power or as a source of heat and light in industry and the home. The world is dependent for most of its power and heat (apart from that of the sun) on the burning of fuels, and for many centuries wood and coal were the main fuels. The advent of liquid petroleum fuels revolutionized our way of life by making possible the development of the internal combustion engine and hence the motor vehicle, the aeroplane and industrial machinery generally.

All fuels need air for burning and the more intimate the mixture of air and fuel, the more complete and efficient the combustion. Gaseous fuels, and liquid fuels that vaporize easily, mix readily with air while liquid fuels that do not vaporize easily can be atomized into minute droplets which disperse rapidly throughout the air. Intimate mixing of the fuel with air permits the extremely rapid burning that takes place in the internal combustion engine. Solid fuels cannot be so easily dispersed in air, and consequently are difficult to burn quickly and efficiently. Petroleum fuels thus have an inherent advantage over solid fuels in their ease of dispersion and combustion. They also have the advantage of being almost completely combustible, with little ash, and of being easily stored and handled.

Petroleum fuels comprise both gaseous and liquid fuels and the latter can be classified according to their volatility into gasoline, kerosine, gas oil, diesel fuel and fuel oil. These various types are described below.

Natural gas

Natural gas is produced either associated or non-associated with crude oil and is a ready-made fuel which, after removal of undesirable constituents such as sulphur compounds and of valuable liquid constituents, can be used for many industrial and domestic applications. As delivered to the customer it consists essentially of methane, CH_4.

Natural gas has long been used as a fuel in the USA, but its use outside the USA has been restricted hitherto by limited availability. Recent discoveries of natural gas in other parts of the world, especially in Europe and North Africa, will make it much more widely available.

Natural gas is more fully discussed in the chapter, Natural gas, p. 67.

Liquefied petroleum gas

Liquefied petroleum gas (LPG) consists of petroleum hydrocarbons which, although gaseous at normal ambient temperatures and pressures, can be liquefied by the application of pressures of the order of a few atmospheres, and can therefore be conveniently stored and transported as liquid in light pressure containers.

In the production of gasoline, whether from wet gas (natural gasoline) or from refinery operations, considerable quantities of hydrocarbon gases are obtained. The heavier gases are compressed to yield various grades of LPG: commercial propane, mainly C_3 hydrocarbons, commercial butane, mainly C_4 hydrocarbons, and commercial mixtures of these two, often blended in a prescribed ratio. They are supplied in steel cylinders (bottles) or in bulk.

The quality of LPG is closely controlled by specifications which usually impose strict limits on vapour pressure, sulphur content and moisture content, and since the product is supplied in closed pressure vessels there is no opportunity for its quality to deteriorate.

Gasoline

The term 'gasoline' covers the volatile liquid fuels used in spark ignition engines (motor and aviation gasolines) and the 'special boiling point spirits' (SBP) used for various industrial purposes. Only the former will be dealt with under the heading of oil products, the SBP being dealt with under Solvents, p. 201.

The product marketed as gasoline is not usually a single refinery fraction, but a blend of various streams from different processes, with the addition of tetraethyl lead (TEL), or tetramethyl lead (TML) or mixtures of the two and other additives to meet marketing specifications. As produced at the refinery, gasolines are colourless, highly inflammable liquids boiling between 30–200°C (85–390°F).

The most important property of a gasoline as an engine fuel is its octane number (ON) which indicates whether it will knock in an engine (Test methods, p. 181). Practically all aviation and motor gasolines contain TEL/TML or mixtures of the two to control knocking and increase the ON. Since these fluids are dyed to indicate their poisonous nature, most marketed gasolines are coloured.

Volatility is also an important property and depends on the relative proportions of the various hydrocarbons present. It is assessed and controlled by a standard ASTM distillation test and by a Reid vapour pressure test (Test methods, p. 192).

Gasolines normally contain traces of sulphur compounds. These can form corrosive gases on combustion and the sulphur content is therefore reduced to a practicable minimum by refinery treatment (p. 107). Gasoline should be stable in storage and contain no non-volatile material.

When crude oil was first processed, the internal combustion engine had not been developed and there was little use for the volatile gasoline fractions; kerosine for burning in lamps was the product most in demand, the gasoline fractions being too inflammable. The development of the internal combustion engine completely changed the picture, and the demand for motor and later aviation gasoline became so great that new manufacturing methods (cracking) had to be devised. The demand for gasoline today far exceeds that for kerosine, and progressive development of refinery methods has enabled the quality of gasoline to keep pace with the ever increasing demand.

Motor gasolines are available with octane numbers ranging from 70–102, and with volatilities adjusted to suit the climatic conditions of the area in which they are used. Three grades are generally recognized; Regular, for commercial vehicles and cars with low compression ratios; Premium, for the general run of private cars; and Super, for high performance, high compression-ratio cars.

Aviation gasolines have higher octane numbers than those of motor gasolines and are also available in several grades with octane numbers ranging from 73–115/145 (p. 182).

Kerosine

Kerosine, or paraffin oil as it is often called in the UK, was for fifty years the most important petroleum product. Although it has long lost its leading place to gasoline, it is still in considerable demand. Its use as an illuminant persists in many parts of the world, the development of clean, efficient burners has increased its demand for domestic heating and cooking and still more recently the development of turbo-prop and turbo-jet aircraft has resulted in a considerable increase in consumption.

Kerosine, as produced in the refinery, is a colourless liquid, but commercial grades are sometimes dyed. It is less volatile and less inflammable than gasoline, boiling between 140–300°C (285–570°F), thus overlapping the gasoline range.

Kerosines with a high content of aromatics are unsuitable in lamps or white-flame appliances with wicks since they cause smoking. For such uses the kerosine is treated to reduce the aromatic content, leaving a predominantly paraffinic product (p. 90). The sulphur content must also be kept as low as possible.

For use as a tractor fuel kerosine must have as high an octane number as possible, and the inclusion of aromatics, which have high ON, is advantageous. Grades suitable for use in tractors are marketed as tractor vaporizing oil and preferably have a high aromatic content.

For aviation purposes two widely different grades are used, a low-freezing point kerosine and a wide-range distillate (a kerosine including gasoline fractions). Both are rigidly controlled by official British and USA specifications.

Gas oil

Petroleum distillates heavier than kerosine and lighter than spindle oil are commonly known as 'gas oil' because their earliest use was to enrich water-gas (a low calorific value gas produced by passing steam over red hot coal or coke) in the manufacture of town gas. Gas oil is still used for this purpose although, owing to the scarcity of such middle distillates, there is a tendency to use residual fuels wherever possible. Gas oil is also used as fuel for diesel engines, for domestic and industrial heating and as a feedstock for cracking processes in which it is converted to high-grade gasoline.

Gas oil is a brownish coloured distillate, mostly boiling between 180–370°C (355–700°F), obtained in a number of refinery operations, crude oil distillation, vacuum distillation of lubricating oil stock, thermal and catalytic cracking.

Diesel fuels

As the name implies, diesel fuels are the petroleum fractions used as fuel in diesel engines. Various qualities are marketed to suit the type of engine operated. The small high-speed automotive engine uses a distillate fuel little different from gas oil, the most important characteristic of which is its ignition quality or cetane number (Test methods, p. 182). Engine performance also depends on volatility, which is controlled by the distillation range.

Stationary diesel engines, which are larger and slower than automotive diesels, do not make such great demands on the fuel and run satisfactorily on lower octane number fuels, which are generally distillates somewhat less volatile than the automotive fuels.

Marine propulsion diesels, still larger and slower, are even less critical of fuel quality and can run on more viscous fuel oils, either distillate or residual. The use of the cheaper residual fuels was precluded by the heavy deposits and cylinder wear they caused, but the development of special lubricants has permitted their use with no greater deposits or wear than occur with distillate marine fuels.

The sulphur content of diesel fuels is higher than that of gasolines or kerosines, up to 1%w in automotive fuels, up to 1·8%w in marine distillate fuels and up to 4%w in marine residual fuels.

Fuel oils

Fuel oils consist largely or entirely of the residue from the distillation of the more asphaltic crude oils. There are various grades with viscosities ranging from 200 to 6000 sec. Redwood I at 100°F, and since it is impossible to produce all these as primary refinery products, they are made by blending residue with distillate in accordance with the viscosity requirements.

Fuel oil is burnt to raise steam for ships, locomotives and

general heating purposes, and as a fuel in large marine propulsion diesels. There is a tendency to describe the fuel according to its use, for example bunker fuel, under-boiler fuel, industrial fuel.

Fuel oils are generally difficult to vaporize and must be atomized in special burners if they are to burn completely and efficiently. The viscosity of viscous oils must be reduced by heating before they can be atomized. Sulphur content is also important since sulphur compounds in the combustion gases can cause corrosion of low temperature surfaces.

All fuel oils, being largely residues, contain traces of mineral matter derived from the crude or picked up during processing. When the oil is burnt this mineral matter appears as ash, usually less than 0·1 %w of the oil, which may contain compounds of sodium, calcium, iron, nickel and vanadium. Even in these small amounts they can be harmful in certain applications.

Lubricants

Lubricants were at one time almost exclusively animal or vegetable oils or fats, but modern requirements in both nature and volume have made petroleum the main source of supply. Fatty oils still have their uses although generally in an ancillary role.

By its very nature lubrication consumes much less material than do operations involving fuel, with the result that in volume lubricants represent only about 2 % of all petroleum products. But their uses are multifarious and the technical problems associated with them are particularly numerous and complex.

The main function of a lubricant is to reduce the friction between moving surfaces and so facilitate motion. Its second most important function is to remove heat generated in the equipment being lubricated, such as engine pistons, enclosed gears and machine tools. It has also to remove debris from the contact area, e.g. combustion products in the engine cylinder, swarf in metal cutting operations. Sometimes it has to protect the lubricated or adjacent parts against corrosion by moisture, as in turbines, textile machinery and antifriction bearings.

Lubrication

To understand how a lubricant functions it is necessary to know something about the nature of surfaces. Even the most carefully finished metallic surface is not truly flat but has a certain sub-microscopic roughness – something like a sandpaper on a much smaller scale. When two dry surfaces are in contact, the asperities tend to interlock and resist any effort to slide one surface over the other. This resistance is called friction, and before sliding takes place sufficient force must be applied to overcome it.

The main object of lubrication is to replace this solid friction between the two interlocking surfaces by the much lower internal friction in a film of lubricant maintained between them and keeping them apart so that the asperities no longer touch. The viscosity of the lubricant is a measure of its internal friction.

When two surfaces are in relative motion at moderately high speeds with a copious supply of lubricant, a film of lubricant is dragged in between them and is maintained so long as the load is insufficient to squeeze it out. This condition, known as hydrodynamic or fluid lubrication, is the ideal state of affairs for effective lubrication, not only as regards the main function of reducing friction but also as regards cooling and removing debris.

Fluid lubrication is best exemplified by a journal bearing where the rotation of the journal draws in the oil between the journal and the bearing so that the two metal surfaces are separated by a film of oil. The film is very thin by ordinary standards but is thick enough to prevent any actual metallic contact. Friction is very low, depending on the viscosity of the oil, the speed of rotation and the load on the journal; the journal floats on the film of oil.

When the journal stops rotating, it will sink through the lubricant and squeeze out most of the oil from between the surfaces, allowing some direct contact between the asperities on the lower surfaces of the bearing and journal. If the journal then rotates slowly, it may not drag in enough oil to float the surfaces apart, and the much greater friction will be independent of the viscosity of the oil but dependent on the load and a property of the oil called 'oiliness'. This property is related to the ability of the oil to stick tightly to metal surfaces, and depends on the physico-chemical nature of some of its constituents, either naturally present or deliberately added, which are said to be 'adsorbed' on the metal surface. This condition, called 'boundary lubrication', is liable to occur not only in journals but in any mechanism where the speed is insufficient to maintain a film, or the load becomes high enough to reduce the film thickness. It is an undesirable state of affairs since the high friction may generate sufficient heat to damage the surfaces, and it is wasteful in consuming energy. Machines are therefore designed to avoid it as far as possible, but there are many instances in practice where it is unavoidable, and the lubricant must cope with it.

If the film thickness is still further reduced, as by increasing the load, metal-to-metal contact will occur between the asperities, there will be a great increase in friction, and sufficiently high temperatures may be generated at the points of contact to melt the metal and damage the surface. This can happen not only at low sliding speeds and high loads but also at high sliding speeds where the contact between the metals is concentrated in a small area, as in gears or heavy duty metal working operations.

In a journal bearing it is customary to make the bearing of a metal, such as white metal, that is softer than that of the journal, so that if metal-to-metal contact occurs the bearing metal will melt, and provide sufficient lubrication to avoid damage to the more expensive journal. It is not always possible, however, to have dissimilar metals in contact, and the development of local high temperatures is sometimes unavoidable. Under such conditions lubrication can often be maintained by lubricants containing 'extreme-pressure' (EP) agents which react chemically with the local hot-spots to form compounds that shear more easily than the original metal, and so facilitate sliding, and at the same time provide a larger area of contact with a consequent decrease in local pressure. In this way motion can be maintained without excessive damage to the surfaces.

Lubricating oils

Lubricating oils can be produced by modern methods of refining from most crudes. They may be distillates or residues derived from the vacuum distillation of a primary distillate with a boiling range above that of gas oil. They range from thin, easily flowing spindle oils to thick cylinder oils. The uses of lubricating oils are legion, and it would be impossible to make direct from the crude oil all the various grades required. A limited number of primary oils are therefore manufactured at the refinery and these are blended together in various proportions with or without additives (p. 118) to produce oils with the required properties.

The most important property of a lubricating oil is its viscosity, which is a measure of its internal friction or ability to flow, and largely determines its suitability for any particular application. Absolute viscosity is determined either as kinematic viscosity, in centistokes, or as dynamic viscosity, in centipoises, obtained by multiplying the kinematic viscosity by the density of the oil at the temperature of measurement (Test methods, p. 189). Lubricating oils have viscosities ranging from 10–1000 centistokes at 100°F at which temperature water has a viscosity of about 1 centistoke.

In the oil industry, old established, less accurate viscometers have long been used, the Redwood I and Redwood II in the UK, the Saybolt Furol and the Saybolt Universal in the USA and the Engler on the continent of Europe. The viscosity is expressed as seconds Redwood or Saybolt or degrees Engler, at the temperature of measurement (Test methods, p. 190). Although these viscometers are now rarely used, viscosities are still expressed in these terms, in spite of all efforts to persuade the industry to use absolute units. The kinematic viscosity is determined and converted to the older system by means of conversion tables. The viscosities are customarily abbreviated as sec. Red. I, sec. Red. II, sec. SU or SSU, sec. SF or SSF, and lubricating oils are normally specified in terms of viscosity grades.

For crankcase oils, for both gasoline and diesel engines, the Society of Automotive Engineers (SAE) in America has adopted a system which grades the oils into seven categories with their viscosities specified at 210°F. The lightest three, SAE 5W, 10W and 20W oils, are known as Winter or W grades: they have the same viscosity requirement at 210°F but also have to meet a viscosity requirement at 0°F increasing from the 5W to the 20W oil. The other four grades, SAE 20, 30, 40 and 50 oils, have viscosities at 210°F increasing in that order but no requirement at 0°F. In recent years multigrade oils have been developed, i.e. oils that fall within more than one SAE grade classification. They cover in one oil a winter grade and a normal grade specification thus ensuring good lubrication at high temperatures but sufficient fluidity at low ones. They are designated by the appropriate two grade numbers, e.g. SAE 10W/30, 20W/40. Pure mineral oils do not usually fulfil this requirement, and to improve the viscosity index (VI) additives have to be used. A similar classification is used for transmission and axle lubricants for which SAE grades 75, 85, 90, 140 and 250 are specified in terms of viscosities at 210°F and 0°F.

Oils become thinner on heating and thicker on cooling, and a viscosity figure must always be accompanied by the temperature of determination. The relationship between viscosity and temperature is of considerable importance in many applications where a range of operating temperatures is experienced, and it is obviously desirable that the viscosity should change as little as possible with change in temperature. Oils vary considerably in their susceptibility to temperature and it is customary to speak of oils having a 'flat' or a 'steep' viscosity curve to mean that the viscosity temperature curve changes little or a lot in its slope, i.e. an oil with a 'flat' curve shows less change in viscosity with temperature than does an oil with a 'steep' curve. There are many ways of expressing this relationship numerically but the one most commonly used in the oil industry is the 'viscosity index' (VI) system whereby oils are given an index from 0 to 100, the higher the index the less the change in viscosity. To accommodate more recently developed types of oils, synthetic oils and mineral oils with VI improvers, the system has been extended to values above 100. Oils are generally classed as high, medium and low viscosity index oils (HVI, MVI, LVI). There are no precise definitions of these terms or strict lines of demarcation, but HVI usually means above 85, LVI below about 30 and MVI between these (Test methods, p. 190).

Distillate oils

LVI oils are made from naphthenic lubricating oil distillates which usually have such low wax contents that no costly dewaxing is required to obtain low pour points. LVI oils are used whenever viscosity-temperature characteristics and oxidation stability are of secondary importance. Their colour and colour stability are important marketing characteristics, and LVI oils are acid treated to remove coloured and unstable compounds.

MVI oils are produced from both naphthenic and paraffinic distillates and are distinguished as MVIN and MVIP oils; the MVIP oils have to be dewaxed. MVI oils are used as general purpose lubricants for applications where the low viscosity index of LVI oils is a disadvantage.

HVI oils are prepared by solvent extraction and dewaxing of paraffinic distillates. Solvent extraction improves not only the VI but also the oxidation and colour stability. HVI oils are used wherever an oil of good viscosity-temperature and oxidation characteristics is needed, as in motor oils and turbine oils.

White oils are produced by more drastic refining of MVI distillates to remove unsaturated compounds and constituents that impart colour, odour and taste. They are usually solvent extracted and then repeatedly treated with strong sulphuric acid or oleum and alkali. Two varieties are made, medicinal oils and technical white oils, differing in the extent of refining, the latter being rather less severely treated.

Several grades of medicinal oil are manufactured to comply with the various national pharmacopoeia specifications, which differ amongst themselves in minor details but all demanding a water-white oil, free from all harmful components, odour and taste. In addition to their medical use as 'liquid paraffin', medicinal oils are used as lubricants for food-handling machinery, where oil may come into contact with food, and as ingredients in cosmetics and other pharmaceutical preparations.

Technical white oils are either water-white or semi-pale (half-white oils) and are made in several viscosity grades. They are used as lubricants where light-coloured oils are required, for example in textile machinery, and in the UK are required by a government regulation for the lubrication of spinning mules as being non-carcinogenic. Their main use, however, is in the cosmetic industry for the manufacture of hair oils and creams and other preparations. They are also used in horticultural sprays and for the impregnation of some types of wrapping papers.

Residual oils

The residue that cannot be volatilized by vacuum distillation, known as 'short residue', is further refined to produce very viscous lubricants (stock or bright stock).

Bright stocks are usually made by propane de-asphalting, solvent extracting and de-waxing paraffinic short residues. Some crudes, Pennsylvanian for example, yield asphalt-free short residues which need no de-asphalting or extracting. Bright stocks are used as blending components of the heavier engine lubricants and as steam cylinder oils.

Compounded oils

Animal and vegetable oils are excellent lubricants, but are now seldom used because they are thermally unstable and readily oxidized. But fatty oils spread readily over metal surfaces to which they adhere firmly – the property of oiliness previously mentioned (p. 116) – and they emulsify readily with water, an advantage in some applications. It is therefore sometimes of advantage to incorporate some fatty oil in a mineral oil blend, and such blends are known as 'compounded oils'. Rapeseed oil and various fish oils are commonly used in amounts from 1–20 %w.

Lubricating greases

Lubricating greases are solid or semi-solid lubricants made by thickening lubricating oils with soaps, clays, silica gel or other thickening agents. They are used when the parts to be lubricated are difficult to get at or are inadequately sealed, or where there is a danger of oil contaminating a product being processed. They are commonly used in anti-friction bearings. Greases range from soft, semi-fluid greases to hard, solid greases, the hardness increasing with increase in the content of the thickener.

Greases are classified according to the type of thickener and their consistency. Consistency is measured in terms of 'penetration', the distance a plunger penetrates into the grease under standard conditions, and greases are classed as 000–6 greases according to the penetration classification of the National Lubricating Grease Institute (NLGI) in America, 000 being the softest, 6 the hardest.

Greases in which soap is the thickener are known as soap-base greases and are subdivided according to the type of soap into aluminium, calcium, lithium or sodium greases. Aluminium greases are smooth, water-resistant and adhesive and are often used as chassis lubricants. Calcium greases are general-purpose greases suitable for temperatures of operation up to 50°C (120°F). They have drop points around 100°C (212°F) and are unaffected by water. Sodium greases have higher drop points, about 160°C (320°F), and can be used where temperatures are too high for calcium greases. However, they tend to emulsify with water. Lithium greases combine high drop point, up to 200°C (390°F), with good low temperature properties and resistance to water. They were first introduced as aviation greases because of their wide temperature range, but are now used extensively for automotive and industrial applications as multi-purpose greases obviating the use of several greases of other types, each for its own specific purpose.

Greases thickened with inorganic thickeners such as clays and silica gel are known as clay base or microgel greases. They have very high drop points of the order of 300°C (570°F) or do not melt at all and can therefore be used to lubricate bearings at high temperatures at which soap-base greases cannot be used.

Synthetic lubricants

Aviation use of the gas turbine engine has created a demand for lubricants that will operate over a wider range of temperature than can be obtained with conventional mineral oils.

Various organic liquids have the required properties of very high VI, low volatility at high temperatures, thermal and oxidation stability and good lubricating properties. Carboxylic esters are generally used.

These synthetic lubricants are very expensive products and are not likely to have wide-scale use outside their essential applications.

Luboil additives

Straight mineral oils, together with compounded oils, were once able to meet all normal lubrication requirements of automotive and industrial practice. As these requirements become more severe with the progressive development of engines and general machinery it became necessary firstly to improve the quality of lubricating oils by new methods of refining and eventually to use 'additives' either to reinforce existing qualities or to confer additional properties. In the early days of their use additives were regarded with suspicion – an oil that needed an additive was necessarily an inferior oil; today additives are an accepted feature of lubricants – as of other petroleum products – and most lubricants now contain one or more additives.

Additives are substances that, in small quantities – from a few parts per million to a few per cent – confer specific properties on the lubricant. It is impossible in this book to do more than mention some of the more important.

Additives are usually called after their particular function, but many additives are multi-functional; it will give some idea of their multiplicity to name the chief functions they fulfil: to improve the viscosity index (VI improvers); to increase oxidation stability (anti-oxidants); to keep contaminants in suspension (dispersants); to prevent wear (anti-wear); to prevent scuffing (extreme-pressure, EP, agents); to depress the pour point (pour point depressants); to prevent rusting (anti-rust); and to prevent foaming (anti-foam).

Selection of lubricant

In selecting a lubricating oil for an application the primary consideration is usually viscosity and viscosity-temperature characteristics. Where movement is desired the least viscous oil consistent with the load should be used, the more viscous the oil the greater the resistance to motion and the more energy wastefully consumed in overcoming it. On the other hand, where heavy loads are to be sustained with little or no movement or with movement at slow speeds, the most viscous oil may be desirable. If the application involves a wide temperature range a HVI oil will be preferable to a LVI or MVI oil.

Viscosity having been satisfied, other requirements of the application may govern the type of oil to be used, for instance the need for high oxidation resistance or the ability to separate from water. Where high oxidation resistance is required, either because of high temperature or because of a need for long life, a HVI or a MVIN oil is used, not because of its viscosity index, but because of its chemical stability. Moreover such oils respond well to oxidation inhibitors, and their stability can be still further ensured in this way.

Under some conditions it is impossible to use an oil, because of inadequate sealing for example, or it may be undesirable to use it, because of the risk of splashing or dripping on to fabrics, and grease is then used. Here again the choice of grease depends on the requirements of the application, and will be influenced by such factors as speed, load and temperature and whether contact with water is likely.

Lubricating oils are usually described and supplied in terms of their applications, together with an indication of their viscosity grades. For motor oils and transmission and axle oils, this is almost universally in terms of an SAE grading; for other oils it may be given as a viscosity (in absolute or conventional units) or as some viscosity number or code peculiar to the supplier.

Lubricating greases are similarly described according to application, for example chassis grease, water-pump grease, with an indication of penetration grade, usually in terms of the NLGI classification.

Petroleum waxes

Solid waxy hydrocarbons are present in some crude oils, especially in paraffinic crudes. When such a crude is distilled, some of the wax distils over with the lubricating oil fraction, some remains in the residue and must be removed before these fractions can be used as lubricating oils as otherwise they would solidify at low ambient temperatures. The wax so removed is known as 'slack-wax' (p. 88).

Petroleum waxes are crystalline solids at normal atmospheric temperatures and consist essentially of high molecular weight paraffin hydrocarbons but differ considerably among themselves in composition. It is convenient to classify them into two main types – paraffin waxes and microcrystalline waxes.

Paraffin waxes

Paraffin waxes have a macrocrystalline structure and consist mainly of normal paraffins together with some iso- and cycloparaffins. They are produced from light and medium lubricating oil distillates and have melting points ranging from 43–71°C (110–160°F).

Fully refined paraffin waxes are white solid materials substantially free from oil (less than 0·5 %w), odourless and tasteless, with melting points from 50–71°C (122–160°F). They are marketed in grades each with a melting point range of 2–3°C (3–5°F). A low oil content is important not only because oil is undesirable in the major applications, e.g. waxed paper, but also because it may result in some odour and taste.

Semi-refined paraffin waxes or candle-waxes (after their original use) are off-white waxes with a slightly higher oil content (1·5 %w maximum) and not free from odour or taste.

Scale waxes and match waxes are still less refined, with oil contents up to 2–3 %w.

Microcrystalline waxes

Microcrystalline waxes have a microcrystalline structure, and consist mainly of iso- and cycloparaffins together with some aromatics. They are produced mainly from heavy lubricating oil residues, and have melting points from 60–90°C (140–200°F).

Microcrystalline waxes are sometimes white but more usually yellow, amber or brown and sometimes even black. They vary in consistency from a hard brittle solid to a soft plastic material and have oil contents usually between 0·5–5 %w.

Ceresin is a special kind of microcrystalline wax with a dense microcrystalline structure, manufactured from certain residual stocks, but also occurring as deposits in tank bottoms and in pipelines – in which case it is known as rod-wax. Ceresins have melting points from 80–105°C (180–220°F).

Petrolatum or petroleum jelly is a microcrystalline wax with a high oil content.

Wax blends

For many applications paraffin and microcrystalline waxes are commonly blended together with or without other materials such as polymers. Such blends are sometimes marketed ready made, either for specific applications or to suit individual customer requirements.

Wax emulsions

Paraffin wax is sometimes used as an aqueous emulsion containing from 40–60 %w of wax. Emulsions are used especially for coating or impregnating fibrous materials, e.g. textiles and paper, and for water-proofing building structures. In some emulsions the wax particles are negatively charged (anionic emulsions), in others positively charged (cationic emulsions). The positive charge is an advantage in treating fibres that are negatively charged and therefore tend to repel similarly charged materials.

Bitumen

In the UK the term 'bitumen' is applied to the solid or semi-solid residues from the distillation of suitable crudes. The same products are known as 'asphalts' in the USA, a term reserved in the UK for natural or mechanical mixtures of bitumen and mineral matter.

Bitumen also occurs naturally, alone or mixed with mineral matter, and was first known to man as seepages exuding from the ground. Substantially pure bitumen deposits occur in various parts of the world, the best known being gilsonite in Utah and Colorado, USA. Natural rock asphalts, impregnated with up to 14 %w bitumen, are quarried in several parts of Europe, and the names Val de Travers, Neuchatel and Ragusa are well known. The most renowned natural asphalt deposit is the Trinidad Lake containing a mixture of about 39 %w bitumen, 32 %w mineral matter and 29 %w water and gas.

Bitumen obtained by distillation of crude oil is generally a black or dark brown material ranging from a highly viscous to an almost solid substance at normal ambient temperatures, depending on the amount of light fractions removed. Light brown varieties known as 'albino' bitumens are produced from a few crudes. On heating, bitumen softens gradually and eventually becomes fluid; the temperature at which it reaches a certain consistency under arbitrary conditions is called the softening point (Test methods, p. 185). Commercial grades have softening points ranging from 25 to about 170°C (77–340°F). The hardness or consistency of a bitumen is determined by measuring the distance in tenths of a millimetre to which a needle penetrates into the bitumen under standard conditions of load, temperature and time, and ranges from 0 for very hard to

500 for very soft bitumens as measured at 25°C (77°F). (Test methods, p. 182).

Bitumen can be oxidized, or rather dehydrogenated, by blowing air through it at high temperatures. 'Blown' grades have a somewhat rubbery consistency and are less temperature sensitive than are the straight grades.

Both straight and blown bitumens are made in a number of grades with fairly narrow ranges of penetration and softening point. The straight grades are usually designated solely by their softening points for hard grades or their penetrations for medium and soft grades while the blown grades are described by the combination softening point/penetration. They all have to be heated to well above their softening points in order to apply them. There are, however, alternative methods of using bitumen at lower temperatures – as a solution in a suitable solvent or as an emulsion in water.

Bitumen cutbacks

Cutbacks consist of bitumen, usually 100 penetration grade, 'cut back' with a solvent, usually kerosine or creosote but sometimes white spirit or gas oil. Cutbacks become more viscous and bind more firmly as they lose solvent, and the rate of 'setting' or 'curing' depends on the nature and content of solvent. The particular type and grade to be used depends entirely on the application. Cutbacks are seldom used cold but generally at 90–100°C (190–212°F), considerably below the temperature necessary for straight bitumens.

Bitumen emulsions

Bitumen emulsions are made by emulsifying 50–65%w of bitumen in water in the presence of 0·5–1·0%w of an emulsifying agent, usually a soap. They are generally used cold for both road-making and industrial purposes.

Road emulsions are generally made with 200–300 penetration bitumen: they must remain stable in storage and during transport but 'break' soon after application to the road, and be of suitable viscosity for spraying.

Industrial emulsions generally use somewhat harder bitumens, and usually contain various admixtures such as clay. They are used for roofing and flooring and in the paper industry, in all of which applications they are required to mix with other materials without breaking and to break only slowly after application. 40–50 penetration grades are used in roofing and flooring emulsions and very hard, high melting point grades in emulsions for paper.

The bitumen particles in these emulsions are negatively charged (anionic emulsions). Many aggregates such as quartzite are also negatively charged and difficulty is sometimes experienced in coating them, especially when damp, the bitumen failing to adhere. Special emulsions are made in which the bitumen particles are positively charged (cationic emulsions) and adhere readily to the aggregate.

Fuels and lubricants for automotive IC engines

The road transport industry is the largest consumer of petroleum products, and its development has been closely associated with that of the petroleum industry. The IC engine is still the predominant prime mover, and its requirements for fuels and lubricants have become ever greater and more exacting.

There are two types of IC engine: those operating on intermittent combustion (reciprocating piston engines) and those operating on continuous combustion (gas turbines). Piston engines may in turn be divided into two classes: spark-ignition engines and compression-ignition engines. Although gas turbines may possibly be used some time in the future for automotive purposes – and experimental models have been operated – they are not yet established and will not be further considered in this chapter. Aviation and industrial gas turbines are described on p. 135 and p. 142 and should automotive use develop the general requirements are likely to be similar.

Rotary engines of novel design, both gasoline and diesel, are being developed, *inter alia*, by Daimler/Benz, NSU/Wankel, and Renault/American Motors Corporation (manufacturers of the Rambler engine). In the Daimler/Benz and NSU/Wankel engines a three-sided piston rotates eccentrically in a two lobed combustion chamber as shown in Fig. 111. In the Renault/Rambler engine a four-lobed piston rotates in a five-lobed housing which forms five combustion chambers.

The spark-ignition engine

The engine

The spark-ignition engine is used extensively in passenger cars, trucks, motor cycles, outboard motors, agricultural tractors and aeroplanes (Fuels and lubricants for aviation IC engines p. 132). In the spark-ignition engine a charge of vaporized and atomized fuel is drawn with air into a cylinder where it is compressed by the forward motion of the piston. The compressed mixture of fuel and air is then ignited by a spark, and the resulting expansion develops a pressure that forces the piston back and provides the driving power. The gases, having done their work, are exhausted from the cylinder and a fresh charge is introduced. This cycle of operations can be accomplished during four or two strokes of the piston. All aviation piston engines and most spark-ignition automotive engines, with some important exceptions, operate on the four-stroke cycle [Fig. 112]. Motor cycles and motor-assisted cycles may be either four-stroke or two-stroke [Fig. 113]. Except for motor cycles, outboard motors and small appliances such as electric generating sets, lawn mowers, etc, nearly all spark-ignition engines are multi-cylinder; motor cars generally have from four to eight cylinders although some have twelve.

The fuel is pumped from the tank to the carburettor where a supply is maintained in the float chamber. Air is drawn through the carburettor by the suction of the piston and carries fuel with it, partly as vapour, partly as liquid droplets, into the inlet manifold, through the inlet valves into the cylinders.

The combustion process

When the mixture of fuel and air is compressed in the cylinder and then ignited by the spark, the resulting flame travels rapidly from the sparking plug across the combustion space. The combustion causes a great increase in pressure, and the unburnt mixture beyond the advancing flame front is rapidly compressed, whereby its temperature is raised. It should continue to burn smoothly until all the fuel is burnt, and should provide a steady thrust to the piston.

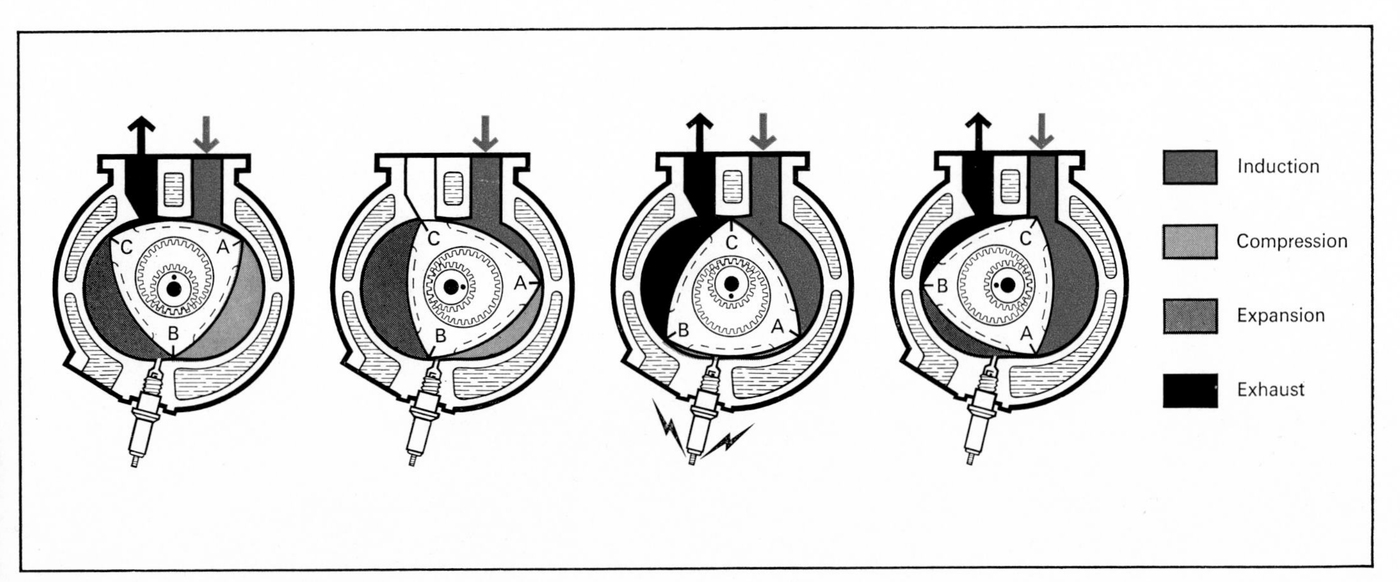

Fig. 111 The rotary cycle of the Wankel engine

Knocking

Under certain conditions, however, the temperature of the unburnt mixture may rise to a point at which it self-ignites, and a very rapid burning – almost explosion – of the residual mixture occurs. The effect is like a hammer blow on the cylinder, and the resulting vibrations give rise to a sharp metallic ping known as 'detonation' or 'knocking'. This sequence of events obviously increases the mechanical and thermal stresses on the engine, and is therefore to be avoided.

Knocking depends partly on the design and operating conditions of the engine and partly on the type of fuel. It is promoted by high temperatures and pressures during combustion, and any engine factors resulting in these conditions

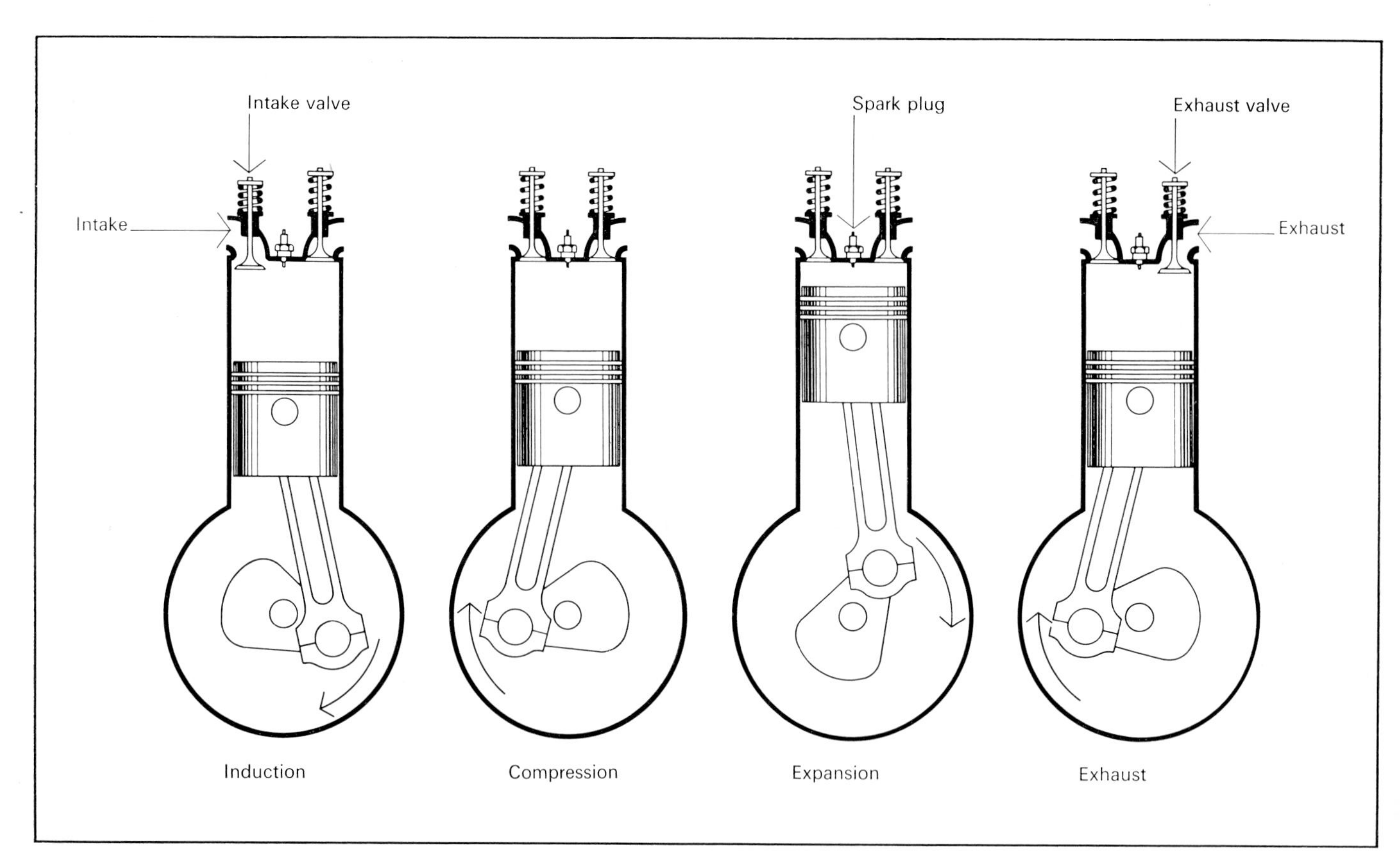

Fig. 112 The four-stroke spark-ignition cycle

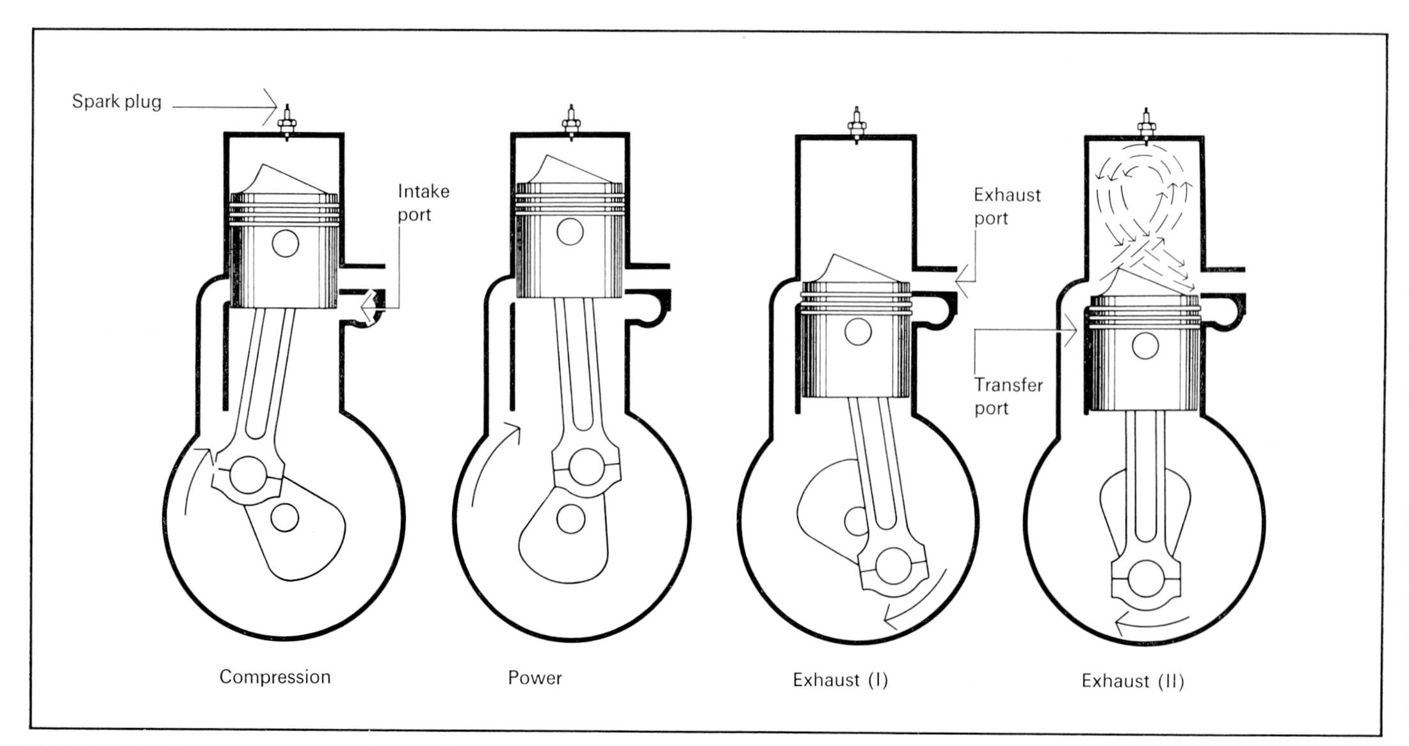

Fig. 113 The two-stroke spark-ignition cycle

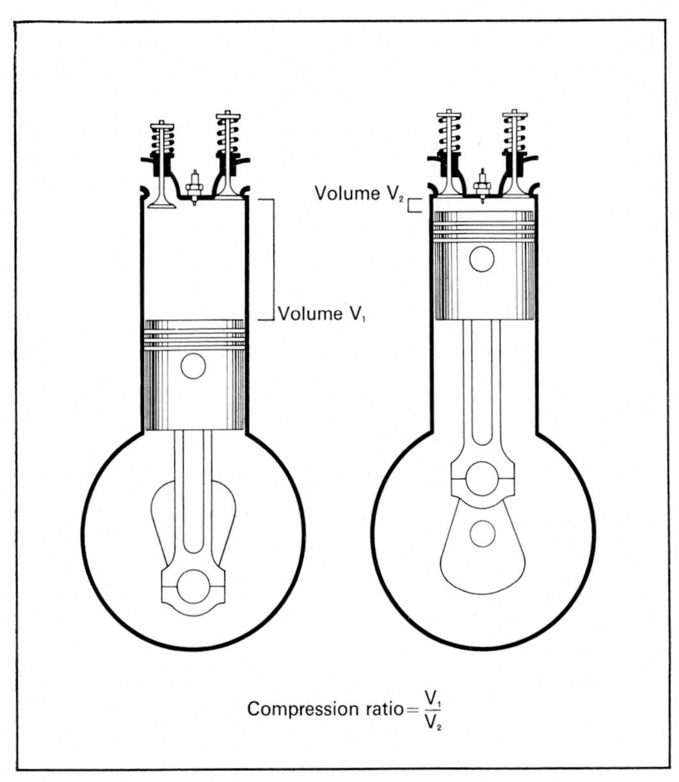

Fig. 114 Compression ratio

tend to cause knock. Such factors include spark adjustment, throttle opening, intake air or coolant temperature and compression ratio. Compression ratio is the ratio of the volume of air and fuel when the piston is at the lower end of the cylinder to the volume when the mixture is compressed and the piston is in its topmost position [Fig. 114]. It affects the combustion performance of the fuel more than any other single factor, and increasing the compression ratio increases the tendency to knock. The higher the compression ratio the higher is the thermal efficiency of the engine, i.e. the ratio of power obtained from the engine to the maximum power available in the fuel, but the limiting compression ratio that can be utilized is set by the knock characteristics of the fuel. Increasing the octane number of the fuel permits the use of a higher compression ratio, and gives more power, higher efficiency and lower fuel consumption. However no advantage is gained by increasing the octane number beyond that necessary to give knock-free performance.

Deposits

During the running of an engine, deposits derived from the fuel, the lubricant and atmospheric dust, form within the combustion chamber, and may have an important effect on the combustion process and the efficiency of the engine. An appreciable proportion of the deposits is derived from the additives that are incorporated in engine fuels and lubricants to improve their performance in various ways.

The deposits decrease the volume of the combustion space, thus in effect increasing the compression ratio; they prevent the loss of heat by conduction, and increase the thermal capacity, thus causing higher cylinder temperatures; they provide local hot spots that encourage abnormal ignition. The first two of these effects lead to what is known as 'octane requirement increase' (ORI), i.e. the engine demands a fuel of higher octane number to give the same performance as previously. ORI is common to all types of spark-ignition engine and reaches an equilibrium level between four and six thousand miles of operation, the level varying between two and five octane numbers for fuels with octane numbers of 90 or more. With lower octane fuels the variation may be much greater.

There are several types of abnormal ignition. Combustion should be initiated only by the spark from the plug; sometimes, however, a hot component in the cylinder – a hot plug electrode or a glowing deposit – may fire the mixture, a phenomenon known as surface ignition, pre-ignition if it occurs before the normal plug spark, post-ignition if it occurs afterwards. Depending on when and how surface ignition is initiated it can give rise to various noises described as 'wild ping' and 'rumble'.

Combustion chamber deposits may also lead to spark fouling and exhaust valve failure. Spark plug fouling is largely due to deposits rich in lead derived from the anti-knock additives in the fuel, and is particularly likely to occur under low temperature operating conditions. The deposits can cause misfiring by reducing the electrical resistance of the insulator, and can also corrode the electrodes and reduce the life of the plug.

Exhaust valve failures result from deposits on the valve stem or the valve seat which interfere with correct operation and cause valve burning.

Cylinder wear and corrosion

Mechanical wear of the cylinder by the reciprocating motion of the piston with its rings in contact with the cylinder wall is largely prevented by a film of lubricating oil. When the engine is running there is usually a sufficient supply of oil, and wear is negligible, but when starting there is a short period before circulation of the oil is established, during which some abrasive wear takes place.

Cylinder wear can also be caused by corrosion. All petroleum fuels contain sulphur compounds, and most motor gasolines contain halogen compounds associated with TEL as 'scavengers', both of which form acidic gases on combustion. Water is also formed when petroleum fuels are burnt. When the engine is hot, the water passes out of the exhaust pipe as steam, and the corrosive gases go with it. When the engine is cool, liquid water condenses on the cylinder walls, and the corrosive gases dissolve in it to form acids which can attack the surface of the cylinder, particularly when starting from cold, before the lubricant has had an opportunity to establish a protective film. Corrosion of this type is thus more evident when the vehicle is used for a number of short journeys with much stopping and starting, and the engine does not reach its normal working temperature. However, it is less evident now than formerly, owing to the more effective thermostatic control of engine temperatures and the use of more resistant materials.

Cam and tappet wear

With the higher power outputs of modern engines the stresses on the engine, and particularly on the valve mechanism, have increased to such an extent that severe scuffing wear on cams and tappets may occur during normal running of the engine. Although this is primarily a metallurgical and design problem, and may eventually be overcome by structural design, the wear can be alleviated by the use of certain EP additives in the lubricating oil and, at least for the time being, reliance is placed on the lubricant to deal with such wear. However, these additives can accelerate fatigue pitting of chilled cast iron, which is still widely used for cams and tappets, and great care is necessary in oil formulations to avoid this.

Fuels for spark-ignition engines

The spark-ignition engine requires a fuel that will readily evaporate in the air stream drawn into the carburettor, be readily ignited in the cylinder by a spark, and burn smoothly without knocking or other operational difficulties. Petroleum gases, town gas, gasoline, kerosine, benzole, and alcohol can all be used, but gasoline is the preferred fuel in almost universal use.

Gasoline

The performance of the engine depends very much on the quality of the gasoline, the most important properties in this respect being volatility, knock characteristics (or anti-knock value) and stability.

Volatility

The volatility of a gasoline affects engine performance in several ways. If it is too low, insufficient vapour may be drawn into the cylinder to allow easy starting from cold, and warm-up will be slow. On the other hand, too high a volatility is apt to cause carburettor icing or vapour lock. A balance must be struck between these extremes. Volatility is assessed by a laboratory distillation test and by a Reid vapour pressure determination (Test methods, p. 192).

Cold starting and warm-up

A mixture of air and gasoline vapour is inflammable only if the air/fuel ratio by weight lies between 6:1 and 18:1, and unless sufficient fuel vaporizes to give at least 1 part of vapour to 18 parts of air the engine will not fire. Easy starting at low temperatures depends on the more volatile fractions of the gasoline; the lower the temperature at which 10%v distils over in the standard distillation test, or the higher the Reid vapour pressure the easier will the engine start. The temperature at which 10%v distils varies from a minimum of 38°C (100°F) in winter to a maximum of 71°C (160°F) in summer, and Reid vapour pressures vary from 6·5 lb/in^2 to 13 lb/in^2.

By restricting the air supply on starting, an excess of fuel is supplied which compensates for the smaller proportion that will evaporate at low temperatures, and thus produces an inflammable mixture in the cylinder. If such an excess of fuel, or too volatile a fuel, were delivered when the engine was warm, evaporation would be so great that too much fuel vapour would be produced, the fuel/air mixture might be too rich to fire, and hot starting would be difficult.

After the engine has started from cold, some time elapses before it becomes completely flexible in operation without fuel enrichment; this is the 'warm-up period'. Whereas under cold conditions of starting about 10%v of gasoline vaporizes, about 50%v vaporizes during the warm-up period, the remainder entering the cylinder as fine droplets. When the engine has warmed up, and is running normally, the gasoline should be completely vaporized. This is ensured by limiting the final boiling point of the gasoline – the temperature at which all distils over in the standard distillation test.

Carburettor icing

For efficient engine operation a large proportion of the fuel should be vaporized before it enters the cylinder. Heat is required to vaporize a liquid, and the gasoline in the carburettor takes this heat from the surrounding air and metal, thereby cooling them. If the air entering the carburettor is already cold and damp owing to the prevailing weather, the extra cooling due to gasoline evaporation may reduce the temperature sufficiently for ice to form. This ice may so interfere with the normal flow of fuel and air through the carburettor that fuel consumption can increase, or the engine stall. The more volatile the gasoline, the greater is the tendency to ice formation. The icing tendency of a gasoline correlates approximately with the temperature at which 50%v distils over in the standard distillation test. If the volatility of the gasoline were reduced sufficiently to eliminate carburettor icing, cold starting and warm-up would be exceedingly difficult. An alternative method is therefore used, the incorporation of anti-icing additives. These act either by depressing the freezing point of water or by lessening adhesion of the ice crystals to the internal surfaces of the carburettor.

Atmospheric conditions most conducive to icing are a temperature about 4·5°C (40°F) with a relative humidity about 70% but it can occur over the range –6·5 to +10°C (20–50°F) at humidities over 60%.

Vapour lock

The maximum permissible volatility of a gasoline is governed by its liability to cause vapour lock. The fuel pump in the average car can supply much more fuel than the engine requires. If the fuel becomes hot, however, and evolves a lot of vapour, the fuel pump supplies a mixture of liquid and vapour, and the total fuel supply may be insufficient for normal running. Moreover, gasoline with a high vapour pressure may form bubbles in the fuel lines or in the carburettor which will impede the flow of fuel. Alternatively a very rapid evolution of vapour may occur in the fuel pipe between pump and carburettor – usually when the car is standing hot after a long run – and force the liquid gasoline from the float chamber into the inlet manifold. Too rich a mixture, above the upper limit of inflammability, may then enter the cylinder, ignition fails to occur, and the engine will not restart.

Vapour lock tendency is greatly influenced by the design of the fuel system, but for a given car it depends on fuel volatility, atmospheric temperature and altitude. The effect of altitude can be marked since atmospheric pressure decreases with altitude, and the evolution of vapour from a liquid increases as pressure decreases. Increase in altitude thus causes the fuel to give off more vapour, and thereby encourages vapour lock.

The risk of vapour lock is reduced to a minimum by control of fuel volatility to suit the season and the locality. For many years the Reid vapour pressure was used as the criterion, but this does not altogether correlate with practice, and various systems are now used in which Reid vapour pressure is linked with distillation characteristics. Another method measures the volume of vapour which a given volume of gasoline will evolve over a range of practical temperature.

Mixture distribution

When the gasoline is completely vaporized before entering the cylinder the air and fuel are more or less evenly distributed among the cylinders. When it is atomized into liquid droplets, uniform distribution is not so readily achieved and some cylinders undoubtedly receive a richer mixture than others, and general efficiency suffers.

A limitation on the final boiling point of the gasoline helps to overcome this trouble since it is the higher boiling parts of the fuel that are most difficult to vaporize. Heating the manifold also assists in the evaporation of the droplets and is achieved by running the exhaust pipe alongside the inlet manifold.

Knock rating

The tendency of a gasoline to knock – its 'knock rating' or 'anti-knock value' – can only be determined in an engine; the type of engine used and the method of determination are dealt with in Test methods (p. 181). It is expressed as an octane number (ON), the percentage volume of iso-octane in a blend with normal heptane that matches the gasoline in knock characteristics in the test engine, run under standard conditions.

The anti-knock value of gasolines varies considerably with their composition. The straight-chain paraffins are poor in this respect while aromatics and branched-chain paraffins have high octane numbers. When two gasoline components are blended the mixture may have knocking characteristics proportional to the amounts of the two components, or it may have a higher or a lower octane number than that calculated on the basis of simple proportion. For example, a blend of one volume of a 90 ON compound and four volumes of a 70 ON gasoline would be expected to have an ON of 74. If, on testing, it had an ON of 76 then by simple proportion the 90 ON component is behaving as if it had an ON of 100. The component is said to have a 'blending ON' of 100 in relation to the basic fuel. A knowledge of blending octane numbers is of considerable advantage in deciding the composition of a gasoline to meet a given octane requirement.

The addition of certain metallic compounds to gasolines materially increases their anti-knock value. Many such compounds have been investigated but tetraethyl lead (TEL) and tetramethyl lead (TML) are in almost universal use. They are added in quantities up to 4 ml/US gal (4·8 ml/UK gal) equivalent to 0·23%w, depending on the required octane level. As the quantity of TEL/TML added to a gasoline is increased, its effect on the octane number decreases and addition of more than 6 ml/US gal has very little effect. Moreover, on combustion, these lead compounds form a non-volatile oxide which is deposited in the combustion chamber, on the exhaust valves and the sparking plug, and contributes to the generally undesirable effects of combustion chamber deposits. To counteract this, 'scavenger' components such as ethylene dibromide and ethylene dichloride are added to the TEL/TML. These compounds convert the lead, on combustion, into the relatively volatile lead bromide and lead chloride which pass out with the exhaust gas. The TEL/TML, together with the scavengers and a dye to indicate the poisonous nature of the compounds, are known as ethyl or methyl fluids. Other additives, both metallic and non-metallic, are sometimes used in conjunction with the lead compounds as 'co-anti-knock agents'.

Although the scavengers effect a reduction of 97–98%w in lead deposits, the remaining 2–3%w, combined with deposits from the lubricants and air borne dust, is still sufficient to have adverse effects. Various additives, of which the best known is ICA (ignition control additive), are now commonly used to modify the deposits chemically to a form in which they are less harmful. The electrical resistance of the deposits is increased, so that they interfere less with spark plug performance, and their ignition temperature is increased, so that they are less likely to provide 'hot spots' that cause surface ignition.

Since the power output of the engine increases with increase in compression ratio, there has been a continuous effort on the part of engine builders to increase the ratio, and a corresponding requirement for ever increasing octane number in the gasoline. These requirements could not be met by straight-run gasolines, where octane numbers rarely exceed 65, and new methods of refining had to be developed to achieve higher octane numbers. By the various cracking and reforming processes now used (Oil products–manufacture, p. 94 and p. 100), octane numbers of 100 are achieved in the unleaded fuel and further increase is obtained by the use of anti-knock additives.

The efficiency of TEL/TML depends on the composition of the fuel to which they are added. Increasing octane number without lead by the above-mentioned refining methods is an expensive business, and it becomes a question of economics to what extent high octane components or lead compounds are used to obtain the required quality.

Stability

Gasolines that have been inadequately refined may contain unstable compounds that will oxidize or polymerize to form deposits of gum or lacquer both during storage – particularly at high temperature – and in the engine. Deposits will form in the carburettor, in the inlet manifold, on the inlet valve stem, and in severe cases, can cause engine failure or serious damage. Even in mild cases, gummy deposits on the inlet valve stem may restrict the movement of the valve, causing loss of power and, when cold, the valve may stick fast so that the engine will not re-start.

Gum is a resinous substance which in the early stages of formation remains in solution in the gasoline, but later becomes insoluble and precipitates from the fuel. In its soluble form it tends to be left behind as the gasoline evaporates in the carburettor and inlet manifold. Its formation is appreciably accelerated by even small traces of copper.

The stability of a gasoline is ensured by adequate refinery treatment to remove the unstable gum precursors, and by the addition of anti-oxidants and copper deactivators that counteract the effects of oxygen and copper.

Liquefied petroleum gas (LPG)

In the USA and some parts of Europe, LPG has been used to a certain extent as an automotive fuel. It has a high octane number and gives clean, complete combustion with even mixture distribution.

Benzole

A suitably refined benzole, produced from coal, is sometimes blended into motor fuels. It has good anti-knock properties and a higher specific gravity (more pounds per gallon) than most gasolines. It is highy volatile and requires a specially prepared base gasoline if vapour lock and carburettor icing are to be avoided.

Ethyl alcohol

Ethyl alcohol has been used in cars both unmixed and blended with gasoline. It has a high octane number but, owing to its low calorific value, gives a higher fuel consumption than does gasoline for the same power output. It is poor in low temperature starting and is inclined to vapour lock. Moreover, owing to its affinity for water, blends with gasoline may separate into two layers through absorption of water. It is not widely used because its value to the chemical industry has made it too expensive, but in a few areas local supplies are so plentiful that the government requires its admixture with gasoline.

Kerosine

Where gasoline is much more highly taxed than kerosine, operators of spark-ignition agricultural tractors naturally turned to kerosine as a fuel. Since kerosine has a lower octane number than that of gasoline, a lower compression ratio must be used to prevent detonation. Moreover, because of its lower volatility, insufficient fuel would be supplied to the cylinder when cold to permit satisfactory combustion, and gasoline from a subsidiary tank has to be used to start the engine. The heat of the exhaust gases is used to operate a vaporizor fitted between the carburettor and the inlet manifold so that the kerosine can be more readily vaporized. The change over from gasoline to kerosine after the engine has started is not made until the vaporizor has warmed up sufficiently.

Kerosine used in spark-ignition engines should be free from gum and gum-forming components, should be sufficiently volatile, and have a sufficiently high octane number. Suitable kerosines for the purpose are supplied as 'tractor vaporizing oil'; they contain more aromatics than would be desirable in kerosines used in lamps.

The compression-ignition engine

The engine

The compression-ignition engine is commonly called the diesel engine, after Dr Rudolph Diesel, one of the pioneers in developing this type of engine; it is also known as an 'oil engine' as opposed to a gasoline engine. In mechanical principles diesel engines are similar to gasoline engines, but there are fundamental differences in the method of mixing fuel and air, and in the mode of ignition.

When a gas is compressed, its temperature rises; the more it is compressed the hotter it gets, and the more quickly it is compressed the less chance is there for the heat to escape. In the diesel engine, air is drawn into the cylinder where it is compressed, and the liquid fuel is then injected. The high temperature of the compressed air raises the fuel to its self-ignition temperature so that it burns, thereby increasing the pressure still further and providing power. The compression ratio in a diesel engine is much higher than that in a spark-ignition engine in order to attain the self-ignition temperature of the fuel.

The liquid fuel is sprayed into each cylinder by means of a fuel injector which breaks up the liquid into a fine mist and so facilitates vaporization, easy mixing with air and satisfactory combustion. Also to facilitate mixing, the air entering the cylinder is usually given a swirling motion by virtue of the design of the combustion chamber.

Diesel engines can operate on either the four-stroke or the two-stroke principle. They are made in a wide range of size and speed from small single-cylinder engines to the very large multi-cylinder marine propulsion engines. Small, high-speed models are used extensively in taxis and light vans and to some extent in private cars; larger models are used in trucks.

Compared with spark-ignition engines, diesel engines are more expensive to make because their high compression ratios require correspondingly stronger components and their injection equipment requires precision engineering. Their fuel consumption, however, is significantly smaller and this, together with lower maintenance costs, makes them attractive for many forms of transport – especially where gasoline is more heavily taxed than is diesel fuel.

The automotive diesel may have either a separate combustion chamber or one consisting simply of a basin-shaped depression in the crown of the piston. The former is known as a separate-chamber or indirect-injection engine, the latter

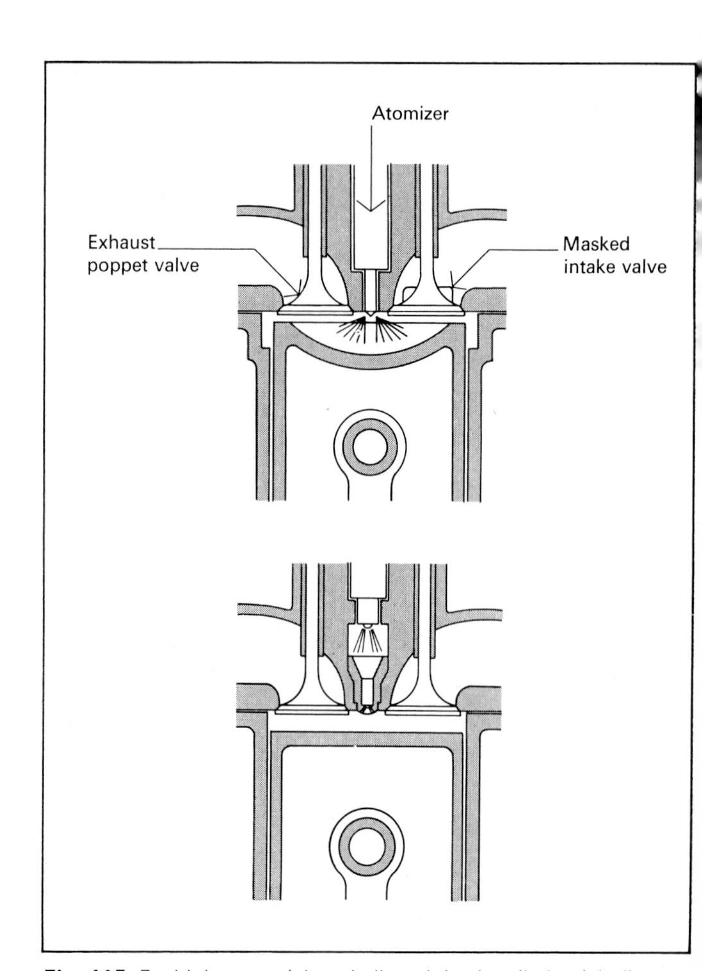

Fig. 115 Fuel injectors: (above) direct injection (below) indirect injection

as an open-chamber or direct-injection engine. Separate-chamber engines are usually fitted with a pintle nozzle which delivers a compact spray of fuel as a hollow cone, the movement of the air being relied on to give good distribution. Open-chamber engines usually employ a multi-hole nozzle giving a well distributed spray since air movement alone is generally insufficient to give effective mixing. The injection pump delivers measured quantities of fuel in rotation along separate pipes to the injector fitted into each cylinder, at pressures of 2000–10 000 lb/in² (140–705 kg/cm²) [Fig. 115].

Because of the high compression ratios used in diesel engines only the smaller engines can be started by hand. A minimum compression of 400 lb/in² (28 kg/cm²) is necessary for good starting, but an ordinary self-starter suffices. An electrical heater plug, switched on before starting, is often incorporated in separate-chamber engines, but is not necessary in open-chamber engines. Ease of starting is mainly influenced by the ignition quality of the fuel and by its overall volatility.

Diesel engines are relatively noisier than gasoline engines in operation, particularly when idling. This combustion noise can be diminished within certain limits by varying either engine settings or fuel properties.

The combustion process

The sequence of events that occur when fuel is sprayed into the cylinder may be considered as happening in three separate phases. In the initial phase the fuel is admitted but does not burn; some of the fuel evaporates, and the vapour is raised to its self-ignition temperature. In the second phase rapid combustion occurs as the flame spreads, and there is a sharp rise in pressure. Finally, in the third phase, the rest of the charge burns as it enters the combustion chamber, and this maintains or increases the pressure. In the small high-speed automotive engine these three stages may occur in about one-thousandth of a second.

The first phase is of the greatest importance. If ignition is delayed too long, too much fuel will have been injected and will all fire at once, producing a rapid pressure rise accompanied by 'diesel knock'. If, however, the delay is short, combustion will commence when relatively little fuel has been injected, and will proceed smoothly as the rest of the fuel enters and burns to produce a smooth pressure rise.

The ignition delay period is related to engine design and operating conditions as well as to fuel properties. The formation of an intimate mixture of fuel and air, necessary for the rapid initiation of combustion, is affected by combustion chamber design, injector characteristics and the induced movement in the air charge. Ignition delay is most pronounced at low loads and is decreased by increasing the compression ratio or the intake air pressure. An increase in engine load and temperature tends to improve the smoothness of running owing to the shorter delay period.

Exhaust smoking is a sign of faulty combustion, and is mainly due to some deficiency in the injection system – either mechanical or due to the fuel. Satisfactory combustion depends on the proper spraying of the fuel into the cylinder, and anything that interferes with the spray pattern is liable to cause smoking. Fuel pumps and injectors are designed to handle fuels of a reasonable but limited range of viscosity. Too low a viscosity may cause leakage in the pump and poor penetration into the cylinder; too high a viscosity leads to poor atomization and over-penetration. Deposits on the injector nozzle and needle may cause needle sticking thus spoiling the spray and causing the fuel to dribble into the cylinder and be incompletely burnt. Over-fuelling is a frequent cause of smoking; it may be caused by wear or maladjustment in the injection system or by unauthorized tampering with the fuel pump setting.

Diesel exhaust smoke can be divided into three categories; black, white or grey and blue smoke. Black smoke is the result of too much fuel, bad atomization of fuel or uneven mixing of fuel with air. White or grey smoke is caused by the slow and incomplete combustion of the fuel at low temperature, as when first starting, but can also be due to loss of compression from worn piston rings, leaky valves, restricted air intake at high altitudes or late injection timing. Blue smoke is caused by mis-fire and incomplete burning of the fuel or by over-lubrication. Both blue and grey smoke are associated with a strong acrid smell in the exhaust gases. Once an engine is warmed up there is generally little tendency to produce grey or blue smoke, and most trouble with black smoke is due to excess fuel injection or faulty operation of injectors. Injectors should therefore be serviced regularly and kept in good condition to avoid atmospheric pollution.

Fuels for the compression-ignition engine

The automotive diesel engine uses a distillate fuel very little different from gas oil but generally known as 'diesel fuel'. Its most important characteristic is its ignition quality. This is expressed as a 'cetane number', the percentage volume of cetane in a mixture with alpha-methlynaphthalene equivalent in ignition qualities to the fuel under test in a standard diesel engine under standard conditions of test (Test methods, p. 182). An alternative method of rating is by an index figure derived from certain laboratory data; the 'diesel index' and the 'calculated cetane index' are in common use (Test methods, p. 182).

The ignition quality depends on the composition of the fuel. In gasoline engines, aromatic fuels resist self-ignition and have high anti-knock values, and paraffinic fuels have lower self-ignition temperatures and lower anti-knock values. In diesel engines these properties make paraffinic fuels superior to aromatic fuels. The ignition quality can be improved by removal of aromatics and the inclusion of additives, usually substances that are chemically and thermally unstable, that initiate the chain reactions of the combustion process.

The diesel engine is less sensitive than the gasoline engine to fuel properties although it is important that the fuel should be clean. Volatility is generally not so important, but needs attention in connexion with cold starting and smoking, and in the USA, in city bus operations, more volatile (Premium) diesel fuels are in demand. A wide range of viscosity is permissable but must not be exceeded. General recommendations are a minimum of 2·0 cS at 100°F (31 sec. Red. I) and a maximum of about 24 cS at 100°F (100 sec. Red. I).

Diesel fuels usually contain organic sulphur compounds which may give rise to low-temperature corrosion due to the condensation of acid combustion products and water on the cylinder walls. Although corrosive wear in the engine can be effectively counteracted by the use of additives in the lubricating oil, there is a definite trend towards lower sulphur contents in diesel fuels, partly due to their contribution to atmospheric pollution. The allowable sulphur content, expressed as %w of elemental sulphur, is often limited by specifications.

A diesel fuel should be sufficiently stable to avoid sludge formation, filter clogging, needle lacquering or persistent emulsion formation. This is achieved by suitable selection of distillates and adequate refining.

Engine lubricants

Whether in gasoline or in diesel engines, the lubricant has the same basic function of lubricating the moving parts to enable them to work without undue friction or wear. Again, in both engines, the lubricating system is essentially of the same design. A circulating system is used whereby a relatively large supply of oil is kept in circulation, and is distributed under pressure to the various bearings and other mechanisms. In most automobile engines the oil is contained in a sump at the base of the engine, containing half to two gallons of oil for gasoline engines and two to six gallons for diesels, depending on the size of the engine. Generally a force-feed system is used; a pump driven by the engine picks up oil from the sump and circulates it under pressure through pipes and oilways to the main bearings, connecting rod bearings, cam shaft bearings, timing gears and valve mechanism. The oil escaping from the big end is flung on to the cylinder walls, and the crankcase is filled with a mist of small oil droplets which settle on all exposed surfaces. Excess lubricant drains by gravity back to the crankcase. A typical engine lubrication system is shown in Fig. 116. In addition to lubricating the moving parts the oil also acts as a coolant, and helps to dissipate the heat from the working parts.

Some small two-stroke gasoline engines in lightweight motor cycles, motor-assisted cycles and scooters, lawnmowers, outboard motors, etc, use a different system in which the lubricant is mixed in suitable proportions with the gasoline to make a 'petroil' mixture. This blend passes from the fuel tank to the carburettor and from there the air/fuel mixture proceeds to the closed crankcase where it is compressed. The compressed charge then enters the combustion chamber where it is fired by a spark. During its passage through the engine some of the heavier and unevaporated petroil fractions are deposited on bearing surfaces and so provide lubrication.

The American Petroleum Institute (API) has defined several types of service requirements for gasoline and diesel engines on the basis of engine type, operating conditions and fuel type and provided a simple code for oils meeting these requirements. There are three definitions of service for gasoline engines MS, MM, ML and three for diesel engines, DS, DM, DL, covering respectively severe, moderate and light conditions of operation.

Oils for automotive diesel engines are often required to meet specifications which define not only physical properties, but also minimum performance levels. These specifications originated from the Service authorities of the USA but have since been widely adopted for general use. They call for the carrying out of engine tests (Test methods, p. 184).

For some time past many of the major motor manufacturers have required lubricating oils to meet engine test requirements to suit their particular engine. The American Society for Testing and Materials has standardized a series of five engine tests which are generally accepted in the USA as covering all individual requirements.

The essential properties of a lubricant to meet these various requirements are that it should be of appropriate viscosity, should not deteriorate rapidly under the given conditions and should protect the engine.

Viscosity

Viscosity is an important property of an engine oil. It controls the speed of flow and the ease of getting to the points to be lubricated. When an engine is at rest there are thin films of oil between the piston rings and the cylinder walls, in the bearings and on the various parts that need lubrication. In cold weather this oil will thicken so that there will be more resistance to movement when the engine is started. For ease of starting, therefore, an oil that is not too viscous at low temperatures is required. When the engine has warmed up, the oil also increases in temperature and will thus become thinner. It must not thin out too much, however, or it will not lubricate efficiently. The desirable lubricant is consequently one that does not become too thick at low temperature or too thin at high temperature, i.e. a high viscosity index (HVI) oil.

The advent of HVI oils has encouraged the use of lower viscosity oils for engine lubrication. An oil of high viscosity increases the resistance to movement of the parts and in effect increases engine friction, and much of the energy of the fuel is used up in overcoming this friction. A reduction in the oil viscosity can effect an appreciable decrease in fuel consumption although there is a limit to the viscosity reduction beyond which there is little significant improvement in fuel economy. Moreover, there may be a danger of inadequate lubrication with too thin an oil.

Another disadvantage in using viscous oils is the delay in establishing normal lubrication when starting the engine from cold. When an engine is shut down, most of the oil drains back to the crankcase, leaving only a thin film on the moving parts. When the engine is re-started, this thin film is all the lubrication available until the oil is circulating. The major part of the wear in the cylinder takes place in the first few minutes after starting, and some of this is mechanical wear due to insufficient lubrication.

It is always advisable therefore to use as thin an oil as possible consistent with good lubrication at all temperatures of operation, and HVI oils permit this to be done without risk of undue thinning at high temperature. For some time the only way to obtain HVI oils was by selection of the crude and the manufacturing process; nowadays, however, the same result can be achieved by the use of additives known as VI improvers (viscosity index improvers).

With modern engines and HVI oils, lower viscosity oils than those formerly used are in general use, and in the UK, SAE 20 and 30 grades are mostly favoured for both gasoline and diesel engines. Multigrade oils SAE 10W/30, 20W/40 and 10W/40 are also in common use in gasoline engines and to a lesser, but increasing, extent in diesel engines. They ensure easy starting and less engine drag leading to reduced fuel consumption and rapid establishment of lubricant circulation whilst at the same time maintaining good lubrication by adequate viscosity at high temperatures.

Deterioration of oil in use

Lubricating oil in the engine deteriorates in two ways; it undergoes chemical and physical changes due mainly to oxidation, and it becomes contaminated by material from

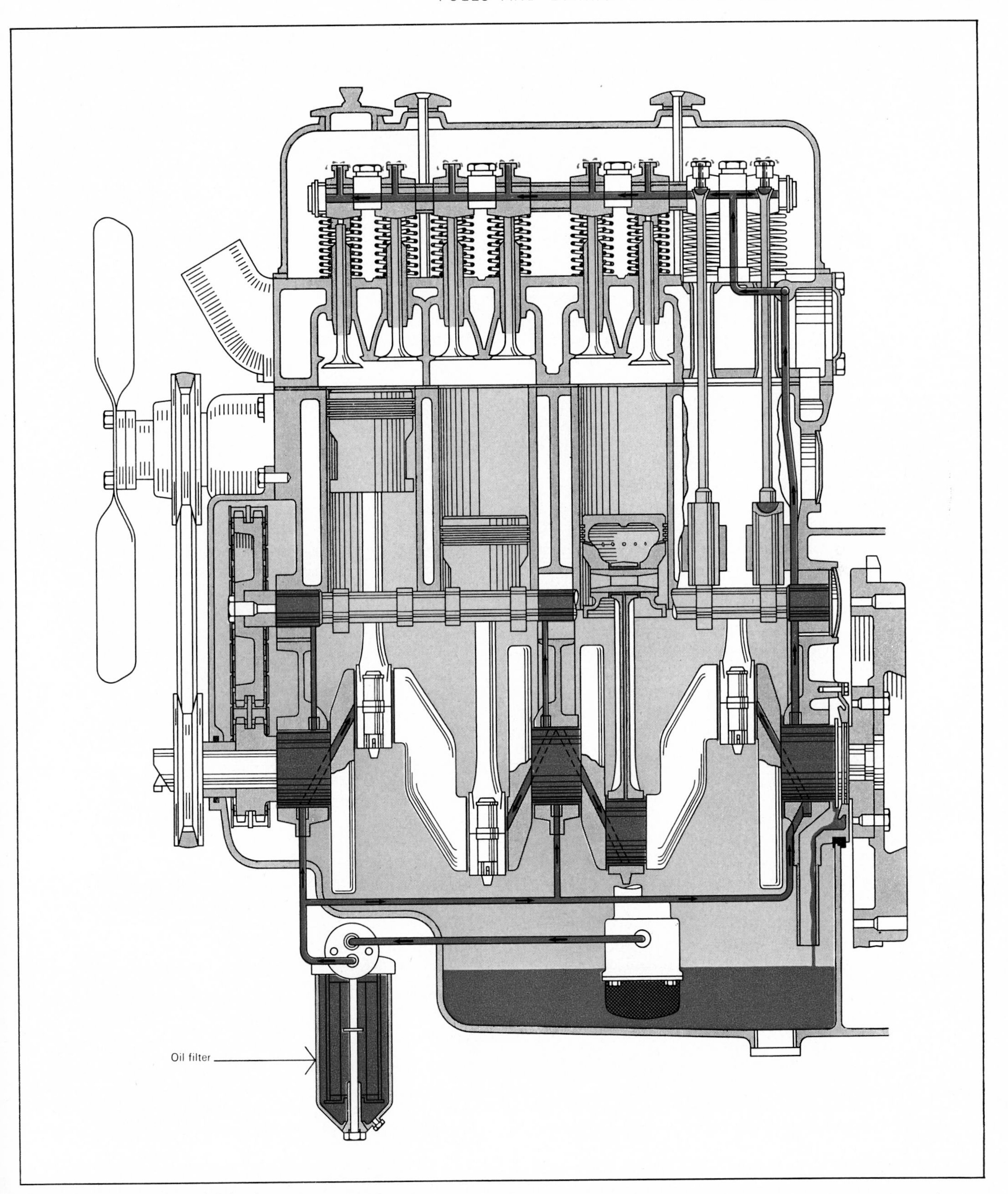

Fig. 116 A typical engine lubrication system

the combustion chamber, its own degradation products and airborne dust. Contamination is the main factor in determining when the oil should be changed. The main contaminants from the combustion chamber are unburnt fuel, water and 'soot'. Unburnt fuel drains from the combustion chamber into the crankcase where it dilutes the lubricating oil. This may be due to poor vaporization of the fuel or to the use of an over-rich mixture, as when starting from cold. Also if the fuel contains too many high-boiling constituents, these may not all be burnt. Contamination in this way is to some extent counterbalanced by evaporation of the contaminant as the oil gets hot, and under normal conditions an equilbrium is reached. Severe dilution of the lubricant could have serious results in reducing the viscosity of the oil below the desirable level.

The combustion of fuel produces something like its own weight of water. When the engine is hot, the water is formed as steam which passes out of the exhaust, but when running cool or on starting, liquid water is formed and can drain into the sump. Moreover, this water may be acidic through solution of the combustion gases. Contamination with water can also take place by leakage from the cooling system, and can be particularly harmful if anti-freeze solutions are in use.

'Soot' is formed as a result of imperfect combustion such as when idling or running under rich-mixture conditions. Most of this is blown out by the exhaust, but some contaminates the oil on the pistons and cylinders and then drains down to the crankcase. In gasoline engines, lead compounds are produced from the fuel oil additives and pass into the oil with the soot. These solid contaminants, in conjunction with oil and water, may form a sludge which is essentially an emulsion of water in oil, stabilized by the solids. This sludge may settle out in the crankcase or be circulated with the oil and block oilways. Oil filters are incorporated in the oil circulation system to remove these contaminants as far as possible as well as any air-borne dust that escapes the air filter in the air intake system. There is a limit to what the oil filter can remove and it too may be blocked if sludge is excessive.

The conditions under which oil is used in an engine are very conducive to oxidation. Oil mist is in intimate contact with air at a fairly high temperature in the crankcase and at even higher temperatures in the combustion chamber, and films of oil are subjected to high temperatures on the cylinder walls, the pistons and the piston rings. Oxidation products are formed, their nature depending largely on the temperature. In the crankcase, acidic material and complex carbonaceous products known as 'asphaltenes' are produced, and, in association with the fuel contaminants already mentioned, help to form the stable sludge that is characteristic of low temperature operation. In the combustion chamber and around the piston rings, the oil forms deposits of 'carbon' by a combustion of oxidation and thermal degradation. Part of this deposit is washed back to the sump, and part remains in the combustion space, on the piston head and in the ring grooves. All these effects of oxidation aggravate the contamination of the oil beyond that resulting from the fuel and the net result is an acidic oil that may corrode bearing metals such as copper-lead, and containing resinous material that may deposit as lacquer on hot metal surfaces such as the piston.

Engine oil additives

Well-refined HVI oils go far in providing the requirements of appropriate viscosity and resistance to oxidation, but still not sufficiently so for the lubrication of modern automotive engines. Nor do they prevent the harmful effects of contaminants. To improve the oil still further in these respects various additives are incorporated and are now an essential feature of all high-quality engine oils.

As already mentioned, the viscosity-temperature characteristics are improved by 'VI improvers', resistance to oxidation is enhanced by anti-oxidants, and wear on cams and tappets is prevented by EP additives. Corrosive wear in the cylinder is prevented either by alkaline additives, which neutralize the acids reponsible for corrosion, or by additives that absorb them and prevent their reaching metal surfaces. Oil-insoluble contaminants are kept in suspension by dispersant additives and thereby prevented from settling out from the oil or adhering to metal surfaces. In this way the engine is kept clean, and although the oil may look darker than a corresponding non-additive oil, the suspended contaminants are in such a fine state of division that they are relatively harmless and do not block oilways or filters. Anti-rust additives may also be used; they are adsorbed on metal surfaces and prevent the access of water and oxygen.

These various additives have been mentioned individually in terms of their functions, and separate additives may indeed be used, but there are now many additives that are multi-functional. The selection of the right additive or of the most suitable combination of additives depends very much on the specific use of the oil, and in this respect there are certain notable differences between gasoline engine and diesel engine lubricants.

Automotive gasoline engine lubricants (motor oils)

Both single grade and multigrade motor oils are invariably based on HVI oils in which appropriate additives are incorporated. The tendency to form deposits in the piston and ring belt area is less in the gasoline engine than in the diesel engine, and the lubricant does not need such marked anti-ring-sticking qualities. The emphasis is rather on the prevention of low temperature sludge and the maintenance of adequate dispersancy to keep the engine clean, although the effects of high temperature, rusting, and corrosive wear have also to be catered for. The low viscosity-temperature sensitivity provided by multigrade oils is important in facilitating cold starting whilst maintaining adequate lubrication at high temperatures, and with these grades no seasonal change from one viscosity grade to another is necessary. The prevention of cam and tappet wear is a special feature of motor oils.

Two-stroke engines demand somewhat different lubricants because part of the lubricant is burnt with the fuel; an undue amount of carbon deposits from the oil must therefore be avoided.

Automotive diesel engine lubricants

Diesel fuels contain more sulphur than do gasolines and therefore produce more corrosive gases when burnt. Diesel engines usually run at higher loadings than do gasoline engines, and are therefore more likely to form high temperature deposits and are more subject to ring sticking and ring packing. Low temperature sludge is, however, not unknown. Diesel lubricants are therefore formulated principally with a view to preventing interference with ring action by deposits, and the emphasis is on anti-oxidation and dispersancy. Viscosity temperature characteristics are of relatively little importance although multigrade diesel lubricants are being increasingly used.

Oil change periods

With continued use in the engine the lubricant changes in various ways. Its viscosity is decreased by fuel dilution, but increased by soluble and insoluble oxidation products. The insoluble contaminants, although largely kept in suspension by dispersants, still have an effect on viscosity. Moreover, there is a limit to the amount that can be kept in suspension, and eventually the oil may become too contaminated to be serviceable. Contamination is, in fact, the main factor in determining oil change, and the degree of contamination depends mainly on the service conditions under which the engine operates. It is, of course, cumulative and not resolved by the addition of make-up oil.

The various additives are consumed or 'depleted' as they fulfil their respective functions, but this has relatively little effect on oil change period because sufficient additive is normally incorporated initially to remain active throughout the expected life of the oil, and is continuously replenished by the make-up oil.

Oil change periods for diesel engines operating under known service conditions (as they often do) can be predicted with reasonable accuracy from laboratory test data on a series of used oil samples taken at appropriate intervals, but this is not practicable for gasoline engines under the random service conditions of private car operation, and it is always advisable to follow the maker's recommendations on oil change period.

Fuels and lubricants for aviation IC engines

Two types of engines are used in aeroplanes: the reciprocating piston engine burning gasoline and the gas turbine or jet engine burning either kerosine or a similar distillate that distils over a rather wider temperature range. The lead in aero-engine development has hitherto been mainly on the military side, engines for civil aircraft being modified versions of Service models, but military and civil requirements now diverge so much that engines are being designed specifically for each purpose.

The piston engine is no longer used for military purposes except for training, transport aircraft and helicopters. The very high powers required of modern military craft are beyond the range of piston engines, which become too large, heavy and complex above about 3500 hp. Piston engines are still used in civil aircraft but are being rapidly superseded by jet engines which permit greater speeds and larger planes. Fuel consumption is much higher but fuel quality is less critical. Super Constellations took 10 hours for the flight from London to New York with forty passengers, using 5500 gal (25 000 litres) of aviation gasoline. Modern jet planes do the trip in 6 hours with ninety passengers, but consume some 20 000 gal (90 000 litres) of kerosine. There are no new piston engines under development for either military or civil aircraft.

The conditions under which aircraft engines have to operate are different from those associated with automotive engines. Aero-engines have to develop maximum power for relatively short periods for take-off, yet to maintain sustained economical low-power operation whilst cruising. Moreover, they operate at altitudes where the density and temperature of the air are lower than those at ground level. These factors have a great influence on the design of aero-engines as well as on their fuel and lubricant requirements.

The aviation piston engine

There is little difference in principle between the automotive and the aviation piston engines although there are significant differences in detail. The fuel is stored in tanks, situated usually in the wings, and is pumped from there to a carburettor where it is vaporized and atomized by the induced air. The air/fuel mixture is compressed in the cylinder and fired by a spark. The power generated depends basically on the amount of the charge, and is thus limited by the size of the cylinder. The amount of the charge depends also on the density of the air, and decreases as the air thins out at altitude. With a reduced quantity of air the power would fall off and flying at altitude would be impossible. The engine is therefore 'supercharged' or 'boosted'; the air, instead of being drawn in through the carburettor by the motion of the pistons, is drawn in by a pump fitted between the carburettor and the cylinder, and the air/fuel mixture is forced into the cylinder under pressure – the boost pressure.

Supercharging has an effect similar to increasing the compression ratio since more charge is delivered and compressed into the volume of the combustion space. Normally aero-engines have compression ratios about 6:1 to 8·7:1 as compared with 7:1 to 10:1 for automotive engines. By supercharging, power output can be increased at will, to suit operating conditions, by increasing the boost pressure to the required extent. All possible power is thus obtainable when it is wanted, as at take-off or in combat, albeit at the expense of economy.

Aero-engines may be air-cooled or liquid-cooled according to the arrangement of cylinders. The former were used extensively in past generations of fighters, but the latter predominate in civil aircraft. Water is unsuitable as a coolant because aero-engines run hotter than motor car engines, and weight limitations preclude large coolers; a mixture of glycol and water is normally used.

The number of cylinders in an aircraft engine can range from four to twenty-eight and may be arranged in line [Fig. 117] or radially [Fig. 118]. In-line engines are often liquid-cooled and have four or six cylinders in a bank with up to four banks. Light aeroplanes may have air-cooled, in-line engines with four or six cylinders. Radial engines are always air-cooled and have up to nine cylinders in a bank with a maximum of four banks of seven cylinders.

Mixture distribution

With increase in the number of cylinders per engine, mixture distribution becomes a problem. The fuel is largely, but not completely, vaporized before entering the cylinder, and although the mixture of vaporized fuel and air is evenly distributed, the uniform distribution of the unvaporized, atomized fuel to the various cylinders is no easy matter, especially with in-line engines. Some cylinders will receive a richer mixture, some a weaker mixture, and these latter may 'knock', a far more serious matter in an aero-engine than in a car. Most aviation gasolines contain tetraethyl lead (TEL) which, in the form of either Octel or Ethyl fluid, boils at 200°C (392°F) and thus tends to remain in the unvaporized fuel. The cylinders receiving the weaker mixtures will thus get even less than their due proportion of lead, and this will still further increase their tendency to detonation.

Mal-distribution is reduced by curtailing the distillation range of the gasoline by leaving out the volatile fractions. Baffles in the main intake manifold and charge heaters to more completely vaporize the fuel are sometimes used. But the only positive method of ensuring even distribution is the use of a fuel injector similar to that used in diesel engines. A like charge of fuel can then be metered directly into each cylinder. Half way between this and the normal carburettor is the injection-carburettor in which the fuel is metered by a pump direct into the supercharger.

Most aero-engines now incorporate some form of injection system.

Fuels for aviation piston engines

Aviation piston engines use gasoline as a fuel. A failure that might only be inconvenient in a motor car may lead to a

Fig. 117 An in-line aircraft engine, the Rolls-Royce Merlin 724

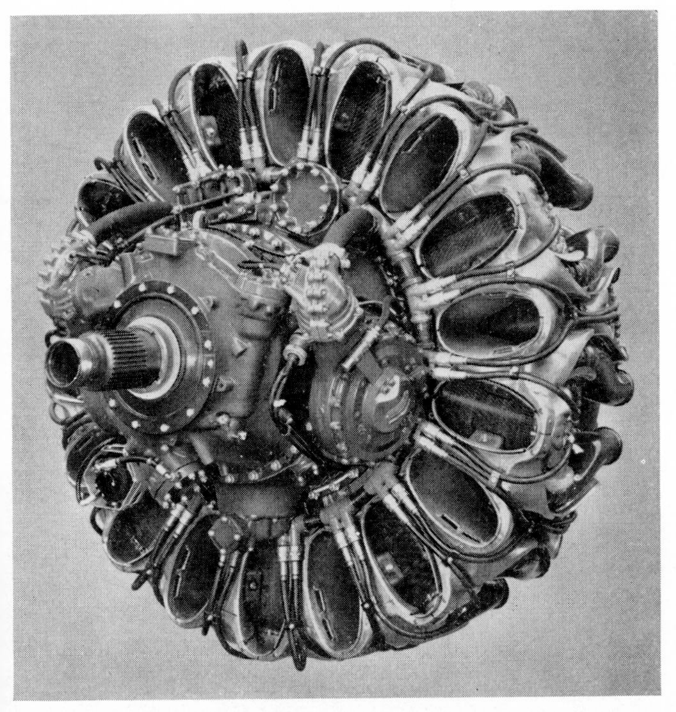

Fig. 118 A radial aircraft engine, the Bristol Centaurus

disaster in an aeroplane, and an aviation fuel must therefore conform to quite rigid specifications, most of which have been laid down by the armed services. In the UK there are five normal grades of aviation gasoline ranging in anti-knock value (octane number) from 73–115/145; in the USA there are four grades ranging from 80–115/145. These must be stable and clean products without appreciable gum or gum-forming compounds.

Carburettor icing

Carburettor icing is common to aero and motor engines and is discussed in detail in the preceding chapter (p. 124). It is avoided in aero-engines by the use of fuel injectors or injector-carburettors and by heating the intake air when necessary.

Vapour lock

The mechanism of vapour lock is discussed in the previous chapter (p. 124). The vapour locking tendencies of a gasoline increase with altitude and vapour lock can occur when an aircraft, after standing on the ground in a warm atmosphere, climbs quickly to high altitudes. The vapour pressure of aviation gasoline must therefore be lower than that of motor gasoline and the distillation curve must be modified accordingly. On the other hand, to avoid uneven fuel distribution, aviation gasoline must contain fewer higher-boiling constituents than does motor gasoline, and consequently must have a lower final boiling point.

Freezing point

The atmospheric temperature falls continuously as altitude increases and it is essential that the fuel should not freeze solid. A maximum freezing point is therefore specified for aviation gasolines, a control unnecessary for motor gasoline; a maximum of –60°C (–76°F) is generally specified.

Another potential hazard of low temperature operation is the freezing of entrained water to form ice particles which could clog filters and reduce fuel flow. Aviation fuel does not normally come into contact with water, but if this should happen by some mischance it is desirable that the water should separate cleanly from the fuel, and not become emulsified in it. It is therefore a specification requirement that aviation gasoline should separate cleanly from water.

Anti-knock value

Detonation is common to all spark-ignition engines and is discussed in detail in the previous chapter (p. 125). It does little actual harm in the automotive engine, but can be very serious in the aero-engine with its large cylinders and high specific output – it can lead to the burning of the piston. Moreover, it is not always easy to detect the onset of detonation, and it may proceed until it becomes uncontrollable. It is essential therefore that aviation gasolines should have good anti-knock properties.

The CFR Motor and Research methods used for rating motor gasolines are of limited use for aviation gasoline because of the different conditions of operation and the use of fuels with knock ratings above 100. Two other methods are used, known respectively as the F3 or 1C method and the F4 or 3C method (Test methods, p. 182). The F4 method rates a fuel higher than does the F3 method since it is run under richer mixture conditions, and in practice it is usual to characterize a fuel by both figures, e.g. the 115/145 grade has an F3 performance of 115 and an F4 of 145.

Combustion chamber deposits

The use of greater quantities of TEL in aviation gasolines to obtain the higher anti-knock ratings has given rise to problems. The scavenge compound in the TEL is theoretically sufficient to convert all the lead to a volatile material which escapes via the exhaust. In practice not all the lead leaves the combustion chamber, and that remaining can cause trouble. Exhaust valve failures traceable to such compounds were common in the immediate post-war period, but are now less frequent as a result of improvements in valve and cylinder head design that have reduced the severity of operation.

Premature spark plug failures, due to lead deposits, were also common in certain engines. These again have been considerably reduced by improvements in plug design and changes in operating techniques as well as by the use of ignition control additives in the fuel.

Lubricants for aviation piston engines

In aircraft operation it is obviously undesirable to have a crankcase or sump full of oil, as in the motor vehicle, and the conventional sump system could not be used at all with radial engines. Aviation piston engines therefore operate on the dry sump principle [Fig. 119]. The oil is stored in a tank separate from the engine and pumped under pressure via a filter, through pipes and oilways to the main crankshaft bearings and big ends and to other parts. Oil is flung from the big end on to the cylinder walls and lubricates the piston,

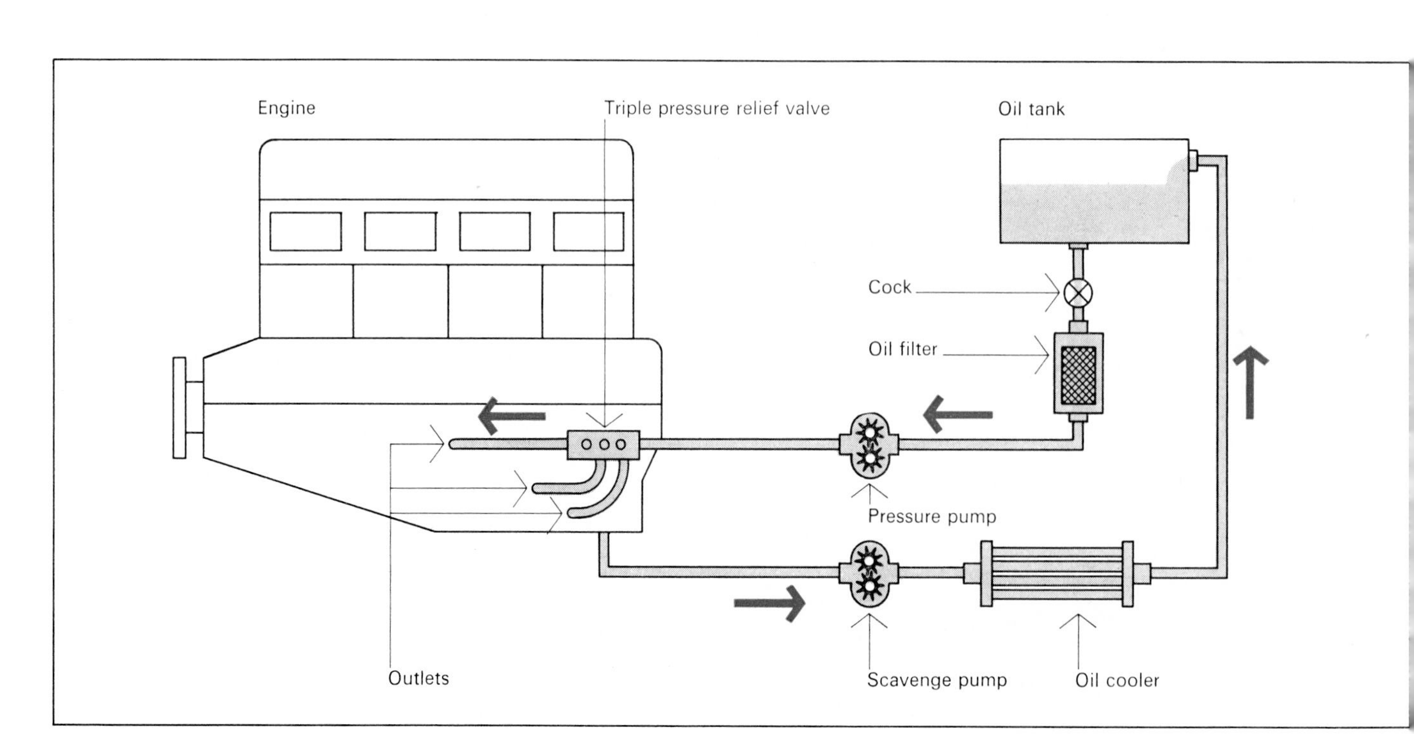

Fig. 119 Lubrication system of an aircraft engine

but is often supplemented by oil jets either in the crankshaft webs or mounted inside the crankcase. Excess oil drains back to the crankcase from which it is immediately returned via an oil cooler to the reservoir by a scavenge pump having a capacity higher than that of the pressure pump.

The lubricating oil is subjected to higher temperatures than those in the automotive engine because of the higher specific output of the aero-engine and the relatively small quantity of oil used. Aviation oils therefore have higher viscosities than those of motor oil and to ensure good oxidation resistance are blended from highly refined solvent extracted stocks. The use of additives to confer anti-oxidant and dispersant properties has hitherto been allowed only in certain cases, for fear of harmful deposits, but the advent of ashless additives has permitted the use of aviation lubricants containing additives that confer good anti-oxidant and dispersant properties as well as acting as VI improvers.

Deterioration of oil in use

Engine oils inevitably deteriorate in use either through contamination or as a result of oxidation or thermal degradation, and this subject is discussed in detail in the previous chapter.

Contamination from the combustion chamber is less serious in aircraft engines, in spite of the higher lead content of the fuel, because the oil consumption is high and there is consequently a high rate of new oil make-up. Nevertheless, the lead compounds tend to centrifuge out of suspension in the oil in the crankpins and supercharger drive clutches. This is minimized by the use of additive oils.

Aviation lubricants do not suffer contamination by condensed water as do motor oils because the engine operates at a higher working temperature. Low temperature sludge – an important factor in motor oils – does not form. The absence of acidic gases – due to the low sulphur content of the fuel – and the relatively high oil make-up remove any danger of corrosive wear. The majority of aviation piston engines are therefore able to operate successfully on straight mineral oils without additives although, as stated above, ashless additives have now enabled oils of greater stability and dispersancy to be used.

Flow properties at low ambient temperatures are important since the oil has to circulate rapidly when starting from cold in any part of the world. A low pour point and a high viscosity index are essential. Again ashless additive oils have facilitated this. To improve ease of starting in cold climates, oil dilution systems are sometimes used. The oil tanks may be divided into two parts and before shutting down, the oil in the smaller compartment is diluted with gasoline to reduce its viscosity. This diluted oil is used on starting and when the engine has warmed up the gasoline boils off and the oil reverts to its original viscosity.

Foaming of oils

The dry sump system, with its scavenge pump of greater capacity than that of the feed pump, encourages foaming of the oil because the scavenge pump sucks in a lot of air with the oil. This air is dispersed in the lubricant, goes into solution in the high pressure part of the system, and is released in the low pressure regions. An intimate mixture of oil and air may thus be delivered to the oil tank and carried to the engine by the feed pump. This type of aeration can build up a large amount of foam which the pressure pump cannot

deal with. At the worst the entire oil charge may be blown through the crankcase system and the engine starved of oil so that it fails.

This trouble used to be prevalent in aero-engines, but has been largely overcome by improved design of tanks, sumps and pipelines. Nevertheless, all aero-oils are tested for foaming characteristics and, if necessary, an anti-foam additive is included.

The aviation gas turbine engine

The first aeroplane powered by a gas turbine flew just before World War II, since when development has been rapid and continuous. Fundamentally the gas turbine works on the same principle as the piston engine; air is taken in, compressed, heated and expanded. Combustion in the gas turbine is, however, continuous, that in the piston engine is intermittent. As there is no need for valves or sparking plugs in the gas turbine, the whole mechanism is simpler and lighter in weight. Moreover, since power is developed continuously, much power can be produced by a relatively small engine. The fuel is burnt in the combustion chamber at constant pressure, there are no peak or fluctuating pressures, and the combustion chamber can be of comparatively light construction. The peak pressures in the piston engine, often reaching over 1000 lb/in^2 (70 kg/cm^2), promote detonation and necessitate the use of high octane fuel; the absence of such pressures in the gas turbine permits the use of low octane fuels. Moreover the smoothness of operation associated with a rotary system of small mass is enhanced by the continuous process of combustion.

Propulsion depends basically on Newton's law that every action has an equal and opposite reaction. A man walks forward by pushing himself along with his feet, at the same time pushing back the earth. Since the man is very light and the earth very heavy, the effect on the earth is negligible. When water squirts at high pressure from a fire hose, the nozzle is forced back in the opposite direction, as is very apparent to anyone holding it; a similar reaction is used to operate a revolving water-spray in the garden. To propel an aeroplane a large mass of air or gas is moved in a rearward direction, and the reaction pushes the aeroplane forward. The efficiency of this means of propulsion depends on the speed of the ejected air in relation to the speed of the aircraft, the highest efficiency being obtained when the forward speed of the aircraft is the same as the rearward speed of the air or gas. The pure jet engine ejects its gases at supersonic speeds while the propeller engine moves the air at much lower speeds. The jet is therefore more efficient at very high speeds, the propeller at lower speeds. Propeller efficiency falls away rapidly at speeds above 450 mph and also at lower air densities, i.e. at high altitudes. At low speeds the efficiency of the jet is low, but it increases continuously with speed, and exceeds that of the propeller at about 500–550 mph.

In operation, air is sucked into the front of the unit [Fig. 120] and compressed in the compressor before delivery to the combustion chamber where fuel is injected, atomized and burnt. The expansion of the air due to the heat of combustion operates the turbine driving the compressor, and in the process the gases lose part of their energy. They are then ejected at high speed from the jet at the rear, and their momentum (mass multiplied by velocity) propels the aircraft.

The combustion temperature is very high, and if the

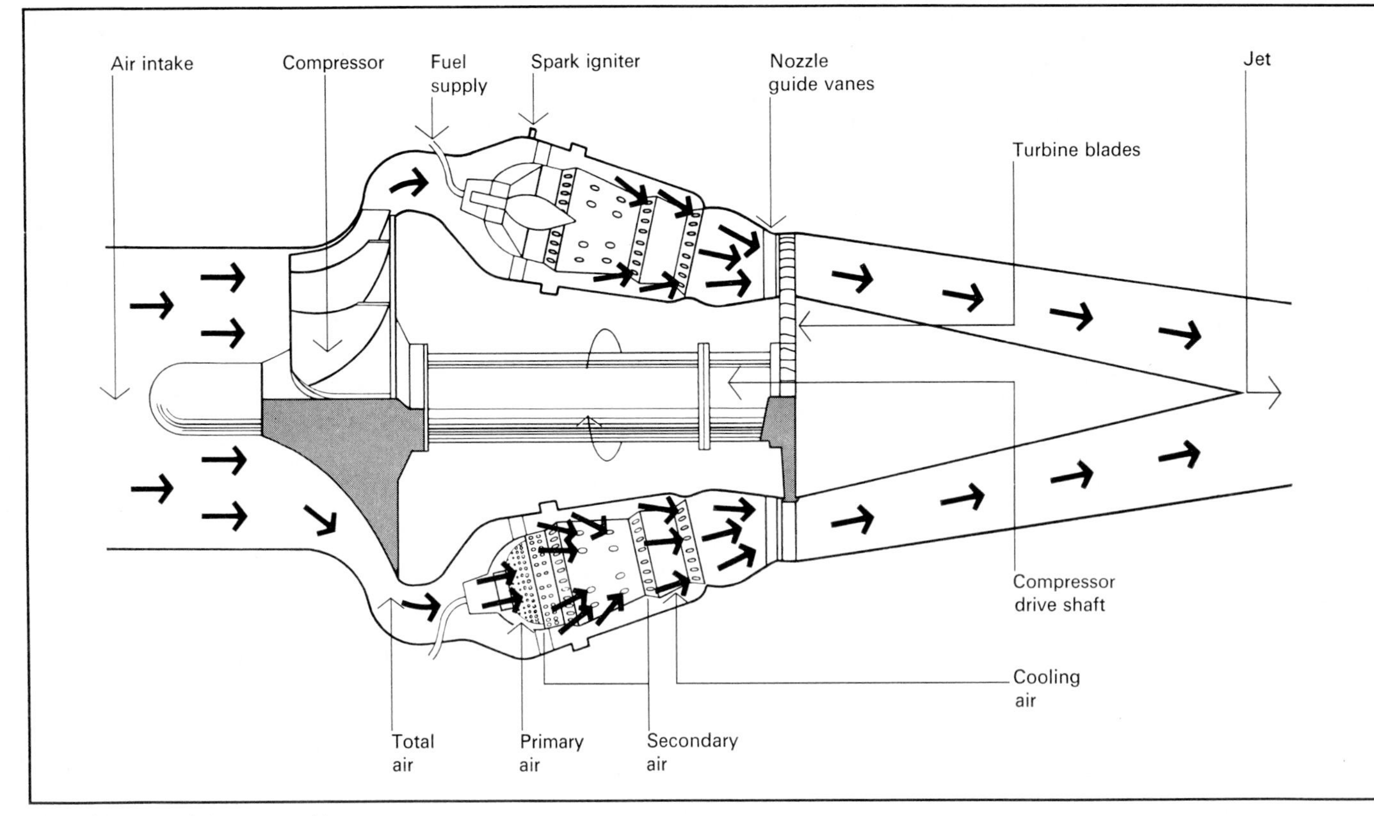

Fig. 120 The aviation gas turbine

gases were allowed to impinge directly on the turbine blades these latter would soon deteriorate. The gases are therefore cooled by the addition of excess air before passing to the turbine with some loss in efficiency.

The weight of air drawn in by the compressor decreases with altitude as the density of the air decreases. This diminished throughput of air reduces the power output of the unit, but this is more than compensated for by the reduced drag in thin air at altitude. Thus the power required to maintain the aircraft at a given speed is reduced as altitude increases, and it is therefore more economical to operate jet aircraft at high altitudes; in general they fly at heights of up to 40 000 ft.

In the pure jet engine (turbo-jet) the turbine is just large enough to drive the compressor, and the surplus energy provides the jet propulsion. The gas turbine can also be used in conjunction with a propeller (turbo-prop), in which case the energy of the gases is absorbed in the turbine which drives both the compressor and the propeller, which is coupled to it through gearing. A propeller cannot work efficiently in a rarified atmosphere and turbo-prop aircraft therefore operate generally at 20 000–30 000 ft and at lower speeds than those of turbo-jet aircraft. Fig. 121 shows a turbo-jet aircraft.

Fuels for aviation gas turbine engines

Basically the gas turbine is not particularly fuel conscious, and can operate on any clean burning fuel. Kerosine is a suitable fuel and is widely used, but since there is only a limited amount of kerosine in any crude a distillate of wider distillation range–'wide range distillate'–is also used. Wide range distillate is produced by including some of the gasoline fraction, and this naturally introduces a somewhat greater fire hazard which has led to some controversy in the use of this type of fuel for civil aircraft.

Combustion characteristics

The aviation gas turbine uses simple all-metal combustion chambers. In one type the fuel is sprayed in as an atomized liquid, in another the fuel is introduced through a heated vaporizing tube and enters as a vapour.

In the spray type the ease of ignition, the stability of the flame and the efficiency of combustion depend mainly on the voltality of the fuel and the fineness of its atomization. Volatility is controlled by the distillation range while the degree of atomization depends mainly on viscosity, and it is necessary to specify a low-temperature viscosity.

Fuel requirements are less critical in the vaporizing type of chamber, and it is only necessary to specify a volatility sufficiently high to ensure complete vaporization. The influence of low fuel temperature on combustion is slight, except for the starting device which is usually a pilot flame from a small atomizer.

The formation of carbonaceous deposits in the spray type of chamber and on the burners was formerly a problem, but is no longer so owing mainly to improvements in chamber design. The formation of deposits in the vaporizing type of chamber has also been practically eliminated by improvements in design. So far as fuel properties are concerned, the tendency to form deposits is related to the aromatic content, particularly in the heavier fractions, the more aromatics the less is the tendency to form deposits. For fuels of similar distillation range, the aromatic content of the fraction boiling above 200°C (390°F) may be used to assess their deposition tendency, and since aromatics have a higher specific gravity than other hydrocarbons the specific gravity of the fuel can be taken as a guide.

Low temperature characteristics

Water can exist in a fuel either in suspension or in solution. It is essential that aviation turbine fuel be entirely free from suspended water because of the low temperatures to which it is exposed. Considerable attention is therefore paid to the handling and storage of these fuels to avoid the ingress of water. Should suspended water be present it can generally be removed by settling although this may take a long time, particularly with kerosine. Water in solution is a more difficult matter, it cannot be removed by any practical means. Ice particles may form below 0°C (32°F) and although there is only about 0·005–0·01 %w of dissolved water in the fuel, the large quantity of fuel used in a long high-altitude flight may produce sufficient ice to block the fine filters used for the removal of extraneous solids. Dissolved water has given less trouble in practice than had been expected because exposure of the fuel to low temperatures and pressures during flight greatly reduces the amount of dissolved water. Nevertheless it is general practice to heat the fuel on the way to the filters.

At extremely low temperatures a fuel may have a high viscosity. Although a booster pump is used to deliver fuel to the engine, the oil feed to this pump from the oil tank is by gravity and it is essential that it should not be impeded by too high viscosity. Fuels with final boiling points below 300°C (570°F) generally have viscosities sufficiently low for them to flow to the pump at temperatures down to their freezing point. The limiting temperature of use would be determined by solidification of the fuel in the tanks, and this would not occur until well below the freezing point, firstly because the freezing point is the temperature at which solids begin to separate under arbitrary test conditions (Test methods, p. 184) and not the temperature at which the fuel solidifies, and secondly because of mechanical agitation inherent in the system. In practice therefore the specification of a maximum freezing point corresponding to the lowest service temperature likely to be experienced provides an ample margin of safety. A maximum freezing point of –40°C or –60°C (–40°F or –76°F), according to the type of service, ensures adequate flow under all practical conditions, including starting at very low temperatures.

Supersonic conditions

The advent of supersonic flight has imposed still more rigorous conditions for aviation gas turbine fuels in that, owing to the high speeds, very high skin temperatures are achieved on all external metal parts. Supersonic speeds are designated as 'mach numbers' equal to the ratio of the speed of the aircraft to the speed of sound, i.e. a mach number of 1 equals the speed of sound, a mach number of 2 equals twice the speed of sound. At a mach number of 2·2 the skin temperature of the fuel tank may attain 120°C (250°F), at a mach number of 3 it may be 260°C (500°F). The fuel must therefore be stable at high temperatures; present normal grades are satisfactory up to mach 2·2 but better stability is likely to be required at higher speeds.

Corrosion

Fuels for gas turbines must be free from acidic material and corrosive sulphur compounds to prevent corrosion of metal equipment and there is a rigid specification to ensure this. Although combustion of the fuel inevitably produces sulphur gases little or no effect on the combustion chamber or turbine blades is experienced provided the sulphur content of the fuel is within the 0·4 %w generally specified by service authorities.

Lubricants for aviation gas turbine engines

The gas turbine engine is far simpler to lubricate than is the piston engine. No moving parts are involved in the combustion process, and lubrication is required solely for the turbine and compressor bearings, the reduction gear and propeller of the turbo-prop engine, and the various auxiliary equipment drives. However, though the machinery makes little demand on the oil, the wide range of temperatures encountered in aircraft operations introduces problems.

For military purposes an aviation gas turbine engine must be able to start at –40°C (–40°F) and the lubricant must be

Fig. 121 The Vickers VC 10 four-engined turbo-jet aircraft

free flowing at that temperature. If an engine stops and has to be restarted at altitude, even lower temperatures may be encountered, perhaps down to –80°C (–112°F). An aviation gas turbine lubricant must therefore be able to function down to very low temperatures.

On the other hand, many of the bearings run at temperatures above 250°C (480°F), and an oil that will withstand such conditions without undue oxidation or deposit formation is required.

It is not easy to find a petroleum oil to conform to these requirements, but certain organic liquids which remain liquid at very low temperatures but do not evaporate at the high temperatures involved in turbine lubrication are effective lubricants under these conditions. These organic liquids are manufactured products, and hence are known as 'synthetic' lubricants. Most current aviation gas turbine lubricants are based on carboxylic esters – the products of a reaction between a carboxylic acid and an alcohol.

Two types of gas turbine lubricants are available, one having a minimum viscosity of 7·5 cS at 210°F, meeting a British specification, the other having a minimum viscosity of 3·0 cS at 210°F, meeting a USA specification. These lubricants have to pass certain oxidation, corrosion, load-carrying and shear-stability tests.

Fire hazards

The ignition or explosion of aviation fuel is an ever-present risk in the event of a crash, and may be a hazard in certain circumstances during flight. In a crash, fuel from ruptured tanks may be ignited by contact with hot engine components and give rise to a general conflagration. In view of the nature of the fuel little can be done fuel-wise to remove this risk. With jet aircraft there is a suggestion that the spread of flame may be slower with the less volatile fuel, kerosine, thus allowing more time for escape.

So far as fuel tanks are concerned, aviation gasoline is so volatile that the vapour/air mixture above the liquid is generally too rich to explode. Aviation kerosine, on the other hand, is much less volatile and at the low temperature experienced in flight the vapour/air mixture would be too weak to explode. The only risk of an explosive mixture would be following take-off with a warm fuel after climbing to altitude. Sudden release of dissolved air from the fuel on rapid ascent can increase the risk since a foam may be formed more inflammable than the bulk fuel.

The fuelling of aircraft gives rise to a fire or explosion hazard from ignition by sparks due to static electrical charges. Static electricity is generated by liquids in motion at the interface between the liquid and another phase which may be solid, liquid or even gaseous. The faster the liquid flows the more it becomes electrified. The hazard has thus increased as the fuelling rates of aircraft have increased, and consequently increasing attention has been given to the fuelling of aircraft, especially large turbine-powered craft, which have much greater fuel requirements yet demand shorter turn-round times. In addition to the usual precautions of coupling all equipment and hoses to provide a continuous electrical conductor, it is now possible to reduce the hazard by incorporating 'anti-static' additives in the fuel, which even at one part per million or less, are very effective in preventing the build up of static electricity by increasing the conductivity of the fuel.

Fuels and lubricants for marine, industrial and locomotive IC engines

This chapter deals with the requirements of diesel engines used in marine, locomotive and general industrial practice as well as with those of the industrial gas turbine.

Marine diesel propulsion engines

Marine diesel propulsion engines operate basically on the principles described in Fuels and lubricants for automotive IC engines (p. 126) although there are certain differences in design and in fuel and lubricant requirements. They are generally large, slow-speed engines (with speeds up to 130 rev/min) coupled direct to the propeller, but medium-speed engines (with speeds from about 400–750 rev/min), with geared or electric drives, are also used in large vessels.

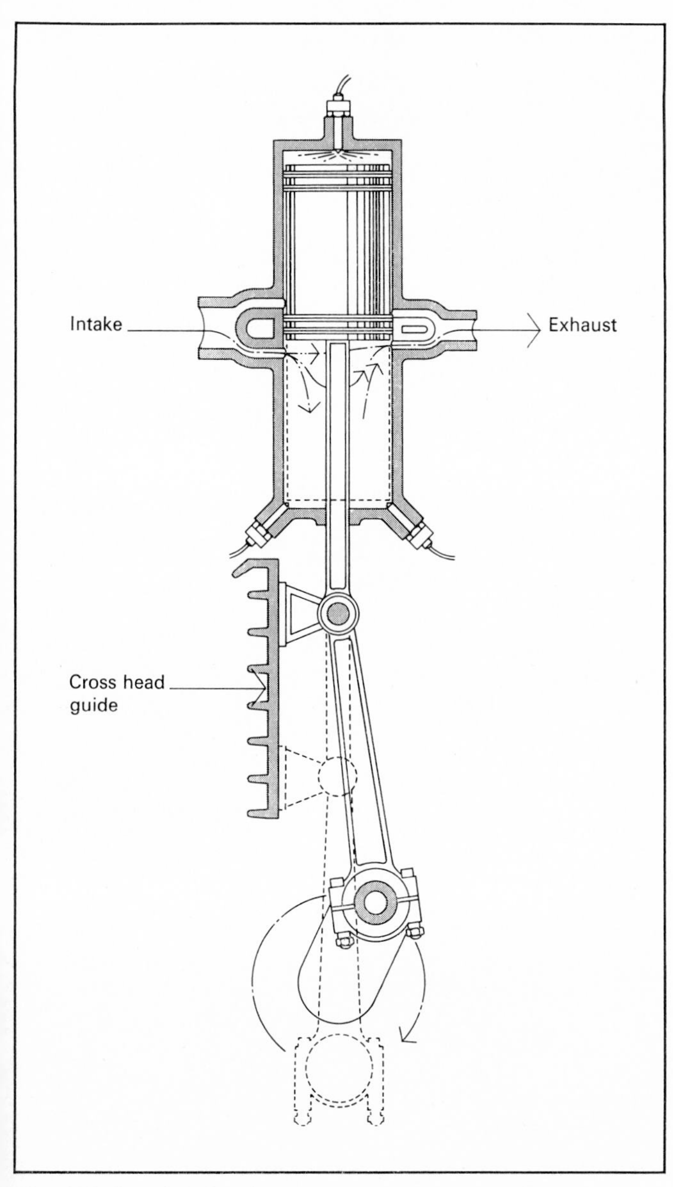

Fig. 122 Crosshead engine

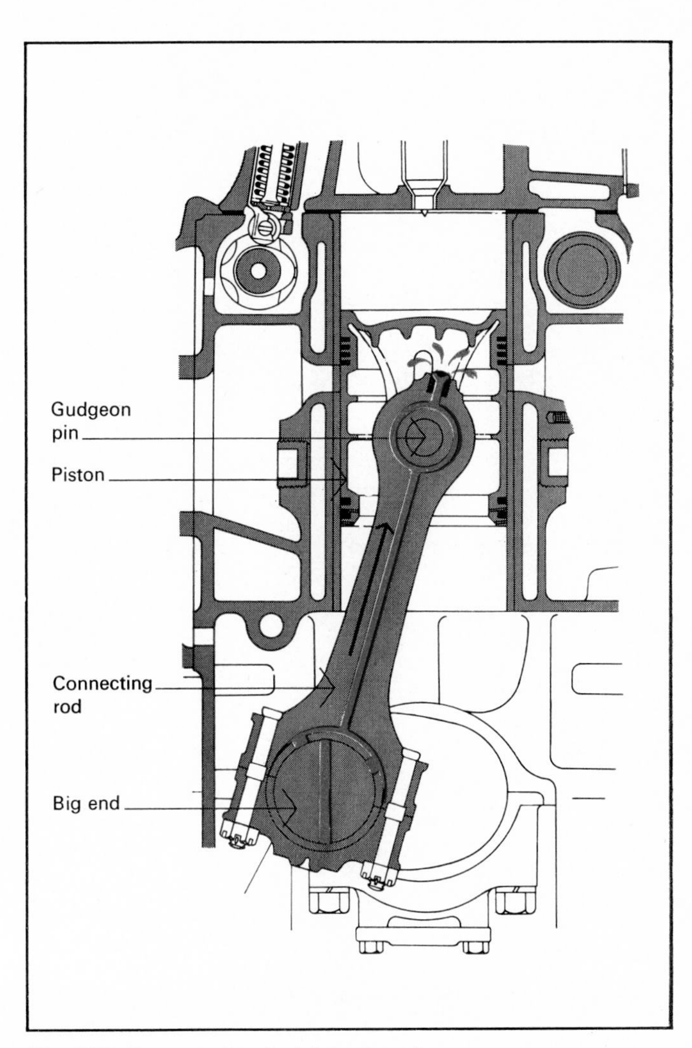

Fig. 123 Piston cooling by lubricating oil

Marine diesels may be four-stroke or two-stroke engines but are always vertical.

With the large bores and long strokes of the large marine diesel, a rigid connecting rod between piston and crankshaft would introduce an undue strain in the connecting rod and a high side thrust between piston and cylinder. This is avoided by making the connecting rod in two sections joined by a link called the 'crosshead' which allows the piston and the short piston rod to move back and forth parallel to the cylinder walls. Such engines are referred to as 'crosshead' engines [Fig. 122] whilst those employing the conventional connecting rod are called 'trunk-piston' engines.

Practically all large marine diesels are of the direct-injection type, the fuel being sprayed direct into the combustion space. Multi-hole injectors are usually used to obtain adequate mixing of air and fuel.

These large engines require positive cooling of the pistons which must be made of some metal that expands as little as possible on heating. The aluminium alloys used for smaller engines are unsuitable, and cast iron or steel is used. Owing to the low heat conductivity and the large diameter of the pistons, piston crown temperatures are relatively high and special arrangements for cooling the piston are provided, generally as shown in Fig. 123, by circulating the crankcase lubricating oil through the connecting rod to the underside of the piston from which it drains back to the crankcase. Water is also used for piston cooling because of its greater specific heat, but may be troublesome if there are leaky glands.

Cooling liquids, whether oil or water, can build up deposits in the cooling system, which may reduce heat removal or even block up the system. This can be avoided by careful selection of the cooling medium and periodical cleaning of the system.

The following types of diesel engine are used in marine practice.

The four-stroke single-acting engine

This works on the conventional four-stroke cycle (p. 121). Air is drawn into the cylinder during the suction stroke and compressed by the piston moving up the cylinder. This compression heats the air charge so that when the fuel is injected it vaporizes, and the mixture reaches its self-ignition temperature. The burning of the fuel forces down the piston, constituting the power stroke, and the products of combustion are expelled in the fourth or exhaust stroke.

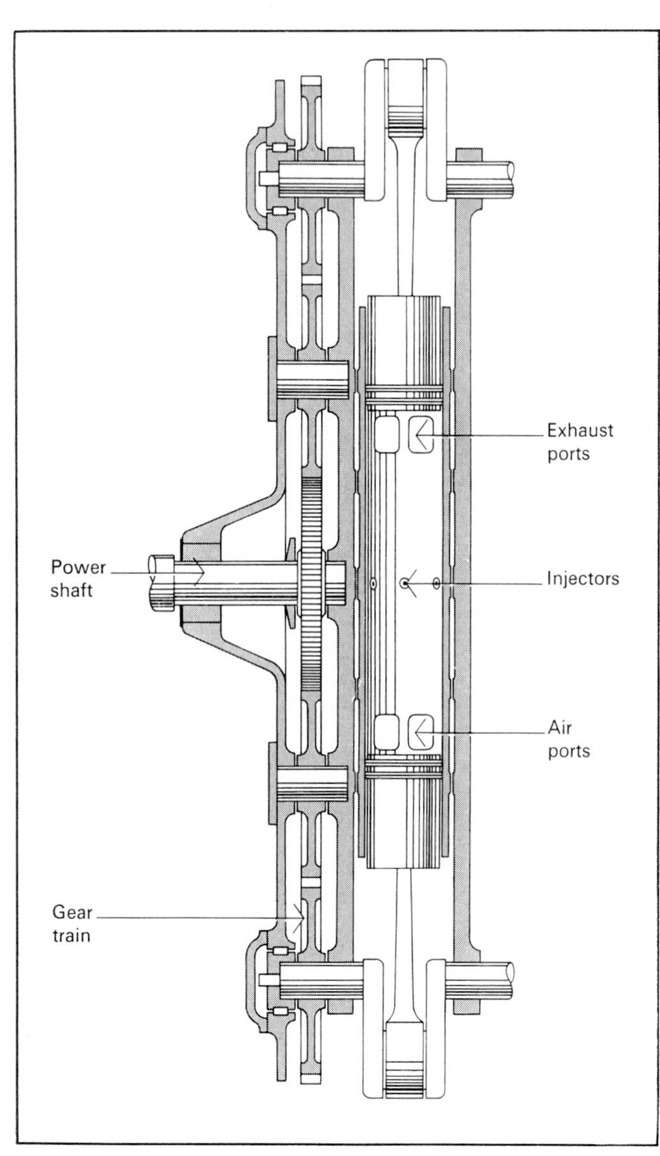

Fig. 124 Opposed piston engine

The two-stroke single-acting engine

In two-stroke engines the complete cycle takes place in one up and one down movement of the piston (p. 121). At the end of the exhaust stroke, and the commencement of the compression stroke, air is blown through the cylinder from scavenge ports uncovered by the piston. This scavenging air sweeps out any gases remaining from the previous power stroke, usually through exhaust ports opposite the scavenge ports. As the piston continues its upward stroke it closes the ports and compresses the air in the cylinder; fuel is injected just before the completion of the stroke and combustion occurs. The piston is forced down, developing power and expelling the exhaust gases. As an alternative to both scavenge and exhaust ports being controlled by one piston, an auxiliary piston forms the cylinder head and hence such engines are called 'coverless'.

Double-acting engines

By closing the cylinder at the bottom and effecting combustion alternately above and below the piston, two power strokes per revolution are achieved thus enabling more power to be obtained from the cylinder without increasing its diameter. An effective seal has to be provided where the piston rod passes through the bottom cover.

Both four-stroke and two-stroke double-acting engines were popular for a time, but are now virtually obsolete, increase in power being more simply achieved by 'supercharging' single-acting engines, by blowing medium pressure air into the cylinder. In this way power output can be increased by about 50%.

The opposed piston two-stroke engine

This engine has two pistons in the same cylinder; in some engines the lower piston drives the main crankshaft by the connecting rod and the upper piston adds its driving power through gear linkages; in others both pistons act through linkages.

On the compression stroke both pistons move inward, fuel is injected between them and, on burning, forces them apart. When the top piston reaches the end of its stroke it uncovers the exhaust port and vents the combustion gases. Immediately afterwards the lower piston uncovers the scavenge ports, the residual gases are swept out and the combustion space is filled anew with air. An engine of this type is illustrated in Fig. 124.

Fuels for marine diesel engines

The low-speed diesel engine is not so critical of its fuel as is its high-speed counterpart. In the high-speed engine, combustion is completed rapidly and any delay in the onset of ignition has quite a pronounced effect. In the slow-speed engine there is a relatively long combustion period and, in the large marine engine, ample space for complete combustion of even coarsely atomized fuel before it impinges on the cylinder wall and causes deposits. They can therefore run not only on distillate fuels but on mixtures of distillate and residual fuels or even on residual fuels alone. Nevertheless distillate fuels with a viscosity of 35–60 sec. Red. I at 100°F have hitherto been the preferred fuels because of their generally clean combustion, low cylinder wear and freedom from port blocking.

The use of residual or boiler fuels is economically attractive on fuel costs but their inherent disadvantages have hitherto outweighed this advantage. They have high viscosities (Bunker C oil has a viscosity of 6500 sec. Red. I at 100°F) and must be heated to reduce the viscosity sufficiently for efficient injection and atomization. Whilst still hot they must be centrifuged to remove matter, either derived from the crude oil or picked up during processing, that would otherwise wear or block injectors or form deposits in the combustion chamber. But their greatest drawback has been the high cylinder wear associated with their high sulphur contents and the cost of replacing worn cylinder liners, which far outweighed any saving on the cost of fuel.

Within the past few years, however, special lubricants have been developed that reduce cylinder liner wear with residual fuels to at least that previously experienced with distillate fuels, and often to an even lower level, and also prevent engine fouling. This has caused a revolution in marine practice in favour of the use of residual fuels which are now used in the majority of marine main propulsion diesel engines.

Lubricants for marine diesel engines

In the lubricating systems described in Fuels and lubricants for automotive IC engines (p. 128) oil is circulated by a pump from a reservoir to the various parts to be lubricated, subsequently draining or being pumped back to the reservoir. This same system is used for lubricating the bearings of marine diesels, but for large bore engines the cylinders and pistons are lubricated by a separate system in which the oil is fed by a mechanical lubricator driven from the engine to a number of injection points or quills dispersed around the cylinder. The used oil drains from the cylinder into a catch tank, and is either burnt as fuel or disposed of as waste.

This system is necessary for crosshead engines since the cylinders are isolated or remote from the crankcase, and splash lubrication would be inadequate or impossible. Moreover, in view of the long stroke and large bore and the position of the inlet and exhaust ports, it is essential to feed the oil in the right quantity to the right place at the right time – all of which can be more readily achieved if the cylinder is separately lubricated. It is also possible to use different oils for the cylinders and the bearings – a distinct advantage when residual fuels are being burnt.

Trunk piston engines may or may not have separate cylinder lubrication. In the medium-speed and high-speed types sufficient oil is thrown from the bearings on to the cylinder walls, but in the large low-speed models used in marine practice sufficient oil may not reach the cylinders by this means, and mechanical lubricators metering a feed direct to the cylinders may have to provide supplementary lubrication. In these engines the oil draining from the cylinders goes back to the crankcase.

Oils used for lubricating marine diesel engines should be of suitable viscosity for the operating conditions and be resistant to oxidation, particularly when the crankcase oil is used for piston cooling and may be exposed to high temperatures. It is usual to have filters or centrifuges in the circulating system to remove sludge or other contaminants. SAE 30 and 40 grade oils are in general use, and well-refined straight oils are usually adequate for both cylinder and crankcase use in engines running on marine diesel fuel. Where heavy fuel is burnt, however, oil oxidation is often more rapid, associated with entry into the system of cylinder drainings containing pro-oxidation catalysts. Lacquer and sludge may then form in the crankcase and could lead to bearing failures, and deposits may build up in piston-cooling spaces leading to piston over-heating and cracking. Acids may also be formed leading to bearing or crankshaft corrosion. Oils containing anti-oxidant and basic additives are required under these conditions.

For engines running on residual fuels, cylinder lubricants containing basic additives to neutralize the corrosive acids are used. The most successful hitherto is an emulsion of water in an SAE 30 grade lubricating oil, the water containing in solution salts that neutralize the corrosive products of combustion and improve engine cleanliness; but oils containing oil soluble additives with similar properties are now available.

Marine gas turbine

The gas turbine has little or no advantage over the steam turbine or the diesel engine for general marine use, but its low maintenance requirements make it attractive for tanker propulsion since the turn round times of tankers are too short to permit more than very minor overhauls in port. Ash deposition is still the major problem limiting its development.

The fuel and lubricant requirements for marine gas turbines are similar to those for industrial turbines as described on p. 142.

Industrial diesel engines

Diesel engines are used in industry to generate electricity in power stations, and as auxiliary engines to drive all sorts of equipment. Whilst they range from small high-speed engines to large low-speed engines, they are mostly of the medium-speed trunk-piston type running at 350–1000 rev/min. Their design, fuel and lubricant requirements differ only in degree from those described under automotive and marine engines.

Locomotive diesel engines

These, in general, are medium-speed to high-speed engines with speeds up to 1500 rev/min, four- or two-stroke, single-acting, although opposed piston designs are also employed. Locomotive engines are generally highly rated because of space limitations and therefore usually operate on distillate fuels. Supercharging, that is, feeding the air into the cylinder under pressure so that additional fuel can be burnt for a given cylinder size, is frequently employed.

Additive oils with dispersant and anti-oxidant properties similar to those for the high-speed automotive engines (p. 130) are used as lubricant.

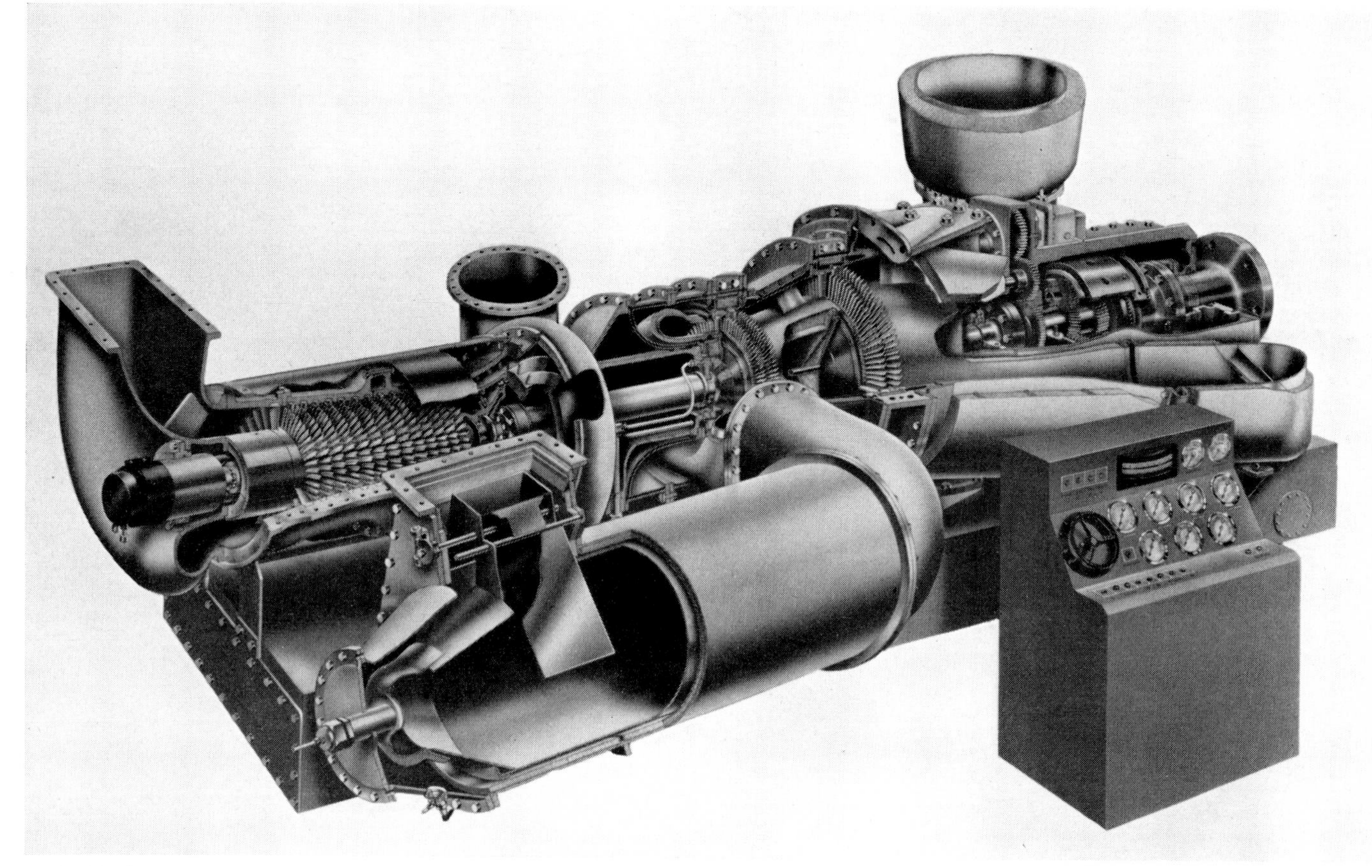

Fig. 125 An industrial gas turbine (cutaway view)

The industrial gas turbine

In a gas turbine unit, the energy from the fuel is used to drive a turbine or turbines. A unit consists essentially of a compressor, a combustion chamber and the turbine or turbines operated by the hot gases issuing at pressure from the combustion zone. A typical engine is shown in Fig. 125.

Air enters the compressor and is forced into the combustion chamber, passing on its way through a heat exchanger where it absorbs heat from the outgoing exhaust gases. Part of this air is used to burn the fuel, the remainder passes along the walls, keeping them reasonably cool, and then enters a mixing zone where it mixes with the products of combustion and cools them to a temperature suitable for delivery to the turbine. This cooling is necessary since the turbine blades could not withstand the temperatures generated in the combustion zone. The gases leave the turbine not much above atmospheric temperature, but still hot enough to warm incoming air in the heat exchanger through which they pass to the atmosphere.

The turbine drives the compressor, which absorbs about 60% of the power generated, leaving about 40% available for external work. Sometimes two turbines are used, the second being driven by the exhaust gases from the first. The whole of the power of the first turbine may be employed in driving the compressor while the power from the second is the useful output of the unit.

The gas turbine has a low efficiency under part-load conditions, and cannot compete with other methods of power generation under such conditions. This has prevented its adoption for automotive, locomotive or marine propulsion, where load factors are generally less than 50%. It can, however, be used to advantage in rail haulage of heavy freight trains.

The gas turbine is used successfully, however, in some other fields in which low efficiency is less important, and the high fuel consumption is offset by ease of installation and low maintenance costs. For example, gas turbines are used to generate electric power in oilfields and refineries where large quantities of gas are available, and are widely used in the USA for gas-line pumping, using the gas as fuel. There is no case for oil-fired gas turbines where coal is available since this fuel can be used by steam turbines at least as efficient as the best gas turbines.

Fuels for industrial gas turbines

The choice of fuel for the aviation gas turbine is limited by the necessity for pumpability at low temperature and clean, complete combustion; a distillate fuel is therefore obligatory. For industrial and marine purposes, however, these requirements do not operate, economical running is far more important and the gas turbine must be able to utilize cheap fuel. Since the fuel is burnt continuously in a combustion chamber and the products of combustion pass to the turbine, any type of fuel should be acceptable – even the most viscous residues. This is true so far as combustion is concerned, but all residual fuels contain incombustible material which, even though only about 0·1%w, can produce serious difficulties by forming deposits on the turbine blades or corroding them. At low inlet temperature carbon particles in the combustion gases will keep the turbine clean, partly by encasing the sticky ash particles in non-adherent carbon and partly by a mild abrasive action on the blades. Certain additives, particularly silicon compounds, will prevent deposition, but since all the cheaper ones are insoluble in oil or water they must be dispersed as a powder in the fuel, and this leads to handling difficulties.

The choking of the turbine or the spoiling of the blade profiles by deposits can reduce the output of a unit to zero within 100 hours. The performance can be restored to its original level by cleaning the turbine.

Corrosion of the blades is more insidious. With suitable alloys it will not occur to any great extent below 650°C (1200°F), but above this temperature it proceeds at an ever-increasing rate. Corrosion may not be noticed until it has done irreparable damage, and must be prevented if blades are to have an economic life. The addition of magnesium or zinc salts to the fuel considerably reduces corrosion.

The all-metal combustion chambers of aircraft gas turbines, suitable for the rapid burning and low carbon formation of kerosine or light distillate fuels, are quite unsuitable for use with residual fuels. A larger combustion chamber is required because the more viscous fuel takes longer to burn and must remain for a longer time in the combustion zones. Moreover, fuel oils have greater heat radiation so that it is necessary to protect the metal walls of the combustion chamber by lining it with refractory materials. An alternative method of keeping them sufficiently cool to ensure long life is to make the chamber on the louvre principle, by having a series of thin rings separated from each other by narrow gaps through which some of the air from the compressor flows.

The use of distillate fuels avoids all these troubles, and most industrial gas turbines use gas oil as fuel.

Lubricants for industrial gas turbines

Lubrication presents few problems in the gas turbine since there are no moving parts in the combustion system and the oil is not exposed to the high temperatures of the combustion chamber. Lubrication is required solely for the turbine and compressor bearings and normal steam turbine oil grades are used. These are relatively low viscosity HVI oils containing anti-oxidant and anti-rust additives. Where reduction gearing is included in the drive the turbine oil lubricates this as well.

The free-piston engine

This engine consists of two distinct parts, the free-piston unit which provides the compressed gas and the gas turbine from which the power output is obtained.

As shown in Fig. 126 the free-piston component comprises two horizontally opposed pistons moving in a cylinder and operating as a two-stroke supercharged diesel. The pistons are called 'free' because there is no connecting rod or crank-

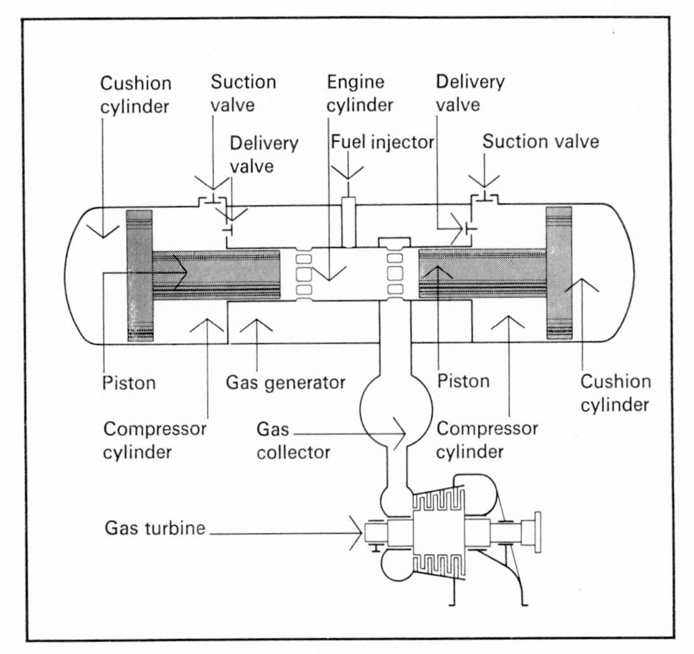

Fig. 126 Free-piston gas turbine

shaft to produce rotary motion of a shaft; they are only tied together by a light linkage to keep them in phase. Each of the pistons is rigidly attached to another piston working in a separate but co-axial cylinder and operating as an air compressor. The compressed air is used partly to supercharge the free piston unit and partly to feed the gas turbine. The exhaust gases from the free-piston unit, diluted and cooled with the compressed air, are passed to the gas turbine to produce power.

The free-piston gas turbine has some advantages over the pure gas turbine. It has greater thermal efficiency since the simple piston reciprocating compressor produces much higher compression ratios than does the rotary compressor normally used with the gas turbine. It has no metal parts operating at the high temperatures of the compressor turbine inlet blades of the normal gas turbine, the temperatures being of the order of 500°C (930°F) as against 800°C (1470°F). Moreover it can use residual fuels with less trouble than they give in the pure gas turbine.

The free-piston engine is being used for electrical power generation and for marine propulsion, but its future is still uncertain.

Fuels and lubricants for free-piston engines

Both distillate and residual fuels are used and lubrication is effected by oils containing anti-oxidant and basic additives such as are used in large marine diesel engines.

Fuels for domestic, industrial and agricultural use

The use of petroleum products in engines for the generation of power has been considered in earlier chapters. Here we are concerned mainly with their use as fuels for the provision of light or heat in domestic, industrial and agricultural practice.

The discovery of coal opened up a vast new source of fuel which soon supplanted all earlier forms such as wood, charcoal and animal or vegetable oils, and was responsible for the rapid development of industrialization. Coal reigned supreme almost to the beginning of the twentieth century but since then liquid and gaseous petroleum fuels have become available in ever increasing quantities to provide alternative sources of energy.

The decision whether to use solid, liquid or gaseous fuels depends on many factors, but liquid and gaseous petroleum fuels are increasingly used instead of solid fuels, mainly because of their convenient physical state and their many technical merits.

Gaseous fuels have many advantages that favour their use even when they are more costly than alternative fuels. They can be distributed through mains and piped direct to the point of application with elimination of customer's storage and handling equipment. Moreover, complete combustion is more readily achieved without smoke or deposits. Petroleum gases have further advantages in that they contain virtually no sulphur and have a higher calorific value than that of coal gas, usually the only alternative gaseous fuel. The absence of sulphur ensures that the products of combustion are non-corrosive, harmless to materials being heated and do not pollute the atmosphere.

Where natural gas is available, as in the USA and Canada, it is widely used for both domestic and industrial applications. It has long been similarly used in Poland and Romania, several other European countries have made extensive use of post-war discoveries of indigenous supplies and the more recent discoveries in the Sahara and the Netherlands will undoubtedly make it available eventually throughout Europe (Natural gas, p. 67).

Liquefied petroleum gas (LPG) is used extensively for cooking, water and space heating, air-conditioning, refrigeration and illumination both in the home and in hotels, restaurants, canteens, hospitals and schools. Its uses in industry are legion – wherever heat is required, LPG can be used. Used with oxygen it is gradually replacing acetylene in steel cutting, flame cleaning, brazing, and welding of non-ferrous metals. It can be supplied in bulk for large scale use or in cylinders or 'bottles' containing up to 100 lb of liquefied gas for smaller offtakes. Bottles containing about 30 lb of liquefied gas yielding about 568 000 Btu are commonly used throughout Europe for domestic use and for many other small-scale operations, such as plumbing, paint-removing and general workshop use. When drawn from a cylinder, the opening of the valve releases the pressure, the liquid boils and gaseous fuel emerges. The operation causes a drop in temperature in the cylinder and if the offtake is substantial the temperature may drop to the boiling point of the liquid, with consequent cessation of gas formation. For large offtakes gas should be drawn from two or more cylinders simultaneously or, better still, from a bulk supply. When bulk supplies are used the LPG is frequently withdrawn from the bulk tank as a liquid and fed to an independent vaporizer which may use the gas itself or any auxiliary fuel to provide the necessary heat.

Liquid fuels have many advantages over solid fuels. They have higher calorific values and lower contents of ash-forming constituents; they are easier to handle, and distribution can be effected quickly and cleanly by pipeline; they permit quick starting up at short notice and quick shutting down when the demand for heat is finished; the regulation of heating operations and the accurate control of temperatures are simplified. Moreover these various operations can be controlled automatically.

Kerosine has long been used as an illuminant and is still used for this purpose in the less developed areas. It is also used extensively for cooking and for space and water heating.

Gas oils are used in small central heating units in dwellings but larger installations use residual fuel oils. Because of their higher price, distillate fuels are not generally used for industrial purposes to anything like the same extent as residual fuel oils, but some industrial users are willing to pay the higher price because of the advantages of lower viscosity, lower sulphur content and virtual absence of ash and asphaltic matter, all of which make it easier to achieve clean and trouble-free combustion.

Combustion of fuels

Heat and light are produced by the combustion of mixtures of fuel and air or oxygen. When a petroleum fuel burns, the carbon and hydrogen of which it is composed combine with oxygen to form carbon dioxide and water or steam. For the reaction to be complete there must be sufficient air intimately mixed with the fuel, failing which the carbon will not be completely burnt and will appear in the combustion gases, some as smoke (carbon) and some as carbon monoxide, together with unburnt fuel and hydrogen. Analysis of the gases from the chimney stack will show whether combustion has been carried out efficiently.

It is difficult to secure an intimate mixture of solid fuel and air; mixing is easier with liquid fuel and still easier with gaseous fuel since mixed gases diffuse into each other immediately. With gases, therefore, provided sufficient air is present, satisfactory combustion is readily achieved.

There is little or no problem with kerosine since it is easily vaporized by heat. The heavier fuels, however, cannot be conveniently vaporized by heat and must be atomized into minute droplets to obtain an intimate mixture with air. This is done in the oil burner. The viscosity of the fuel is important in relation to atomization; viscous liquids cannot be atomized easily and may have to be preheated to reduce their viscosity before reaching the burner. Preheating usually allows the most viscous commercial fuels to be atomized without difficulty.

The satisfactory combustion of a fuel oil depends on its efficient atomization, on the supply of the requisite amount of air and on the correct mixing of fuel and air. The quantity of air required for complete combustion can be calculated from the composition of the fuel, but in practice from 10–40%v excess air is necessary according to the application. Too great an excess will chill the flame, with the danger of incomplete combustion, and will carry more heat up the chimney, thus lowering the efficiency of the plant. Only the oxygen in the air takes part in combustion, the 78%v of nitrogen contributes nothing towards combustion but absorbs heat on being heated to the temperature of the combustion gases. For this reason also, too much excess air is undesirable.

Fuel burning equipment

Whichever petroleum fuel is burnt, some form of burner is required to bring the fuel and air together in the right proportions in a suitable form for mixing and to maintain a constant flame of the desired type and size. The efficiency of combustion depends very much on the design of the burner which must be suitable for the type of fuel to be burnt. The principal types of burners in common use are described below under the headings of the various fuels.

Gas burners

Petroleum gases require five to six times as much air by volume for combustion as does coal gas and have a much lower flame speed; they therefore require burners specifically designed for their use. Three types of gas burners are in common use: atmospheric burners with self-induced air for all domestic and some industrial applications; burners using compressed air, for example in high-temperature furnaces; and oxy-gas burners, in metal cutting and in welding of non-ferrous metals.

Kerosine burners

Because it is easily vaporized, kerosine can be readily burnt in relatively simple burners of which there are five main types: long-drum, short-drum, pressure- or vapour-jet, wall-flame and pot burners. To ensure clean combustion and absence of smell, good quality, clean kerosine should always be used.

Long-drum burners are so called on account of the long drum or chimney mounted over them to induce the air required for combustion. They may produce luminous or non-luminous (blue) flames according to the design of the burner. In the luminous flame type the kerosine is supplied via a cotton wick, and air, induced by the chimney, is supplied to both sides of the wick via perforated galleries or, in the case of a circular wick, via a perforated gallery to the outside and via a central tube to the inside of the wick. The quantity of air is sufficient to maintain a smokeless white flame and the burning rate is controlled by varying the exposed area of the wick. In the blue-flame burners the kerosine is again supplied via a cotton wick, usually circular, and induced air is supplied by a central tube and a perforated gallery to the inside and outside of the wick. The design of the gallery and flame spreader is such, however, that the air is supplied at a greater speed than in the luminous flame type and a non-luminous, blue flame results. The flame may be flat or vertical according to the design of the central flame spreader.

Short-drum burners consist of two concentric perforated steel cylinders or 'shells' mounted above a circular wick. When the flame is first lighted, kerosine vaporizes close to the wick and heats the shells. As the rate of vaporization increases the kerosine vapour burns over the whole height of the shells. Air is introduced internally through the central air tube, and thence through the perforations of the inner shell into the combustion zone, and externally between the air shield and the outer shell, producing a multitude of small blue flames within the combustion space. The air is induced by the chimney effect of the hot burning gases between the shells and no long chimney is needed. Short-drum burners may have adjustable cotton wicks fed by capillary action from the reservoir or a fixed asbestos or glass fibre kindler set in an annular trough fed by gravity from a constant-level device. The burning rate is controlled in the former types by adjusting the wick and in the latter types by a fuel regulator and shut off valve or alternatively by raising or lowering the burner and trough relative to the constant-level device.

Pressure- or vapour-jet burners are fitted with a robust reservoir in which pressure is generated by means of a small hand pump. Kerosine is fed under pressure to the vaporizer, initially preheated by burning methylated spirit in the surrounding cup. Kerosine is vaporized in passing through the burner head and emerges from the jet as vapour under pressure. Air is induced by the injector action of the fuel jet and mixes with the emerging vapour. The mixture burns with a blue flame and sufficient heat is generated to maintain efficient vaporization out-of-doors.

Wall-flame burners are also a vaporizing type. Oil is thrown in coarse droplets on to a flame ring from a rotating oil distributor driven by a small electric motor. The fuel is vaporized from the flame ring and ignited by a high-tension electric spark. Combustion air is supplied by a fan driven by the same electric motor and flame grills are used to ensure efficient combustion.

Pot burners, very simple yet effective burners, consist of an open pot with perforated sides, in the bottom of which a thin layer of kerosine is maintained by gravity feed from a reservoir. The fuel is ignited by means of a spill or piece of rag soaked in the fuel and once alight, the flame, which generally burns above the pot, provides sufficient heat to vaporize the oil. Air is obtained through the holes in the side of the pot and may be provided by a natural draught from a flue or by a forced draught from a low-power fan.

Fuel-oil burners

Fuel oils, both distillate and residual, must be atomized before they can be burnt efficiently. There are four main types of fuel-oil burners, blast, rotary-cup, pressure-jet and pot burners.

Blast burners work similarly to a scent spray; a fast-moving blast of air or steam passing over the orifices of the oil-feed pipe blows the issuing oil into a spray of fine droplets. Low-pressure burners operate with air at one third to 1 lb/in^2, for which a fan can be used, medium- and high-pressure burners use dry steam or air from a compressor at respectively 5–15 lb/in² and about 25 lb/in². The Shell Toroidal burner is a special form of blast burner that gives very efficient mixing of fuel and air to provide a very stable high temperature flame, the shape of which can be varied at will. It can be used with air or oxygen.

Rotary-cup burners employ two-stage atomization: the fuel is fed into a cup rotating at high speed and is flung off by centrifugal force as a thin flat disc. A low-pressure air blast moving axially along the outside of the cup atomizes the fuel. This type of burner will atomize oil of much higher viscosity (300–450 sec. Red. I at the temperature of atomization) than can be dealt with by any other type.

Pressure-jet burners have a jet so designed that when the oil is forced through it at high pressure, it rotates rapidly as it issues from the orifice and forms a hollow conical film which breaks into droplets as it spreads out. Pressures of 70–300 lb/in² are normally used but higher pressures are sometimes employed. Even large burners of this type will not function satisfactorily if the viscosity of the oil is outside the range 70–120 sec. Red. I at the temperature of atomization.

Pot burners for distillate fuel oils are exactly the same as those used for kerosine.

Domestic applications

The various applications listed here under the heading of domestic are also common to hotels, schools, institutions, restaurants, canteens and other 'commercial' consumers.

Cooking

Domestic cookers, ranging from small single burners to complete cooking stoves, can be fired by distillate oil using either atomizing or vaporizing burners. Alternatively they can be fired by either natural gas or LPG. Gaseous fuels are often preferred on account of convenience, ease of operation and absence of smell [Fig. 127].

Kerosine cookers compare favourably with gas appliances and in some countries provide the principal outlet for kerosine. Luminous-flame wick-fed kerosine appliances are almost obsolete, having been superseded by blue-flame types.

Space heating

Natural gas and LPG are both used for domestic space heating. Where the total heating load is limited, kerosine is used extensively in blue-flame burners and can be used to maintain a background temperature by convective heating, with radiant heat locally as required.

Two types of appliances are generally used – the unflued, portable kerosine heater with an output up to 10 000 Btu/h and the flued convector heater with an output up to 50 000 Btu/h.

Several types of kerosine heaters are available to supply both convective and radiant heat. A very popular type employs a blue-flame short-drum burner to heat a hemispherical wire gauze mantle above it; the wire becomes red-hot and provides radiant heat. Another type employs a vapour-jet burner to heat a bank of radiants similar in design to those in the ordinary domestic gas fire. The portable appliance demands a premium quality kerosine.

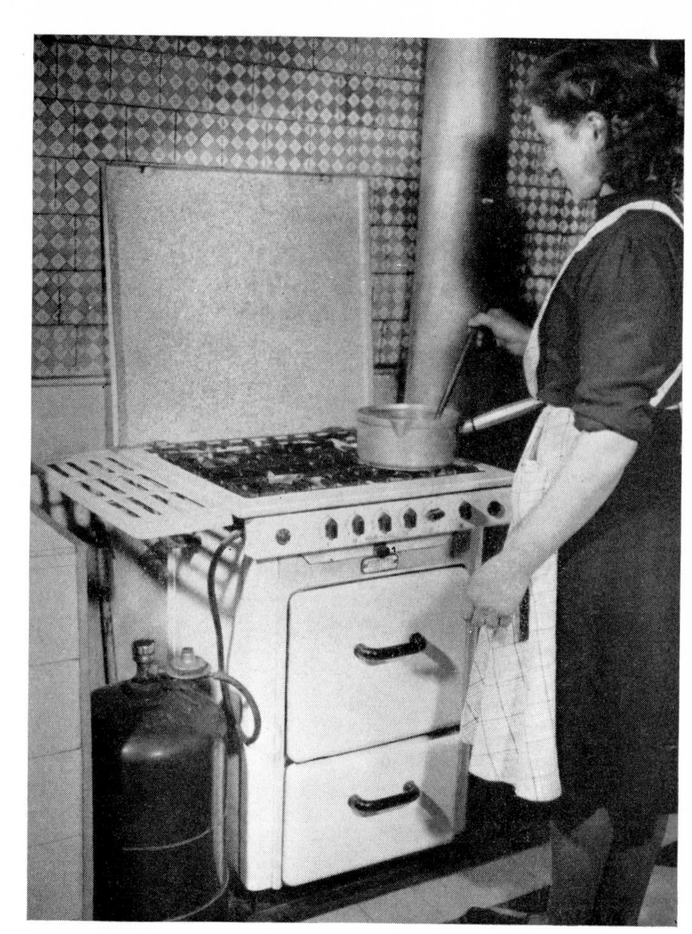

Fig. 127 Domestic cooking stove fired by LPG

Flued convector heaters commonly employ pot burners and the preferred fuel is kerosine, although gas oil is used in many countries where kerosine is highly taxed. An interesting development is a unit with a back boiler that provides hot water for radiators in adjoining rooms.

Central heating

The central heating of houses has long been widespread in North America and some European countries and is now increasingly practised in many others, including the UK. Heating may be effected by the circulation of either hot water or hot air. A certain amount of attention is being devoted to district heating schemes in some countries. Central heating systems usually provide domestic hot water from the same boiler.

The advantages of gaseous or liquid fuels over solid fuels are considerable; they are clean and ashless and their automatic supply and control eliminates much labour. Natural gas is used extensively in the USA and Canada where it is widely available. Outside North America gas is less used because town gas is generally more expensive than other fuels, natural gas is less available and LPG is not convenient. The increasing availability of natural gas, both as such and as a constituent of town gas, will no doubt alter the picture in the near future.

Liquid fuels are used widely for domestic central heating

and two types of installations are in vogue, semi-automatic and fully automatic.

Semi-automatic installations usually rely on pot burners with a forced draught, using either kerosine or gas oil. The installation is semi-automatic in that although it has to be manually started, it burns continuously with a high or low flame according to the heat demand.

Fully automatic installations operate intermittently, the fuel supply being cut off when heat is no longer required, and switched on again and the flame re-established when the demand arises. When the burner is in action it operates at a constant rate. Both pressure-jet and medium-pressure air blast burners are used. The latter is somewhat the noisier but can handle heavier fuel and is less sensitive to fuel quality or to fluctuations of viscosity with temperature.

Some of the smaller installations are equipped with a wall-flame burner, operating on kerosine.

Air conditioning

Air conditioning in homes, offices and workshops not only gives greater comfort to their occupants but leads to greater efficiency in production and sometimes to lower maintenance costs for machinery. Air conditioning includes simultaneous control of air temperature, humidity, cleanliness and distribution. Air-conditioning plants must provide a means of heating the air when required and a means of cooling it, not only to lower its temperature but also to remove excess moisture. Although most air-conditioning plants are operated electrically many installations employ petroleum fuels (gas, kerosine or fuel oil) as the source of energy for both heating and refrigeration.

Water heating

Where hot water is not supplied by a central-heating system, the heating of water for domestic purposes is an important and growing application for kerosine. Natural gas and LPG are also used, the latter being particularly convenient for small local water heaters over sinks and baths.

Refrigeration

Kerosine is used in many domestic refrigerators where gas or electricity is not available. Small luminous-flame or blue-flame burners are used, and since they must operate for long periods without attention good quality fuel is essential. LPG is also used.

Lighting

Town gas has long been used for lighting, initially in luminous bats-wing burners, subsequently in blue-flame burners fitted with incandescent mantles. Natural gas and refinery gases, where available, are sometimes 'reformed' to town gas specifications, fed into the town mains and thus used in equipment made for burning town gas. Natural gas, refinery gases and LPG can also be used as such for lighting, but require burners designed for their use. LPG is a convenient fuel where no mains gas supply is available.

Blue-flame burners with incandescent mantles are used almost exclusively for domestic lighting with petroleum gases.

The use of kerosine as an illuminant was the first extensive application of any petroleum product and the earliest processing of crude oil was directed to the production of oil for lamps.

Kerosine lighting appliances are of three types, those using a luminous-flame wick burner, those using a blue-flame wick burner with an incandescent mantle and those using a pressure burner with an incandescent mantle.

The wick-fed yellow-flame burner is the oldest and least efficient of the three types but is still much used all over the world – often in a home-made form – because of its simplicity Many models are extant from the very primitive to the most elaborate. [Fig. 128]. A carbon-like deposit, known as 'char', tends to form on the top end of the wick and is usually the result of decomposition of the fuel exposed to the head of the flame but may also be caused by contaminants such as heavier fuels or certain sulphur compounds. It is therefore especially important to use clean high-grade kerosine with this type of burner.

Fig. 128 Left: kerosine lamp and cooking stove in an African hut; Right: kerosine lamps and heaters

The wick-fed incandescent lamp is extensively used for domestic lighting and has virtually superseded the yellow-flame type in all but the less developed areas of the world. It is much more efficient than the luminous-flame lamp and is free from smoke or smell.

The pressure-jet lamp is twice as efficient as the wick-fed mantle type but is somewhat noisy in operation. The volatility of the kerosine is important since the fuel must be completely vaporized as it issues from the jet; the kerosine must also be thermally stable and free from contaminants to avoid formation of deposits in the vaporizing tubes.

Industrial applications

Petroleum fuels of all kinds are extensively used in industry for heating purposes – apart from the heating of buildings, etc, where the applications are akin to those already described under domestic applications. The strictly industrial uses fall into three groups, steam raising, furnace heating and miscellaneous general uses.

Where available, natural gas is extensively used, as is LPG, especially where, with direct heating, it is important to have no adverse effect of the fuel on either equipment or processed material. LPG is extremely convenient for small local applications such as plumbing, welding, and general workshop use, on account of its portable supply. Kerosine is relatively little used for large-scale industrial heating except where there is a price advantage compared with gas oil. Heavy distillate and residual fuel oils are extensively used, the choice depending on several factors, such as consumption rate, amount of sulphur and ash that can be tolerated and simplicity of operation.

Steam raising

The greatest proportion of fuel oil consumed is used in the production of steam for industrial processes, electricity generation, ship propulsion, etc. The lower first cost of the combustion equipment, the ease of control of firing and the generally lower cost of maintenance all contribute towards making oil fuel more attractive than solid fuel. Residual fuels are most commonly used.

Fuel oil has almost entirely replaced coal for the firing of marine boilers; in 1919 about 87% of the world tonnage of steam-propelled ships used coal, this figure had dropped to 8% in 1956 and less than 3% in 1964.

For industrial purposes, package boilers, either of the shell type [Fig. 129] or the water-tube type are generally used nowadays instead of the Lancashire and older brick-set water-tube boilers. Being factory assembled, they can be made operational very rapidly on site and, having much higher heat absorption rates, they require less space. The shell and water-tube package boilers have maximum steam outputs of approximately 40 000 and 90 000 lb/h respectively. For greater outputs and higher steam temperatures and pressures, larger water-tube boilers are used.

For electric power generation the trend is towards larger single boiler units which may be fired with 30–40 oil burners and produce more than 1500 tons/h of steam.

Pressure-jet and steam-atomizing burners are most commonly used in the firing of water-tube boilers. The smaller flame angle normally associated with air or steam atomizers and rotary-cup burners make them most suitable for firing the somewhat restricted combustion zone of shell type boilers.

In some parts of the world oil firing is used in locomotives. Steam-atomizing burners are used, the air for combustion

Fig. 129 Package boiler, shell type

being drawn in by a steam injector in the chimney. Oil is usually fed to the burner by gravity and may require preheating. The oil consumption of a steam locomotive is large, some 800–4500 tons/year per engine.

Furnace heating

Solid fuel is still used extensively for furnace heating, but despite the low specific cost in many countries there are several disadvantages in its use, particularly the high ash formation, the difficulty of achieving close control of combustion, and high maintenance costs. Also for high-temperature furnaces, ash formation may limit the intensity of combustion. Pulverized coal provides quicker burning but in no way reduces ash formation. Solid fuel is sometimes used indirectly, being first converted to producer gas – with some loss in calorific value but enabling somewhat closer control.

Gaseous fuels are eminently suitable for furnace heating, and natural gas is extensively used where available. Fuel oil is in general use and is especially useful for high-temperature furnaces on account of closer control and the high level of temperature and radiation even when cold air is used for combustion. Higher levels of flame radiation are achieved by preheating the air. The choice of fuel and the type of equipment used are frequently influenced by the type of material that is processed in the furnace and some of the more specific instances follow.

Iron and steel industry

Most iron is produced by heating iron ore in coke-fired blast furnaces, but output can be increased and coke saved by injecting fuel oil or natural gas into the furnace with the blast air. In modern practice the iron ore is ground to 'fines' and then agglomerated into porous pieces known as 'sinter', by heating with coke fines. This sinter forms the raw material for the blast furnace and fuel oil or natural gas is eminently suitable for igniting the sinter bed. A number of schemes have been proposed to utilize only petroleum fuels in the production of iron, especially in countries rich in ore but poor in coal, but none has so far proved economically attractive.

Improvements in blast furnace operation have resulted in less coke being required per ton of iron produced, with the consequence that the quantity and calorific value of the blast furnace gas are reduced. The calorific value can be raised by injecting light distillate fuel into the gas mains, so enabling the gas to be used in the gas engines commonly used to generate power in the works.

Large quantities of steel are produced in open-hearth furnaces fired by producer gas, natural gas, fuel oil or a combination of gas and oil. When the charge consists mainly or entirely of cold pig iron and steel scrap the melting time can be reduced by the use of oxygen/fuel oil burners.

The Bessemer converter is gradually being replaced by oxygen-blown converters. Converters can absorb only a limited amount of cold steel scrap but more scrap can be used if it is premelted, which can be effected by the use of oxy/fuel burners. The Shell Toroidal burner is being used extensively for this purpose [Fig. 130].

Alloy steels are produced in electric arc furnaces and by melting the charge with oxy/fuel burners the rate of production can be increased and electricity saved.

Liquid and gaseous fuels are used in the many reheating jobs in a steelworks, such as soaking pits, rolling-mill furnaces, forging furnaces, heat-treatment furnaces, galvanizing and tinning baths, as well as in the manufacture of welded pipes, nuts and bolts, etc. In some of these applications, for example annealing, it is most important to avoid any deleterious effect on the goods and distillate fuel oils or, better still, petroleum gases are used.

Fig. 130 Above: scrap metal being charged into an open-hearth furnace fitted with a Shell Toroidal burner; Below: close-up of flame

Ceramic industry

For the firing of heavy clay products such as bricks and tiles, the main factor is thermal cost, since nearly all types of fuel can be used. Solid fuels are giving way to liquid and gaseous fuels on account of reduced labour requirements and greater cleanliness. Closer control of kiln conditions also allows improved products in many cases.

With pottery products such as tableware, electrical and fine porcelain, sanitary ware, etc, the main requirement is quality of product rather than thermal cost of fuel, and hence fuels which allow close control of the kiln temperature and the kiln atmosphere have a distinct advantage. For this reason gaseous fuels are often preferred to liquid fuels, and can command a good premium. Electricity is often the main competitor to gaseous fuels where the firing temperature is limited to 1300°C and where an oxidizing atmosphere is sufficient.

The firing of refractory products usually calls for high kiln temperatures and hence gaseous and liquid fuels are generally preferred on account of closer temperature control and greater thermal efficiency.

For the firing of both intermittent and tunnel kilns conventional premixed gas burners are generally used or, in the case of liquid fuels, either atomizing burners or liquid injection equipment with suitable volumetric metering devices. The latter equipment relies on a high environment temperature rather than on atomization for combustion of the oil, and the ease of metering and distributing the fuel is a distinct advantage. This type of equipment is therefore used extensively on tunnel kilns operating at a constant temperature.

Cement and lime manufacture

Both coal- and oil-fired kilns of various types are in general use for the manufacture of cement, lime and plaster. Natural gas is also used where the price differential allows for the lower flame radiation and hence lower efficiency.

Glass manufacture

Gaseous and liquid petroleum fuels are both used in the manufacture of glass and the advantages of gas frequently outweigh its possibly higher price. Large oil-fired tank furnaces are employed for melting the glass used for the manufacture of standard shaped articles such as bottles and jars and for the production of sheet and plate glass. Special glass such as optical glass may be produced in oil-fired pot furnaces. Glass articles, when first withdrawn from the furnace, are generally in a state of strain and must be annealed by reheating and cooling very slowly. Annealing furnaces may be gas or oil fired.

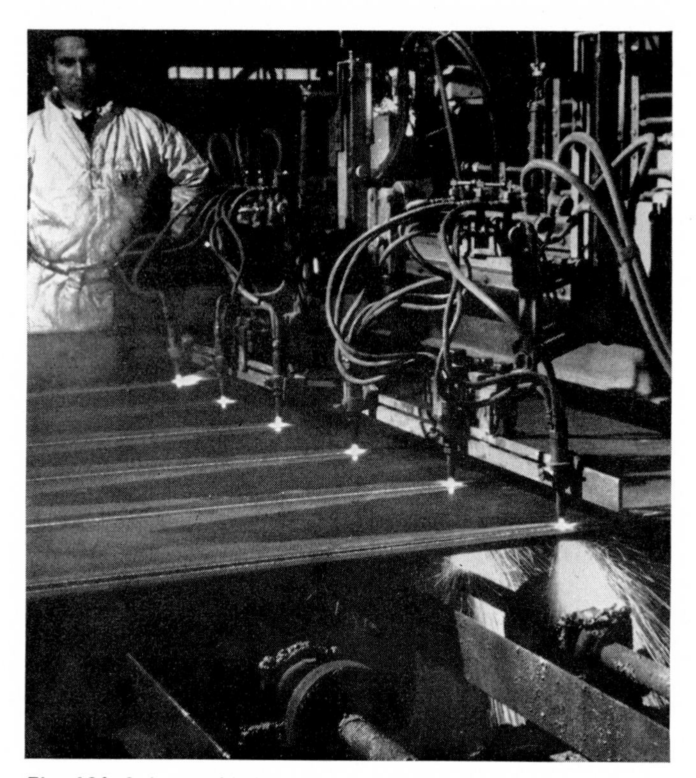

Fig. 131 Strip metal being cut with 6 oxy/LPG torches

Enamelling and stoving

Gas- and oil-fired furnaces are used in the application of vitreous enamel to cast iron or pressed steel goods such as baths, cooking stoves, weighing machines, kitchen sinks, etc. Furnaces for stoving low-temperature enamelled articles and drying ovens for painted articles are similarly fired.

Bread and biscuit baking

The side flue oven widely used for baking was originally heated by solid fuel but is easily converted to liquid fuel, which is now extensively used. Medium- or low-pressure blast burners are generally used, with fully automatic control. Gas firing is also used where natural gas or LPG is available. Advantages of gas lie in the cleanliness and ability to heat directly, giving close control and rapid heating up. Large, continuously operated, tunnel ovens are generally oil or electrically heated.

Controlled atmospheres

Controlled atmospheres are used extensively in the heat-treatment of steel and other metals in order to prevent surface damage, to obtain a desired surface finish or to modify the surface properties. Oxygen, carbon dioxide, carbon monoxide, hydrogen, sulphur compounds and water vapour can all be reactive to metals during heat treatment. The requisite in a controlled atmosphere is to keep these constituents constant within the limits required by the operation in question. Such atmospheres can be readily achieved by burning natural gas or LPG, either partially or completely, under controlled conditions of combustion.

Lighting

Petroleum fuels are little used for general industrial lighting in the way they are still used for domestic lighting. There are, however, a number of special applications deserving of mention.

LPG is used to an increasing extent in place of acetylene for the illumination of buoys. It is also used in lighthouse lamps employing a blue-flame burner with an incandescent mantle.

Luminous-flame kerosine lamps are used as storm lamps, guard lamps on road works, etc, and signal lamps on railways. Blue-flame, incandescent mantle kerosine lamps are still used in some lighthouses.

Miscellaneous industrial uses

Metal cutting, welding, etc

LPG is used extensively in oxy/LPG burners for metal cutting and the welding of non-ferrous metals. The welding of steel has not so far been practicable because the necessary reducing flame is not hot enough for satisfactory welding. Fig. 131 shows strip metal being cut with oxy/LPG torches.

Fig. 132 Grain drier

Manufacture of town gas

Until about 1940, practically all town gas manufactured outside North America was made from coal or its products. In recent years, owing to the shortage of good carbonizing coal and increasing prices, other raw materials, notably petroleum products, have been used.

The oldest application of petroleum fuels for gas making is the carburetted water-gas process developed in the USA about 1872–5. Water gas, made by passing steam over red hot coke was enriched by passing gas oil over the hot coke. The resulting gas, known as carburetted water gas, had a higher calorific value than that of water gas and was used to meet peak load demands.

Town gas is now made to an increasing extent from petroleum fractions by several processes depending mainly on catalytic reforming in the presence of steam. A variety of feed stocks from natural gas to heavy fuel oil is used.

The direct use of natural gas as town gas is dealt with in the chapter on Natural gas (p. 67).

Benzol wash oils

Gas oil is used extensively in gas works for removing benzol and naphthalene from coal gas before its distribution via the mains. The gas and oil are brought into intimate contact in scrubbers, the benzol and naphthalene are dissolved out by the oil and later recovered from it by distillation and crystallization.

Feedstocks for chemical manufacture

Large quantities of natural gas, refinery gases and light distillates are used as feedstocks for the manufacture of chemicals but this subject is dealt with in Raw materials and primary conversion processes (p. 196).

Agricultural applications

Apart from the obvious uses for space and water heating, cooking and lighting, which are dealt with under domestic applications, and the use of fuel for tractors which is dealt with under Fuels and lubricants for automotive IC engines (p. 126), there are a number of specialized agricultural applications of petroleum fuels as follows.

Grain drying

Grain can be stored only when its moisture content is below a certain level, different for each variety. Artificial drying makes the farmer independent of weather conditions and enables him to store grain which would otherwise have to be sold earlier at a less favourable price. Grain can be dried in bulk in tray or silo driers or in sacks, either directly by passing combustion gases through it or indirectly by passing hot air through it, the air having been heated in some form of heat exchanger by combustion gases. In the former case natural gas or LPG is used, being free from sulphur; in the latter case any petroleum fuel can be used. Fig. 132 shows a grain drier that can be heated by gaseous or liquid petroleum fuels.

Grass drying

Haymaking is essentially a slow drying process in the open air. Under adverse weather conditions a serious loss of nutrients (up to 30%w) may occur. To reduce these losses

Fig 133 Kerosine-burning infrared chick brooder

(to below 5%w) freshly cut grass is blown along with hot combustion gases and excess air through a drying tunnel. Gas oil or heavy fuel is used as fuel. Careful regulation is necessary to avoid overheating or scorching the grass.

Quick haymaking

Intermediate between haymaking and grass drying are processes called 'quick haymaking' or 'barn hay drying'. An appreciable amount of moisture is removed by normal field haymaking practices in the swath or windrow and the herbage is then taken into the barn to complete the drying. Slightly warmed air is blown through bales or loose hay on a mesh floor. Either gaseous or liquid petroleum fuel may be used as the source of heat.

Heating of animal quarters

In the intensive rearing of poultry the young chicks have to be kept warm; this is done either by space heating or, more usually, by hover heaters with radiant burners operating on LPG or kerosine.

In pig rearing, similar hover burners provide sufficient warmth for piglets to be kept away from the sow, thus avoiding their being crushed. When fattening pigs, the provision of heated houses allows fewer calories to be used by

Fig. 134 Milking parlour with LPG-fired radiant heaters

the pigs in keeping themselves warm and more for growing; the cost of heating is more than covered by the improvement in food conversion (weight increase per weight of food consumed).

Underfloor heating of cattle pens often obviates the need for expensive straw for litter and reduces labour. Heating of milk parlours prevents accidents to stock and staff under freezing conditions.

Various heating systems are used to suit the particular conditions, and LPG or gas oil is commonly used as fuel. Fig. 133 shows a kerosine-burning infrared chick brooder while Fig. 134 illustrates the heating of a milking parlour by LPG fired radiant heaters.

Flame cultivation

Flame cultivation consists of passing a flame across the crop rows at a time when the crop is large enough to withstand the heat and the weeds are small enough to succumb to it. Only sufficient heat is required to bring the juice in the lower part of the stems to the boil. This causes the cells to rupture and the weed withers and dies in a few hours. The equipment is mounted on a tractor and able to treat four to six rows at a time; LPG is the most commonly used fuel. General burning of fields can be applied prior to crop emergence thus giving the crop a start over the weeds so that it will be strong enough to withstand the flaming of the next weed generation. Two to three flamings are usually sufficient for crops like potatoes, sugar beet, cotton or maize. Fig. 135 shows a flame cultivator fired by LPG.

Flame torches are also used for clearing ditches and roadsides, stubble and potato haulms.

Soil sterilization

In horticultural and greenhouse practice soil sterilization is often effected by steam which may be generated in a gas- or oil-fired boiler. For smaller quantities of soil, as for potting, the soil may be passed through a flame in a rotary drum or oscillating tray machine fired by petroleum gas or kerosine.

Fig. 135 Flame cultivation

Fig. 136 CO_2 enrichment by combustion of LPG

CO_2 enrichment in greenhouses

Under the influence of light, plants assimilate carbon dioxide. Atmospheric air contains about 0·03%v CO_2; increasing this to 0·1 or 0·15%v increases the rate of assimilation and promotes growth. Plants grow more quickly and abundantly and crops can be picked earlier. The CO_2 can be obtained most economically by burning LPG or low sulphur kerosine in the greenhouse through suitable burners Fig. 136 shows a burner producing CO_2 by combustion of LPG.

Crop drying and curing

Many crops require to be dried or cured in the course of preparing the marketed product, for instance tea, tobacco, hops, copra. Gaseous and liquid petroleum fuels are extensively used in these processes.

Biocides

Various petroleum fractions are used as carriers for insecticides, fungicides, herbicides, etc, which, however, are dealt with more fully under Agricultural chemicals (p. 236).

New ways of generating electrical power

Electricity is generated by rotating an assembly of wire coils (the armature) in a magnetic field. The rotary motion

Fig. 137 Fuel cell, methanol as fuel, supplying power to a hammer

is provided by some sort of engine, steam, water or gas turbine, free piston engine or diesel engine, Where steam power is used the heat required to generate the steam is provided by the combustion of coal or petroleum fuels or by nuclear reactions. Where internal combustion engines are used petroleum fuels are again much in evidence.

This whole process involves, therefore, release of heat energy by combustion or nuclear reaction, conversion of heat energy to mechanical energy, and conversion of mechanical energy to electricity. At each stage there is wastage of energy and the total loss can be as much as 70% or even more of the original energy in the fuel.

The needs of space exploration on the one hand, and the increasing awareness of the need to utilize reserves of fossil fuels as efficiently as possible on the other hand, have, in the last decade or so, stimulated efforts to discover new ways of generating electrical power more efficiently. Such new methods are of interest to the petroleum industry, either as potential users of petroleum fuels or as alternative methods not requiring petroleum fuels. Those in the former category are briefly described here as an indication of future possibilities in the application of petroleum fuels, but none has yet reached commercial operation although laboratory models have been successfully achieved.

Fuel cells

The fuel cell converts chemical energy directly to electrical energy by a process that is the reverse of electrolysis. A fuel gas is fed into one of two hollow porous electrodes in a liquid electrolyte whilst oxygen or air is supplied to the other electrode. Ionic reactions similar to those of a primary storage battery occur at the electrode surfaces releasing electrons that flow in the external circuit.

So far only hydrogen, carbon monoxide, methanol, hydrazine and a number of rather exotic fuels have been successfully used (in laboratory models) but the aim is to develop fuel cells that can operate on readily available, cheap hydrocarbon fuels such as natural gas, LPG or kerosine. A very considerable amount of research and development is being devoted to these projects and there is a considerable chance of successful commercial development in the forseeable future. Fig. 137 shows a fuel cell, with methanol as fuel, operating a Kanga electric hammer.

Thermoelectric generators

Thermoelectric generators convert thermal energy directly to electrical energy. When the two ends of a metal rod, wire or strip are maintained at different temperatures the free electrons in the metal migrate to the cooler end and a difference in electrical potential (voltage) is set up between the two ends. If two different metal wires are joined together at one end and this junction is heated to a high temperature while the other ends are kept cold the potential differences between the ends of each wire will be different and there will be a net potential difference between the cool ends which can be tapped to produce an electric current in an external circuit. Thermoelectric materials have been developed capable of producing power outputs of 100 watts and a generator rated at 500 watts is under development.

Any source of heat can be used to heat the hot junction, and petroleum fuels will no doubt be used.

Magnetohydrodynamic generators

Magnetohydrodynamic (MHD) generators convert the kinetic energy of a stream of gas to electrical energy. The conventional generation of electricity by the rotation of loops of wire in a magnetic field stems from Faraday's discovery that a conductor moving in a magnetic field generates electricity. This is true of any conductor, solid, liquid or gaseous. A gas can be made conducting by heating it to a very high temperature, 2000–3000°C, and introducing into it particles of certain metals such as potassium or caesium. In the MHD generator hot conducting gas flows at right angles to a magnetic field and electric power is withdrawn at right angles to the direction of flow and to the magnetic field via electrodes embedded in the walls of the duct that conveys the gas.

Hot conducting gases can be produced by burning petroleum fuels and injecting the seeding element into the gas stream, and high velocities of the gas stream can be achieved by passing through a divergent nozzle. The hot gases from the MHD generator are then passed through a steam boiler and the steam so generated used to drive a conventional turbo generator. In this way a greater proportion of the energy of the fuel can be utilized; a conventional steam turbine generator may achieve at most 40% efficiency, by using a MHD generator in conjunction with it an efficiency of 60% may be reached.

Lubricants for industry

Lubricants for internal combustion engines have been dealt with in previous chapters; in this chapter all other uses are included under the heading of industry even though some are automotive, aviation or marine applications. This is a matter of convenience to save repetitive mention of applications that are fundamentally the same whether in industrial or other usage, for example the operation of an anti-friction bearing is the same in a motor car, an aeroplane or a textile machine and the lubrication of a hypoid gear presents the same problems in the motor car as in industrial equipment. Also included under the heading of lubricants are a number of products that are not lubricants, for instance insulating oils, or are not primarily lubricants, for instance hydraulic fluids, but which are customarily associated with lubricants in research and marketing operations because, on the whole, similar materials are used in their formulation.

Industrial applications of lubricants are so numerous and varied that it would be impossible to deal with them all in a book of this size and scope, and only the more important are described in the following pages where, for convenience, they are listed in alphabetical order.

Bearings

The most common application of lubricants is to bearings, which are included in an endless variety of mechanical equipment. A bearing is a support provided to hold a moving member of a machine in its correct position, and there are two main types, plain bearings and anti-friction bearings.

Plain bearings

In its simplest form the plain bearing [Fig. 138] consists of a hollow cylinder in which a shaft rotates. The portion of the shaft within the bearing is called the journal, and the hollow cylinder is called the journal bearing. If the revolving shaft is subjected to an end load, a thrust bearing must be provided, and may consist of a collar on the shaft rotating against a flange on the support. A plain bearing may also be used to support a shaft or spindle that does not rotate but moves backwards and forwards longitudinally; it is then called a guide-bearing.

It is generally preferable not to use the same metal for surfaces moving in contact with each other, and it is usual to provide the bearing with a liner of softer metal which lessens the risk of damage to the more expensive journal in the event of failure. Plain bearings are usually oil lubricated although grease may be used in some instances, as when sealing arrangements are inadequate for oil. When a journal rotates in a bearing, an oil-film is built up as a result of the rotation, and prevents metallic contact between journal and bearing. The viscosity of the oil should be as low as possible in order to reduce friction, but not so low that the film will break down under the load imposed and permit metal-to-metal contact. Bearing oils have viscosities ranging from

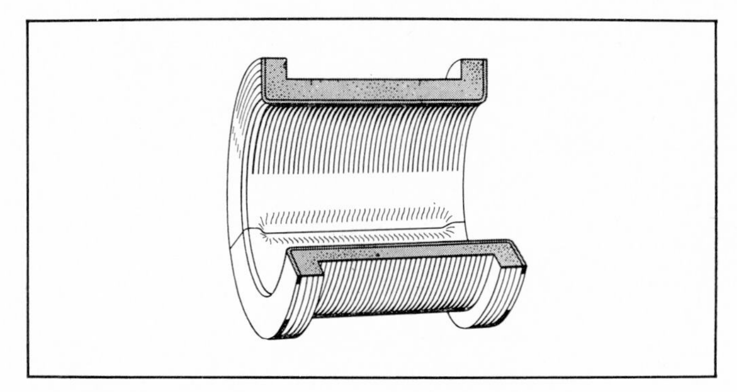

Fig. 138 Plain bearing

that of light spindle oil to that of heavy cylinder oil, the choice depending on speed, load and operating temperature. Under mild operating conditions LVI oils are adequate, but the more stable HVI oils are required for more severe conditions.

The method of lubrication depends mainly on the speed of the shaft in the bearing; an oil bath and splash system is suitable for low and medium speeds, a circulation system for medium speeds and spray and mist systems for high speeds.

A special type of plain bearing is the porous bearing, made of sintered metal powder, usually bronze, and impregnated with oil during manufacture. Porous bearings need no additional lubrication in service, and have been particularly successful in lightly loaded apparatus such as domestic vacuum cleaners.

Some bearings necessarily come into contact with water; in some instances, as in vertical open crankcase steam engines, oils in which water will emulsify are required, in others, as in the Morgoil bearings of steel rolling mills, oils from which water readily separates are required. The former are produced by adding emulsifiers to the oil, the latter by careful selection or by special treatment of straight oils to ensure the absence of trace quantities of emulsion promoting materials.

Anti-friction bearings

In the plain bearing, the moving surfaces slide one over the other. A considerable reduction in friction can be achieved by replacing this sliding motion by a rolling motion, and this is done by attaching hardened steel rings, called races, to the moving and stationary members and inserting between them a row of steel balls or rollers. A cage or separator ensures that the rolling elements are adequately spaced and do not rub together [Fig. 139].

Ball bearings may consist of a single or double row of balls in different kinds of races, depending on the magnitude and direction of loading. Roller bearings are used for heavier loads and more severe conditions. The rollers may be straight, tapered, barrelled or concave, depending on the application; straight rollers are usually used for radial loads

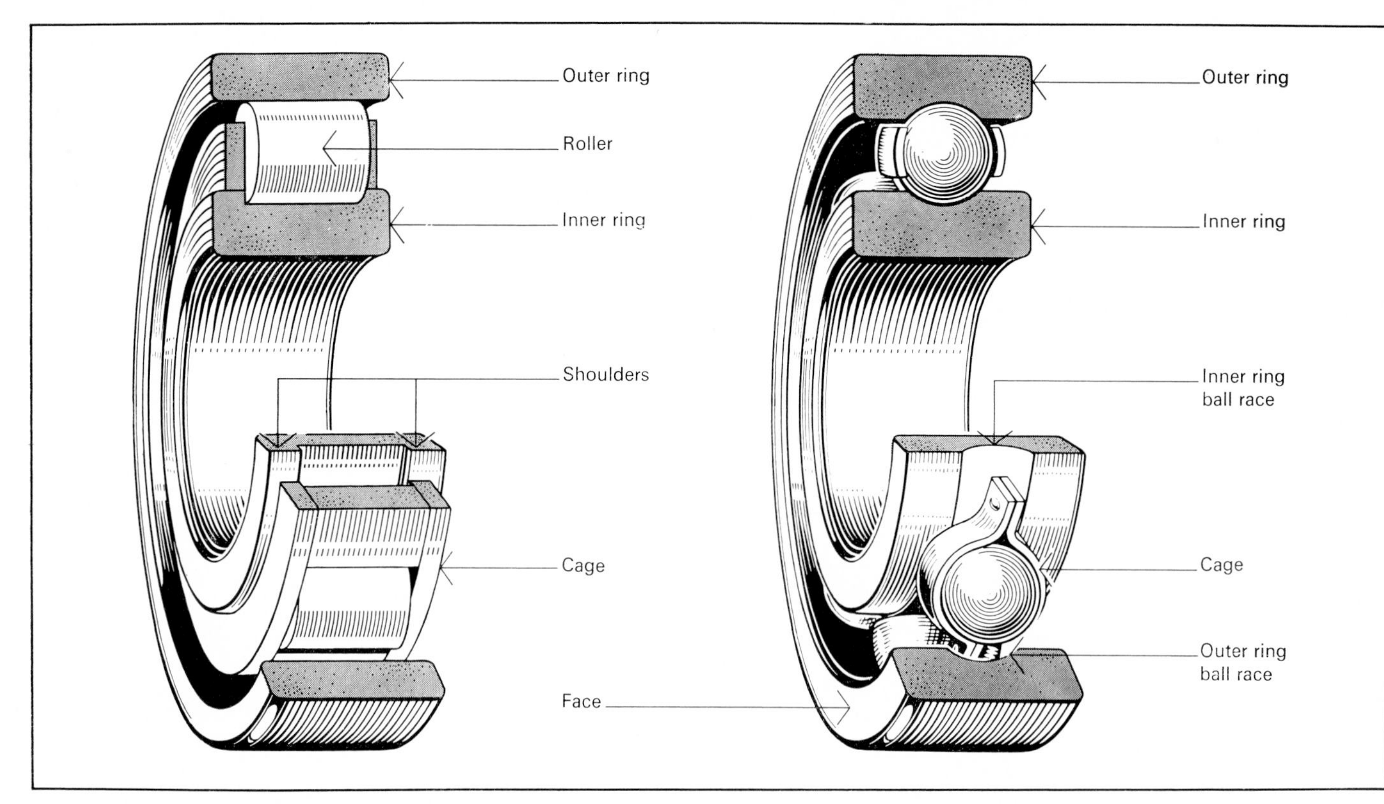

Fig. 139 Anti-friction bearings: roller (left) and ball bearings (right)

whereas tapered rollers can support both radial and thrust loads; barrelled rollers ensure self-alignment. A special type of roller bearing, the needle roller bearing, has thin rollers assembled direct on to a hardened shaft without races; it is used generally for oscillating movements.

Theoretically, rolling contact needs no lubricant, but in practice some sliding occurs in anti-friction bearings, particularly in some types of ball bearings, due to distortion under load. There is also some sliding between the rolling elements and the cages, and a lubricant is therefore necessary to control sliding friction, to act as a seal against ingress of moisture or other contaminant and to protect against corrosion.

Most anti-friction bearings use grease, which stays in place without elaborate sealing, does not need constant replenishing, and is an effective seal against ingress of contaminants. Many bearings are filled with grease on assembly and then sealed, the original grease charge being expected to last the life of the bearing. The choice of grease depends on the speed, load and running temperature of the bearing, but has been considerably simplified by the advent of multipurpose lithium greases (p. 118). There is little difference between general industrial and automotive requirements for greases, but the demands on aviation greases are in general more severe and cover a wider range of conditions for any one grease than those for any other application. In particular, good performance at very high as well as very low temperature is required, which necessitates good oxidation resistance at high temperatures and adequate fluidity at low temperatures. Both automotive and aviation greases require high resistance to water, and little tendency for oil separation.

Oil is sometimes used in anti-friction bearings, but requires very effective sealing unless the bearing is in a totally enclosed, oil lubricated assembly.

Compressors

A compressor is a machine for compressing gases. Compressed air is widely used to provide power to operate tools, to spray liquids, to grease-lubricate vehicles and for a host of other purposes. Gases of all sorts are compressed in order to store large quantities in small cylinders, either as compressed gas or as liquid.

When a gas is compressed its temperature rises in proportion to the degree of compression, and because high compression may cause very high temperatures, it is usually achieved in stages, cooling the gas between successive stages.

There are three main types of compressor, reciprocating, rotary positive displacement and aerodynamic. The reciprocating piston/cylinder type is the simplest and its method of operation is obvious. Rotary positive displacement compressors operate by trapping gas in a succession of cells from which it is driven by the mechanical contraction of the cell enforced by the contour of the casing as the rotor revolves. Aerodynamic or turbo compressors depend on changes in the velocity of the gas whilst in continued motion. There are several types of rotary compressors, depending on the way in which the cells are formed in the positive displacement types or the direction of gas flow in the aerodynamic types.

The method of lubricating a compressor varies with the type and design of the unit. Reciprocating compressors require both cylinder and bearing lubrication; small units are generally splash lubricated, but larger units may have either a circulating system or direct feed by means of a mechanical lubricator. Some rotary compressors need only bearing lubrication, others, such as the sliding-vane compressors, require internal lubrication as well. Some have plain bearings, many have anti-friction bearings either oil or grease lubricated. Depending on the design, rotary compressors may have oil-bath, circulation or direct-feed lubrication. In general a comparatively frugal supply of oil is provided with a minimum carry over from the compressor, but a recent development, as yet confined to sliding-vane compressors but likely to spread to others, is the oil-cooled compressor in which a large quantity of oil is forced into the compressor, and is separated from the compressed gas on the discharge side and recirculated. This results in economy in power, lighter weight equipment and low discharge temperatures, a distinct advantage in the life of hoses when air is being used as an operating force.

Except where no internal lubrication is required, compressors bring lubricating oil and gas into intimate contact under the best possible conditions to promote reaction, i.e. high pressure, high temperature and fine state of subdivision or large area of exposed surface. This must be taken into account in the choice of lubricant. When compressing air, highly stable, oxidation resistant oils are required, when compressing other gases, the possibility of chemical reaction with the lubricant must be borne in mind.

Depending on the severity of the conditions, high-quality straight oils, oils with anti-oxidant and anti-rust additives (as for steam turbines) or anti-oxidant, dispersant oils (as for diesel engines) are used. The latter are particularly preferred for high temperature operations where severe oxidation and deposit formation is to be expected. For grease lubricated anti-friction bearings, multi-purpose lithium greases are preferred.

Corrosion prevention

The protection of metals against corrosion is important because corrosion, especially rusting, can cause very considerable losses to industry in both materials and time. Relatively permanent protection is provided by painting, enamelling, etc, but such durable and expensive coatings are neither justifiable nor desirable in many instances where some measure of protection is nevertheless required to keep the metal surface in good order pending further processing or use. The need arises most frequently during transport or storage, and may be for periods ranging from a few days to a year or more. Products serving this purpose are known as 'temporary protectives', temporary not only in duration but in the sense of 'easily removed', as opposed to paint and such 'permanent' protectives.

Protection from corrosion depends on preventing moist air from coming into contact with the metal, and the application of an impervious coating is a convenient and effective means. Temporary protectives provide coatings ranging from thin oily or hard films to thick grease-like films, and are commonly classified according to the type of film (oily, soft or hard) and the method of application (hot-dip, solvent deposited). The duration of protection depends not only on the type of film but also on the severity of the conditions to which the article is exposed.

Oily films are suitable only for short-term protection, but are easily applied and removed, and in some instances need not be removed at all before further use or treatment. They are used, for example, on precision tools, strip and sheet after rolling, enclosed gears on idle equipment or for indoor storage of spare parts. They are provided by mineral oil with or without rust inhibitors or other protectives such as petrolatum or lanolin.

Soft films give more lasting protection, the duration of which depends on their thickness and consistency, ranging from thin, transparent to thick, grease-like. They are used on metal parts during storage, on the exterior of machinery and on packaged parts and assemblies during transport and storage; thick ones can be used for storage or shipment under severe outdoor conditions. Soft films are provided by petrolatum or lanolin/petrolatum mixtures, lubricating greases or solutions of such substances in a volatile solvent such as white spirit. The solvent types are applied cold, the others either hot or cold.

Hard films provide protection for comparatively longer periods under severe conditions and are not readily disrupted by handling, as are soft or oily films. They are often preferred for this reason and because of their lesser tendency to pick up contaminants, but they are correspondingly more difficult to remove. They are usually deposited from solutions of rosin, waxes, lanolin and similar materials in a volatile solvent.

Special water-displacing grades of solvent-deposited soft-film protectives are used on wet surfaces, the water being displaced from the metal and replaced immediately by a protective film.

'Strippable' coatings, consisting of a thick, tough, rubber-like, transparent coating that envelops but does not adhere to the protected articles, are provided by certain protectives based usually on cellulose derivatives and applied by hot or cold dipping. The coating, which can be stripped off like a banana skin, gives protection against both moisture and mechanical damage, and is particularly useful for the protection of small, high quality spare parts.

Special protective oils are used to protect the interior parts of engines during storage or shipment; new engines may require such protection during shipment abroad, used engines may need it when laid up. Normal engine oil grades are used with added corrosion inhibitors, and they can be used for the initial running of the engine after storage or shipment and be topped up with normal lubricant.

Apart from the engine oils and strippable coatings, temporary protectives are applied, according to their type, by hot or cold dipping, spraying, brushing or swabbing, depending on the size, type and complexity of the article to be protected. They can be removed by wiping with or without the aid of a solvent such as white spirit or kerosine, or by any of the conventional industrial cleaning or degreasing processes.

Electrical equipment

Oil is used in several types of electrical equipment, as a coolant and as an insulating fluid. Oils for this purpose are known as 'insulating oils'.

Transformers

Transformers are used to raise or lower the voltage of electric current to the desired level, and consist essentially of insulated copper windings round an iron core. All but the smallest transformers are immersed in oil which assists in removing heat generated in the coils and core and provides insulation between core parts [Fig. 140].

The oil, which may attain temperatures around 90°C (190°F), is exposed to some extent to air and also to copper, a well-known oxidation catalyst. Under these conditions it will slowly oxidize with the formation of acids and sludge,

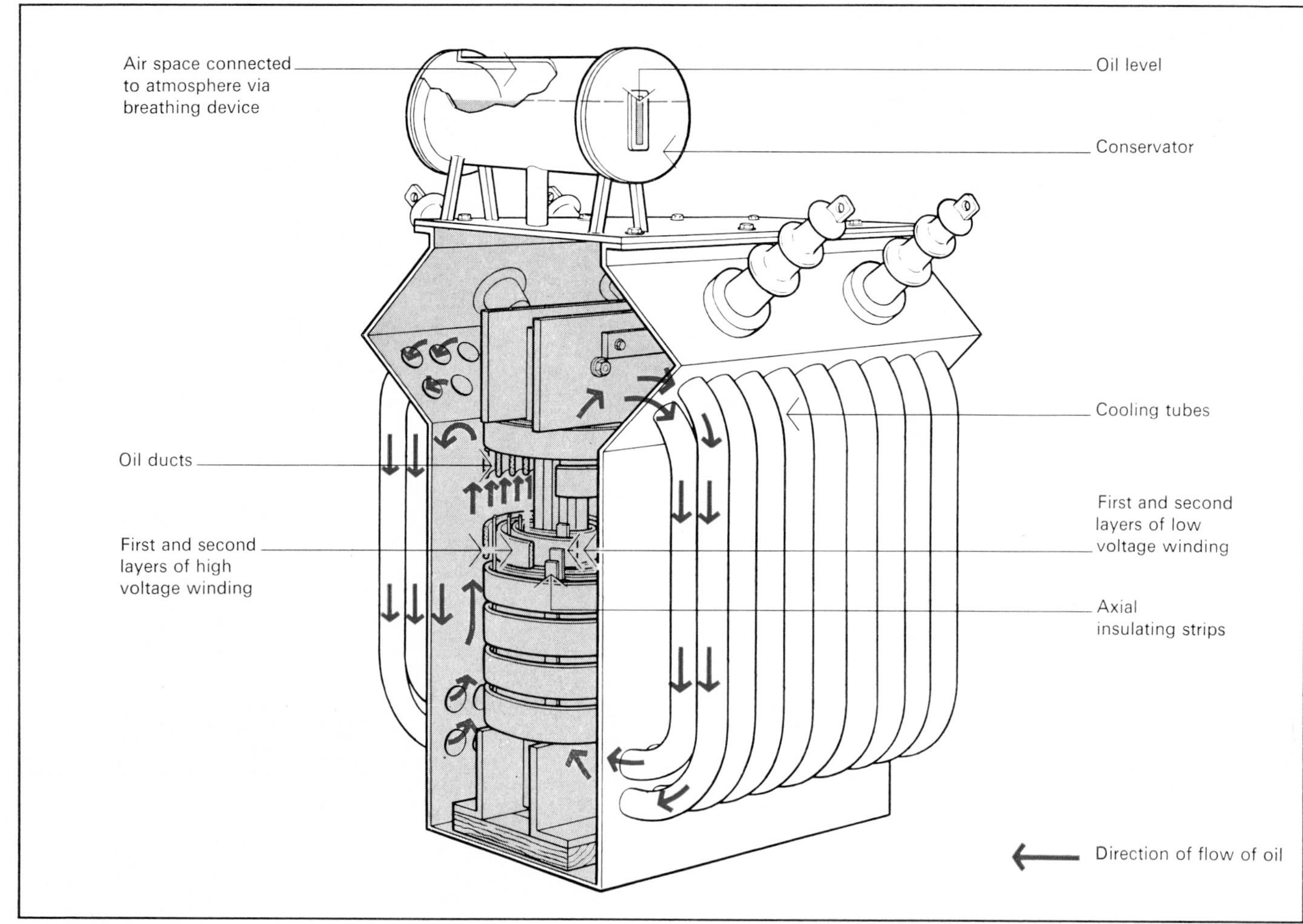

Fig. 140 Use of oil in an electrical transformer

one or other of which may predominate depending on the type of oil and the operating conditions.

Acids are undesirable because they impair the dielectric properties of the oil and are liable to corrode the transformer; sludge is undesirable because it coats the windings and otherwise interferes with cooling. Transformer oils must therefore be resistant to oxidation and of sufficiently low viscosity to ensure adequate cooling without being unduly volatile. Good resistance to oxidation is achieved firstly by special refining techniques and secondly by the use of oxidation inhibitors; copper deactivators and copper passivators are also used to reduce the catalytic action of dissolved and undissolved copper.

The insulating ability of a transformer oil depends largely on its freedom from contaminants, such as dust, fibres, moisture and its own oxidation products, all of which can seriously reduce the electric strength of the oil. For this reason particular care is taken in the packaging, distribution and general handling of transformer oils, and special tests have been devised to assess their performance, e.g. measurements of electrical resistance and of resistance to oxidation.

Although oxidation-inhibited transformer oils are available (inhibited transformer oils) and show much longer life in laboratory oxidation tests, the practical life of uninhibited transformer oils is generally so long that it is usually regarded as adequate, and uninhibited oils are in very general use. Their quality is rigorously controlled by various national specifications all of which have long been established and each of which enjoys almost exclusive merit in its own territory. The variety of oxidation tests in particular, often conflicting in their requirements, has long been an embarrassment to producers and suppliers, if not to consumers, and efforts to establish an internationally accepted test appear to be achieving some success.

Switchgear

Oil-filled switchgear is widely used over an extensive range of voltage. The function of the oil is to quench the arc formed between the contacts when the switch is operated and to prevent it from re-striking. Transformer oils are generally used for this purpose.

Cables

The insulation of solid cables is commonly effected by winding them with paper impregnated with materials of high electrical resistance. Naphthenic mineral oils blended with 25–35 %w of rosin are frequently used as the impregnant.

Oil-filled cables contain one or more internal ducts which are kept full of low-viscosity mineral oil by means of gravity supply tanks situated along the run of the cable. The insulating material of the cable is thus kept saturated with oil which must be stable under high electric stress. Alkylated products such as dodecyl benzene – also produced from petroleum – are sometimes used.

Capacitors

A capacitor or condenser stores electrical energy as stress in insulating material located between conducting surfaces. A common type consists of sheets of metal foil with impregnated paper in between. Petroleum jelly and mineral oils are used as impregnants, although chlorinated hydrocarbons are now extensively used.

Since capacitor oils are not exposed to air to any great extent, and capacitors operate at moderate temperatures, there is comparatively small risk of oxidation. However, even a slight degree of oxidation would have serious consequences and oxidation-stable oils are always used.

The electrical stresses in the insulating material are higher in capacitors than in other electrical equipment, and the impregnant must be able to withstand them, so that leakage currents are very small and little heat is generated. Capacitor oils must therefore have high electrical resistance, and resist chemical decomposition under electrical stress.

Gears

Gears are incorporated in many machines as a means of power transmission, for increasing or decreasing the speeds of shafts or for changing the direction of the drive. There are many types of gears [Fig. 141] to suit varying conditions of operation.

Spur and helical gears connect parallel shafts either without alteration in speed, as in the domestic mangle, or with alteration in speed, as in the gearbox of a motor vehicle. Where speeds and loads are high, straight-tooth spur gears tend to be noisy, and the helical gear with its smoother transfer of load from one tooth to the next is quieter.

Worm, bevel or crossed helical gears are used to change the direction of drive, with or without alteration in speed. A common example is the worm or bevel gear in the rear axle of many modern vehicles. The hypoid gear, a special form of bevel gear, is used in the back axle of most modern cars and operates under very severe conditions in that sliding speeds are great and tooth loading high.

Gears may be either enclosed or open. The enclosed type may be dip lubricated, i.e. the teeth of the bottom wheel dip into a reservoir of oil and convey it to the bearings and other gears, or a circulating system may be used in which the oil is sprayed onto the teeth close to the point of engagement and drains back into the oil reservoir. Dip lubrication is restricted to low- or medium-speed gears since at high speeds churning of the oil may occur, resulting in rise in temperature and loss of power. To reduce losses due to churning, oil levels are kept as low as possible consistent with effective dipping, and baffles to restrict churning are often provided. The more primitive open gears are often lubricated by hand.

The main functions of a gear lubricant are to reduce friction and wear by providing a film of oil between the working surfaces and to carry away the heat generated during tooth contact. If the load conditions are not severe, straight oils are suitable. They must be viscous enough to maintain the film yet sufficiently free flowing to dissipate the

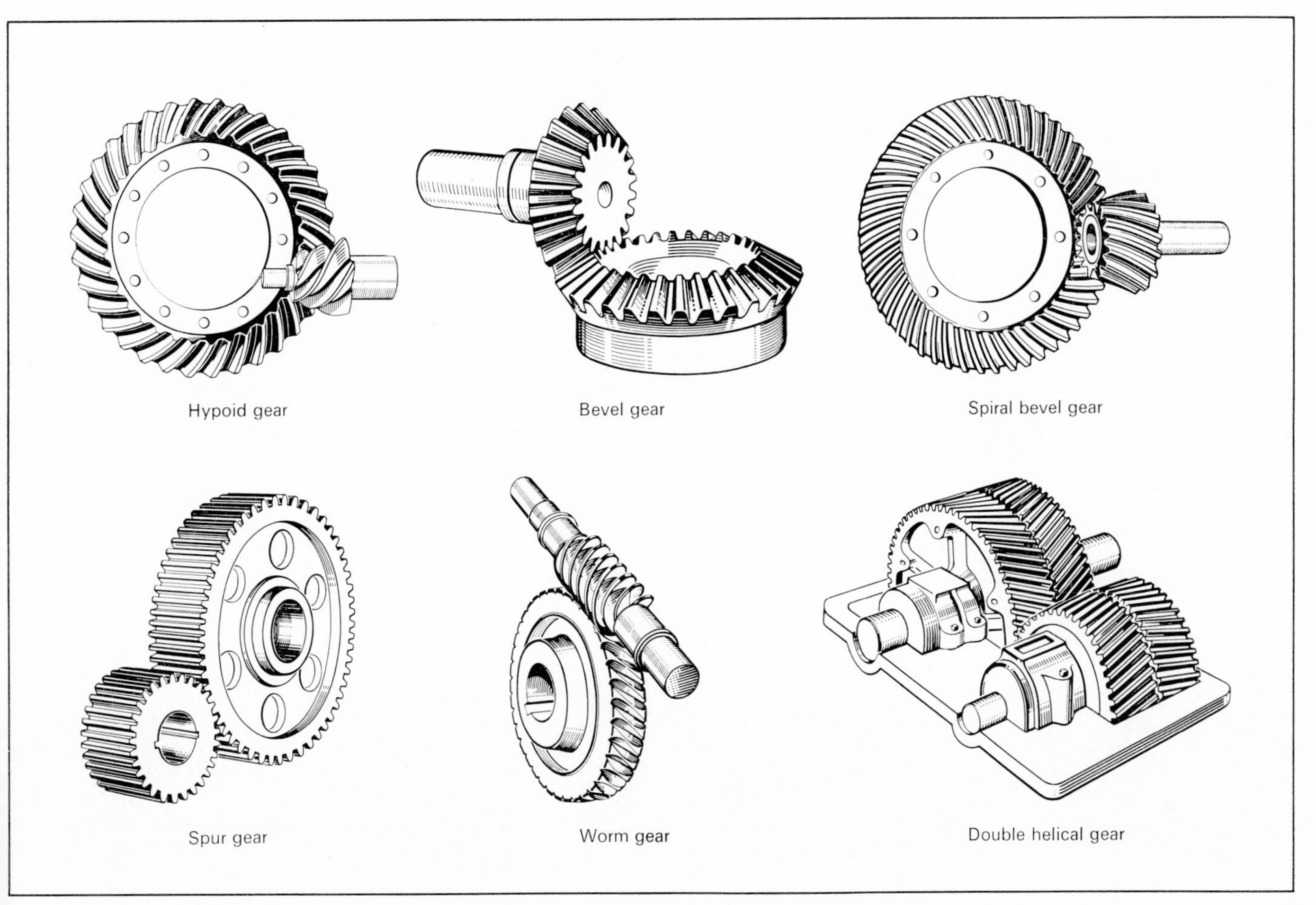

Fig. 141 Typical gears

heat. HVI oils are used, the viscosity depending on the speed. For higher loaded spur, helical and bevel gears, oils containing mild EP additives, such as lead naphthenate and sulphurized fatty oils, are often used. Worm gears are lubricated with high-viscosity HVI oils, compounded oils or mild EP oils.

Hypoid gears require special EP oils to prevent scuffing. Such oils incorporate additives containing sulphur, chlorine or phosphorus which react with the gear surface when local high temperatures are developed, and form a protective film that prevents metal-metal contact. Hypoid lubricants for the back axles of modern cars have to meet stringent specifications imposed by car manufacturers and service authorities, specifications which include severe performance tests.

Whereas in the past the load-carrying capacities of hypoid gear oils were customarily assessed by various laboratory test machines or laboratory rigs involving actual gears, there is a trend nowadays to full-scale axle tests for both development and control purposes.

Heat transmission

Oil is often used as a medium for supplying heat for industrial purposes. It is usually circulated from a heater, through pipes to the required site, and back again to the heater. The oil must be thermally stable so that deposits do not form in lines and heater tubes. In a well-designed system there is minimum contact with air so that oxidation is not

Fig. 142 Comparison of a normal oil with a fire-resistant oil for use as hydraulic fluid. The oils are being sprayed through flames – normal oil (left) and fire-resistant oil (right)

severe. To avoid difficulty in starting the circulation from cold, the oil should have as low a viscosity as is compatible with low volatility at operating temperatures. At one time it was customary to use rather viscous cylinder oils, but medium-viscosity distillates are now generally preferred.

Heat treatment

Heat treatment refers to any thermal operation to which a metal is subjected in the solid state with the object of modifying its physical properties. Two particularly important treatments, hardening and tempering of steel, make considerable use of oils.

Hardening involves heating to a certain minimum temperature and then cooling rapidly (quenching) in some suitable fluid. Tempering consists of re-heating the hardened steel, maintaining it at an elevated temperature for a period, and then cooling again, usually in air. The re-heating is sometimes done in oilbaths.

Quenching

When high carbon steels are heated to a high temperature and cooled slowly, they remain soft, but if cooled quickly they harden. The steel is heated to a temperature ranging from 760–950°C (1400–1740°F), and is cooled rapidly by quenching in cold water or oil, depending on the type of steel. Water, which gives faster cooling, is used with plain carbon steels while oil is used for alloy steels. With the development of alloy steels oil has become much more widely used than water.

Oil viscosity is of primary importance; too viscous an oil gives too slow cooling, too thin an oil is ineffective because its high volatility leads to an excessive vapour blanket around the part being quenched. Thermal stability is required to prevent thickening which reduces quenching power. HVI, high flash spindle oils are commonly used for best performance although cheaper LVI oils are sometimes used. Surface active agents are sometimes added to produce 'rapid quenching oils'. In some quenching operations, the oil is kept at temperatures up to 180°C (355°F) for long periods (marquenching). Oxidation and cracking of the oil inevitably occurs and the oil has to be rejected more frequently.

Tempering

Tempering is carried out to relieve stresses set up by the hardening process, steels being tempered at temperatures ranging from 150–650°C (300–1200°F). Mineral oil is a convenient heating medium for the lower end of the range, up to 320°C (610°F), but must have a high flash point and good oxidation stability; oils of the steam cylinder type are used.

Hydraulic equipment

Hydraulic power transmission serves a wide range of purposes where multiplication of force is required or where accurate and dependable control gear must be provided. Various recent developments, especially automation, have greatly extended the use of hydraulic equipment.

The principal requirements of a hydraulic medium are that it should be relatively incompressible and sufficiently fluid to permit efficient transmission of power. But it must also be a good lubricant for the pumps and bearings in the system and a good seal between the moving parts. It should not foam, should be stable against oxidation and provide good protection against corrosion. If water enters the system it must separate quickly from the oil.

In older and larger hydraulic machinery water is still used, but it is a poor lubricant and causes rusting. Soluble oil emulsions are used in some closed-circuit systems to minimize these defects, but their lubricating properties are not good enough to allow the use of high-speed pumps, and large slow-speed pumps, driven through reduction gears, have to be used. Nor is rusting entirely avoided, and rust particles can cause damage to packings and valves.

Mineral oils eliminate the danger of rusting and permit the use of high-speed, high-pressure pumps directly driven by an electric motor, the hydraulic fluid serving as the lubricant for all working parts. HVI oils in a range of viscosities, with addition of anti-oxidant, anti-rust, anti-foaming and anti-scuffing agents are used.

If the fire risk is very great, as in aeroplanes or in some industries, fire-resistant fluids are used. These can be water-base fluids, containing glycol or the like, water-in-oil emulsions or synthetic materials such as chlorinated or fluorinated hydrocarbons or phosphate esters. Fig. 142 illustrates the reduced inflammability of such fluids.

Metal working

Metal working operations may be divided into two categories, cutting and forming, both of which require rather specialized lubricants.

Metal cutting

Cutting operations include all those in which a portion of the metal is parted from the bulk, as in turning, screw-cutting, tapping, broaching, planing, honing and grinding. A lubricant is required primarily to cool the tool and the work-piece, but also to provide lubrication between tool and work-piece, preventing chips from welding to the tool, to wash away the chips and to protect tool and work-piece against corrosion. In doing all this it ensures longer tool life, higher precision and better surface finish, as well as reduction in power and tool costs and increase in output.

Water is the best coolant known and was indeed the first cutting fluid to be used, either as such or as aqueous solutions of soap or soda. Such liquids are, however, poor lubricants and promote severe rusting of ferrous metals. Fatty oils, mineral oils or mixtures of the two proved to be excellent lubricants and protectives, but not such good coolants, and eventually 'soluble oils' were developed consisting of mixtures of oil and emulsifier that form an emulsion of oil in water when diluted with water, thus combining good cooling with sufficient lubrication for many operations.

Three types of cutting fluid are widely used, soluble oils, water-base fluids and straight cutting oils, the choice depending on the severity of the cutting operation.

Soluble oils are used where cooling is more important than lubrication, as in turning and grinding. They consist of low-viscosity mineral oils containing emulsifiers which on dilution with water form stable oil-in-water emulsions. They are normally used at concentrations of 1–20%v of oil circulating over the seat of the operation [Fig. 143]. Sodium naphtha sulphonate, a by-product of the refining of transformer and technical white oils, is commonly used as the emulsifier. Soluble oils can be adapted to more severe cutting operations by the inclusion of EP additives to produce 'EP soluble oils'. The emulsions formed by normal soluble oils are opaque, milky fluids; 'clear soluble oils', which contain more emulsifiers, produce transparent emulsions which enable the work-piece to be seen more clearly, at least for a limited time until the emulsion becomes opaque with use.

Water-base cutting fluids are used where greater and more permanent clarity is required. They consist of concentrated aqueous solutions of chemicals such as sodium nitrite, triethanolamine sebacate, soaps or polyglycols, and are diluted with water before use. Although they are aqueous liquids they do not promote rusting, and have adequate lubricating ability.

Straight cutting oils are used in more severe operations where the lubrication provided by soluble oils is insufficient. Various grades are used according to the severity of the operation. For machining non-ferrous metals, straight mineral oils or blends of mineral oil with 10–15%w of fatty oil are used; for somewhat heavier operations on low alloy steels and certain non-ferrous metals, mineral oils containing mild EP agents that do not stain copper, such as sulphurized fatty oils, are used. For even more severe operations on steels, more active EP oils are used which may contain free sulphur or compounds containing sulphur, chlorine or phosphorus, individually or mixed.

The cutting performance of cutting oils is impossible to assess by means of ordinary laboratory tests, and actual cutting tests carried out on a statistical basis under rigorously controlled conditions are the only answer.

Fig. 143 Metal cutting using a soluble oil

Metal forming

Metal forming operations include all those in which the metal is deformed to produce the required shape and dimensions, as in rolling, drawing, extruding and forging. Lubricants are used to reduce friction and wear, to remove heat generated in the process and to achieve good surface finish. Two of these operations, rolling and drawing, are of outstanding importance.

Rolling

In the manufacture of metal plates, sheets and strip, heated billets of metal are rolled down to plate thickness of 3–10 mm (hot rolling) and then, if required, reduced in thickness by cold rolling, which gives better surface finish than hot rolling. Occasionally, as with some brasses, the cast ingot is cold rolled.

Hot rolling is done in the presence of water (steel) or dilute soluble oil emulsions (aluminium). For cold rolling of steel to car body thickness, and for mild steel strip generally, special soluble oils are used to give sufficient lubrication to permit great reduction in thickness, but not enough lubrication to cause slipping. The emulsion must also protect against rusting and leave no harmful deposits after annealing. For very thin steel plate (tinplate) palm oil or a palm oil/water emulsion is generally used. For cold rolling of aluminium, copper and copper alloys, straight oils, fatty oils and compounded oils are all used. For aluminium foil, kerosine or spindle oil/kerosine mixtures containing oleic acid, fatty oil or esters are used. They must give no staining on annealing.

Drawing

Many metal articles are manufactured by pressing metal sheets or plates into the required shape by means of suitable punches and dies – 'pressing' and 'deep drawing'. Wire, rod and tubes are produced by cold drawing through dies.

These processes, often carried out in several stages, require lubricants to reduce friction and wear of both die and work-piece, and to produce a good surface finish. A variety of lubricants are used, from viscous mineral oils and compounded oils to aqueous emulsions of fats with or without mineral oils, according to the severity of the operation. Dry powdered soap is used for most steel wire drawing because it permits long die life in spite of the high pressures involved, but for non-ferrous wire drawing, and for some fine steel wire, oils or emulsions are used. 'Drawing compounds', consisting of emulsions of partly saponified fats, are used for deep drawing and tube drawing, and EP agents or solid filler such as talc or zinc oxide are sometimes incorporated in them.

Nuclear power plants

The fuel charging and reactor control mechanisms of CO_2 cooled nuclear power plants operate at temperatures of 50–200°C (120–390°F) in an atmosphere of CO_2 at pressures up to 400 lb/in² (28 kg/cm²) and subjected to more or less

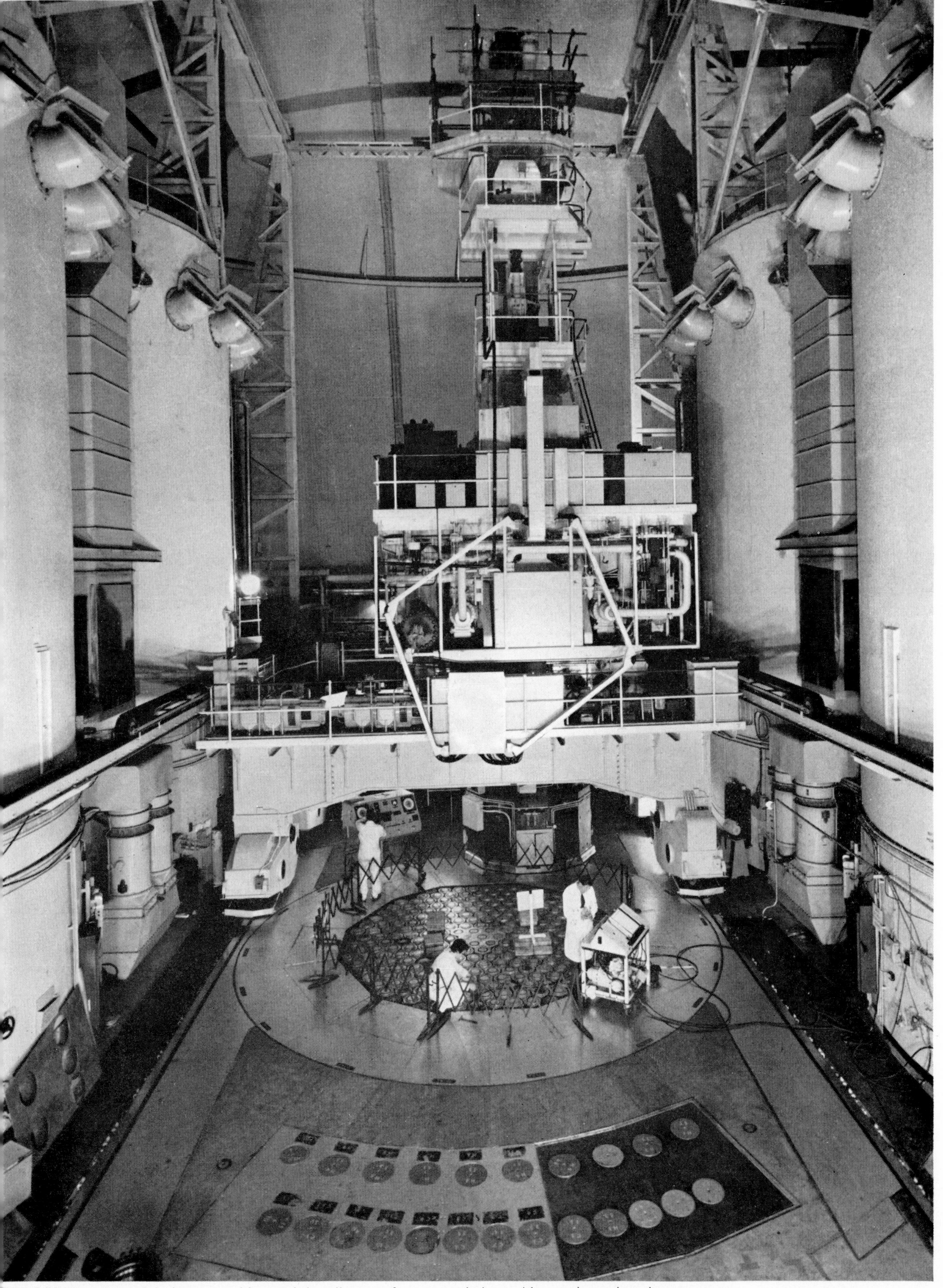

Fig. 144 The charge/discharge machine and the pile cap of a gas-cooled, graphite moderated nuclear reactor

intense atomic radiation depending on their location. Intense irradiation rapidly increases the viscosity of HVI oils until they become jelly-like solids, but affects LVI oils to a lesser extent. Silicones are even less stable than HVI oils under these conditions. Conventional greases are affected in both the oil and soap phases, the soap being decomposed by CO_2 as well as by radiation.

Greases made by thickening mineral oils of reasonable radiation stability with thickeners unaffected by radiation, such as silica gel, are used to lubricate those parts least subjected to radiation but the parts subjected to the most intensive radiation are either designed to need no lubrication or are lubricated by solid lubricants such as graphite or molybdenum disulphide.

In water-cooled nuclear plants there are no corresponding lubrication problems; the reactor controls are operated hydraulically by the water, and bearings are made of plastics or other materials lubricated by water.

Fig. 144 shows the charge/discharge machine and the pile cap of a gas-cooled, graphite moderated nuclear reactor.

Refrigerators

Most refrigerators have compressors, either piston/cylinder or rotary, to compress the refrigerant, the subsequent rapid expansion of which produces the cold. Although the main functions of a refrigerator lubricant are the same as those of compressor lubricants, conditions in the refrigerator impose additional demands such as low viscosity and good low-temperature properties. Moreover, since the refrigerant and the lubricant are brought together, they must not interfere with each other in their respective functions.

Some refrigerants, such as ammonia, carbon dioxide and sulphur dioxide, are immiscible with mineral oil and require an oil of low viscosity and low pour point that will not solidify in the colder parts of the system; others, such as methyl chloride and chlorofluorocarbons (Freons), are miscible wholly or in part with mineral oils. The dilution of the oil reduces its viscosity so that a more viscous oil must be used than would be required for immiscible refrigerants. Dilution also reduces the pour point and facilitates flow at low temperatures. The refrigerant/oil mixture must not deposit solid matter (wax) on cooling since this would block expansion valve openings. Refrigerator oils are commonly assessed by cooling a mixture of oil and refrigerant, and determining the temperature at which insoluble material appears and the amount of the deposit at a given temperature.

Straight MVI oils are generally used, with appropriate viscosities for the particular application.

Steam engines

The steam engine was in existence long before the internal combustion engine, but both work on the same principle in that expansion of a gas or vapour takes place in a cylinder fitted with a piston and produces power. The expanding gas in the steam engine is steam delivered to the cylinder at high pressure.

Steam engines are a dying race, rapidly giving place to diesel engines for road, rail and sea transport, and the demand for steam engine lubricants is now very small.

There are several types of steam engines, slow-speed horizontal engines, usually with an open or exposed crank shaft, medium-speed open vertical engines and high-speed closed vertical engines. In all of them the lubrication requirements of the cylinders and other parts exposed to steam differ from those of the bearings and other external parts.

Cylinders

With all types, the cylinder oil is normally introduced into the steam supply pipe where it is atomized and then carried by the steam to all working parts in the valve chest and cylinders. This method may be supplemented by direct feed to selected points on the cylinder barrels and glands, and some engines have direct feed for their entire cylinder lubrication.

Straight mineral oils are commonly used; unrefined distillate oils for engines running at low temperatures with saturated or mildly superheated steam; viscous residual oils (steam-refined cylinder stock or bright stock) for engines running under more severe conditions. Compounded oils are used with wet steam because they atomize more readily and spread more easily over wet surfaces, but they are not suitable for use with highly superheated steam because fatty oils are unstable at high temperatures; they can sometimes be used with low or moderate superheat.

While low-viscosity oils atomize easily, and in this respect would be suitable, low viscosity usually entails high volatility which is undesirable in steam cylinders as the oil might evaporate and leave the cylinder walls unlubricated. Heavy residual oils are therefore favoured, the more severe the conditions the higher the viscosity and the lower the volatility required.

Bearings

Lubrication of the bearings depends on the type of engine. If the bearings do not come into contact with condensed steam, mineral oils are adequate, but bearings that come into contact with water require oils in which water will emulsify, and oils containing blown rapeseed oil or various water/oil emulsifiers are used.

In horizontal engines, a refined naphthenic distillate of medium viscosity is generally used, applied by drip feed or mechanical lubrication.

In open vertical engines, the lubricating system is of the total loss type, and the oil in the bearings must be able to absorb any water that finds its way down the piston rod. LVI oils containing blown rape or fish oil or other emulsifying agents, and with viscosities of 170–300 cS at 100°F, are used.

In closed vertical engines a circulating system is used and the oil must separate easily from water. HVI oils, as used in steam turbines, are usually employed.

Steam turbines

In the steam turbine, high pressure steam impinges on blades set round the circumference of a rotor, causing it to rotate at high speed. Most turbines have several rows of blades on the rotor alternating with rows of fixed blades on the casing, which direct steam on to the rotor blades.

Oil is supplied by a circulating system to the bearings on which the rotor revolves, to the governor mechanism and to the reduction gears. It also serves as the hydraulic medium to operate the governor controls, acts as a coolant and protects metal parts against rusting. Turbines have become increasingly more compact and steam temperatures higher so that the coolant function of the oil has become increasingly important.

Turbine oils are expected to operate for years without replacement except for occasional topping up, and are sometimes guaranteed to last the life of the turbine. They must therefore be very resistant both to oxidation at operating temperatures and to the catalytic effect of copper, brass and steel. Moreover, since water is always present in the system, due to steam leakage past bearing seals, it is essential that the oil and water should separate cleanly so that the water can be periodically drained off. Even so, it is customary to centrifuge or filter the oil in the course of circulation.

Turbine oils are usually solvent refined oils containing oxidation inhibitors and anti-rust additives, and must have good demulsibility.

When turbines are used as marine power units, reduction gears have to be used and are lubricated by the same oil as for the turbine. Normal turbine oils are satisfactory for this purpose for moderately loaded gears, but for the more heavily loaded gears in modern ships an EP turbine oil is necessary to prevent gear scuffing. Many of the EP agents commonly used in other EP oils are unsuitable for turbine oils because of adverse effects on their anti-oxidant, anti-rusting or demulsification properties, and careful selection is necessary.

Textile machinery

In all machinery a certain amount of power is expended in overcoming friction within the oil film itself. This becomes excessive in the high-speed machinery used in the textile industry, and the lubricant must therefore be as thin as possible consistent with good lubrication. Textile machinery usually operates in humid atmospheres, and the oil must give protection against corrosion. Moreover, care must be taken not to soil the fabric being processed, and the oil is made non-splashing by incorporating small amounts of soap or polymer. Where there is still a risk of contamination, the oil must be easily removed by scouring, or where scouring is inadmissible, the oil must be highly stable and colourless. Suitable additives are used to promote scouring.

The modern high-speed oil bath spindle rotates at 11 000–15 000 rev/min or even higher, and may run for 6000 hours or more on a single charge. Highly refined oils that will not thicken or otherwise deteriorate in use are therefore necessary.

Anti-friction bearings are used extensively in textile machinery under a wide range of temperatures and often in very moist situations. Multi-purpose lithium greases can be used for most of these operations instead of several types of grease, each for its own specific conditions.

A wide range of textile machinery oils is required to cover the many different conditions of operation; they range from oxidation inhibited HVI oils to similar oils containing non-drip, anti-rust, emulsifying or other additives. Where light coloured oils are required to avoid discoloration of textiles technical white oils are used.

Textile manufacture

Oils are also used to lubricate textile fibres, particularly wool, during the various manufacturing processes. Such oils must be removable by scouring at a later stage, and must leave no residues or otherwise affect the fibre in any way that will interfere with subsequent processing. Emulsions of oleic acid or of a mineral oil are generally used. In the latter case the mineral oil, with suitable emulsifiers dissolved in it, is supplied for dilution with water before use.

Synthetic fibres also require lubrication to prevent breaking during processing. Emulsified oils made with low viscosity white mineral oils are generally used.

Straight mineral oil is used as 'batching oil' to soften the fibres in preparing jute for further processing.

Various processes

A considerable quantity of mineral oil is used in a wide variety of industrial processes, and such oils are referred to as 'process oils'.

Typical applications are as ingredients in the manufacture of printing inks, rubber articles (rubber extenders), horticultural sprays, cosmetics, hair creams, etc, and as treating materials in leather dressing, coal briquetting, dust-laying, egg preserving, etc.

The type of oil used naturally depends on the application in question; for many of them low-viscosity naphthenic distillates are suitable, but for others, such as cosmetics, hair creams and the like, where it is important that the oil should be free from odour and colour and absolutely harmless to the skin, only the more highly refined white oils (medicinal oil or technical white oil) can be used.

Petroleum waxes

About 1 million tons of petroleum waxes are produced each year of which about 86% is paraffin wax and 14% microcrystalline wax.

For many years paraffin wax was used almost entirely for the manufacture of candles, first supplementing and eventually supplanting the use of beeswax, stearine (from animal fats) and tallow. Today it has many and varied end uses, of which candle making is but one. The end use pattern varies markedly in different areas according to the degree of industrialization and to local custom. For instance, in the USA, the use of pre-packed foods is far greater than in Europe, and the offtake of wax for frozen food wrappers, bread wrappers, milk and fruit-juice cartons and the like is about 85% of the total demand, whilst in Europe it is only 25%.

The principal applications of petroleum waxes are described in the following pages.

Wax as a combustible

The proportion of the world production of wax used for candle making has been declining for many years, but has now levelled out at about 20%w. The actual quantity used for candles, however, is increasing because, although the demand for household candles has diminished, there has been an increasing demand for decorative and art candles, church candles, nightlights and hot-plate candles.

Candles were once made by repeated dipping in molten wax and draining, starting with the wick and finishing with a candle of the required dimensions. Some art and church candles are still made in this way, but most candles are now made by moulding paraffin wax around a wick in machines such as that described and illustrated in Fig. 145. Semi-refined paraffin wax with a melting point of 50°C (122°F) and upwards is normally used. Paraffin wax candles tend to stick in the mould and to bend when warm and often exhibit mottling. Small proportions of substances such as stearine, microcrystalline wax or polyethylene are added to overcome these difficulties, and they also produce an opaque white candle that is generally preferred to the translucent article produced by straight paraffin wax.

Nightlights are also made by the same process, except that the wicks are inserted after moulding. They usually consist wholly of paraffin wax.

An alternative method of manufacturing candles is by the cold extrusion of powdered wax through a die.

Paraffin wax is used in the manufacture of matches for impregnating the wooden splint so that it readily catches fire and continues to burn. The cheaper, lower melting point grades (match waxes) are used, the splints being dipped in the molten wax at a temperature that will give good penetration. Book matches, using cardboard instead of wood, are similarly treated.

Paraffin wax is also used in the manufacture of explosives and fireworks, and slack wax in the manufacture of fire-lighters from waste paper and wood fragments.

Wax as a waterproofing material

Wax is used for waterproofing a great variety of materials, of which paper and textiles are the most important. The treating of paper and board for packaging purposes has superseded candle making as the major application for petroleum waxes – at least half of all petroleum wax produced being used in this way. Wax is ideal for the purpose; it is clean, odourless, tasteless, harmless and attractive in appearance; it is chemically inert, resisting attack by strong acids, alkalis and oxygen at normal ambient temperatures; it is insoluble in water, practically impervious to air and moisture, even in thin films, and produces a hydrophobic surface that repels water from the treated material.

Although little affected by oxygen in the air at ordinary temperatures, petroleum wax oxidizes more readily if kept molten for prolonged periods, as in dipping baths, and can discolour and develop an unpleasant odour. Therefore when materials are waterproofed by dipping in molten wax, working temperatures are kept as low as possible, small baths are used so that make up with fresh wax is reasonably frequent, and waxes containing oxidation inhibitors may be used.

Waxing of paper

Paper can be either coated or impregnated with wax. In coating, wax is applied to one or both sides of the paper by passing it between heated rollers either or both of which carry molten wax picked up from a heated trough. A continuous film of wax is formed on cooling. Alternatively, the paper may be passed through a bath of molten wax and immediately chilled in cold water or on cold rollers so that the wax forms a continuous glossy film. The weight of wax applied varies considerably according to the application, but may equal or even exceed that of the paper.

Straight paraffin wax is not very suitable for this application; it is too brittle, and the film is liable to crack when the paper is folded or creased, especially at low temperatures. Blends of paraffin wax with about 25%w of microcrystalline wax are used, being much more flexible and less liable to crack. Coated papers are practically impervious to water vapour, and are accordingly used for wrapping foodstuffs, such as bread, that are affected by changes in atmospheric humidity or deteriorate by loss of moisture.

Impregnated papers are made by immersion in a bath of molten wax followed by passage between heated rollers, so that most of the wax is absorbed and little, if any, is left on the surface. Impregnated paper is not impervious to water vapour, but prevents the passage of liquid water and has a hydrophobic surface. It can therefore be used for paper cups and bags. Since cracking or creasing is not a problem with such articles, straight paraffin wax can be used.

Waxing of board

Board is waxed either by coating or by impregnating according to the end use. An important application is in the

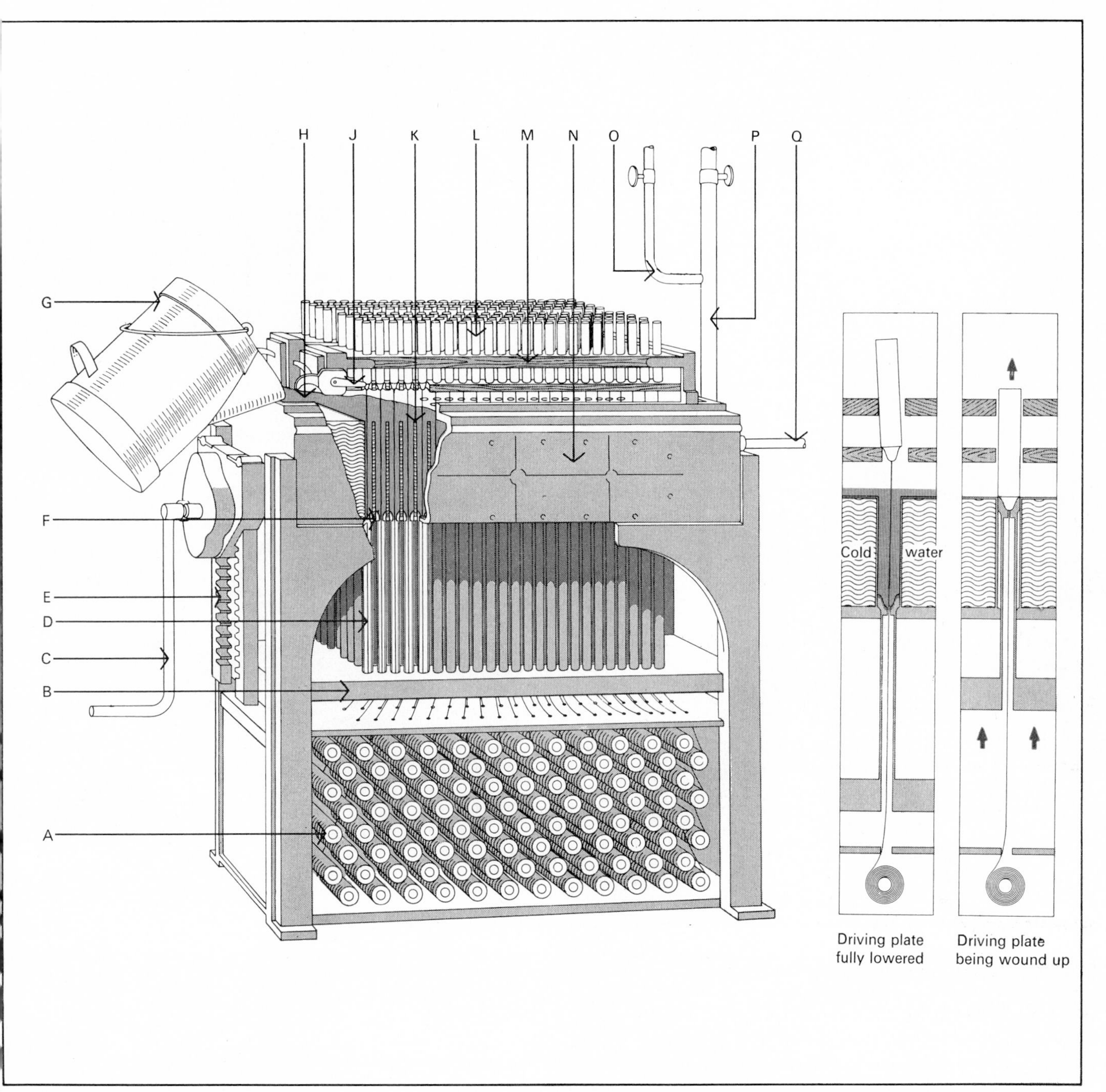

Fig. 145 Candle-making machine

Construction. A metal tank (N), supported by a substantial framework, is fitted with inlet pipes for cold water (P) and steam (O) and an outlet (Q). The candle moulds (K) are fixed in the tank, which may contain as many as 500. The moulds are cast preferably from almost pure tin, which is resistant to corrosion, takes a high polish and is easily re-cast.

The candles are moulded upside down. A small piston called the tip (F), which shapes the tip of the candle, slides inside each mould. The tip is fixed to a hollow tube called a ram (D) which passes through the bottom of the mould, and is attached with some degree of flexibility to the driving or lifting plate (B). This can be raised and lowered by rack and pinion or screw action (E) from a hand-operated crank (C).

Below the driving plate are spindles carrying spools of wick (A), one to each mould. On top of the machine rest two wooden clamps (M) which receive the candles as they are forced up out of the moulds. A clamp consists of two boards spaced one above the other, each drilled with holes corresponding in position and diameter with the moulds. The lower board can be shifted slightly by means of a cam (J) to hold the candles in the clamp.

The wicks stretch down from the ends of the finished candles (L) through the moulds and the tips and rams, to the spools. The tips are a tight sliding fit over the wicks which are thus stretched reasonably tautly.

Operation. Starting with the two clamps full of finished candles from the previous batch or 'lift,' the working of the machine is as follows.

Steam is heating the moulds, the driving plate is fully lowered. Molten wax is poured from a filling pail (G) into two shallow troughs (H) from which it flows to the moulds. The steam is cut off and cold water admitted to the tank. As the moulds cool the wax sets, and when the candles in the moulds are fairly rigid, the wicks below the candles in the clamps are cut with a long knife. The candles are then removed from the clamps for packing, and the newly moulded candles are wound up and locked in the clamps.

The time taken by the full cycle of operations varies according to the nature of the wax, the temperatures of the atmosphere and the cooling water, and the size of the candles. A batch of household candles may be produced under normal conditions in the UK in 20-25 minutes.

manufacture of cartons for milk, fruit-juice and other foodstuffs. Such cartons are coated with wax, either by dipping the preformed carton in molten wax or by assembling the cartons from blanks that have been coated by passing between heated rollers carrying molten wax, as described for paper coating. Fig. 146 shows cartons being coated.

Drinking cups are impregnated with wax by dipping or spraying after assembly and then passing through a hot oven to allow the wax to soak into them.

Blends of paraffin wax with microcrystalline wax or polymers or both are used for coating cartons so as to give a tough, flexible, non-cracking, non-flaking film, and similar blends are used for impregnating.

Waxing of textiles

Wax is used to make textile materials water-repellent or 'shower-proof'. The wax is generally applied as an emulsion, either by spraying or dipping, so that the textile fibres are wax coated but the interstices are not sealed. The fabric remains porous to air – giving adequate ventilation – but is water-repellent. The grade of wax used is not critical.

Wax is also used to treat yarn to facilitate further processing and generally to improve the 'handle' of the finished fabric.

Waxing of foodstuffs

Besides the use of waxed wrappings for the preservation of foodstuffs, wax may be applied direct to the surface of some foods. The wax may be applied as a thick overall covering, surrounding the article with an airtight package, as in the waxing of cheese, or as a thin layer which slows down evaporation of water but still allows breathing to take place, as in the waxing of fruit and vegetables, e.g. oranges and cucumbers.

Thick films are produced by dipping in molten wax at about 66°C (150°F); thin films by dipping in a wax emulsion or by spraying with an emulsion or a solution of wax in volatile solvent.

Wax films hinder or prevent not only drying out but also the growth of moulds and bacteria, as with cheese.

Fig. 146 Coating cartons with wax; (above) cartons passing through bath of molten wax; (below) cartons leaving waxing machine

Polishes

Natural waxes and petroleum wax have long been used in the manufacture of polishes, and about 10%w of the total production of petroleum wax is so used. Natural waxes are undoubtedly superior to all others in their durability and gloss when rubbed to a polish but many of them are too hard to be easily worked and they are, without exception, expensive. On the other hand paraffin wax has little polishing value, giving a dull, easily smeared film and microwax is not much better, giving somewhat sticky films. Blends of natural, paraffin and microcrystalline waxes, however, make excellent polishes, the petroleum waxes serving to modify the consistency and texture of the polish, to assist in solvent retention and to eke out the more expensive natural waxes. Such blends are used in a great variety of polishes, e.g. for boots and shoes, furniture, motor vehicles and leather articles. Beeswax, carnauba and candelilla waxes are the chief natural waxes that are blended with paraffin or microwax or both to give the required consistency and texture.

Wax polishes are prepared in three main types, pastes, creams and liquids, although powdered or flaked waxes, usually blends, are used for treating dance floors.

Paste polishes are mixtures of wax and solvent, usually white spirit, made by dissolving the wax in the hot solvent and allowing to cool. The wax separates out as a network of wax crystals in which the solvent is enmeshed, the whole forming a fine-structured paste, the consistency of which depends largely on the solvent content and the way in which it is dispersed, which in turn is influenced by the nature of the wax blend and its 'solvent retention' properties. When the paste is spread and rubbed out, the solvent evaporates and a continuous film of wax is formed.

Creams may be either dispersions of water in wax-solvent mixtures or dispersions of the wax-solvent mixture in water, stabilized by various dispersing agents. On rubbing out, the water and the solvent evaporate, leaving a wax film.

Liquid polishes are usually wax-solvent mixtures, such as

are used in paste polishes, but with sufficient solvent to give a liquid product, i.e. the solvent is not enmeshed in a crystalline structure, but the wax is either in solution or dispersed in the solvent. Some liquid polishes are dispersions of wax in water with insufficient wax to form a cream.

Miscellaneous uses

Amongst the many other uses of petroleum wax too numerous to mention, the following are some of the most interesting.

Metallurgical

Wax is used in a metal casting process known as the 'lost-wax process'. A replica of the article to be cast is shaped in wax and is then coated with a suitable refractory material. On pouring in the hot metal, the wax melts and is replaced by the metal.

Rubber processing

Wax is blended with rubber to protect it from deterioration or to modify its properties.

Electrical industry

Because they are good insulators and resistant to water, waxes, especially microcrystalline wax, are used in the manufacture of cables as an impregnant for covering fabric or as an external coating.

A recently developed application is the use of petrolatum on ceramic insulators on outdoor high-voltage lines to prevent leakage due to films of moisture.

Chemical industry

Wax is a feedstock in the chemical industry for various processes. It may be cracked to olefins for the production of detergents, oxidized to acids which are then esterified to form wax-like compounds used in the manufacture of polishes and crayons, or chlorinated to make 'chlorinated waxes' used as plasticizers and for electrical insulating purposes.

Medical

Wax baths are used as a heat transfer medium in the physiotherapeutical treatment of limbs affected by arthritis, rheumatism or post-operational stiffness.

Testing of wax and waxed products

Properties of petroleum waxes such as oil content, melting point, hardness, viscosity, density, colour, etc, serve to characterize the various grades of wax, and can be determined by conventional tests, most of which have been standardized by the ASTM or the IP.

These tests, however, have little or no bearing on the performance of wax in many of its applications, and functional tests in which the conditions of the application are simulated are in common use, although few of them have yet been standardized. Some of the more important are listed below.

Tensile strength

Tensile strength is defined as the longitudinal stress required to break a test specimen of specified dimensions in a standard ASTM test (D 1320).

Rigidity modulus

The rigidity modulus is the ratio of stress to strain in a material subjected to a shearing force. It gives an indication of the force required to shear the material and, in the case of paraffin wax, provides a better correlation with product quality for certain applications than do other less precisely defined properties such as hardness or penetration or even the above-mentioned tensile strength.

Sealing strength

Some food wrappers are sealed by pressing the portion to be sealed successively between heated and cooled plates. The force required to pull apart two strips of standard paper, coated with wax to be tested, and sealed together in this way, is a measure of the suitability of the wax for this application.

Blocking point

Waxed papers tend to stick together, which is undesirable. This tendency is measured by a 'blocking test' in which sheets of waxed paper are laid on one another, pressed together by a weight, and kept successively at a range of temperatures; the temperature at which sticking first occurs is the blocking point. The test has been standardized by the ASTM (D 1465).

Flaking

When wax cartons are bent or deformed, as in closing and opening, the wax coating should not flake and allow particles of wax to drop into the contents. This quality is assessed either by flexing tests or by dropping a weight on to wax coated board.

Scuffing

When waxed paper is passed between rollers in the course of waterproofing, the wax should not 'scuff' off the paper and build up on the roller. This quality is assessed by passing a waxed paper strip between two rollers, one of which is loaded, and determining the loss in weight of the strip.

Gloss

The glossiness of a waxed paper and its retention of gloss on storage are important characteristics in relation to customer reaction. Visual inspection, being highly subjective, is liable to give variable ratings, and a more objective method is used in which the reflected light is measured by special instruments.

Permeability

Permeability to water vapour is measured by sealing a moisture-absorbing salt such as calcium chloride in a waxed container, storing it in a humid atmosphere under standard conditions and determining the increase in weight.

Bitumen

Naturally occurring bitumen was used in the Near East for building and hydraulic work thousands of years ago, but its use lapsed with the decline of the ancient civilizations. In modern times the development of the petroleum industry has made large quantities of bitumen available, an important consequence of which has been the development of the modern flexible road surface. The early bituminous roads of modern times were made with natural asphalts (naturally occurring mixtures of bitumen and mineral matter). A bituminous mastic was used on the roads of Paris as far back as 1838, and in 1869–70 compressed rock asphalt was used on roads in London. In 1867 roads in Washington, DC, were surfaced with Trinidad Lake Asphalt, which was also used in London in 1895. Early in the present century refinery-made bitumen from Texan, Californian and Mexican crude oils began to be used in ever-increasing quantities in road construction, and today, although natural asphalts are still used in considerable quantities, petroleum bitumen is by far the commonest medium for the construction of the modern asphalt road.

The production of bitumen from petroleum in the world outside the Sino-Soviet spheres is about 37 million tons/year, most of which is used in the construction of roads and airfields, the remainder in industrial applications and hydraulic construction.

Road construction

There are two classes of modern roads, flexible and rigid. The flexible road consists of a thick layer of crushed stone or similar material, perhaps coated with a bituminous product, with a wearing surface bound with bitumen or tar. The rigid road is made of cement concrete slabs, which carry the load and also serve as a running surface.

The flexible road has many advantages over the rigid road. It permits some settlement of the foundations without cracking or otherwise failing, and is less liable to crack when exposed to wide variations in temperature. It is jointless, gives a better riding surface and is easier to repair. With rigid roads there is no alternative to heavy construction, regardless of the amount of traffic to be carried, whereas with the flexible road there is considerable scope for varying the thickness of the foundation and the type of wearing surface. With flexible construction it is therefore possible to build up in stages as traffic requirements increase, a very great advantage in countries that are developing.

The components of a flexible road are the wearing surface, the base, and the subgrade.

The function of the wearing course is to provide a waterproof, non-skid cover to the road and to withstand the shear and abrasive action of traffic. It may consist of only a very thin layer of bituminous material for a lightly trafficked road or several inches of high quality bituminous mixture for heavy traffic. The function of the base is to carry the traffic load. It is frequently made up of a number of layers of materials of different strength, and in modern road construction, it is becoming increasingly common to build a large part of the base with bitumen-bound material.

In designing a flexible road, the object is to provide sufficient thickness and strength of base and surfacing so that traffic stresses will not deform the subgrade. Until recently flexible pavements were designed by empirical methods which have proved satisfactory with uncoated granular base materials. The advent of bitumen-coated bases with their far superior load-spreading properties has focused the need for a more scientific approach to road design, and roads are now designed more on engineering principles, taking into consideration the stresses involved to calculate the constructional requirements. With the more rational design methods, uncoated base material can now be used to better advantage than hitherto, although the use of bitumen-bound base is preferred.

The simplest form of bitumen application to roads is surface dressing, the bitumen being sprayed over the surface, which is then covered with stone chippings. This method is used either to re-surface existing bitumen roads or to provide a wearing surface on a previously untreated road so as to make it better able to carry traffic, in which case, as traffic increases and the road has to be strengthened, a bituminous carpet of suitable material can be superimposed to whatever thickness is warranted by the traffic.

For road surfacing of a higher quality there are a considerable number of mixes that can be used, the choice depending on the traffic conditions and on the materials and plant available. The most important of these surfacings, bitumen macadam, cold asphalt, sand mixes, asphaltic concrete, hot rolled asphalt and mastic asphalt, are discussed in the following pages.

Aggregates used in making road mixes include broken stone of various sizes, crushed slag, gravel (either natural or crushed), and sand. For certain mixes 'filler' is also sometimes added – a finely ground material most of which passes through a 200 mesh sieve, examples of which are limestone dust and Portland cement. The grading of aggregate is of great importance in the designing of road mixes. The larger stone, in general, forms the main structure, the interstices being filled with the smaller stone, sand and filler, the whole being bound together with bitumen to give a compact durable construction.

Each particle of the aggregate is coated with bitumen, which provides an adhesive, ductile film to bind the particles together and form a resilient, flexible and waterproof structure. The bitumen can be applied as such or in the form of a cutback or an emulsion, the choice depending on the nature of the construction.

Surface dressing

A surface dressing consists of a thin layer of bitumen or other binder sprayed over an existing road surface, and then covered with stone chippings and rolled. Cutbacks or emulsions are usually used for this purpose, but in warm climates hot bitumen may be employed, provided it is

Fig. 147 Bitumen macadam and (below) the surface texture

possible to apply the chippings while the surface is still sticky.

Although the process may appear relatively simple, workmanship of a very high standard is essential for satisfactory results. The binder must be suited to local conditions and applied at the correct rate, whilst the chippings should be clean, dry and cubical in shape. If the weather conditions are bad, either an adhesion agent is used or the chippings are precoated with bitumen in order to ensure that they are not stripped off by traffic.

Bitumen macadam

The expression 'macadam' perpetuates the memory of John Loudon McAdam who did much to revive the science of road making in the nineteenth century. His principle was to apply to an existing surface a layer of broken stone of suitable quality and size which, when compacted, would give inherent strength by interlocking. To provide a denser construction it became the practice to add water and fine aggregate, and this gave rise to the term 'water-bound macadam'. When modern traffic conditions made such surfaces unsuitable, the water slurry was replaced by hot tar or bitumen poured into the interstices of the stone layer, a process known as 'penetration macadam' or 'grouting'. Penetration macadam has, however, been replaced in many countries by precoated material known as tar or bitumen macadam. The name 'tar macadam' or 'tarmac' is often loosely applied to any coated aggregate of this type irrespective of whether tar or bitumen has, in fact, been used. Bitumen macadam consists of a mixture of coarse aggregate and a relatively small quantity of fine aggregate and filler, coated with a bitumen or cutback. The stability or load-bearing capacity of the mix depends to a great extent on the mechanical interlocking of the aggregate particles. Mixes can vary from very densely graded mixtures with low void content to very open graded mixtures of high void content [Fig. 147].

Bitumen macadam can be laid in one or two courses, the thickness varying from half to two inches for the former and two to four inches for the latter. Single-course mixes are used for general resurfacing work and two-course mixes on new roads or roads that need strengthening. The macadam may be spread manually or mechanically [Fig. 148].

Cold asphalt

Cold asphalt provides a clean even surface with a sandpaper finish which remains permanently non-skid. It is normally used as a thin carpet material for the resurfacing of existing roads, but is also very suitable for surfacing footpaths, railway platforms, playgrounds, and for general maintenance and patching work. Two varieties are recognized, fine cold asphalt all passing a $\frac{1}{4}$ in. BS sieve, and coarse cold asphalt, substantially all of which passes a $\frac{3}{8}$ in. BS sieve.

It consists of a finely graded aggregate, the most suitable being crushed slag, coated with a small quantity of soft bituminous binder. Cold asphalt, in contradiction to its name, is always mixed hot and is frequently laid hot. The principle of the design of the mix is the provision of mechanical stability by the interlocking of the aggregate particles on consolidation; the bitumen initially assists compaction by its lubricating effect and then functions as a waterproofing binder giving the necessary cohesion to withstand the combined action of traffic and weather. By virtue of the relatively low binder content the mix is easily workable and, with a suitable choice of binder, it is possible to produce a mix that can be stored and then laid cold.

Sand mixes

In many parts of the world stone aggregate is not readily available, and the only cheap locally available aggregate is sand. Sand can be used in road surfacing work in a variety of ways – hot sand mix, cutback sand mix and wet sand mix – and each of these will be considered briefly.

Fig. 148 Mechanical spreader

Hot sand mix

These mixes are made using naturally occurring sand either as such or blended with quarry fines. They are not so carefully graded as sand sheet asphalt and do not, therefore, have the same durability or stability, but they provide a satisfactory surfacing for roads carrying fairly heavy traffic.

Their stability depends largely on the hardness of the bitumen and therefore as hard a bitumen as convenient is used compatible with the climatic conditions. They can be made in a fairly simple hot mix plant and are frequently laid by grader.

Cutback sand mix

Where dry sand is readily available, sand mixes using a cutback binder will provide a low-cost method of road surfacing. They are suitable only for light and medium pneumatic-tyred traffic, but after a period of service will provide a suitable base on which to lay a better quality surface able to carry heavy traffic. Cutback sand mixes have been used with considerable success for roads and airfields in a number of Middle Eastern and African countries and in the USA.

The sand should be clean and preferably evenly graded as this will increase the stability of the mix. A wide range of cutbacks can be used, the choice depending upon the climate and the type of sand and mixing equipment available. Cutback sand mixes can be spread by hand or mechanically. Initially the mix remains somewhat plastic, but eventually sets up sufficiently to carry traffic, at which stage a final surface dressing is necessary to prevent surface fretting.

Wet sand mix

The wet sand mix was developed in Europe during World War II as a rapid means of airfield construction where only wet sand was available. In order to coat the wet sand, cutbacks containing a wetting agent were developed which worked in conjunction with hydrated lime or cement as an activator. Wet sand mixes proved to be superior to dry sand mixes in that they gained stability or bearing capacity much more rapidly.

Since the war this process has developed in a number of countries where wet sand is the only available aggregate. It has been widely used for minor roads in Belgium, France and the Netherlands, and for roads and airfields in Africa and the Far East.

Very lean wet sand mixes (and other types of lean sand mix) are proving a satisfactory and economical means of stabilizing sand as a road base material, and this form of construction is likely to be used on an increasing scale in developing countries where low-cost roads are urgently needed.

Fig. 149 Asphalt mixing plant

Fig. 150 Asphaltic concrete (section showing three courses)

Asphaltic concrete

Asphaltic concrete consists of a very carefully proportioned mix of coarse aggregate, fine aggregate and mineral filler, coated with bitumen. It provides a surfacing of exceptional durability and is widely used for the surfacing of heavily trafficked roads, motorways and airfield runways under all types of climatic conditions.

An asphaltic concrete mix is designed with a continuous grading from the maximum size down to the filler with the object of obtaining a controlled void content. The amount of bitumen added is related to this void content and to the traffic and climatic conditions. The binder used is normally a penetration bitumen.

For making asphaltic concrete an elaborate hot mix plant is required where the aggregates of various sizes, filler and bitumen can be correctly proportioned [Fig. 149]. Mixing temperature depends on the grade of bitumen but is around 300°F (150°C). The mix must be laid and compacted while still hot. Asphaltic concrete can be laid in two or three layers where a thick surfacing is required or in a single course as a resurfacing material. Careful control must be maintained during manufacture and laying, and on a suitable base, asphaltic concrete should have a life of fifteen to twenty years without requiring any maintenance [Fig. 150].

Hot rolled asphalt

This material evolved from sand sheet asphalt which consisted of a mixture of carefully graded sand, mineral filler and bitumen. The inclusion of a small percentage of stone chippings not only improves the stability but decreases the cost. The material is made in a hot mix plant and is laid by mechanical finisher. Precoated chippings are rolled into the surface to increase its non-skid properties.

Hot rolled asphalt can be laid as a resurfacing material or in new construction, where it is normal practice to lay a two-course construction to a total thickness of 3–4 in. It provides a very durable surfacing with a life of fifteen to twenty years and is widely used in the UK for surfacing heavy duty roads [Fig. 151].

Mastic asphalt

Mastic asphalt consists of a mixture of bitumen, fine limestone aggregate and filler in proportions which give a voidless impermeable material.

The binder may be petroleum bitumen, natural asphalt, or a mixture of the two. The fine aggregate is added in increments to the molten bitumen and cooked in a special boiler which keeps the contents stirred for up to 5 hours. Mastic asphalt is then usually cast into blocks which are remelted at the laying site in a special boiler, and small

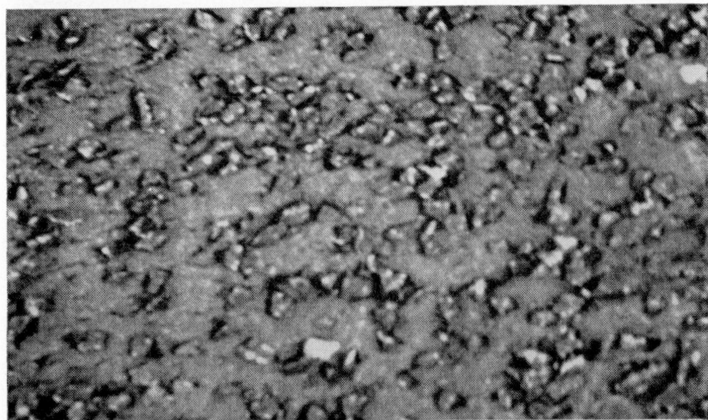

Fig. 151 Hot rolled asphalt and (below) the surface texture with precoated chips

Fig. 152 Bitumen-bound base, showing staggered transverse joints of four layers to total thickness of 10 in.

chippings are added. Mastic asphalt is spread by hand and provides an impermeable and highly durable surface. In order to improve its non-skid properties, precoated chippings are often rolled into the surface or a rough finish given by an indenting roller.

In some European countries a slightly different form of mastic asphalt is made consisting of coarse aggregates with a very high filler content. The material is first mixed in an asphalt plant and then further mixed in a mastic boiler while being taken to the site of work. The asphalt is spread mechanically as a thin wearing surface on an asphaltic concrete base. To provide a non-skid finish the surface is rolled with an indenting roller, and small chippings are rolled in.

Bitumen-bound bases

As mentioned previously when discussing the design of flexible roads, the modern tendency is to use a bitumen-bound base in place of uncoated or cement-bound material. A bitumen-bound base consists of a well compacted, high stone content mix with a low void content. The bitumen should be as hard as is compatible with ease of mixing and laying and its quantity kept to a minimum.

In designing a bitumen-bound base, use can be made of cheap locally available aggregates. Quarry wastes and pit or river gravel and sand are widely used. A bitumen-bound base can be built up in layers to any required thickness. Traffic is usually allowed to use the bitumen-bound base for a period of up to one year, as this allows any settlement to take place before the expensive final surfacing is placed [Fig. 152].

Bitumen-bound bases are also being increasingly used for airfields, where the saving in design thickness provides considerable advantages both from the constructional and the economic point of view.

The quantity and type of bitumen used in these various types of construction are shown in Table 18.

Testing of road materials

So long as bitumen is marketed on the basis of penetration or softening point, the determination of these properties

TABLE 18 Type and quantity of bitumen in road construction

Construction	Bitumen penetration 25 °C	Bitumen content %w on mineral aggregate	Filler content %w on mineral aggregate
Bitumen-bound base	80/100	4	4
Dense bitumen macadam	100/250	5	5
Open bitumen macadam	150/350	4·5	5
Fine cold asphalt	200/500	5·5	12
Asphaltic concrete	60/100	6·5	9
Hot rolled asphalt	40/70	8	9
Mastic asphalt	20/30	12	30

(Test methods, pp. 182 and 185) is useful for identification and control. But they do not in themselves help much in establishing the required properties of a good road-surfacing material, which depends not only on the nature and content of the bituminous binder but also on the nature and grading of the aggregate.

For adequate information about the properties of a road mix and of the road structure formed from it, the material as a whole must be examined on engineering principles. Various tests have been devised for measuring the mechanical properties of road materials, in particular their behaviour under static and dynamic loads, to ensure stability under the various traffic and climatic conditions to which the road is likely to be exposed. It is impossible in this chapter to do more than indicate the type of tests that are used, but a factor that has always to be borne in mind is the difficulty of securing a representative sample. A test piece made in the laboratory is unlikely to be the same as would be produced from the same mix laid on the road, and a section cut from the road is disturbed in the process and is no longer the same as when supported by surrounding material.

The best known mechanical test for the design and control of hot asphalt mixes is the Marshall test, a semi-confined compression type shear test in which a sample of the mix is compressed between two segments of a mould [Fig. 153]. The stability of the mix is assessed in terms of the load required to produce failure, and the plasticity is measured by the amount the upper and lower segments are squeezed together. A more elaborate compression-shear test is the 'triaxial cell test' which assesses the resistance of bituminous mixtures to shear.

Fig. 154 Model road for testing road-surfacing materials

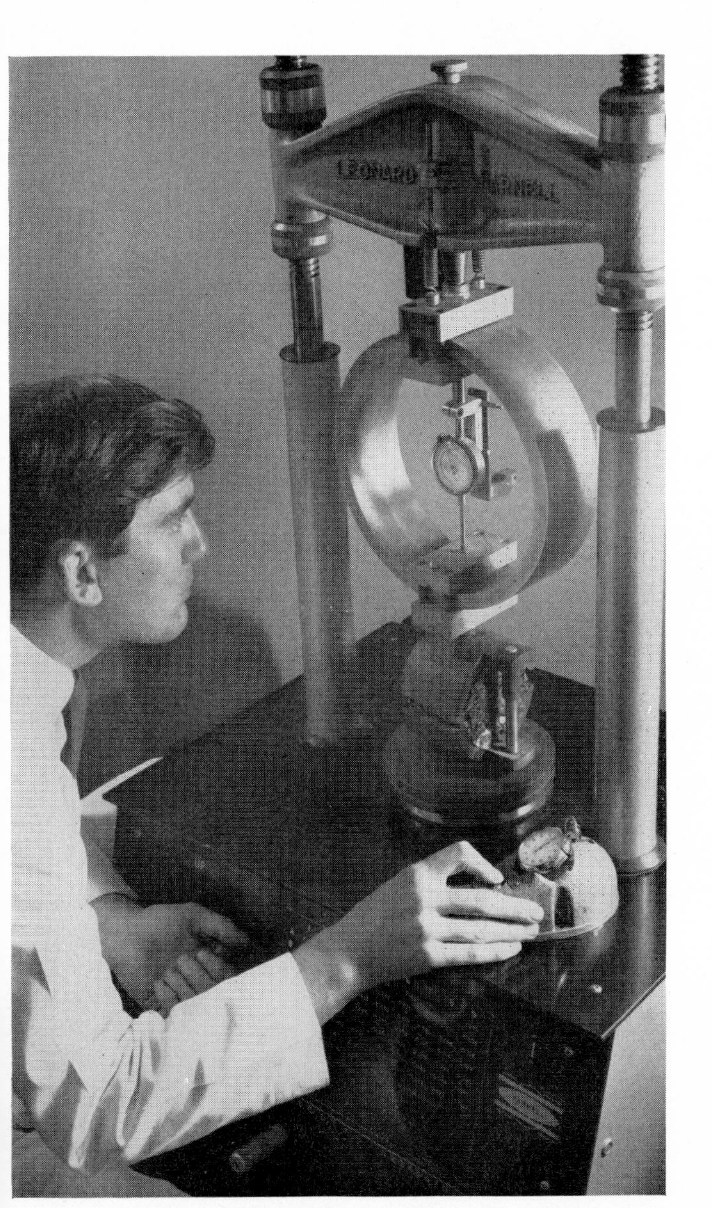

Fig. 153 Marshall test apparatus

Specimens cut from the road or made in the laboratory are sometimes subjected to beam tests in which the specimen is loaded either between supports or at the end of a cantilever, and the deflection is measured.

Road vibration machines are used to measure the stresses and strains set up in a road structure by traffic passing over it, and road mixes can then be examined in the laboratory under similar conditions of load and temperature.

Considerable use is made of 'model roads' to investigate the stability and durability of both carpets and surface dressings. Wheels mounted on an axle are run on a circular road track under controlled conditions of load, speed, temperature and humidity [Fig. 154].

Water can be particularly destructive to road surfaces by causing the bitumen to strip from the aggregate. The adhesion of a bitumen to an aggregate is a function of both the properties of the bitumen and the nature of the aggregate surface. Various laboratory tests, from simple immersion in water to the use of model roads under wet conditions, have been devised to test the resistance of coated aggregates to water, but none is entirely successful in predicting behaviour on the road. They are useful, however, for comparative purposes.

Although much useful information can be obtained from these various tests, the ultimate criterion is behaviour on the road and it is common practice to investigate the behaviour of new types of surface dressing or road carpets and base coats by laying experimental sections on the public highway – with the co-operation of the local highway authority.

Fig. 155 Some industrial applications of bitumen; bituminized roofing felt, bitumen-lined pipe, coal briquettes bound with bitumen, electric cable insulated and protected by bitumen.

Industrial applications

The uses of bitumen in industry are many and diverse [Fig. 155]. It is used because of its waterproofness, durability, flexibility and resistance to chemical action, properties in which it excels. Most grades of bitumen are employed, but the harder grades, blown grades and special filled bitumens find particular outlets in this field.

The following paragraphs describe briefly only a few of these industrial applications.

Construction industry

Bitumen is widely used in construction work of all kinds, and the manufacture of bituminous products for use in this field often forms an industry in itself, for example mastic asphalt and roofing felt manufacture.

Mastic asphalt

Mastic asphalt, which has been referred to previously in connection with roads, is also employed for heavy-duty industrial flooring, as a base for other types of floor coverings, as a damp-proof course, for waterproofing below-ground structures, and for waterproofing and protecting insulation and other materials. In addition to the normal mastic that is mixed and laid hot, clay-filled bitumen emulsions provide a type of cold-worked mastic.

Bituminized felts

Bitumen is used extensively in the manufacture of roofing felts which consist of felt impregnated with a penetration grade of bitumen, and then coated on one or both sides with a blown grade. Blown bitumen is used for the coating because it resists flow at high temperatures and cracking at low temperatures. The coated felt is normally dusted with a fine mineral powder to prevent sticking in the roll or is sometimes finished with relatively coarse granular material.

Roofing shingles are manufactured in a similar way, but a harder bitumen is used for impregnation, and special coloured granules are often employed for the surface finish. The treated felt is then cut into the required shapes and sizes.

Bituminzied felts are also used for damp-proof courses and for tanking applications of all kinds. For this purpose impregnated, but uncoated, felts are sometimes used.

Linoleum substitutes are a specialized form of bituminized felt provided with a decorative finish. The bitumen used for impregnation must be hard enough to resist indentation by furniture but sufficiently flexible to resist cracking during rolling and unrolling.

Protective coatings

Bitumen is used extensively for waterproofing and protecting all types of surface against attack by corrosive atmospheres, agressive soils, and chemicals. Depending on the degree of protection required, various thicknesses and types of coating can be provided, and the grade of bitumen and technique employed are selected according to the application and exposure conditions.

Thin coatings can be provided by the use of solutions of bitumen in volatile solvents, sprayed or brushed onto the prepared surface to be protected. Such applications provide a relatively cheap, simple protection for a limited time. Somewhat more expensive but more durable thin coats are provided by more specialized bituminous paints in which drying oils, resins and other additives are incorporated. Such paints may be coloured by the addition of pigments or dyes, but colours are confined to the darker shades.

Heavier coatings for more lasting protection and for more critical conditions are provided by spraying with or dipping in hot bitumen, normally a blown grade, possibly containing

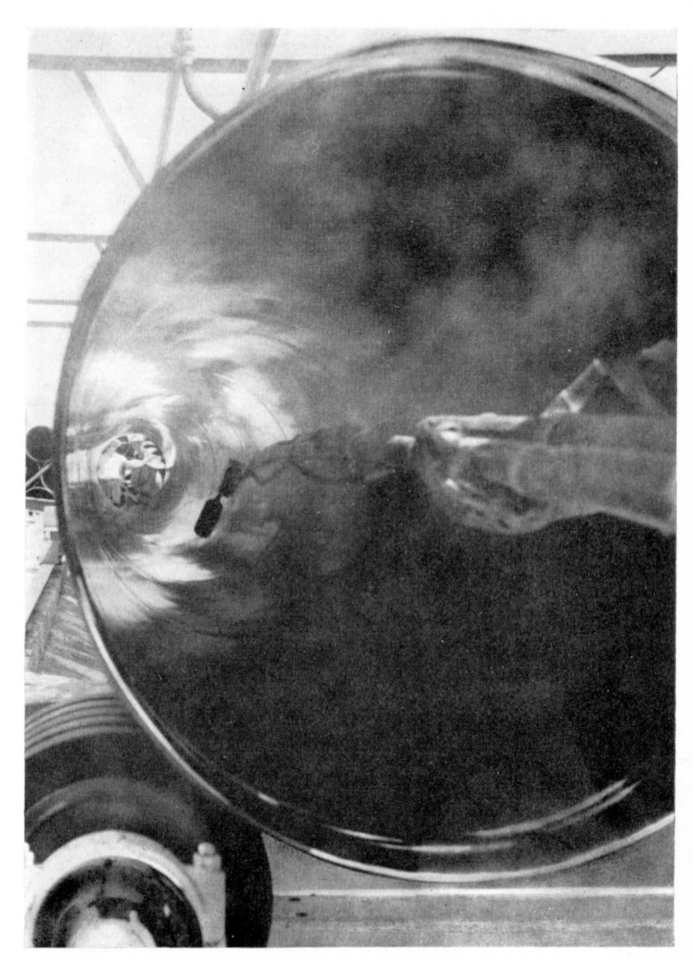

Fig. 156 Pipe being treated internally with bitumen

Fig. 157 Crude oil pipeline being protected with a coat of bitumen and wrapped with fibre glass

filler. Alternatively the filled bitumen may be applied cold either as an emulsion or mixed with a volatile solvent.

Bitumen is extensively used for the internal protection of pipes carrying water and other liquids except of course those, such as petroleum products, that would attack the coating [Fig. 156]. External protection of all types of pipeline, including oil lines, is effected by coating with bitumen. A filled, blown grade is frequently used and a coating thickness of up to about 4 mm adopted. If the pipeline is to be buried the external coating often incorporates a membrane reinforcement and, for particularly severe conditions, an outer wrapping [Fig. 157].

Mine shaft lining

A rather unusual application for bitumen is in the construction of mine shafts. Modern shafts have to be sunk to increasingly greater depths to exploit deep coal seams, and this accentuates the difficulties due to stresses on the shaft lining resulting from movements of the surrounding soil. Application of a layer of bitumen has provided a solution to the problem, and this method has been adopted for a number of mine shafts in Europe using bitumen compounds specially designed to meet the particular conditions obtaining at each shaft.

Tunnel lining

Effective tunnel linings must be impermeable, durable and crack resistant. In the Netherlands and Germany bitumen and bituminized felt have been employed to waterproof new road tunnels under canals and waterways.

Bitumen as an adhesive

Bitumen is widely used as an adhesive in the building and other industries. Particular applications include the laying of roofing felts, floor tiles, and insulating materials. The type of bitumen employed depends on the temperature conditions and the slope of the surface on which it is to be applied. Blown and penetration grades are used as such or as solutions or emulsions.

Paper and boards

Bitumen is used in the manufacture of various types of waterproof paper. The paper is impregnated or coated with bitumen or prepared in the form of duplex paper, which consists of leaves of plain paper laminated with a continuous film of bitumen. More complex systems of paper, reinforcing membrane and bitumen are employed for paper sacks for fertilizers, etc.

The grade of bitumen employed depends on the type of paper being produced; a medium or hard grade is used for impregnated paper and blown grades for coated and duplex papers. Paraffin wax is often added to coating bitumen to reduce stickiness.

Bitumen boards are made either by impregnating the board with bitumen or by incorporating the bitumen during the course of the board manufacture.

Coal briquetting

Coal briquetting has long been practiced in many countries and bitumen is a most suitable binder because of its non-toxic nature, resulting in better working conditions during manufacture, and its lower level of smoking during burning. Briquettes are manufactured either by the 'dry process', in which the binder is mixed in a pulverized state with the coal fines, or by the 'wet process', in which the bitumen binder is sprayed hot onto the coal fines before pressing. The grade of bitumen employed depends on the type of coal and on the briquetting process. Special grades with high temperature susceptibility are sometimes used.

Hydraulic construction

A more complete knowledge of bitumen as an engineering material has facilitated its use in major hydraulic works such as the lining of irrigation canals, navigation canals and reservoirs, the construction of dams and the protection of coasts and harbours.

Bitumen is particularly suitable for these applications because of its impermeability, flexibility and binding properties, which govern its behaviour under stress and its durability during the working life of the structure of which it is part. It is used either as such or in combination with fillers and aggregates such as limestone dust, sand and crushed stone. The type of mix used depends on the nature of the application, availability of plant, labour and materials, the size of job, the speed with which work has to be done, such as between tides, and, of course, cost.

Bituminous layers used in hydraulic construction have two distinct functions; firstly as an impermeable layer to prevent the seepage of water and the possibility of resultant structure failure in the underlying material, and secondly as a protective layer to prevent erosion of underlying material by waves and currents. These two functions may be

Fig. 158 Asphaltic concrete being placed on Zoccolo dam, Italy

incorporated in the one layer, as in a dam-facing subject to wave and ice action.

Some of the forms in which bitumen and bituminous layers are used are described below.

Buried membranes

Blown bitumen, sprayed hot, and then buried beneath a protective layer of soil or gravel is used to form thin impermeable linings for canals and water courses. This method has been adopted for use in irrigation schemes in the USA, the Middle East and elsewhere.

Revetments and linings

Mixtures of stone, sand, filler and bitumen are used to form layers of varying degrees of impermeability and resistance to erosion for the lining of irrigation canals, navigation canals and rivers, the protection of sea walls, and the facing of the upstream slopes of earth and rock fill dams. For large works hot mixes manufactured and placed by techniques similar to those used for road construction are employed. Asphaltic concrete is used extensively for facing dams and lining reservoirs in some European countries [Fig. 158].

Mastic grouted stone layers

The use of stone layers, either hand pitched or bulldozed into place and then grouted with a hot mastic of sand, filler and bitumen, is well established for coast and river protection works. Such layers are not impermeable, but afford durable flexible protection for banks, breakwaters, groynes, etc. The recent introduction of mastic grouted, stone filled, wire-mesh gabions has enabled the use of smaller stone than would otherwise be possible for protective layers, even on quite steep banks. A variant of this method is the use of precast concrete blocks grouted into position with a hot mixture of bitumen and asbestos filler.

Protective layers applied under water

Special apparatus has been developed in the Netherlands to deposit hot mastic under water at considerable depths to form durable protective layers for the founding of caissons necessary for the closure of large estuaries, or to grout stone layers for the protection of banks. Similar, though simpler, apparatus has also been used in Italy for grouting stone layers on river banks.

Prefabricated linings and mattresses

Prefabricated linings of varying degrees of complexity, from simple bitumen coated and impregnated felt to more complex steel reinforced mattresses laid 2 in. thick in hot-mix asphalt, are used for lining irrigation canals, navigation canals and other water courses. Factory made linings that can easily be laid by unskilled labour have been used in farming areas in the USA. They offer the advantage of speedy construction, but the larger linings are sometimes expensive and may require special handling equipment.

Prefabricated mattresses used to protect the banks of waterways are usually laid at or about water level. They are often fairly heavy in construction and in one method of application are placed off the barges on which they have been fabricated, by fixing one edge to the bank to be protected and floating the barge away.

Test methods and their significance

It is essential to maintain the quality of the various oil products at all stages from their manufacture to their delivery to the customer. This is done by testing the products at various stages in their life history, such as manufacture, storage and distribution. Throughout the petroleum industry testing laboratories are found, in refineries, in installations and attached to the marketing function, whose duty it is to keep constant watch over the quality of the products.

Tests are of two kinds: those that control quality by the determination of some chemical or physical property, for example sulphur content and flash point, and those that indicate performance characteristics, for example octane number of gasolines and engine tests of lubricating oils. There is naturally some overlap between these two groups in that chemical or physical properties used for control purposes may also have some bearing on performance.

Only relatively few properties of oil products, for instance sulphur content and kinematic viscosity, are absolute quantities that can be determined by any scientifically sound procedure. Most properties, for instance flash point and distillation range, are not scientifically defined properties, and the results obtained in their determination depend on the test method employed. In many cases the arbitrary nature of the test is associated with the fact that the oil product is not a simple substance but a mixture of substances, the behaviour of which depends on the composition. It is essential that such arbitrary methods should be standardized if the results are to be of equal significance wherever determined, and it is desirable that even absolute methods should be standardized to ensure that they are reliable, of sufficient accuracy, and suitable for routine laboratory use. Standardization entails the precise specification of both the apparatus and the procedure to be used, and in expressing results it is essential to mention the relevant method.

Most of the test methods used in the petroleum industry have been standardized by the American Society for Testing and Materials (ASTM) or The Institute of Petroleum (IP) or both. Many ASTM and IP methods are identical or technically equivalent though differing in some details, and these are now being unified as joint ASTM/IP methods. These same methods have been largely adopted by national standardizing bodies in many other countries and there is therefore a considerable degree of uniformity in methods for testing oil products. In any case, in view of the international nature of the industry, the tendency is to use exclusively ASTM methods in manufacturing and marketing specifications throughout the world.

This chapter gives a general description of the most important methods and briefly discusses their significance; fuller details can be obtained by consulting the publications of the ASTM and the IP both of which issue annual volumes of their standard methods. These methods are constantly under review and are brought up to date whenever necessary: new methods are included and obsolete ones removed as dictated by the changing requirements of the industry.

In the following pages the tests are arranged alphabetically in groups according to the property they measure and not on a product basis.

In addition to these 'standard' methods used in the control laboratories, an important feature of modern quality control is the use of measuring devices installed in the product flow lines in a refinery to detect some significant change in product quality, for example density, viscosity or refractive index, that necessitates a change in process operation. The instrument may merely register the change or may automatically effect the necessary adjustment of process conditions. (Measurement and loss control, p. 282.)

Many of the standard tests have also been automated and automatic apparatus for the determination of, *inter alia*, distillation, flash point, cloud point, penetration and sulphur content are now used in control laboratories to speed up routine testing. Fig. 159 shows an automatic distillation apparatus.

Yet another interesting development is the introduction of 'do it yourself' test kits whereby engine and plant operators in the field can keep a check on the quality of their lubricating oils, with special reference to oil-change period. Viscosity can be judged relative to that of standard oils by the rate of flow of the oil down an inclined plate. Acidity can be gauged by the change in colour of a spot of oil on a filter paper when treated with a given reagent. 'Soot' and dispersancy can be assessed by the density of the oil spot on the filter paper and the rate at which relatively clean oil spreads outwards from it.

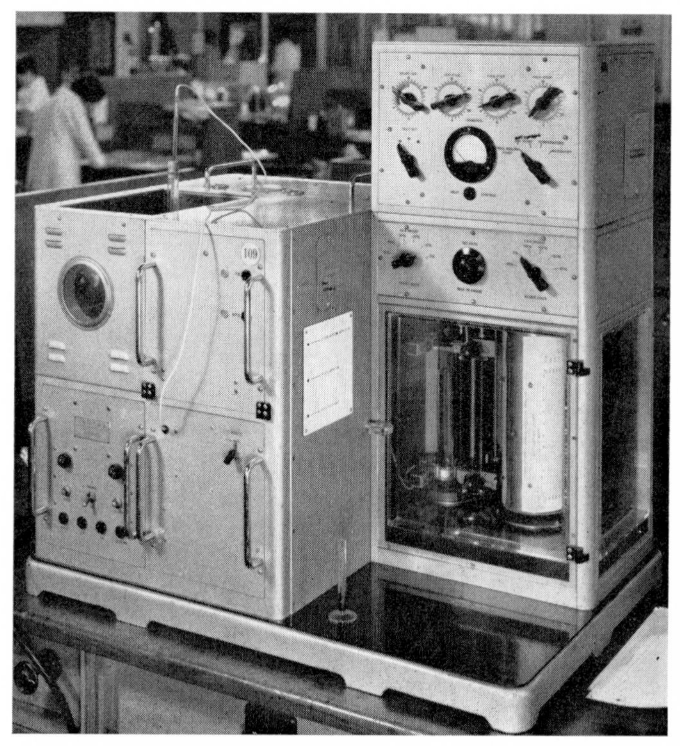

Fig. 159 Automatic distillation apparatus

Fig. 160 Spot tests in the field

These 'spot' tests are commonly applied to used diesel engine lubricants, less commonly to used gasoline engine lubricants, and sometimes to turbine oils. They are usually specific to a particular brand of oil, the kit being supplied by the oil supplier, although more general application is claimed for some motor oil test kits. Fig. 160 shows such a kit being used.

Combustion

Petroleum fuels are burnt under widely differing conditions and each type of fuel must have combustion characteristics appropriate to its use. These properties are determined in laboratory engines, for gasolines and diesel fuels, and in lamps for kerosines. The quantity of heat or energy available when a fuel is burnt is determined for all fuels as a calorific value.

Anti-knock quality of gasoline

The knock characteristics of a gasoline have to be determined in an engine, and to get reproducible results both the engine and the method of operation must be standardized. Sir Harry Ricardo was the first, in 1919, to develop an engine suitable for the purpose, a single-cylinder engine on which the compression ratio could be varied by raising or lowering the cylinder head while the engine was running. In testing a gasoline the compression ratio was increased until an audible detonation, knocking, occurred. This critical compression ratio was called the HUCR (highest useful compression ratio) and represented the conditions for maximum power output from the given gasoline.

In 1930 the Co-ordinating Fuel Research Committee in the USA developed a similar engine – the CFR engine – in which again the compression ratio is increased until knock occurs, but the knock is determined by a detonation meter and not by ear. The gasoline under test is matched at the critical compression ratio with a blend of two reference fuels, iso-octane with a high anti-knock value and normal heptane with a low anti-knock value. The result is expressed as an octane number, the percentage of iso-octane in the blend which matches the gasoline under test, for example a gasoline which is matched by a blend of 80%v iso-octane and 20%v normal heptane would have an octane number of 80. Gasolines having anti-knock values better than that of iso-octane are rated against iso-octane containing tetraethyl lead in sufficient quantity to match the gasoline under test. The anti-knock value is then derived in terms of an octane number greater than 100 from an arbitrary scale relating quantity of TEL in ml/US gal to octane numbers above 100.

Motor gasolines are normally rated in the CFR engine under two sets of conditions differing in severity: the Research or F1 method gives a rating more applicable to mild conditions while the Motor or F2 method is a better criterion for operation at higher speeds and loads. The F1 rating tends to be higher than the F2 rating; the difference indicates the sensitivity of the fuel to changes in operating conditions and is an important characteristic with respect to its performance on the road.

The aviation piston engine operates under two sets of conditions: normal cruising, using weak fuel mixtures, and maximum power for take-off or combat, necessitating rich fuel mixtures. The anti-knock quality of aviation gasolines is therefore determined under both these conditions.

The CFR engine is used but the F1 and F2 procedures used for motor gasolines are not suitable because of the difference in operating conditions. Two other procedures, the F3 or 1C method and the F4 or 3C method, are used.

The F3 method determines the knock rating under weak mixture conditions and is based on a temperature rise rather than a pressure increase due to detonation. For octane numbers below 100 the same reference fuels as for motor gasolines are used, and for octane numbers above 100 the octane containing TEL is used.

The F4 method determines the knock rating under supercharged rich mixture conditions. The engine is operated at a constant compression ratio, detonation being induced by increase in boost. The gasoline under test and the reference fuels are compared on the basis of power output at the fuel/air ratio at which the maximum power output with the reference fuel occurs.

The F4 method rates a gasoline higher than does the F3 method. Aviation gasolines are often characterized by both ratings, for example 115/145 grade indicates F3 performance of 115 and F4 of 145.

Burning quality of kerosine

Kerosine, whether used for illumination or for heating, must burn freely and steadily for reasonable periods without attention.

A burning test is carried out for 24 hours in a standard lamp with a flame of specified size and shape. The consumption of kerosine and the amount of char formed on the wick are measured, and a qualitative assessment is made of any bloom on the lamp chimney.

A smoke point test determines the maximum flame height in millimetres at which a kerosine will burn without smoking when burnt in a special wick-fed lamp in which the flame height can be viewed against a background of a graduated millimetre scale.

Calorific value

Calorific value, or heat of combustion, is the heat liberated when a fuel is burnt completely under standard conditions, and is a measure of the energy that can be obtained from its use. It is an important criterion of all fuels, gaseous, liquid or solid.

A weighed sample of the liquid or solid fuel is burnt in oxygen under pressure in a pressure vessel – a bomb – immersed in water in a calorimeter. The calorific value is calculated from the rise in temperature of the water resulting from the burning of the fuel. The calorific value of gases is determined, on the same principle, in a special form of calorimeter, or can be calculated from the known calorific values of the constituents.

Carbon residue

When a petroleum product is heated in the absence of air, or in the presence of insufficient air for complete combustion, the lighter fractions will evaporate, but the heavier, more complex compounds will decompose forming carbonaceous deposits. Two tests are used to determine the 'carbon residue' or 'coke number' of petroleum products.

In the Conradson method the sample is heated in a crucible under controlled conditions with the virtual exclusion of air, and the residue is weighed. In the Ramsbottom test the sample is sucked into a small glass bulb with a capillary opening and heated in this bulb to 550°C (1022°F) by immersion in a bath of molten metal. The residual coke is weighed. The Conradson method is used for fuels, the Ramsbottom sometimes for fuels but mainly for lubricating oils.

The coke number of distillate fuels is so small that it is usual to distil the fuel first and then to carry out the test on the 10%v residue.

The carbon residue of fuels is sometimes associated with their tendency to form carbonaceous deposits in IC engines and oil-burning equipment, but this is of doubtful validity since the design of equipment and the operating conditions exercise a very great influence. Similarly the carbon residue of lubricants has been considered to indicate their tendency to form combustion chamber deposits, but this is equally dubious.

Ignition quality of diesel fuels

In a diesel engine there is always some delay between injection of the fuel and ignition; for smooth running this delay should be as short as possible. The determination of ignition quality is related to this delay period.

In the ASTM method a standard single-cylinder variable compression engine – the CFR diesel – is used. The fuel under test is compared with a blend of two reference fuels, cetane with a high ignition quality and alpha-methyl naphthalene with a low ignition quality. The cetane number of the fuel is the volume percentage of cetane in the blend of the two fuels that is equivalent in ignition quality to the fuel under test.

The cetane number of a diesel fuel cannot be determined with the same degree of accuracy as can the octane number of gasolines and alternative methods of estimating it from laboratory data are sometimes used. Since the ignition quality is related to the chemical composition of the fuel a correlation is to be expected between aromaticity and cetane number. Aromatics differ appreciably from non-aromatics in physical properties and various empirical relationships between such properties and cetane number have been used. The best known are the 'diesel index' and the 'calculated cetane index'. The former is calculated from a formula involving the gravity of the fuel and its aniline point (the lowest temperature at which it is completely miscible with aniline), the latter from a formula involving the gravity and the mid-boiling point.

Consistency

Penetration tests

The hardness or consistency of solid or semi-solid products such as bitumen, lubricating grease and wax is measured by penetration tests in which the depth is measured to which a loaded needle or plunger sinks into the material under standard conditions of temperature and time. These tests are arbitrary, do not yield absolute values of any fundamental physical property, and are of little value in relation to performance. They are useful, however, for grading and quality control.

For bitumen and microcrystalline wax the penetration is determined by measuring the distance in tenths of a millimetre that a standard needle penetrates in 5 seconds under a load of 100 grammes, usually at a temperature of 25°C (77°F) [Fig. 161]. The sample is prepared by melting the material under specified conditions and pouring into a container where it cools and solidifies.

Grease and petrolatum are tested with a conical plunger, and the depth of penetration in 5 seconds is determined at 25°C (77°F) under a load of 150 grammes. Since greases cannot be melted without decomposition they are filled cold into the test container. The consistency of a grease depends on the structure built up by the thickener in the oil, and this structure is affected by mechanical disturbance. A grease has a different consistency immediately after being stirred or churned from that after it has been undisturbed for a long time. Since greases in use are apt to be churned by the motion of the parts they lubricate, they are usually tested after being 'worked' to a standard amount in a container fitted with a perforated plate that can be forced up and down through the grease.

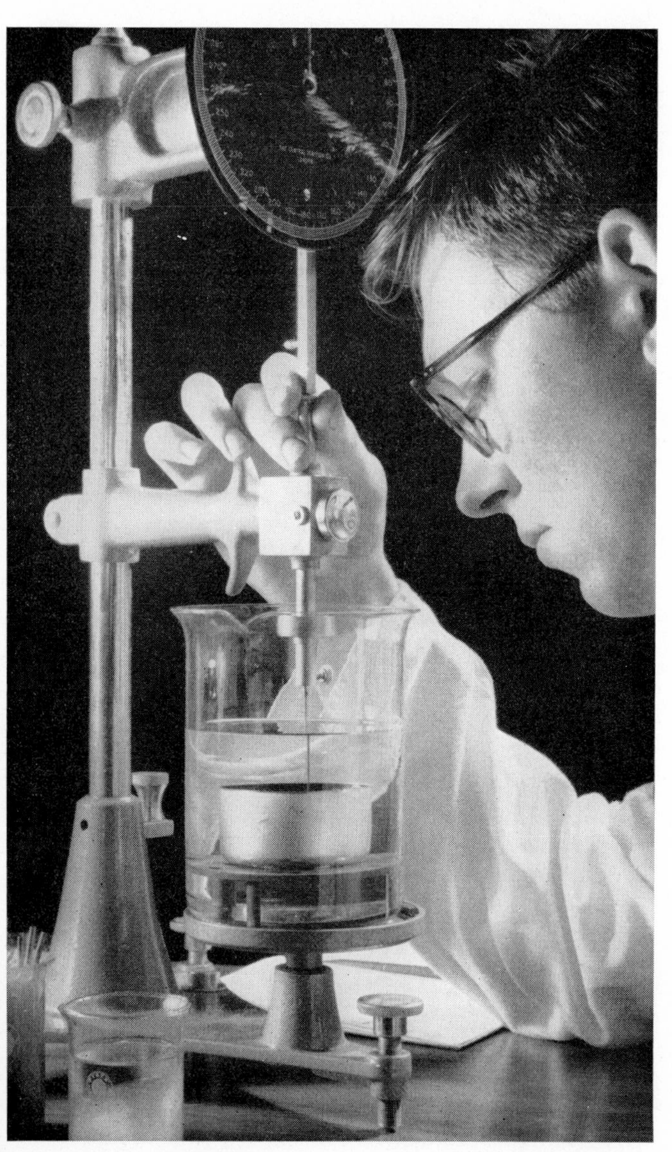

Fig. 161 Penetration test

Corrosion and protection

Nearly all petroleum products are used under conditions that bring them into contact with metallic surfaces, and it is important that these surfaces should not be corroded thereby. Petroleum products must therefore be non-corrosive in themselves and should not become corrosive during use and, in some instances, are also expected to provide positive protection against corrosive attack by moisture or other agents.

Sulphur is a common source of corrosion, even though present in only small quantities, and products are therefore tested to ensure either its absence or its limitation to relatively harmless amounts. Oxidation with formation of acids is another potential cause of corrosion and this is one reason why oxidation stability is of such great importance.

Protection against corrosion

Protective properties are generally assessed by coating mild steel plates with the product in question in a manner simulating its normal usage and then exposing them to a corrosive atmosphere under specified conditions. The plates are inspected at intervals and the degree of protection assessed by the length of time before any, or a specified amount of corrosion occurs, or by the general state of the plates in comparison with others coated with different protectives. Exposure may be outdoor, outdoor under cover, indoor or in a 'humidity cabinet' in which the temperature and humidity are controlled, either to a constant level or in a cycle.

Alternatively exposure may be in a beaker in which water or other liquid is mildly heated by an underlying hotplate and vapour condensed by cooling coils surrounding the upper part of the beaker. In this apparatus, by suitable selection of the liquid, various corrosive atmospheres can be generated.

Sulphur (corrosive)

Qualitative tests for corrosive sulphur – which should have been removed during refining – are carried out on almost all liquid products. A cleaned strip of copper is immersed in the sample for a prescribed time at a specified temperature, depending on the product. Any staining or discoloration of the strip is reported in terms of a set of standards.

Sulphur (total)

Petroleum gases and the lighter liquid products can be examined by a lamp method in which the product is completely burnt in a small wick lamp and the combustion gases are absorbed in an aqueous alkaline solution which is then analysed for sulphur content. Gas oils and aromatic products which might burn with a smoky flame can also be tested by this method if first diluted with a sulphur-free diluent.

Non-volatile products, which cannot be tested by the lamp method, are burnt in a bomb in the presence of oxygen under pressure. The combustion products are absorbed in aqueous alkali which is then analysed for sulphur content. Alternatively the sample is vaporized in a heated quartz tube and the vapour is swept by purified air over quartz chips maintained at 950–1000°C (1740–1830°F). The combustion products are absorbed and analysed as previously.

Engine tests of lubricants

The performance of a lubricating oil in an engine can be inferred to a certain extent from conventional tests for oxidation stability, carbon formation, volatility, etc, but engine tests are necessary to get a more realistic assessment. Even so, in view of the wide variety of engines in which any engine oil is used and of the conditions under which they operate, no single engine test can be expected to assess all aspects of performance. It is customary therefore to apply a number of engine tests in each of which the conditions are adjusted to provide rather more than normal severity to a particular aspect, for example ring sticking, cold sludge, cam and tappet wear. Some of these tests have become more or less universally used, the Caterpillar for ring sticking, wear and deposits, the Fowler for ring sticking, the Chevrolet for oxidation stability and bearing corrosion, the Gardner for piston cleanliness and general performance, and the Petter for engine cleanliness. Although the Caterpillar, Fowler and Gardner are diesel engines they are used also for the evaluation of lubricating oils for gasoline engines.

Many of the major manufacturers have developed engine tests in which lubricants must show good performance before being recommended for use in their engines. The ASTM have standardized a sequence of engine tests for evaluating automotive lubricants for API Service MS (*ASTM Special Technical Publications 315 and 315A*) which is generally accepted in the USA as covering all individual engine requirements. There are five tests which evaluate, respectively, low-temperature, medium-speed operation (including scuffing and wear), low-temperature deposits and rusting, high-temperature oxidation, high-temperature high-speed scuffing and wear, insoluble sludging and screen clogging. The Co-operative European Committee is attempting to standardize a similar sequence for European use.

Load-carrying capacity

Under hydrodynamic conditions the ability of an oil to carry a load depends on its viscosity, but when metal-to-metal contact is imminent its ability depends on the effectiveness of the EP agent to prevent catastrophic wear.

Various laboratory machines have been devised to assess this property by causing test pieces to rub together under load in the presence of the lubricant and measuring the extent of wear, the maximum permissible load without undue wear, the load to cause seizure, or some other parameter dependent on the ability of the lubricant to facilitate lubrication under the conditions imposed. The best known machines of this type are the Almen (or Almen-Wieland), Falex, SAE, Shell Four Ball and Timken machines. Although these machines undoubtedly give some indication of EP activity, their results are often mutually contradictory and show no precise correlation with service performance. They are, however, useful for comparative testing of oils and additives.

Load-carrying capacity is of particular interest in gear lubrication, and as an alternative to the above-mentioned machines laboratory rigs in which actual gears are run are used. The best known are the IAE Gear Machine designed by the Institute of Automotive Engineers (UK), the Ryder Machine (USA) and the VZG Machine (Germany). But these also do not always agree amongst themselves in the rating of lubricants or correlate with practice. Moreover all these rigs use spur gears whereas the major problems in gear lubrication arise with hypoid gears.

More recently, tests in actual vehicle hypoid axles have been developed to assess lubricant performance and some are now specified in official specifications (USA military, MIL Specifications) or in motor or gear manufacturers' specifications. Two in particular have been developed for the testing of hypoid gear oils under conditions of high torque/low speed and high speed/shock loads. These tests appear to correlate better with practice than do any laboratory machine or rig tests [Fig. 162].

Melting and freezing points

The changing of a solid into a liquid by heat is called melting while the reverse change is called freezing. Individual substances melt and freeze sharply at a definite temperature – the melting and freezing points – but mixtures of compounds such as petroleum products do not melt or freeze sharply; they gradually soften or set over a range of temperatures. It is therefore strictly incorrect to speak of melting point or freezing point of a petroleum product and the terms 'softening point' and 'setting point' are used to define a transition under arbitrarily specified conditions. An even more specific term, 'drop point', is used to define the temperature at which greases drop from the orifice of a cup in which they are gradually heated.

Drop point of grease

The grease is steadily heated at a specified rate in a small cup with an orifice in the bottom, the cup full of grease being clipped over the bulb of a thermometer. The drop point is the temperature at which a drop of the sample first falls from the cup. The drop point is no indication of the maximum temperature at which a grease can be used, many greases would flow from a bearing at temperatures far below their drop points. The drop point is useful only for control purposes.

Freezing point of aviation fuel

Freezing point is an important characteristic of aviation fuels and must be sufficiently low to avoid solidification and consequent blocking of filters at the low temperatures prevailing at high altitudes.

The freezing point test (ASTM) or cold test (IP) of aviation fuels is carried out by cooling a quantity of the fuel (freed from water) under specified conditions until crystals of hydrocarbon appear. The temperature at which this occurs is reported as the freezing point or cold test temperature; it is not the temperature at which the fuel solidifies.

Pour point

When liquid petroleum products are cooled a point is reached at which some of the constituents begin to solidify, and if cooling is continued the oil eventually ceases to flow. The temperature at which this occurs under the conditions set out below is recorded as the setting or solid point and the pour point is defined as the temperature 5°F (3°C) above it.

To determine the pour point a sample of the oil in a cylindrical glass jar with a flat bottom is heated to 115°F (46°C) or to a temperature 15°F (8°C) above the expected

Fig. 162 Hypoid axle test

pour point if this is above 90°F (32°C). The sample is then cooled at a specified rate until there is no apparent movement of the surface of the oil when the jar is held horizontally for 5 seconds. This is the setting point.

Pour points are generally determined on distillate fuels, fuel oils and lubricants. The pour point of an oil indicates its ability to flow at normal or low temperatures. Solidification may be due to either separation of wax or a considerable increase in viscosity. It may be possible to pump an oil at temperatures below its pour point because the stirring action of the pump breaks up the restraining structure of the solidified oil but only, of course, if the oil can enter the pump. In most cases, therefore, the pour point is actually the limiting factor and the product may have to be heated in order to remain pumpable.

Setting point of paraffin wax

Molten wax is cooled under specified conditions and the temperature recorded at frequent intervals. At first the temperature falls continuously but as solidification occurs the temperature remains constant or nearly constant for a short time and then falls again. The setting point is the temperature recorded during this brief interval of constant temperature. The test is used to classify waxes and as a guide to the grade to be used for a given application.

Softening point of bitumen

Two brass rings resting on a plate are filled with molten bitumen and allowed to cool. Excess bitumen is cut off and the rings removed from the plate and placed in a frame immersed in a beaker of water. A steel ball of specified weight is placed on the disc of bitumen in each ring, and the water is heated at a specified rate until the bitumen softens sufficiently to allow the ball to carry it through the ring onto a plate fixed at a specified distance below the ring. The temperature at which this occurs is the softening point. Glycerin is substituted for water when determining softening points above 80°C (176°F).

The test is used to specify the various grades.

Oxidation characteristics

All petroleum products under normal conditions of storage and use come into contact with air and hence with oxygen, often at high temperatures, and sometimes when in a finely divided state, for example as a mist in an engine. Such conditions are very favourable for oxidation to take place. Hydrocarbons vary in their susceptibility to oxidation, paraffins or saturated chain compounds are generally more resistant than aromatic ring compounds, and unsaturated compounds are readily oxidized.

Although there are many oxidation tests differing appreciably in their details, they mostly follow the same general procedure. The product being examined is exposed to excess air or oxygen at a temperature commensurable with that to which it is subjected in practice, or somewhat higher to expedite the process, and the amount of oxygen absorbed is determined or the quantity and quality of the oxidation products are assessed. Gasolines, lubricating oils, insulating oils and greases are all commonly subjected to such tests.

A major difficulty of such tests is the choice of conditions. If these conditions, especially the temperature, are similar to those in practice, the oxidation may be so slow that the test is too long to be serviceable for control or specification purposes. However, if the conditions are made more severe, as by increasing the temperature, or using oxygen instead of air, in order to shorten the test to a serviceable time, the nature of the reaction is altered and the results may have little bearing on what happens in practice.

Gasoline

The oxidation stability of motor gasoline is determined by placing a quantity in a steel bomb, charging with oxygen at a pressure of 100–102 lb/in², immersing the bomb in a bath of boiling water and recording the pressure at intervals. After an initial rise due to increase in temperature, the pressure remains substantially constant since oxidation is proceeding very slowly, but after an interval (induction period) it begins to fall as oxygen is absorbed in the course of the reaction. The induction period is taken as a measure of the oxidation or gum stability of the gasoline.

Another method applied to aviation and motor gasolines, as well as to kerosine fuels for aviation gas turbines, consists in evaporating the sample to dryness in a suitably heated dish, assisted by a jet of air or steam passing slowly over the surface of the liquid. The residue at the end of the test is weighed. The result, expressed as mg/100 ml gasoline, is the 'existent gum', and gives some indication of the tendency of the fuel to deposit gum if used immediately, but does not indicate the likelihood of gum formation during storage.

To determine the 'potential gum', that likely to be formed on long storage, the sample is heated in a bomb at 100°C (212°F) in the presence of oxygen under pressure, for a specified time. The bomb is then cooled, and the sample is removed and evaporated to dryness with the aid of a jet of air. The residue, expressed as mg/100 ml of gasoline, is the 'x hour aging gum' or 'potential gum'.

Insulating oil

Many tests have been devised for measuring the stability of transformer oil, and most national standardization bodies and some transformer manufacturers have their own particular tests – to the general embarrassment and inconvenience of all concerned with the manufacture and international supply of transformer oils. Although the tests differ considerably in detail and give incompatible results, they are mostly based on the same principle – the oil is exposed to air or oxygen for a certain time at a specified temperature and the oxidized oil is tested for acidity and/or the amount of sludge formed. The International Electrotechnical Commission (IEC) have for many years been endeavouring to formulate an internationally acceptable test.

The accepted British test, once known as the Michie Sludge Test after its originator, now known as the BSI (British Standards Institution) test, involves the blowing of air through the oil at 150°C (302°F) for 45 hours in the presence of copper foil, after which the oxidized oil is tested for acidity and sludge.

In the IEC test, which has now been accepted in some but not all countries, oxygen is blown through the oil for 164 hours at 100°C (212°F) in the presence of solid copper, after which acidity and sludge content are determined.

Lubricating grease

When grease-filled anti-friction bearings are stored for long periods corrosion can occur due to oxidation of the grease and formation of acids. Grease is tested for stability under such conditions by exposing it in thin layers on trays in a steel pressure bomb filled with oxygen at a pressure of 100 lb/in² and maintained for 100 hours at 100°C (212°F). If oxidation occurs the pressure drops and a usual specification is that it should not drop more than 5 lb/in² in 100 hours.

The test is not intended to predict stability of the grease in use or in bulk storage.

Fig. 163 Turbine Oil Stability Test (TOST)

Lubricating oil

Many oxidation tests for lubricating oil are in vogue, the temperature and other conditions being selected appropriate to the use of the oil. One of the oldest is the BAM (British Air Ministry) test. This test was once the main specification test for aviation oils but is no longer included in any aviation specification; it is still used, however, for quality control and classification of engine and other lubricants, although its validity is somewhat doubtful. A quantity of oil is maintained at 200°C (392°F) for two periods of six hours with air bubbled through it at a specified rate. The oxidized oil is compared with the original oil for viscosity and carbon residue.

Turbine oils are expected to remain in use without appreciable oxidation for very long periods. In the Turbine Oil Stability Test (TOST), the oil is maintained for 90 hours at 110°C (230°F) in the presence of iron and copper catalysts. Portions of the oil are withdrawn at intervals and tested for acidity. The acidity rises very slowly for a period (induction period) and then rises rapidly; the induction period is regarded as a measure of the resistance of the oil to oxidation. The test primarily determines the life of the oxidation inhibitor and may not indicate the stability of the base oil once the inhibitor has been exhausted. Results show some correlation with practice in that the life of the oil increases with the length of the induction period. Fig. 163 shows the TOST apparatus.

Sundry tests

Acidity and alkalinity

The acidity or alkalinity of petroleum products is determined by dissolving the product in a suitable neutral solvent and neutralizing the solution with either standard alkali or standard acid as the case may be. The neutral point may be indicated by a colour indicator or electrometrically.

Most unrefined petroleum products contain small quantities of weak organic acids which are normally removed during refining to give substantially neutral refined products. The test therefore serves to indicate how much acid is present in the unrefined product and to ensure its absence in the refined product. In particular it may be used to ensure the absence of corrosive acids.

Fuel oils and bitumens, which are not further refined, may still retain these organic acids, naphthenic acids, and their presence is sometimes an advantage – as in the manufacture of bitumen emulsions. Again the test is used to determine the amount present.

Greases may contain small quantities of free acid, free alkali or both and their presence or absence may profoundly affect the properties.

Oxidation of petroleum products more often than not produces acids and the progress of deterioration can be followed by measuring acidity.

Acidity determinations can therefore be used as a refinery control test or as a measure of change during use. The normal acidity test measures total acidity and makes no distinction between organic and inorganic or weak and strong acids. The weak organic acids – naphthenic acids – present in some products and the organic acids formed by oxidation are not nearly as corrosive as the acids formed by the combustion or other oxidation of sulphur compounds and, in the proportions in which they are usually present, have little effect on metallic surfaces. The main objection to their presence is the greater tendency for the oil to form emulsions or sludges.

Ash

Inorganic matter in petroleum products may be due to complex organometallic compounds in solution in the crude oil, to contaminants, e.g. salt, associated with the crude, to impurities picked up during processing or, very commonly, to additives used to improve the product. Distillates may contain some small traces of inorganic matter derived from the crude but most of it will be left in the residues, i.e. residual fuel oil and bitumen.

When an oil is burnt most of the inorganic matter remains as 'ash' although some mineral salts are volatile and would be lost if not prevented. The ash of an oil is normally determined by burning a quantity in a dish and heating the residue strongly until no carbonaceous material remains. If volatile salts are present the residue on burning is heated carefully until nearly free from carbon and is then moistened with a little sulphuric acid which converts any volatile salts to non-volatile sulphates and permits the remaining carbon to be burned off without loss of inorganic matter. In this case the ash is described as 'sulphated ash' and will be more than the straight, unsulphated ash, not only because loss of ash has been prevented but because of the extra sulphur and oxygen combined in the sulphate. The ash may be qualitatively or quantitatively analysed for its constituents either chemically or spectrographically.

The ash test is widely used for quality control of refined products. Applied to used engine oils with due allowance for the ash of the unused oil, it indicates the amount of mineral matter – wear products or road dust – picked up during circulation. With natural or mechanical asphalts it indicates the amount of mineral matter present.

Asphaltenes

Practically all crude oils contain asphaltic matter. This is non-volatile and therefore not found in the lighter distillates but in the residual fractions, heavy lubricating oils, residual fuels and bitumen. It is generally removed from lubricating oils during refining, but may be present in some that are not fully refined, such as steam cylinder oils and some industrial gear oils.

The quantity of asphaltic matter or 'asphaltenes' is determined by diluting the product with a paraffinic solvent, for example n-heptane, in which the asphaltenes are insoluble. The precipitate includes any carbon and inorganic matter that may also be present; the asphaltenes are separated from them by redissolving in an aromatic solvent, for example benzene, filtering, evaporating the solution to dryness and weighing the residue.

For liquid products the test is used mostly for classifying but for bitumens the asphaltenes are an essential part of the product profoundly influencing its performance – a high asphaltene content being associated with low susceptibility to temperature change.

Demulsification

In some applications lubricating oils come into contact with water or steam, for example turbine oils and steam cylinder oils. In some instances emulsification of the oil with water is desirable (steam cylinder oils in engines operating with wet steam) but in most cases emulsification is undesirable.

Oils are tested for emulsification or demulsification by blowing with steam under specified conditions and measuring the stability of the emulsion so formed. Where emulsification is undesirable the demulsibility is expressed as the time in seconds required for complete separation of oil and water.

Alternatively specified quantities of oil and water may be violently stirred together by a paddle rotating in a narrow glass cylinder under specified conditions of temperature and time, and again observing the time required for complete separation (demulsibility) or the time during which the emulsion remains stable (emulsibility).

Diluent

In an IC engine unburnt fuel may find its way into the lubricating oil in the crankcase, the amount depending on the mechanical condition of the engine and the volatility of the fuel. Dilution reduces the viscosity of the oil and, if excessive, impairs its lubricating properties.

The diluent content is estimated by distilling a sample of crankcase oil with steam and measuring the amount of oily distillate. It is not a very precise test since there is no clear demarcation between heavy ends of fuel and light ends of lubricating oil, and the results depend very much on the type of fuel and oil used. It gives a rough indication of dilution, however, and will indicate excessive dilution. The test is usually confined to gasoline engine lubricants since the demarcation between fuel and lubricant is still more indefinite in diesel engines.

Electric strength

The electric strength of transformer oils and bitumens is measured by subjecting them to an increasing alternating voltage under specified conditions of cell dimensions, electrode shape and dimensions of gap, until either breakdown occurs or a specified voltage is maintained for a specified period.

The electric strength of a petroleum product is inherently high; low electric strength is mostly a result of contamination with water or finely divided solids, especially fibrous materials. The test is therefore an indication of contamination.

Foaming

Foaming tests are applied to aviation piston engine lubricants, turbine oils and hydraulic oils.

The oil is blown with air under standardized conditions

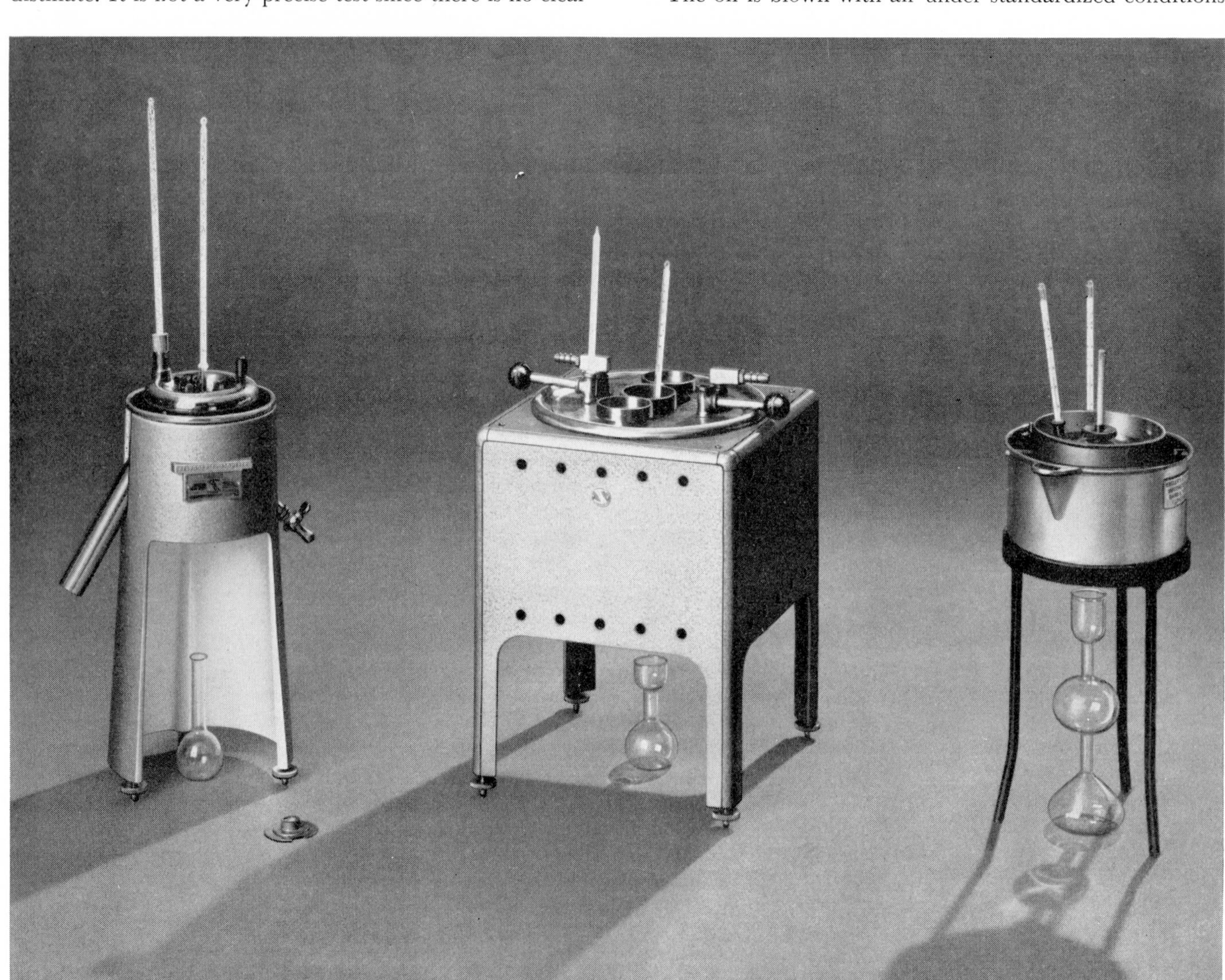

Fig. 164 Conventional viscometers, left to right, Redwood, Saybolt, Engler

and the build-up of foam and the speed with which it collapses are measured.

Viscosity

The viscosity of a liquid is a measure of its resistance to flow and is a property of great importance for all petroleum products. It influences the flow of kerosine up a wick, the atomization of fuel oils, the impregnation of fibrous materials by paraffin wax or bitumen, the circulation of lubricating oils in an engine or a bearing, and the spreading of bitumen on aggregates and roads. It is therefore determined on many petroleum products both as a routine control test and as a means of assessing suitability for or behaviour in any given application. Viscosity depends on temperature and decreases as temperature increases; the temperature must therefore always be specified in stating the viscosity of a material, otherwise the figure has no meaning.

Viscosity is a fundamental property of a liquid, i.e. it can be expressed in units which do not depend on the instrument or the method used for its determination; a viscosity so expressed is referred to as 'absolute viscosity'. Viscosity can also be expressed in ways that depend on the instrument and the method used and such viscosities are referred to as 'conventional viscosities'.

In the petroleum industry a number of conventional viscometers have been used almost since the beginning of the industry, i.e. the Redwood, Saybolt and Engler viscometers [Fig. 164], they are now being gradually superseded by the more accurate and scientific absolute capillary viscometers [Fig. 165]. Nevertheless it is still customary to characterize petroleum products in terms of conventional viscosities even though the absolute viscosity is determined and the conventional viscosity derived from conversion tables.

Absolute viscosity

Absolute viscosities can be expressed in many ways depending on the units used but in the petroleum industry it is usual to express kinematic viscosities in centistokes and dynamic viscosities in centipoises, the two being related by the equation:

dynamic viscosity = kinematic viscosity × density

Absolute viscosity is determined in a capillary viscometer [Fig. 166] by measuring the time required for a fixed volume of the sample to flow through a glass capillary under the pressure of a fixed and reproducible head of liquid.

The time of flow depends on the length and diameter of

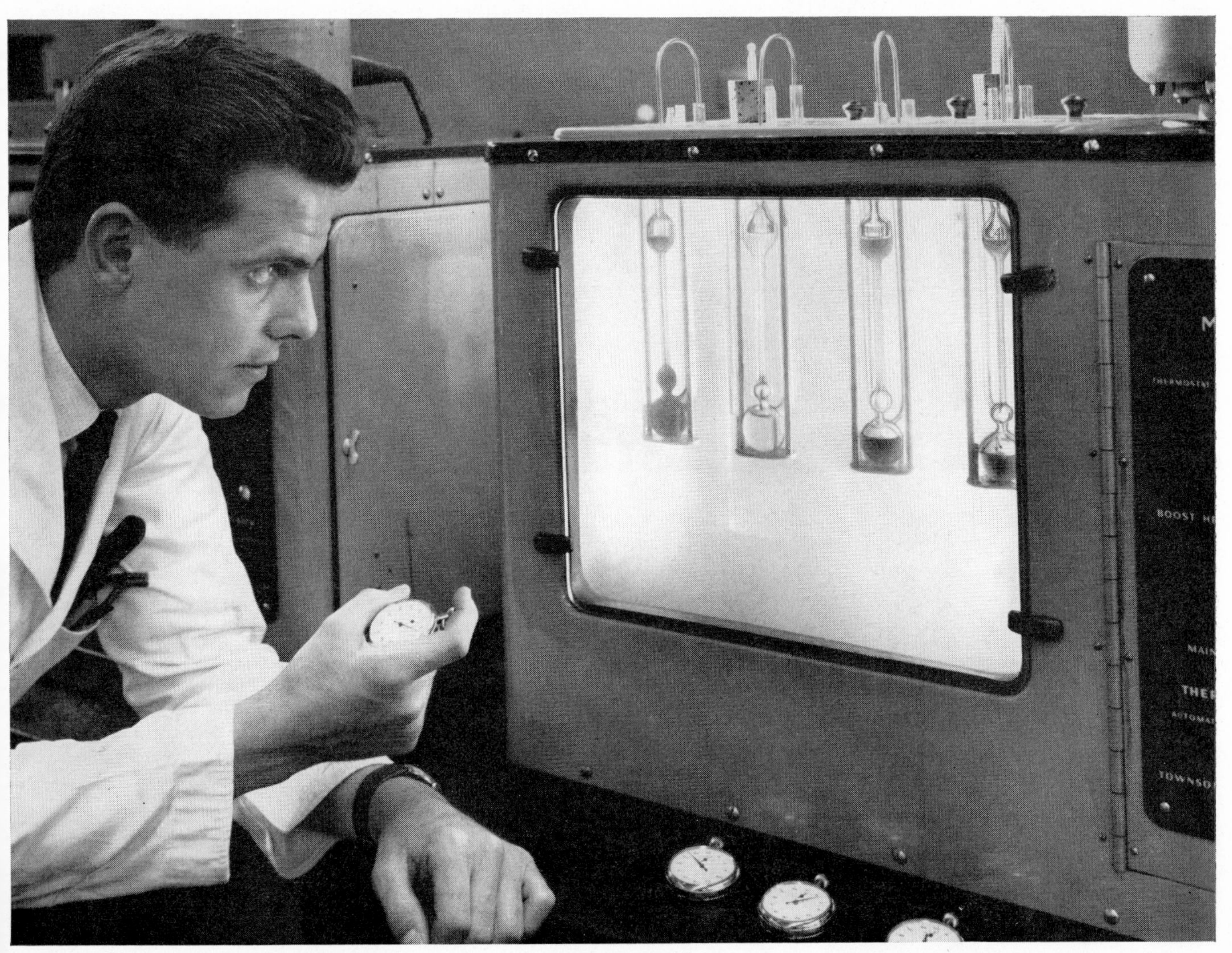

Fig. 165 Suspended level capillary viscometer

the capillary, but each instrument is calibrated and assigned a 'calibration factor' with which to multiply the time to give the viscosity. The temperature of the liquid under test must be controlled within very fine limits, a variation not exceeding ±0·02°F (0·01°C) being usually required. The viscometer is accordingly all but immersed in a large bath of water or other liquid controlled to the required temperature. Determinations are normally made at 100° or 122°F (37·8° or 50°C) for fuels and at 100° and 210°F (37·8° and 98·9°C) for lubricants, the viscosities at these temperatures being those required for calculating 'viscosity index'.

Conventional viscosity

Conventional viscosities were measured by the Redwood I and Redwood II viscometers in the UK, the Saybolt Universal and the Saybolt Furol in the USA, and the Engler on the European continent [Fig. 164]. These all consist of a container with a hole or jet of standard size in the bottom, the container being jacketed by a bath in which water or oil can be heated and maintained at the required temperature. In the Redwood and Saybolt instruments the second of each pair mentioned has a larger orifice and is used for more viscous oils. Measurement is made of the time taken for a specified volume of oil to flow out of the container into a graduated flask. Results with the Redwood and Saybolt viscometers are expressed in terms of time in seconds. With the Engler, however, the viscosity is reported as the ratio of the time of flow of the oil to the time of flow of water, and is given as Engler degrees. There is no general agreement regarding the temperatures to be used with these instruments: Redwood viscosities are customarily reported at 70°F (21·1°C), 100°F (37·8°C), 140°F (60°C) and 212°F (100°C); Saybolt at 100°F (37·8°C) and 210°F (98·9°C); and Engler at 20°C (68°F), 50°C (122°F) and 100°C (212°F).

Viscosity index

The viscosity of an oil decreases with rise in temperature but to a varying degree depending on the type of crude from which it is derived and the refining treatment to which it has been subjected. The relationship between viscosity and temperature is of significance for lubricating oils since most oils have to operate over a range of temperature. There are many ways of expressing this relationship but the one firmly established in the petroleum industry is the viscosity index (VI) system, even though it is an arbitrary system and more fundamental methods have been suggested.

When the system was first introduced, distillates from Pennsylvanian crudes had the flattest viscosity/temperature curves (i.e. the least change in viscosity with temperature) of any oils known, while distillates from Gulf crudes had the steepest known curves. These oils were accordingly assigned viscosity indexes of 100 and 0 respectively, and the viscosity/temperature curve of an oil is compared with these two standards and the oil given a VI indicating its behaviour relative to them.

There are now many lubricants with VI values outside the original limits of 0 and 100, and although the system has been extended to include them the arrangement is not altogether satisfactory. This has led to renewed attention to more fundamental methods of expressing the viscosity-temperature relationship but none has so far been accepted.

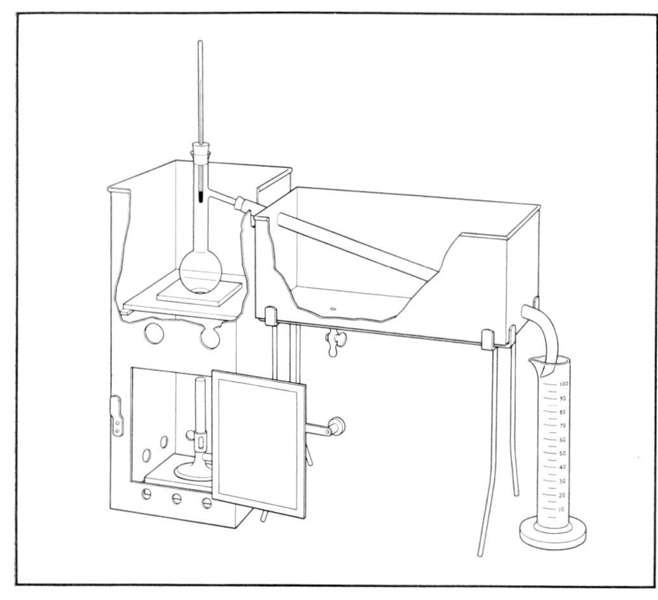

Fig. 166 Distillation apparatus

Volatility and inflammability

Volatility is of considerable importance for most distillate fuels, for some lubricants and for bitumen cutbacks; it is of some significance also for straight bitumens.

In gasolines it affects easy starting, vapour lock and dilution of crankcase oil; in diesel engine fuels it is of less importance, but has some influence on startability and combustion characteristics. In these products and in kerosines, volatility is assessed by determining the distillation range, the vapour pressure and the flash point. The flash point is also an indication of inflammability.

In the less volatile products, lubricating oils and bitumens, only a small fraction is volatile and then only at high temperatures or at very low pressures. Such volatiles may, however, limit the use of the product in some applications and the volatility is then commonly assessed by determining the loss in weight on heating to some specified temperature.

In cutback bitumens the volatility is again high due to the volatile solvent and has a bearing on the setting performance of the product. It is determined by a distillation test similar to that applied to fuels.

Distillation test

When a simple liquid such as water is heated, it boils at a constant temperature, its boiling point, and is converted to a vapour, steam. If this steam comes into contact with a cold surface it condenses back again to the liquid form, water. Petroleum products, however, are not simple liquids but mixtures of many compounds each having its own boiling point. Instead of a simple boiling point these products therefore have a 'distillation range' which varies according to the type of product.

Distillation tests are normally carried out on all liquid petroleum products other than lubricants and residual fuels. A quantity of the liquid is heated in a glass flask carrying a thermometer and fitted to a condenser and a receiving cylinder [Fig. 166]. The most volatile compound boils first, turns to vapour, passes up the neck of the flask, over the thermometer bulb, into the condenser where it

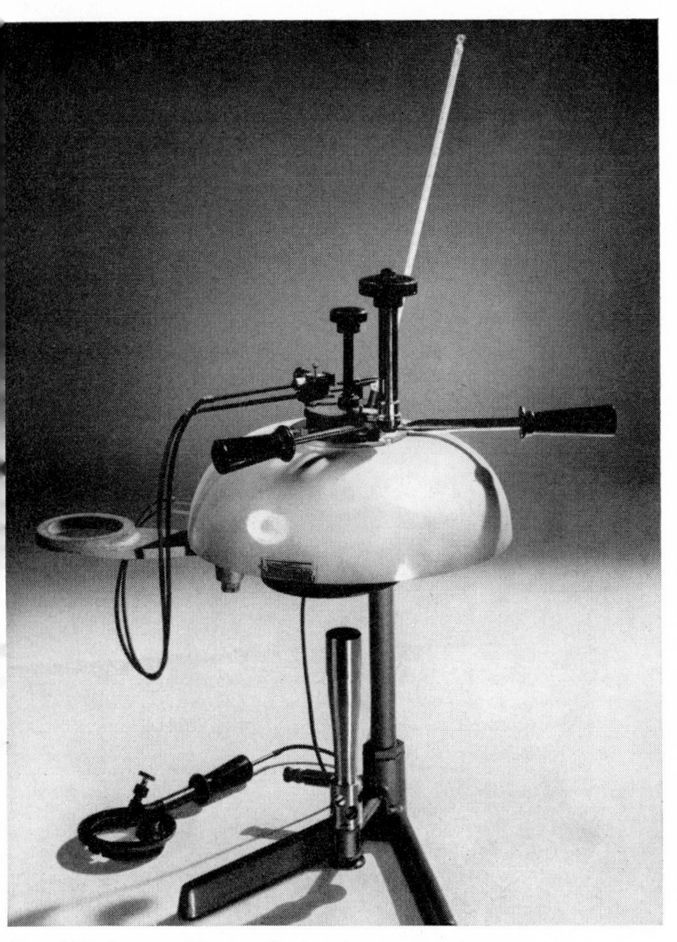

Fig. 167 Pensky-Martens flash point apparatus

condenses back to a liquid and flows into the graduated receiver. As the temperature in the flask is increased, the less volatile compounds in their turn distil, condense and pass into the receiver until eventually either all the liquid in the flask has been boiled off or only a small quantity remains and cannot be distilled over without decomposition.

The temperature at which the first drop of liquid falls into the receiver is recorded as the 'initial boiling point', IBP, and the highest temperature at the end of the distillation as the 'final boiling point', FBP. The temperatures at which each 10 %v is recovered in the flask are also recorded as well as the %v collected at various selected temperatures.

When the distillation test is applied to cutback bitumens the distillation is stopped at a selected temperature according to the nature of the solvent, instead of being carried to the highest attainable temperature, and the amount recovered indicates the amount of solvent present in the cutback.

Flash point and fire point

Flash point tests are carried out to assess both the volatility and the inflammability of a product. The flash point is the lowest temperature at which a combustible material will give off enough vapour to form an inflammable mixture with air. In general, the relative volumes of liquid and vapour spaces, as well as the accessibility of air to the vapour space, will affect the flash point.

Two types of test are carried out, the closed and the open flash point tests. In the former, a measured quantity of the product is placed in a cup fitted with a lid carrying a thermometer. The oil is heated slowly at a uniform rate and a small test flame is directed into the cup at regular intervals. The closed flash point is recorded as the lowest temperature at which a distinct flash occurs inside the cup on applying the flame. The open flash point is often determined immediately following the closed flash, by removing the lid and continuing to heat the oil until the vapour flashes under these new conditions. Alternatively, the open flash point may be determined without going through the closed flash point stage, and this is generally done with the heavier products, lubricating oils and bitumen.

After the open flash point has been recorded, heating may still be continued until the oil burns continually on applying the test flame and the temperature at which this occurs is the 'fire point'.

There are several methods of determining flash point, each with its own design of apparatus, e.g. the Tagliabue (Tag), Abel, Pensky-Martens and Cleveland methods, all of which have been standardized by either the ASTM or the IP [Fig. 167].

Flash point determinations are not usually carried out on volatile products such as gasoline and light solvents since they have flash points well below normal atmospheric temperatures. The flash point of kerosine is an assessment of inflammability, that of heavier fuels is an indication of volatility. The test is carried out on lubricating oils mainly

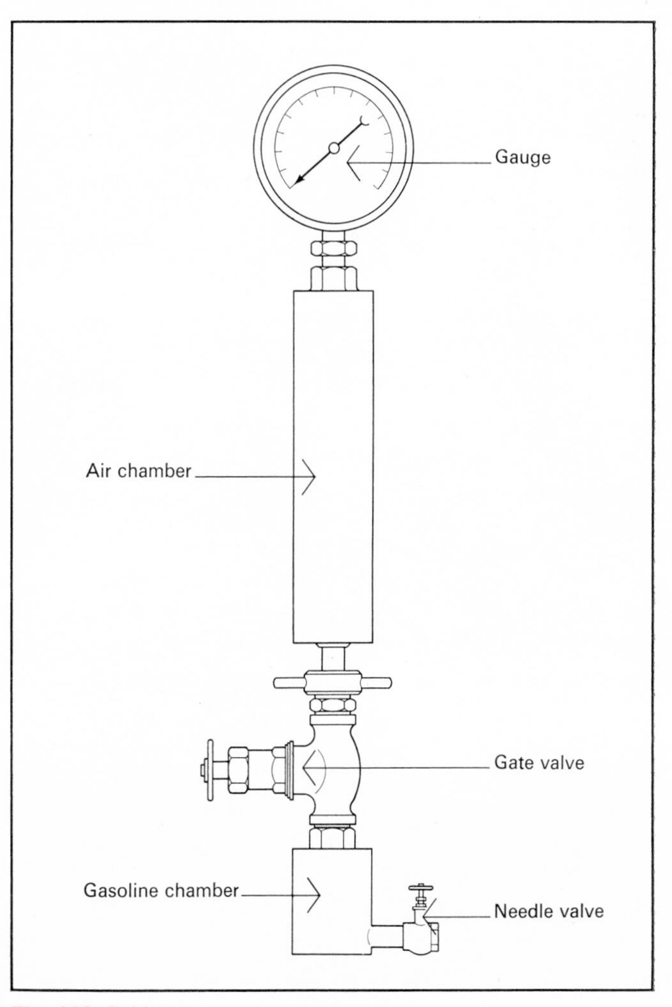

Fig. 168 Reid vapour pressure apparatus

as a manufacturing control and for classification; it has no relation to the usefulness of a lubricant.

Vapour pressure (Reid)

Vapour pressure is a measure of the tendency of a liquid or solid to evaporate; it increases with the temperature and when it equals the atmospheric pressure the liquid boils. In a simple liquid like water the vapour pressure depends solely on temperature and the same liquid-vapour equilibrium is established at a given temperature irrespective of the volume of the vapour space. With mixtures, however, the vapour pressure depends on the ratio of liquid volume to vapour volume as well as on the temperature and both these factors must be controlled if repeatable results are to be obtained when measuring it.

The vapour pressure of gasoline is determined by the Reid method [Fig. 168]. The lower chamber is filled with the gasoline and connected to the upper air chamber fitted with a pressure gauge. The whole apparatus is placed in a water bath at 100°F (38°C) and is frequently removed and shaken. The increase in pressure due to the vapour pressure of the liquid at 100°F is then measured.

This test not only measures the volatility of the gasoline but also gives some indication of the pressure that may develop in ships' tanks, drums and other containers in which gasoline is stored.

ASTM/IP methods

The ASTM and IP methods mentioned in this chapter are shown in Table 19, which also serves as an index to the methods. Only the numbers of the methods are given since the date of the method, e.g. ASTM D 357/*60*, IP 44/*60*, indicates when it was last revised, and is therefore subject to change.

The methods fall into four categories as follows:

1 Joint ASTM/IP Methods: methods that are identical and have been accepted as joint methods for which both organizations are responsible.

2 Technically Equivalent Methods: methods that differ in certain respects but are technically equivalent, i.e. give substantially the same results.

3 Corresponding Methods: methods that are designed to determine the same property or quality, but which differ significantly in some respects so that they do not give the same results, i.e. are not technically equivalent.

4 Methods for which there is no corresponding method in the other organization.

The publication of joint ASTM/IP methods is a new feature. The first list was published in the 1964 editions of the respective books of Standards, a second list has been agreed for publication in the 1965 editions, and further lists will be published as more methods become approved.

For further details of these and other methods reference should be made to the current volumes of *ASTM Standards on Petroleum Products* and *IP Standards for Petroleum and its Products*.

Table 19 ASTM and IP methods

Test	Page	ASTM D	IP	Category
Combustion				
Anti-knock quality,	181	357	44	1
motor method		1948	150	1
Anti-knock quality,	181	908	126	1
research method		1656	172	1
Anti-knock quality, aviation	182	614	42	2
Burning quality, kerosine	182	187	10	3
Burning quality, kerosine, long-time	182	219	11	3
Burning quality, kerosine, smoke point	182	1322	57	3
Calorific value	182	240	12	3
Carbon residue, Conradson	182	189	13	1
Carbon residue, Ramsbottom	182	524	14	1
Ignition quality, diesel fuels	182	613	41	3
Consistency				
Penetration, bitumen	182	5	49	3
Penetration, grease	182	217	50	3
Penetration, petrolatum	182	937	179	1
Corrosion				
Corrosive sulphur	183	130	154	1
Protection against corrosion	183	—	153	4
Total sulphur, bomb	183	129	61	1
Total sulphur, lamp	183	1266	107	1
Total sulphur, quartz tube	183	1551	63	3
Engine tests of lubricants	184	—	124/173/174/175	4
Load-carrying capacity				
ASTM (Ryder) IP (IAE)	184	proposed	166	4
Melting and freezing				
Drop point of grease	184	566	132	1
Freezing point of aviation fuel	184	1477	16	3
Pour point	184	97	15	1
Setting point of paraffin wax (cooling curve)	185	87	55	1
Setting point of paraffin wax (rotating thermometer)	185	938	76	1
Setting point of paraffin wax (drop point)	185	127	133	1
Softening point of bitumen	185	36	58	3
Oxidation characteristics				
Gasoline (aviation)	186	873	138	1
Gasoline (motor)	186	525	40	1
Grease	186	942	142	1
Lubricating oil	187	—	48	4
Transformer oil	186	1314	56	3
Turbine oil (TOST)	187	943	157	1
Turbine oil	187	—	114	4
Sundry				
Acidity, colorimetric	187	974	139	1
Acidity, potentiometric	187	664	177	1
Ash, straight	187	482	4	1
Ash, sulphated	187	874	163	1
Asphaltenes	187	—	143	4
Demulsification	187	1401	19	3
Diluent	188	322	23	2
Electric strength	188	877	20	3
Foaming	188	892	146	1
Viscosity				
Absolute viscosity	189	445	71	1
Conventional viscosity	190	88	70	3
Viscosity index	190	567	73	2
Volatility and inflammability				
Distillation	190	86	123	1
Flash point, Abel	191	—	170	4
Flash point, Pensky-Martens	191	93	34	1
Flash point, Cleveland	191	92	36	1
Vapour pressure, Reid	191	323	69	1

Chemicals – manufacture and applications

The petroleum-chemical industry

Raw materials and primary conversion processes

Solvents

Detergents

Synthetic resins – plastics

Synthetic textile fibres

Synthetic rubbers

Industrial chemicals

Agricultural chemicals

The petroleum-chemical industry

Origin and development

The chemical side of the petroleum industry has developed enormously during recent years and is now an important and integral part of the chemical industry. It is sometimes referred to as the 'petrochemical industry' and its products as 'petrochemicals'. 'Petrochemical' is etymologically undesirable, especially in latin derived languages, and although 'petroleochemical' would be less misleading, it has not been used to any great extent. The terms 'petroleum-chemical industry' and 'chemicals derived from petroleum' are therefore used in this book.

The petroleum-chemical industry as we know it today is of comparatively recent origin, but it has some interesting antecedents. In 1854, before Drake's oil well was drilled, Professor Silliman of Yale University, after analysing samples of Pennsylvanian oil, mentioned the possibility of using petroleum products for purposes other than lighting and heating. In 1872 the famous Russian chemist Mendeleyev, after a visit to Pennsylvania, reported to his government: 'This material (oil) is far too precious to be burnt. When burning oil, we burn money; it should be used as a chemical base material.'

The Rhenania Ossag Oil Company (a predecessor of Deutsche Shell) was one of the first to use a petroleum fraction in a chemical process. In 1908 at Reisholz near Düsseldorf they nitrated a Balik Papan gasoline fraction, rich in toluene, to produce mononitrotoluene as a dyestuff intermediate for Badische Anilin. The process was later extended to the manufacture of trinitrotoluene, TNT, an explosive widely used during World Wars I and II.

About 1917 Standard Oil of New Jersey developed a process for the production of acetone from propylene, derived from the cracking of petroleum fractions. The acetone was to be used as a lacquer solvent, but the war ended before the process was commercially developed. Around 1925 Esso produced ethylene glycol from ethylene, and around 1930 larger scale petroleum-chemical developments were started in the USA by Esso, Shell, Dow, Dupont and Hercules. Shell produced isopropyl alcohol from propylene and secondary and tertiary butyl alcohols from butylenes, the olefins being derived from thermal cracking of petroleum fractions.

After the war, with the reconstruction and extension of the petroleum industry in Western Europe, a petroleum-chemical industry developed there even more rapidly than in the USA, and has since grown to its present dimensions.

Comparison with the petroleum industry

Quantitatively the petroleum-chemical industry is not very large compared with the petroleum industry as a whole, only 2–3% of the oil and natural gas produced being used as a base material for the manufacture of chemicals. But the value of the products per unit weight is considerably higher than that of oil products, and the manufacturing processes are much more complex than the relatively simple separation, conversion and treating processes of oil manufacture (p. 78).

Oil products are manufactured in large amounts in a relatively small number of standard grades; chemicals are manufactured in relatively smaller amounts in great diversity. Oil products and their manufacturing processes tend to remain stable for long periods; chemical manufacturing processes are subject to more frequent change as new processes are developed or new catalysts discovered for quicker or cheaper production.

The sequence of operations in oil and chemical manufacture is practically the same; feedstock is selected and processed, the product is treated to bring it up to marketing specification, or various products are blended together to a formulation for specific applications. In both the oil and the chemical industries more care has to be taken in the selection of feedstocks for catalytic processes than for non-catalytic processes. For example, to produce isopropyl alcohol from the propane/propylene fraction of cracking gas, a propane content of about 40% will suffice, but for the manufacture of polypropylene plastic by a catalytic process, a minimum of 99·5% is essential.

Oil refining is based on continuous operations, with few exceptions. Continuous operations are employed wherever possible for chemical manufacture, but there are more occasions when batch operation is advantageous in carrying out a complicated process.

Many chemicals, especially fine chemicals, are produced to specifications calling for a high degree of purity, and therefore often require some final treatment to bring them up to specification. Where chemicals have to be blended to produce products for specific applications the formulae are apt to be rather more complex than those of oil products. Pesticides, containing toxic compounds, have to be blended to be specific for particular pests and crops without undue hazard to other living organisms, including man; detergents must have balanced wetting, cleaning and foaming properties as well as being readily degraded biologically in sewage treatment.

Types of chemicals

Chemicals from petroleum can be divided into two main groups, organic and inorganic. The former have a carbon skeleton and are basically composed of carbon, hydrogen and certain other elements, notably oxygen, chlorine, sulphur and nitrogen. The latter, for example, ammonia, sulphur and hydrogen peroxide, do not contain carbon and are much less numerous than the former, but are nevertheless manufactured in considerable quantities.

Chemicals can be further classified as 'specification' chemicals and 'performance' chemicals. Specification chemicals, for example, ammonia, ethyl alcohol, acetone, glycerol, are in the main well-established chemicals common to the chemical industry as a whole, irrespective of their origin. They are produced to established specifications,

Fig. 169 Aerial view of chemicals plant, Houston, Texas

and are marketed as such for whatever purpose the buyer has in mind. Performance chemicals, on the other hand, have usually been developed for some specific application and many of them owe their existence to the petroleum-chemical industry, for example synthetic detergents, pesticides, synthetic resins. Many of them, as marketed, are blends of several chemicals, often to a proprietary formulation.

The range of products now derived from petroleum is so wide that they cannot all be discussed in this book, and the range will undoubtedly continue to grow. Moreover, chemicals from petroleum are often not final products but intermediates and starting materials for other industries. The great variety of chemicals from petroleum is shown in the chart inserted at the end of this book.

Raw materials

The main starting materials of the petroleum-chemical industry are hydrocarbons, particularly those present in natural gas and those obtained as products and by-products in oil refining, such as olefins, aromatics and certain higher normal paraffins. Because of their reactivity, the olefins are most important and, where they are not available in sufficient quantities, special processes have been developed to produce them.

The raw materials and the primary processes that are applied to them are more fully described in the next chapter.

Chemical plants

Chemical plants in the petroleum-chemical industry are analogous to refineries in the petroleum industry. They employ a number of continuous physical operations such as distillation, extraction, filtration, mixing, and pumping during which no change in the chemical structure of the materials occurs. The equipment used is very similar to that used in the corresponding oil operations, but the individual units are usually smaller, since the volume of chemicals handled by a chemical plant is generally less than the output of an oil refinery [Fig. 169].

The manufacture of chemicals also involves many complex chemical conversion processes, the reaction conditions of which are very precise, requiring careful control of temperature, pressure, reaction velocity and throughput, and these factors determine the nature and dimensions of the equipment.

Although fully continuous processes similar to those in the oil industry are preferred, batch reactions are not uncommon in the production of rather complex and expensive chemicals in relatively small quantities.

Many chemicals are corrosive and the materials used in the construction of equipment must be suitably chosen. Stainless steel and special alloys incorporating metals such as titanium and tantalum are widely employed, but are expensive. Glass and plastics are frequently used as linings of reaction vessels where lead was formerly used.

Raw materials and primary conversion processes

Chemicals are produced from a variety of petroleum fractions, firstly in what may be termed 'primary conversion processes', in which the petroleum fraction is directly converted to a derivative that is used as a chemical, either as such or as an intermediate for further processing, and secondly by more complex processes involving the synthesis of chemicals from these primary products. This chapter describes the petroleum fractions and the primary processes that are applied to them. Subsequent chapters will describe the manufacture and applications of various classes of derived products.

Natural gas

Natural gas is produced either in association with crude oil (associated gas) or on its own (non-associated gas). Its principal constituent, and the one of interest for the production of chemicals, is methane, CH_4. The production and properties of natural gas are more fully described in the chapter on Natural gas (p. 67).

Although enormous quantities of natural gas are produced, and the reserves are still greater, only a relatively small amount is used as a base material for chemicals, 3%v in the USA, 5%v in France, 7%v in Italy, 17%v in Japan. The main products derived directly from natural gas are as follows.

Carbon black is produced by the incomplete combustion of natural gas in sooty flames cooled on iron bars (channel black) or by the partial combustion of residual oils in a furnace (furnace black) at temperatures from 1200–1400°C (2200–2500°F). The yield of furnace blacks (30–40%w of carbon in the feed) is much higher than that of channel blacks (2%w). The effluent gas from the furnace, entraining the carbon black, is cooled and washed with water, and the carbon black is separated in filters, cyclones or electric precipitators.

Carbon black is used in many industries, the principal offtakes being as a pigment in printing inks and for reinforcing rubber in the manufacture of tyres.

Hydrogen is obtained from natural gas either by cracking or by steam conversion.

$$\underset{\text{methane}}{CH_4} \longrightarrow \underset{\text{soot}}{C} + \underset{\text{hydrogen}}{2\,H_2}$$

$$\underset{\text{methane}}{CH_4} + \underset{\text{steam}}{2\,H_2O} \longrightarrow \underset{\text{carbon dioxide}}{CO_2} + \underset{\text{hydrogen}}{4\,H_2}$$

Hydrogen is used on a very large scale for binding atmospheric nitrogen to form ammonia, the nitrogen being obtained by distillation of liquid air. Fertilizers are produced from ammonia, either directly as ammonium salts or via urea or nitric acid derived from it (p. 237).

Synthesis gas, a mixture of carbon monoxide and hydrogen, is produced from methane and steam.

$$\underset{\text{methane}}{CH_4} + \underset{\text{steam}}{H_2O} \longrightarrow \underset{\text{carbon monoxide}}{CO} + \underset{\text{hydrogen}}{3\,H_2}$$

It is used in the manufacture of methyl alcohol, higher alcohols, OXO alcohols and synthetic gasoline (Fischer-Tropsch process).

Chlorinated solvents are produced by the reaction of methane with chlorine, the product depending on the number of chlorine atoms attached.

$$CH_4 + 1\,Cl_2 \longrightarrow CH_3Cl \text{ (methyl chloride)} + 1\,HCl$$
$$CH_4 + 2\,Cl_2 \longrightarrow CH_2Cl_2 \text{ (methylene chloride)} + 2\,HCl$$
$$CH_4 + 3\,Cl_2 \longrightarrow CHCl_3 \text{ (chloroform)} + 3\,HCl$$
$$CH_4 + 4\,Cl_2 \longrightarrow CCl_4 \text{ (carbon tetrachloride)} + 4\,HCl$$

methane chlorine ... hydrochloric acid

Carbon disulphide, CS_2, is produced by the reaction of methane with sulphur.

$$\underset{\text{methane}}{CH_4} + \underset{\text{sulphur}}{4S} \longrightarrow \underset{\text{carbon disulphide}}{CS_2} + \underset{\text{hydrogen sulphide}}{2\,H_2S}$$

Hydrocyanic acid, HCN, is formed by passing methane and ammonia over a catalyst.

$$\underset{\text{methane}}{CH_4} + \underset{\text{ammonia}}{NH_3} \longrightarrow \underset{\text{hydrocyanic acid}}{HCN} + \underset{\text{hydrogen}}{3\,H_2}$$

Acetylene, C_2H_2, can be produced from natural gas (or other hydrocarbon fractions) by pyrolysis (p. 63). At high temperatures highly reactive, electrically charged particles of molecules (free radicals) are formed by temporary rupture of chemical bonds. At lower temperatures the free radicals recombine to form firstly acetylene and hydrogen and then benzene and other aromatics. By cooling the reaction gases quickly the secondary reactions are prevented and high yields of acetylene obtained.

$$\underset{\text{methane}}{CH_4} \rightarrow \underset{\text{free radicals}}{(\equiv CH), (=CH_2), (-CH_3), (-H)} \rightarrow \underset{\text{acetylene}}{CH\equiv CH} \longrightarrow$$

$\longrightarrow$ 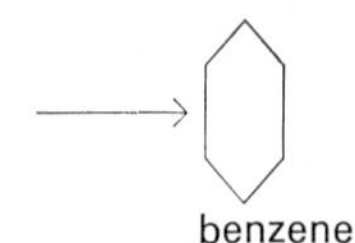

benzene

Several processes are used:

Natural gas (or light fractions) is passed through an electric arc or through externally heated tubes (Hüls, BASF, Dupont, and Montecatini processes).

Natural gas is partially burnt with oxygen in specially

Fig. 170 Fractionating columns separating high purity hydrocarbons

shaped burners in the high temperature zone of which pyrolysis takes place (Sachsse process).

Natural gas is passed in a special oven over bricks, preheated to a very high temperature by combustion of a gas/air mixture. The bricks lose their heat in the process and when the temperature becomes too low, *in situ* combustion is restarted (Wulff process).

Natural gas is passed through an externally overheated flame (Hoechst process).

The effluent gases of all these processes have to be quenched with water to stop unwanted recombination reactions. The acetylene content is generally 8–12% but the electric arc process gives 16–17%w. The acetylene is extracted, concentrated and purified by solvents and the higher acetylenes are frozen out. Large quantities of carbon monoxide, hydrogen and ethylene are produced as by-products, and these are also important base materials for chemicals.

Several important organic syntheses are based on acetylene (p. 227), but for many of them competitive processes have been developed starting from cheaper ethylene.

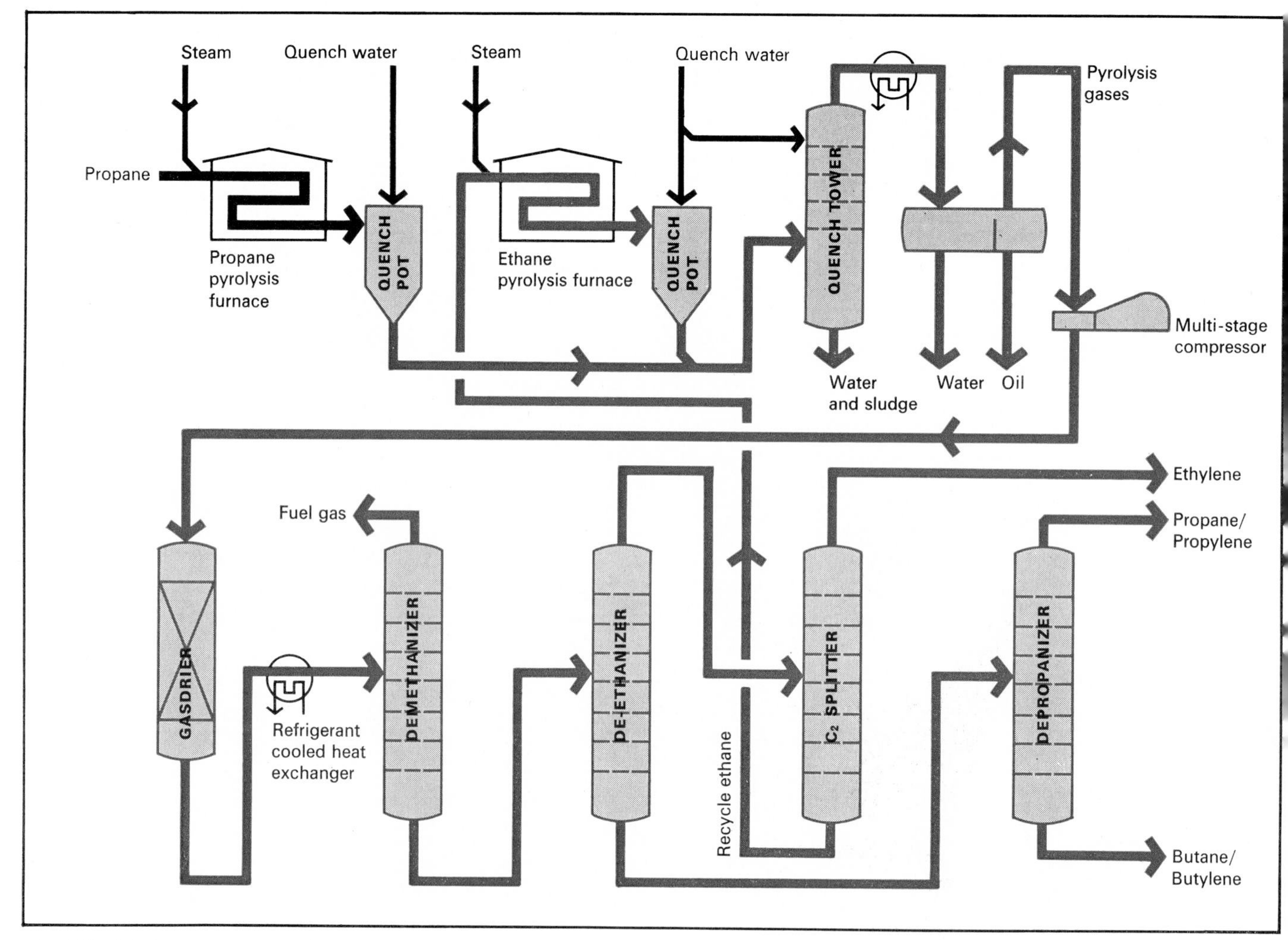

Fig. 171 Ethylene manufacture by cracking propane, with ethane recycle

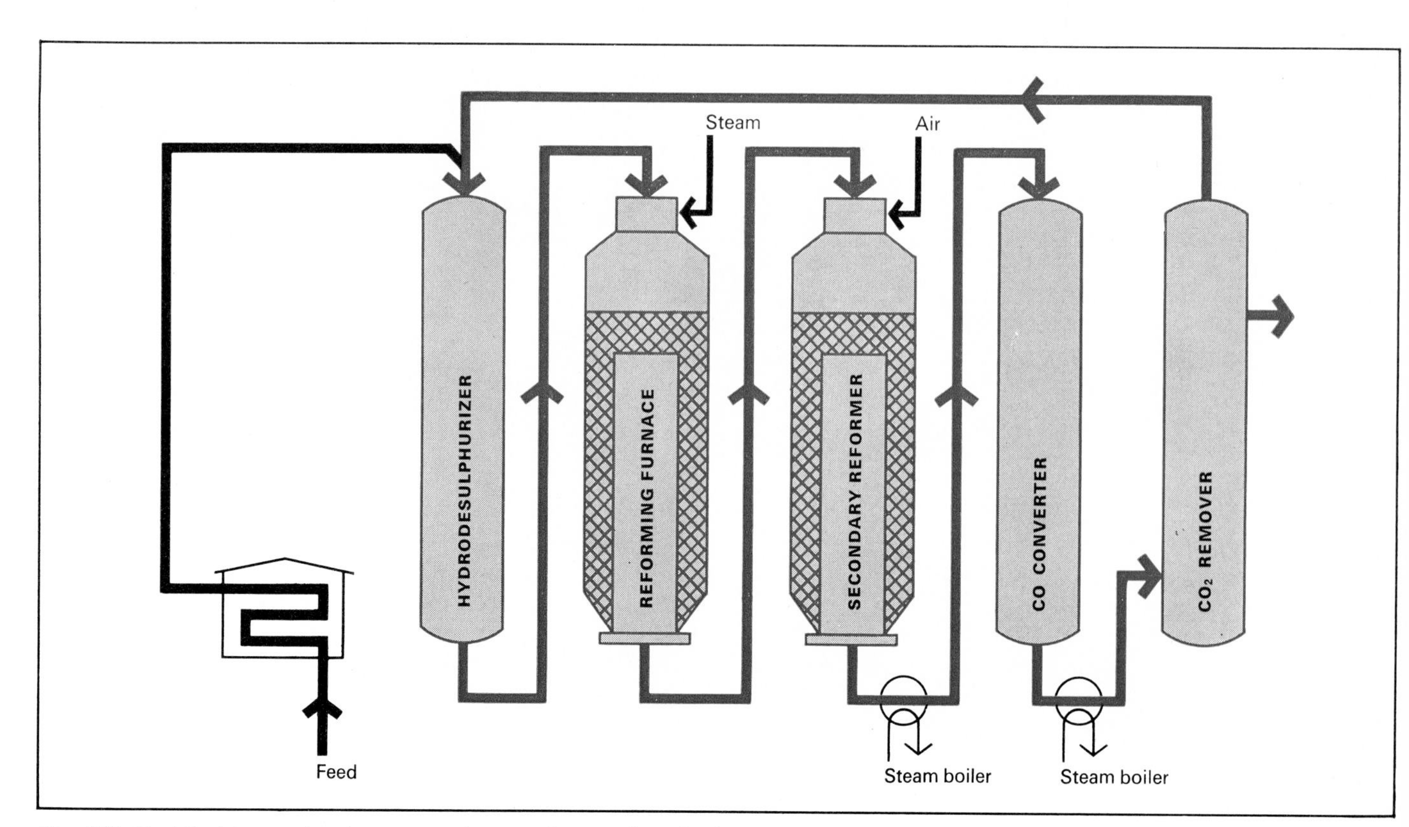

Fig. 172 Naphtha/steam reforming process for manufacture of synthesis gas

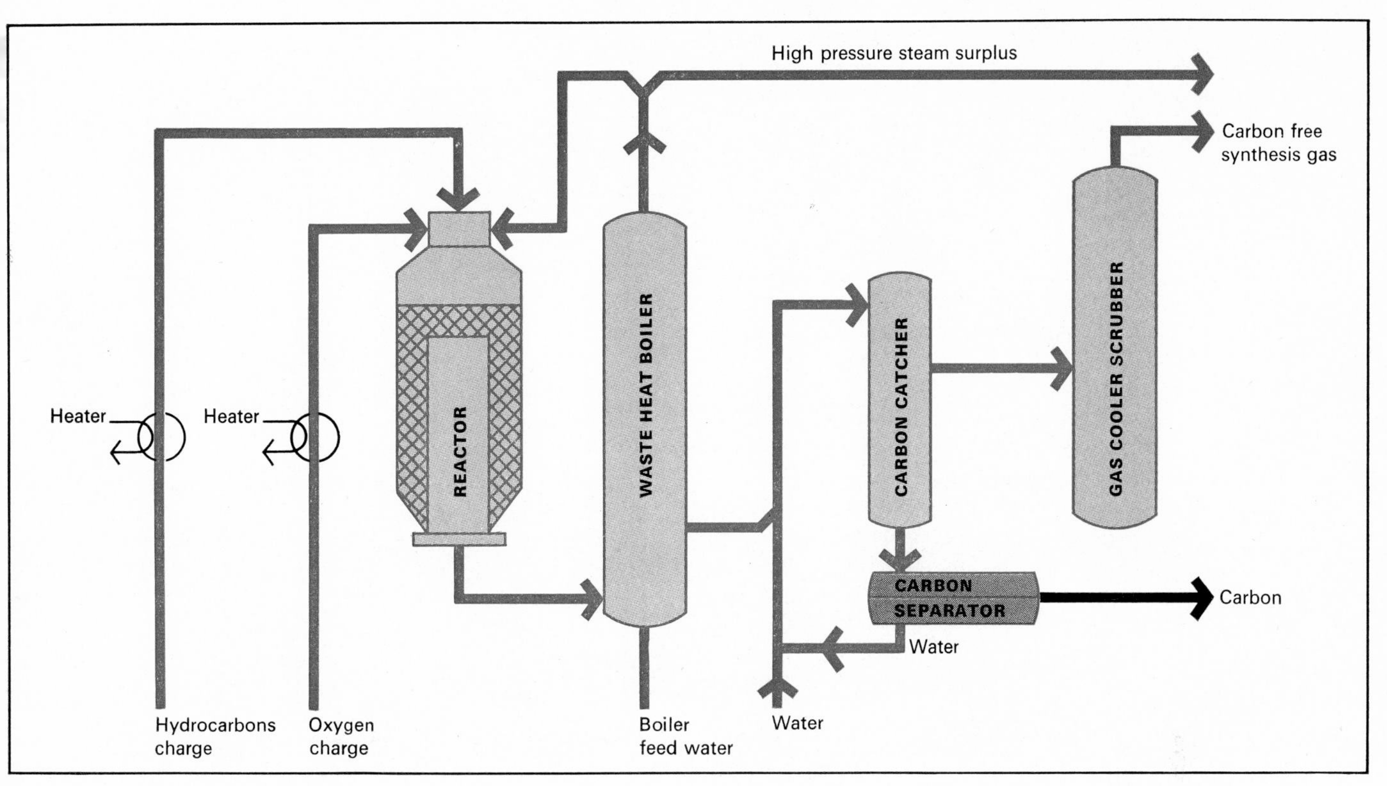

Fig. 173 The Shell gasification process

Formaldehyde, CH_2O, can be obtained in good yields by direct oxidation of methane at relatively low temperatures over silver catalysts.

Refinery gas

Refinery gas contains the lower olefins (ethylene, propylene, butylenes) as by-products of cracking operations. Ethylene and propylene are increasingly used as base materials for resins and plastics, and the supply from refinery cracking gas is insufficient; other base materials are therefore specially cracked to produce them. The olefins can be recovered by distillation or adsorption, primarily as ethane/ethylene (C_2), propane/propylene (C_3), and butanes/butylenes (C_4) fractions. Fig. 171 illustrates the production of ethylene by pyrolysis of propane, the ethylene being separated by fractionation of the liquefied gases.

The main characteristic of olefins is the double bond, the reactivity of which is utilized in such further processes as oxidation, polymerization and addition.

Light tops

Light tops or 'naphtha' are the lower normal paraffinic gasoline fractions, unsuitable for blending into high octane gasolines or for conversion by catalytic reforming. They are an important source of lower olefins and diolefins (butadiene) by cracking as such or in the presence of steam. Electric arc cracking is also employed for the production of acetylene.

An important development is the ICI naphtha/steam reforming process for the manufacture of synthesis gas [Fig. 172]. The process is carried out in two stages, desulphurization and steam reforming. The naphtha feed stock has to be desulphurized because the catalyst used in the reforming stage is very sensitive to sulphur. Easily removed sulphur compounds such as H_2S, COS and CS_2 are eliminated in the liquid phase by washing with sulphuric acid or by conducting the naphtha over a zinc oxide catalyst. More resistant sulphur compounds are decomposed and removed by hydrodesulphurization at about 400°C (750°F) over the same type of catalyst.

The sulphur-free naphtha vapour is mixed with steam in an externally heated tube furnace and reformed over a very rigid and active catalyst developed by ICI. The temperature rises to about 700°C (1300°F) and pressures up to 27 kg/cm^2 (400 lb/in^2) are used. The heat developed is used to generate steam, as is also the heat developed in the subsequent conversion of carbon monoxide to carbon dioxide. After washing out carbon dioxide, the end gas (hydrogen or synthesis gas) is further purified. By introducing air into the secondary reformer between the main reformer and the CO converter, an end gas ($3H_2+N_2$) suitable for ammonia synthesis can be obtained.

Since its inception on a commercial scale in 1962, the use of the ICI process has rapidly increased, the total capacity either in operation or under construction in 1965 amounting to 500 tons of naphtha per hour.

A similar naphtha/steam reforming process has been developed by Badische Anilin in Germany for the manufacture of synthesis gas or ammonia synthesis gas, using a combined nickel-platinum catalyst that is sufficiently resistant to sulphur to obviate the necessity for desulphurization.

Heavy fractions

Heavy fractions such as fuel oil can be cracked as such or in the presence of steam to produce olefins and diolefins. They can also be converted into synthesis gas by treatment with steam and oxygen, as in the Shell gasification process, by which all hydrocarbon fractions from natural gas to bitumen can be converted. The process is important for the manufacture of ammonia in countries where natural gas is not available [Fig. 173]. Oxygen must be available, but is a by-product in the production of nitrogen from liquid air.

The process is based on the non-catalytic partial oxidation of hydrocarbons. Preheated hydrocarbons and oxidant (air or oxygen) are fed to the reactor and intimately mixed before they reach the reaction zone where the final product gas, consisting mainly of carbon monoxide and hydrogen, is formed at a temperature of 1100 to 1400°C (2100 to 2640°F). With oxygen as oxidant, steam is included in the reaction mixture to moderate the temperature; when air is used as oxidant, the nitrogen acts as a moderator.

The gas from the reactor passes to a waste-heat boiler which it leaves at a temperature close to that of the steam produced in the boiler. The gas then passes into the carbon separator from which the carbon emerges as a slurry with water, leaving the gas virtually free from carbon. The carbon is removed from the slurry in the form of pellets 3–15 mm in diameter, suitable for burning or for other uses, and the water is used again for carbon removal.

The synthesis gas can be used as feedstock for the manufacture of ammonia, methane, town gas or reducing gas for iron ore reduction. Depending on the feedstock, the hydrogen and carbon monoxide content of the synthesis gas may vary from 45 to 60 %v and 35 to 47 %v respectively.

More than enough steam is generated in the waste-heat boiler to cover the requirements of the process, the excess being of the order of 1.5 to 2.3 kg/kg of feedstock.

Aromatics

Aromatics occur naturally in certain petroleum fractions or are produced in catalytic reforming operations. They can be concentrated by extractive distillation (p. 91), by liquid/liquid extraction with a diethylene glycol/water mixture or with sulfolane (p. 91), or by adsorption on silica gel.

Conversion processes for the manufacture of aromatics were developed during World War II. Toluene was made in the USA by dehydrogenation of methylcyclohexane. They may also be produced by catalytic reforming. Aromatics with side chains may be converted into benzene by hydrodealkylation in a hydrogen atmosphere in the presence of a catalyst.

The main aromatics for further processing are benzene, toluene (methylbenzene) and the xylenes (dimethylbenzenes) of which there are three isomers (ortho, meta and para).

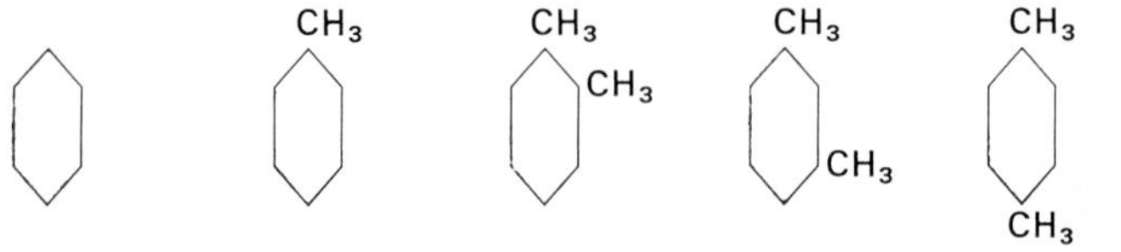

CH_3 CH_3 CH_3 CH_3 CH_3 CH_3 CH_3

benzene toluene o-xylene m-xylene p-xylene

These xylenes have different chemical and physical properties and are used as base materials for different chemicals. They can be separated and isolated by distillation and freezing out. Oxidation of the three isomers gives respectively ortho-phthalic, isophthalic and terephthalic acids, base materials for important synthetic resins (p. 212).

Slack wax

Slack wax, obtained in the dewaxing of lubricating oils (p. 87), contains the higher paraffins, mostly straight-chain paraffins with 20–30 carbon atoms in the molecule. For the main applications as chemical base material the absence of branched chains is an advantage, and they can be excluded by extractive crystallization with urea with which the straight-chain, but not the branched-chain, paraffins crystallize out.

By thermal cracking of slack wax in the vapour phase in the presence of steam, the higher molecular olefins with six or more carbon atoms are obtained. The double bond is formed preferentially at the end of the molecule, the α position, and the presence of catalysts should be avoided as causing displacement of the double bond along the chain. The difference in boiling points between the C_6, C_7, C_8, etc, olefins is large enough for their separation by distillation so that fairly pure fractions (mixed with the corresponding saturates) are obtained. They are used in the manufacture of detergents, lubricating oil additives, higher alcohols, OXO alcohols and higher aliphatic carboxylic acids (Versatic acids).

Solvents

Petroleum derived solvents can be divided into two main classes: hydrocarbon solvents and chemical solvents.

Hydrocarbon solvents

Hydrocarbon solvents consist chemically of carbon and hydrogen only, and are manufactured in the course of normal refinery operations for gasoline manufacture. They are sub-divided into special boiling point spirits (SBP), white spirits and pure aromatics.

Chemical solvents

Chemical solvents usually consists of carbon, hydrogen and oxygen and are manufactured from the refinery gases ethylene, propylene and the butylenes by chemical synthesis to a high degree of purity. The alcohols, ethers, ketones, esters and glycol ethers fall into this group. Chlorinated hydrocarbons made from petroleum fractions by the action of chlorine or hydrochloric acid are also classified as chemical solvents.

The products discussed in this chapter are widely used in industry, not only as solvents but also as intermediates for further chemical synthesis.

Fig. 174 Distillation unit for final purification of solvents

Manufacture, properties and general applications

Special boiling point spirits (SBP)

Special boiling point spirits (SBP) are gasoline fractions distilled to specially selected boiling ranges and subsequently refined. The manufacture of a series of SBP of different volatilities makes it possible for a suitable grade to be chosen for any particular industrial purpose, for example for use in oil seed extraction or as a rubber solvent. The boiling range of an individual SBP may be either narrow or wide, but generally falls within the limits of 35–160°C (95–320°F). SBP are usually classified by means of their boiling ranges, for example SBP 62/82°C (144/180°F).

White spirits

White spirits are fractions intermediate between gasoline and kerosine with a boiling range of 150–200°C (300–390°F). They are usually classified by their aromatic content, which is around 15%w in typical low aromatic grades and up to 45%w or more in high aromatic grades.

By virtue of their volatility and solvent power both low and high aromatic white spirits are particularly suitable for use in paints and lacquers as thinners, and the former are widely used in dry cleaning and wool degreasing. 'Odourless' white spirits are also manufactured, primarily for use in the paint industry (turpentine substitute), especially for interior decoration.

Aromatics

The aromatic hydrocarbons benzene, toluene and xylene, mentioned in the previous chapter, are produced from petroleum to a high degree of purity, and have almost entirely superseded the chemically identical products manufactured from coal.

The boiling points of benzene and toluene are 81°C (178°F) and 110°C (230°F) respectively. Xylene is produced as a mixture of the three isomers with a boiling range 138–141°C (280–286°F). This group also includes high-boiling hydrocarbon solvents with aromatic contents of 80–100%w derived from refinery streams based on compounds with nine or more carbon atoms in the molecule. These solvents are complex mixtures of similar components and although their properties cannot be specified as accurately as those of single solvents such as toluene, they provide a very useful extension of the aromatic hydrocarbon range, often at low cost. Their boiling ranges vary in width, but usually fall within the range 110–300°C (240–570°F).

All of these solvents, except benzene, are used extensively in paints because of their ability to dissolve resins when used alone or in combination with other solvents. Benzene is usually considered too toxic for use in paints, but is very important as a chemical intermediate, as also are toluene and xylene.

Alcohols

The principal alcohols are:

		Boiling point (°C)
Methyl alcohol	(methanol)	65 (low boiling)
Ethyl alcohol	(ethanol)	78 (low boiling)
Isopropyl alcohol	(IPA)	82 (low boiling)
Secondary butyl alcohol	(SBA)	100 (medium boiling)
Isobutyl alcohol	(IBA)	107 (medium boiling)
Normal butyl alcohol	(NBA)	118 (medium boiling)
Methyl isobutyl carbinol	(MIBC)	132 (medium boiling)

These alcohols are valuable ingredients for many paints and lacquers and are also used in extraction processes, in the pharmaceutical industry, and as intermediates in a variety of chemical syntheses. IPA and methanol are also used in anti-freeze mixtures.

Methyl alcohol is made via synthesis gas ($CO + H_2$) from various oil fractions, or natural gas, as mentioned in the previous chapter. The reaction is carried out in the presence of zinc oxide as a catalyst at pressures of 150–300 kg/cm² (2000–4000 lb/in²) and at temperatures around 300°C (500°F).

$$\underset{\text{carbon monoxide}}{CO} + \underset{\text{hydrogen}}{2\,H_2} \longrightarrow \underset{\text{methyl alcohol}}{CH_3OH}$$

An important group of alcohols is obtained by the hydration of olefins. Ethylene (C_2H_4) yields ethyl alcohol (C_2H_5OH), propylene (C_3H_6), isopropyl alcohol (C_3H_7OH) and the butylenes (C_4H_8), various butyl alcohols (C_4H_9OH).

$$\underset{\text{propylene}}{CH_3{-}CH{=}CH_2} + \underset{\text{water}}{H_2O} \longrightarrow \underset{\text{isopropyl alcohol}}{CH_3{-}CHOH{-}CH_3}$$

There are two methods of carrying out this hydration, the sulphuric acid process and the direct hydration process.

Sulphuric acid process

The olefin is absorbed in sulphuric acid and the resulting sulphonic acid is decomposed by water, thus liberating the alcohol which is separated from the acid by stripping with steam. The crude alcohol is purified by distillation. The dilute sulphuric acid can be recovered and returned to the reaction system after concentration [Fig. 175].

$$\underset{\text{propylene}}{CH_3{-}CH{=}CH_2} + \underset{\text{sulphuric acid}}{H_2SO_4} \longrightarrow \underset{\text{propane sulphonic acid}}{CH_3{-}\underset{\displaystyle O{-}SO_3H}{\underset{|}{CH}}{-}CH_3} + H_2O \longrightarrow$$

$$\underset{\text{isopropyl alcohol}}{CH_3{-}CHOH{-}CH_3} + \underset{\text{sulphuric acid}}{H_2SO_4}$$

A by-product is diisopropyl ether $C_3H_7{-}O{-}C_3H_7$.

In the butanes/butylenes fraction three butylenes (α, β and γ) are present:

$CH_2{=}CH{-}CH_2{-}CH_3$ α–butylene
$CH_3{-}CH{=}CH{-}CH_3$ β–butylene
$CH_3{-}\underset{\displaystyle CH_2}{\underset{\|}{C}}{-}CH_3$ γ–butylene

The sulphuric acid process converts both α- and β-butylenes into secondary butyl alcohol and γ-butylene into tertiary butyl alcohol.

$CH_3{-}CHOH{-}CH_2{-}CH_3$ secondary butyl alcohol

$CH_3{-}\overset{\displaystyle CH_3}{\overset{|}{\underset{\displaystyle OH}{\underset{|}{C}}}}{-}CH_3$ tertiary butyl alcohol

The C_4/C_4 fraction is first contacted with 65% sulphuric acid, which selectively absorbs γ-butylene. By dilution and steam stripping, tertiary butyl alcohol is produced.

A further treatment of the extracted C_4/C_4 fraction with concentrated sulphuric acid, with subsequent dilution and stripping, yields secondary butyl alcohol.

Direct hydration process

The direct hydration process obviates the drawbacks of the sulphuric acid process: the necessity of handling a corrosive chemical (sulphuric acid) and the need of reconcentrating the acid. The olefin is hydrated with steam in the presence of a catalyst (phosphoric acid, H_3PO_4) supported by a carrier. This process was first applied for the manufacture of ethyl alcohol by the Shell Chemical Corporation at Houston, Texas.

$$\underset{\text{ethylene}}{C_2H_4} + \underset{\text{water}}{H_2O} \longrightarrow \underset{\text{ethyl alcohol}}{C_2H_5OH}$$

The direct hydration process cannot be carried out with propylene and butylene.

By direct oxidation of propane and butane at elevated pressures, a mixture of alcohols, aldehydes and organic acids (such as acetic acid) is obtained which, however, is not always easy to separate.

OXO process

An important method for the manufacture of primary alcohols from olefins is the OXO process, which yields alcohols with one carbon atom more in the molecule than in the starting olefin. It consists essentially of the addition of carbon monoxide and hydrogen to the olefinic double bond, and takes place at pressures ranging between 100–250 kg/cm² (1400–3500 lb/in²) and temperatures between 100–150°C (210–300°F) in the presence of a cobalt catalyst.

$$\underset{\text{n-octene}}{C_6H_{13}CH{=}CH_2} + \underset{\text{carbon monoxide}}{CO} + \underset{\text{hydrogen}}{2\,H_2} \longrightarrow \underset{\text{nonyl alcohol}}{C_6H_{13}CH_2{-}\underset{\displaystyle CH_2OH}{\underset{|}{CH_3}}}$$

The reaction can take a more complicated route by modifying the catalyst. An OXO synthesis carried out by Shell on a commercial scale is the reaction of propylene (C_3H_6) with carbon monoxide and hydrogen (Shell hydroformylation process). This leads to the formation of n-butyl alcohol and 2–ethyl hexanol.

$$\underset{\text{n–butyl alcohol}}{CH_3CH_2CH_2CH_2OH} \qquad \underset{\text{2–ethyl hexanol}}{CH_3{-}\overset{\displaystyle C_2H_5}{\overset{|}{CH}}{-}CH_2{-}CH_2{-}CH_2{-}CH_2OH}$$

The lower alcohols such as methyl alcohol, ethyl alcohol, isopropyl alcohol and the butyl alcohols may be sold as such, but are often used as intermediates for the manufacture of other chemicals. Thus, oxidation of methyl alcohol

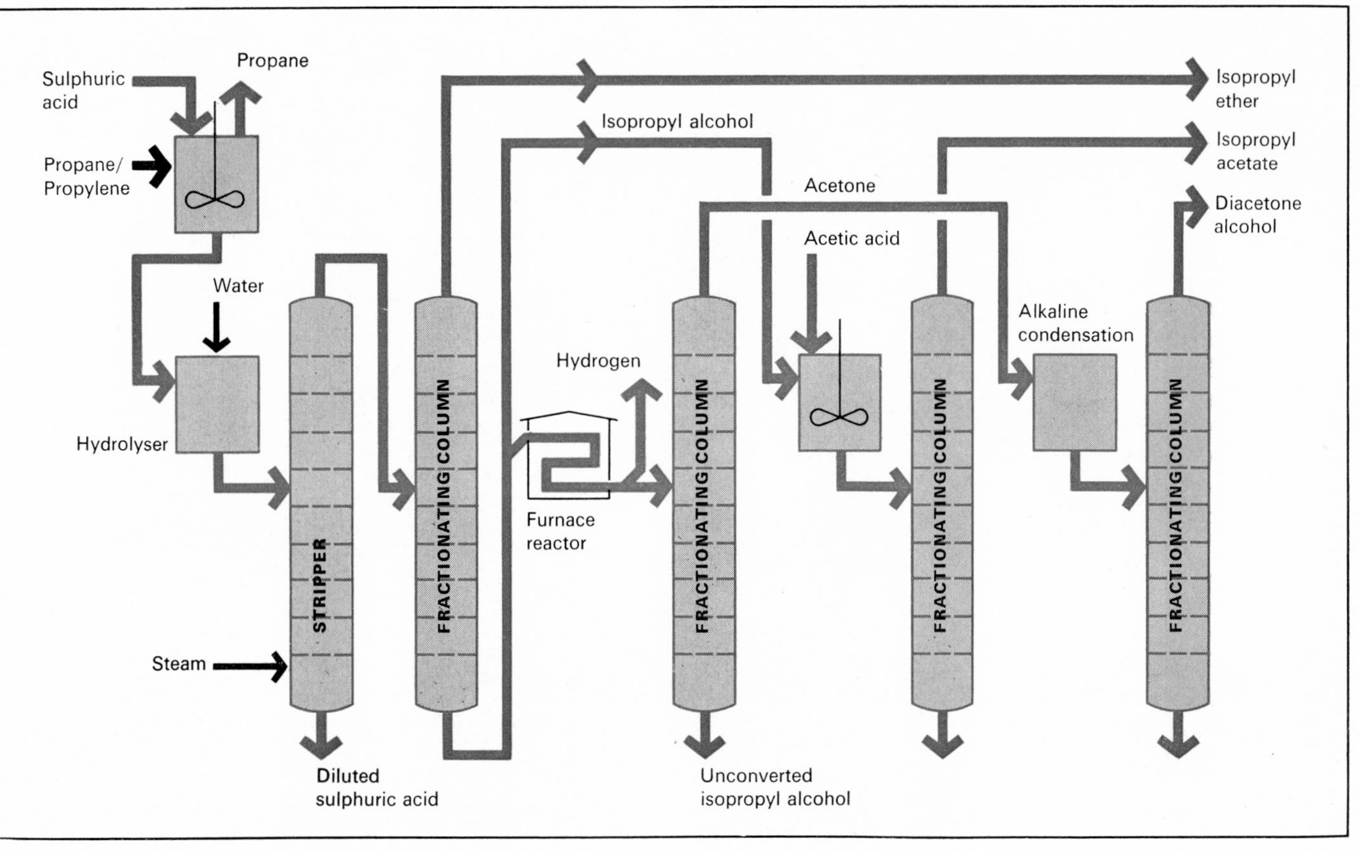

Fig. 175 Manufacture of isopropyl alcohol and derivatives

and ethyl alcohol leads to the formation of formaldehyde and acetaldehyde respectively.

$$2\ CH_3OH + O_2 \longrightarrow 2\ CH_2O + H_2O$$
methyl alcohol — formaldehyde

$$2\ C_2H_5OH + O_2 \longrightarrow 2\ CH_3CHO + H_2O$$
ethyl alcohol — acetaldehyde

Formaldehyde and acetaldehyde are important ingredients for the manufacture of synthetic resins.

Ketones

The principal ketones are:

		Boiling point (°C)	
Acetone or dimethyl ketone	(DMK)	56	(low boiling)
Methyl ethyl ketone	(MEK)	80	(low boiling)
Methyl isobutyl ketone	(MIBK)	116	(medium boiling)
PENToXONE	(ME-6K)	157–162	(high boiling)
Diacetone alcohol	(DAA)	166	(high boiling)
Ethyl amyl ketone	(EAK)	168	(high boiling)
Isophorone		215	(very high boiling)

Because of their high solvent power the ketones are very useful in formulating surface coatings and in extraction processes. Ketones, in particular acetone, are also important intermediates for further chemical synthesis.

Dehydrogenation of isopropyl alcohol leads to the formation of acetone, the simplest member of the group.

$$CH_3{-}CHOH{-}CH_3 \longrightarrow CH_3{-}CO{-}CH_3 + H_2$$
isopropyl alcohol — acetone — hydrogen

Dehydrogenation is effected by passing the alcohol over a catalyst at a relatively high temperature. (A brass catalyst and 450°C are often used). In the same way secondary butyl alcohol yields methyl ethyl ketone ($CH_3COCH_2CH_3$).

The lower ketones are sold as low boiling solvents, but they are also used as starting material in the production of higher boiling solvents. Thus acetone, which has an extensive industrial use as a solvent, is also the base for the manufacture of higher boiling solvents by a combination of processes such as condensation, dehydration and hydrogenation. The first condensation product is diacetone alcohol,

$$CH_3{-}\underset{\underset{O}{\|}}{C}{-}CH_2{-}\underset{\underset{OH}{|}}{C}(CH_3)_2$$

from which several products with the same carbon skeleton are derived: mesityl oxide, hexylene glycol, methyl isobutyl ketone, methyl isobutyl carbinol, isophorone, PENToXONE (Shell ME—6K), PENToXOL (Shell ME–6C). (PENToXONE and PENToXOL are registered trade names in the USA).

Methyl isobutyl ketone, $CH_3{-}CO{-}CH_2{-}CH(CH_3)_2$, is a very useful higher-boiling solvent. A similar high-boiling ketone, ethyl isoamyl ketone, $C_2H_2{-}CO{-}i.C_5H_{11}$, is derived from methyl ethyl ketone.

Esters

Esters are an important group of products, and until the introduction of the ketone solvents made from petroleum they were in general use for most applications, mainly in the lacquer industry. They are still widely used, the commonest being:

	Boiling point (°C)
Methyl acetate	57 (low boiling)
Ethyl acetate	77 (low boiling)
Isopropyl acetate	88 (low boiling)
Isobutyl acetate	118 (medium boiling)
Normal butyl acetate	126 (medium boiling)
Methyl amyl acetate	146 (high boiling)
Ethylene glycol monoethyl ether acetate (Oxitol acetate)	156 (high boiling)

Two grades of these materials are normally available commercially, one with a purity of about 80–85% and the other of 98–99%, the 'impurity' being mainly the alcohol from which the ester has been derived. They are generally made by esterification, the chemical combination of an alcohol with an (organic) acid, usually in the presence of a small amount of sulphuric acid as a catalyst, for example:

$$\underset{\text{ethyl alcohol}}{C_2H_5OH} + \underset{\text{acetic acid}}{CH_3COOH} \longrightarrow \underset{\text{ethyl acetate}}{CH_3COOC_2H_5} + \underset{\text{water}}{H_2O}$$

$$\underset{\text{isopropyl alcohol}}{CH_3CHOHCH_3} + \underset{\text{acetic acid}}{CH_3COOH} \longrightarrow \underset{\text{isopropyl acetate}}{CH_3COO\text{–i.}C_3H_7} + \underset{\text{water}}{H_2O}$$

Acetic acid, ethyl alcohol and isopropyl alcohol can be made from petroleum, although the first two are also made by fermentation of other raw materials. Ester solvents are used in the lacquer industry, in extraction processes and in the manufacture of flavourings, the acetates being the most widely used.

Chlorinated hydrocarbons

As mentioned under natural gas as base material (p. 196), the hydrogen atoms in methane can be progressively substituted by chlorine.

$$\underset{\text{methane}}{CH_4} + \underset{\text{chlorine}}{Cl_2} \longrightarrow \begin{cases} CH_3Cl & \text{methyl chloride} \\ CH_2Cl_2 & \text{methylene chloride} \\ CHCl_3 & \text{chloroform} \\ CCl_4 & \text{carbon tetrachloride} \end{cases}$$

When four chlorine atoms are added to acetylene, tetrachloroethane is formed. This is in itself a good solvent, but toxic. It can be converted into the less toxic trichloroethylene by reaction with a hot lime slurry, extracting hydrochloric acid from the molecule.

$$\underset{\text{acetylene}}{CH{\equiv}CH} + \underset{\text{chlorine}}{2\,Cl_2} \longrightarrow \underset{\text{tetrachloroethane}}{CHCl_2\text{—}CHCl_2} \xrightarrow{\text{lime}} \underset{\text{trichloroethylene}}{CHCl{=}CCl_2} + HCl$$

Further chlorination of trichloroethylene, followed by dehydrochlorination, yields perchloroethylene, $CCl_2{=}CCl_2$. These two are perhaps the most widely used of the chlorinated hydrocarbon solvents, mostly in dry-cleaning and metal degreasing. They have excellent solvent properties and are non-inflammable, but should be handled with care.

Chlorination of pentane fractions gives a mixture of chloropentanes, which was used as a solvent for special purposes, but is now of decreasing importance.

Carbon disulphide

Reaction of methane with sulphur vapour yields carbon disulphide, CS_2, usually made by leading sulphur vapour over glowing coke. It is a good but dangerous solvent for it is highly inflammable and toxic. The main application is in the rayon industry for converting cellulose into spinnable cellulose xanthate.

Xanthates of lower alcohols are used as collectors in the flotation of sulphidic ores in order to concentrate the metal sulphides, separating them from silicates.

Glycol ethers and glycol-ether esters

These are a group of solvents with boiling points ranging from 124–250°C (255–480°F), which are made by reacting an alcohol with ethylene oxide or propylene oxide.

$$\underset{\text{ethylene oxide}}{\begin{matrix} CH_2 \\ \vert\;\;\diagdown \\ \vert\;\;\;\;O \\ \vert\;\;\diagup \\ CH_2 \end{matrix}} + \underset{\text{ethyl alcohol}}{C_2H_5OH} \longrightarrow \underset{\text{ethylene glycol monoethyl ether}}{\begin{matrix} CH_2OC_2H_5 \\ \vert \\ CH_2OH \end{matrix}}$$

Further reaction with ethyl alcohol gives ethylene glycol diethyl ether. Esterification of glycol monoethyl ether with acetic acid gives the corresponding ester, ethylene glycol monoethyl ether acetate.

These products with long chemical names are usually known by simpler trade names, Oxitol or Cellosolve.

Oxitol	ethylene glycol monoethyl ether
Methyl Oxitol	ethylene glycol monomethyl ether
Isopropyl Oxitol	ethylene glycol monoisopropyl ether
Butyl Oxitol	ethylene glycol mono n-butyl ether
Dioxitol	diethylene glycol monoethyl ether
Methyl Dioxitol	diethylene glycol monomethyl ether
Butyl Dioxitol	diethylene glycol mono n-butyl ether
Oxitol acetate	ethylene glycol monoethyl ether acetate
Methyl Oxitol acetate	ethylene glycol monomethyl ether acetate
Butyl Dioxitol acetate	diethylene glycol mono n-butyl ether acetate

Complete miscibility with water and most organic solvents makes the glycol ethers useful coupling agents between liquids that will not normally mix. Apart from their use as coupling agents, notably in cutting oils, the glycol ethers are used extensively in the production of hydraulic brake fluids, and they are also good solvents for a number of surface coating resins.

Specific industrial applications

Paints

Solvents are used extensively in surface coating paints, lacquers and varnishes of which there are two main types.

Coatings formed by evaporation of volatile solvents

The film is formed simply by evaporation of volatile solvents, leaving a solid coating which undergoes no further physical or chemical change. The most important in this class are the nitrocellulose and vinyl lacquers. Other well-

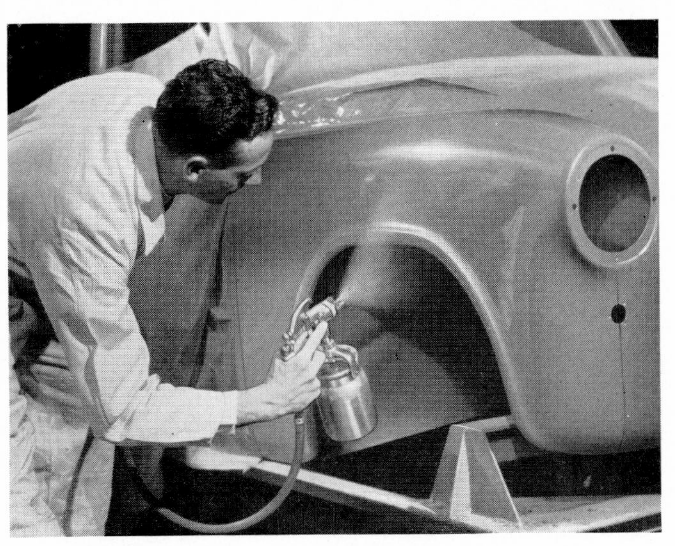

Fig. 176 Paint spraying a car body

known examples are spirit varnishes, French polish (a solution of shellac in methylated spirits) and solutions of bitumen in white spirit.

Nitrocellulose lacquers consist of nitrocellulose with other solid ingredients such as resins, plasticizers, dyes and pigments dissolved in a mixture of volatile solvents. The total content of solids is usually about 25–35 %w. The solvent is complex, containing ketones, esters and glycol ethers, which readily dissolve nitrocellulose and resins, and alcohols and hydrocarbons, which as such do not dissolve them, but which are added as thinners. The alcohols and hydrocarbons are cheaper than the other solvents and can be added in fairly large quantities without precipitating either the nitrocellulose or the resin.

The composition of the solvent mixture is chosen to obtain an adequate solvency for the solids and a suitable drying time for the lacquer. During evaporation no precipitation should occur. Therefore, the volatility (boiling point) of the solvents and the solubility of the ingredients must be carefully balanced. Acetone is, for instance, a good solvent, but too volatile; it disappears rapidly and higher boiling ingredients are used. The main advantage of nitrocellulose lacquers is their short drying time.

Ketones, in particular methyl ethyl ketone and methyl isobutyl ketone, are excellent solvents for vinyl resins and are widely used in vinyl lacquers, often in blends with aromatics. Vinyl lacquers are based on polymers and copolymers of vinyl chloride, vinyl acetate and vinylidene chloride.

Solvents used in paints that form a coat by evaporation of the solvent are generally divided into three classes: low-boiling (below 100°C), medium-boiling (100–150°C), and high-boiling (150–220°C), as indicated in the lists of solvents given in the preceding pages.

Fig. 177 P & O–Orient line's *Oriana.* Paint used on the hull and superstructure contained Epikote resins

Coatings formed by polymerization and oxidation

This is a very extensive group since a wide variety of polymerization reactions involving one or more resin components can be used to form a hard film. The coatings are based on natural or synthetic resins (either as such or modified with drying oils) thinned with volatile solvents. The film is formed by evaporation of the solvent at normal or elevated temperature, followed by oxidation or polymerization (or both) of the resin (air drying). The natural resins are derived from chemically unsaturated vegetable oils such as linseed oil, and many of the synthetic resins are based wholly or partly on petroleum (p. 212). In addition to the film-forming material and the thinner, paints may contain pigments, fillers and a 'drier' to speed the hardening process, when this depends on air oxidation.

The original paint thinner was vegetable turpentine, but the supply became totally inadequate and the petroleum industry produced substitutes such as white spirits which are used either alone or in conjunction with chemical solvents.

Both low and high aromatic white spirits are used. A high aromatic content gives greater solvent power, but a stronger odour. Isoparaffin hydrocarbons have good solvent power, but little odour. They are the basis of the 'odourless' white spirits now on the market.

Chemical solvents are also used in this class of surface coatings where special solvency characteristics are required. Ketones, alcohols, esters and glycol ethers, in combination with hydrocarbons (for economy), are used in coating systems based on epoxide resins, polyester resins, vinyl resins and formaldehyde containing resins [Figs 176 and 177].

The choice of solvent depends on many factors of which the following are of the utmost importance.

Solvency – The thinner must be capable of dissolving the film-forming material to produce a homogeneous mixture.

Volatility – The thinner must remain in the paint during manufacture and handling, but during and after application it must leave the paint at such a rate as to ensure good flow and no sagging.

Odour – Excessive odour during the drying period is undesirable in certain applications, notably with indoor paints.

Paint removers

In the course of time paint films deteriorate, no longer give protection and have to be replaced. A convenient method for removing small areas of old paint is to use a solvent mixture which will dissolve or soften the old film. The solvent mixture is usually composed of chlorinated solvents, such as methylene chloride and carbon tetrachloride, together with other types such as acetone and isopropyl alcohol. Hydrocarbon solvents, such as white spirits or toluene, are sometimes incorporated.

Oil seed extraction

Vegetable oils and fats, obtained from such materials as olives, coconuts, groundnuts, soya beans and linseed, are used as foodstuffs and in the manufacture of paints, soaps and polishes. The traditional method of production is pressing, but larger yields can be obtained by means of solvent extraction, which is now widely used. The fatty material is dissolved out in a suitable solvent, which is recovered by distillation for re-use. A narrow boiling hydrocarbon solvent such as SBP 62/82°C (144/180°F) is generally accepted as nearly the ideal solvent for oil seed extraction, although in the USA normal hexane is widely used.

Cleaning processes

Low aromatic white spirits are widely used in the dry-cleaning industry, since they are stable and non-toxic, and are able to dissolve grease and similar substances that are insoluble in water, without affecting the fabric to be cleaned. The performance of white spirits in dry-cleaning operations can be improved by the addition of products based on naphtha sulphonates. Such dry-cleaning aids make it possible for a small quantity of water to be dispersed in the solvent, which makes the product more effective in removing water-soluble stains.

Degreasing

Degreasing of engine parts and of metals prior to plating may be carried out by detergents or solvents or by a combination of the two. Both white spirits and chlorinated solvents are used. When used together, clear blends are often obtained by the use of coupling agents such as diethylene glycol mono n-butyl ether (Butyl Dioxitol). Low aromatic white spirits are frequently used for wool degreasing.

Rubber processing

Motor tyres are built up from layers of rubber, rubberized fabric, and extruded rubber sections. In the course of this process it is necessary to treat the rubber surfaces with a solvent to make them tacky so that the layers can be placed together accurately; SBP are used for this purpose.

SBP and chlorinated hydrocarbons are also used in the preparation of rubber solutions employed in fabrication processes such as coating and spreading, and as adhesives.

Printing inks

The printing industry uses a wide variety of inks, most of which incorporate petroleum derived solvents. High boiling petroleum fractions are used in the manufacture of letterpress and offset lithographic inks, which rely mainly on the oxidation of a vegetable oil for drying. Inks used on packaging material for foodstuffs must be virtually odourless, and the petroleum fractions must be selected accordingly. Glycol ethers are used in dry offset and silk screen inks. Alcohols and SBP are important constituents in inks for flexographic printing on surfaces such as polyethylene and other non-absorbent materials. Alcohols, glycol ethers and ketones, as well as volatile hydrocarbons such as toluene, are widely used in the formulation of inks for use in modern high-speed gravure printing [Fig. 178].

Polishes

There are three types of wax polishes: paste polishes, emulsion polishes and abrasive polishes (p. 168).

Paste polishes are essentially a blend of wax or a mixture of waxes with white spirit, to which may be added colouring matter and perfumes. The solvent serves as a carrier for the

Fig. 178 Rotary newspaper printing machine which uses inks containing solvents derived from petroleum

wax, enabling the polish to be spread uniformly. An average polish contains about 75%w of white spirit. Emulsion polishes are essentially emulsions of wax in water with or without the addition of a solvent. The addition of white spirit gives a smoother consistency and enables fat-soluble dyestuffs to be used, which have a better colour stability.

Abrasive polishes remove dirt and stains by mechanical action, assisted by the solvent action of water and white spirit present in the polish.

Pharmaceuticals and cosmetics

The major outlet for solvents in this field is in the production of antibiotics, vitamins, hormones, perfumes, essences and cosmetics. In the preparation of medicinal and pharmaceutical products, chemical solvents such as methyl isobutyl ketone and acetone are used.

Perfumes are extracted from flower petals by hydrocarbon solvents of low boiling range, for example SBP 40/60°C (104/140°F) or SBP 58/72°C (136/162°F).

Many perfumes are based on synthetic chemicals. In the preparation of artificial musks, tertiary butyl alcohol is used as a constituent group, not as a solvent.

Ethyl alcohol and isopropyl alcohol are used in many drugs and cosmetic formulations and IPA, by virtue of its sterilizing and disinfecting properties, is widely used in hospitals.

Miscellaneous

IPA can be added to motor gasolines to prevent water condensation in carburettors and thereby permit easy winter starting; in aviation, isopropyl alcohol is used as a de-icing fluid, while other alcohols such as methanol and ethanol are sometimes injected into aero-engines to produce temporary power boosts for take-off.

Detergents

Before 1939 soap was the only important detergent. New types had already begun to appear in America and in Europe, but they were used almost exclusively by industry for specialized applications. During World War II, and in the years immediately following it, petroleum based raw materials came to be used for the large-scale production of the now familiar synthetic detergent powders and liquids. This development was partly due to the war-time shortage of animal and vegetable oils needed for soap making, and partly because synthetic detergents had certain advantages over soap, notably their freedom from scum formation when used in hard water. From the manufacturers' point of view, however, their great advantage was the ready availability of comparatively cheap raw materials for their manufacture as compared with the then scarce and expensive fats and oils. After the war the synthetic detergent market expanded very rapidly, largely at the expense of soap, and in many countries synthetic detergents have now completely replaced soap for domestic dish and clothes washing, and to a large extent for industrial cleaning and processing.

The theory of detergency is too complex for discussion in this book, but detergent action may be considered as a threefold process. Firstly, the dirty surface, whether of crockery, fabric or other material, must be wetted; secondly, the dirt must be detached from the surface; and thirdly, the dirt must be kept in suspension in the detergent solution so that it is easily rinsed away without being redeposited on the cleaned surface. The process is assisted by heating the detergent solution and keeping it moving relative to the surface being cleaned, as in a washing machine.

There are many different chemical types of detergents but they all have certain features in common. Firstly, they must be soluble in water, and this is bought about by the presence in the molecules of the detergent of certain groups of atoms, for example sulphate, sulphonate and polyether groups, which are termed 'hydrophilic' groups. Secondly, they must have some affinity for oily or greasy dirt, and this is ensured by the presence in the molecules of groups of carbon and hydrogen atoms similar to those in oils and fats and which are termed 'hydrophobic' groups.

Some detergents 'ionize' when dissolved in water, i.e. their molecules split into two electrically charged atoms or groups of atoms known as ions. This behaviour is similar to that of common salt, sodium chloride, which splits into sodium cations (positively charged) and chlorine anions (negatively charged). In detergents, one of the ions is always relatively large and contains both hydrophilic and hydrophobic groups of atoms. Detergents that form large negatively charged surface-active ions are termed anion-active or anionic, whilst those that form positively charged surface-active ions are termed cation-active or cationic. Detergents that do not ionize in solution are termed non-ionic.

All three types of detergents can be solely or partly derived from petroleum. The anionic type is the most important commercially and includes alkyl aryl sulphonates, alkyl sulphates and common soap. The nonionics are the next most important whilst the cationics are mainly used for purposes for which their cationic nature makes them especially suitable.

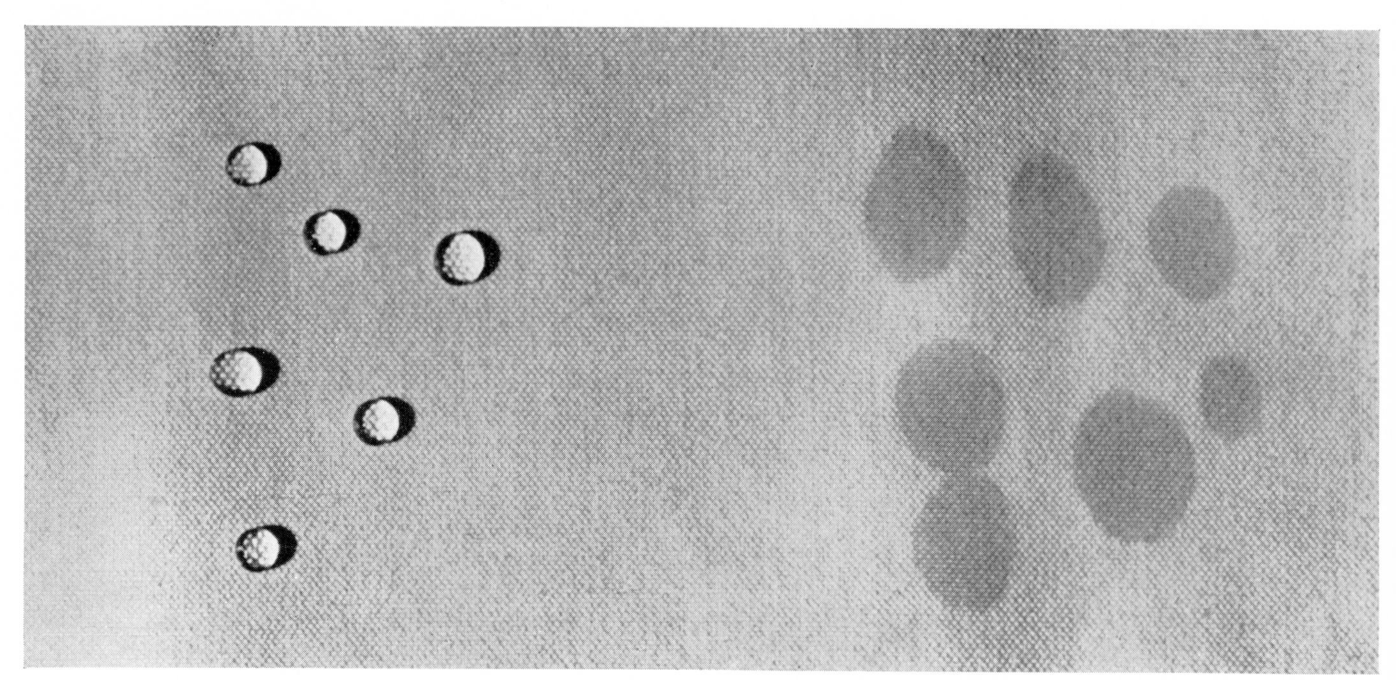

Fig. 179 Wetting power; drops of water on cotton cloth (left) *without* (right) with synthetic detergent

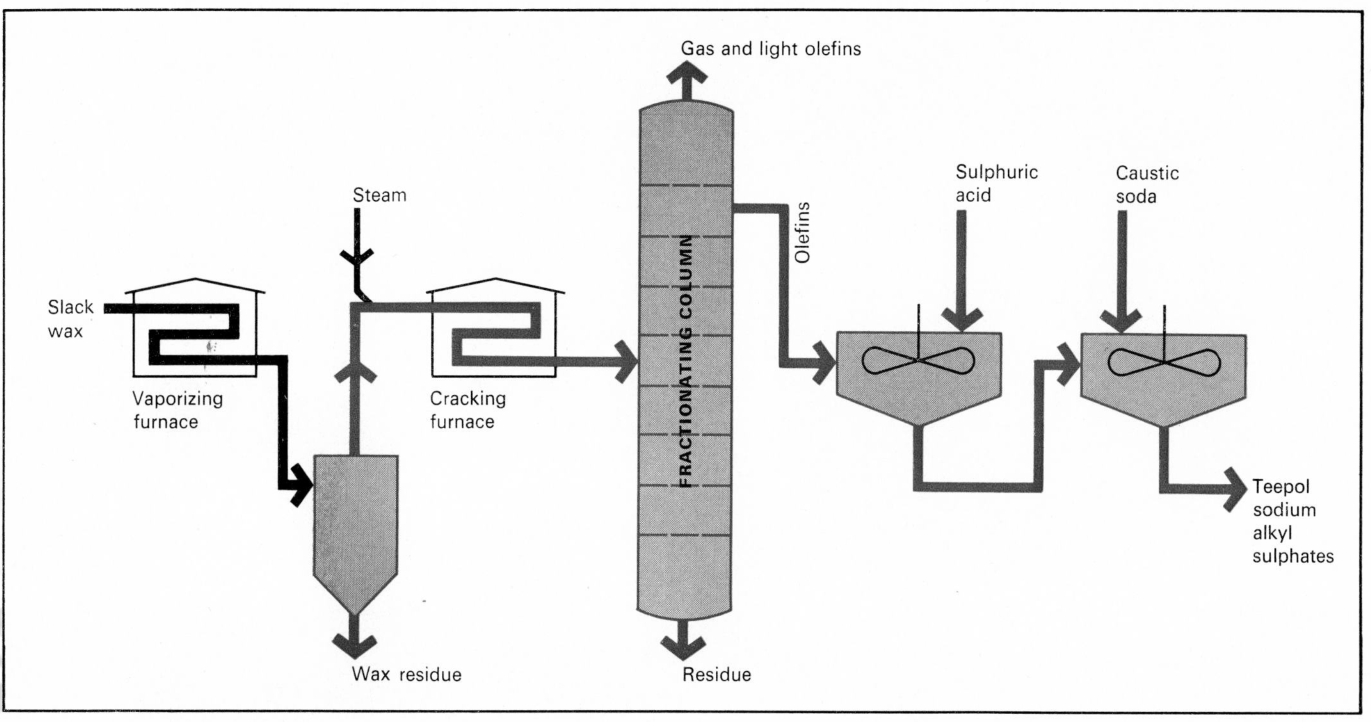

Fig. 180 Manufacture of Teepol

Manufacture

Anionic detergents

Alkyl aryl sulphonates

The manufacture of alkyl aryl sulphonates involves three main steps, the manufacture of an alkylate (p. 63), sulphonation of this alkylate to a sulphonic acid (p. 64), and neutralization of this acid with caustic soda. Alkylation is generally carried out by the petroleum chemical industry whilst the sulphonation, neutralization and formulation of the detergent for the individual markets are generally done by the soap and detergent products industry.

In the alkylation step, benzene and a C_{10}—C_{14} olefin are reacted together in the presence of an acid catalyst. The olefin is either a straight-chain α-olefin, obtained by cracking slack wax, or a branched-chain olefin such as propylene tetramer, made by polymerization of propylene.

$$C_6H_6 + C_{12}H_{24} \longrightarrow C_6H_5C_{12}H_{25}$$

benzene dodecene dodecylbenzene (alkylate)

The alkylate is sulphonated to dodecylbenzene sulphonic acid by means of concentrated sulphuric acid or sulphur trioxide.

$$C_6H_5C_{12}H_{25} \xrightarrow{H_2SO_4} C_{12}H_{25}C_6H_4SO_3H$$

dodecylbenzene dodecylbenzene sulphonic acid

The sulphonic acid is neutralized with caustic soda to form sodium dodecylbenzene sulphonate in which the sulphur atom of the sulphonic acid group is directly linked to a carbon atom of the benzene nucleus.

Alkyl sulphates

These include the original type of Teepol which consists of sodium secondary alkyl sulphates manufactured by a process developed by Shell from straight-chain higher olefins (C_8—C_{18}) obtained by cracking slack wax. The first large Teepol plant was started up in England in 1942 [Fig. 180].

A fraction containing the C_8—C_{18} olefins is treated with sulphuric acid to form a mixture of mono- and di- secondary alkyl sulphates. The latter are hydrolyzed to mono-alkyl sulphates, unsulphated products are removed and the mono-alkyl sulphates are neutralized with caustic soda.

The general formula of the sodium alkyl sulphates is as shown, with the sulphur atom linked to the carbon atom of the alkyl group through an oxygen atom.

$$C_nH_{2n+1}—\underset{H}{\overset{CH_3}{C}}—O—SO_3Na$$

Sodium alkyl sulphate

Primary sodium alkyl sulphates are made from fatty alcohols and sulphuric acid. The alcohols have hitherto been obtained by hydrogenation of fatty acids derived from animal or vegetable oils and fats, but similar alcohols can now be made from petroleum by a process recently developed by Shell.

Nonionic detergents

Nonionic detergents are generally made by a condensation reaction in which alcohols or phenols, which may be partly or wholly derived from petroleum, are combined with ethylene oxide (p. 229), now manufactured in large quantities from petroleum derived ethylene. Many different nonionic detergents, including Shell Nonidet, are made commercially, their properties differing according to the kind of alcohol or phenol used and the number of molecules of ethylene oxide per molecule of alcohol or phenol. This is usually in the range 6–15 but may be less or more, the greater the number, the greater the solubility in water. Such products can also be used as base material for making anionic detergents of the sulphated polyethoxyphenol or polyethoxyalcohol types.

Cationic detergents

Cationic surface-active materials have so far found little application as detergents, but are used in the textile industry to assist dyeing and other finishing processes. Some cationics have bactericidal properties and are therefore incorporated into detergent products intended for use in hospitals and dairies and for seed disinfection. They are often quaternary ammonium compounds or derivatives of pyridine or fatty acid amides.

Applications

Synthetic detergents have the advantage over soap in not forming insoluble calcium and magnesium salts, and can therefore be used in hard or even sea water. When soap is used in hard water, unpleasant scums are formed by the insoluble calcium and magnesium soaps. This is not only objectionable but a waste of soap. Synthetic detergents do not react with calcium or magnesium salts and their detergent qualities are in no way impaired by them. On the contrary, they help to maintain any scum already formed in a finely divided state so that it can be easily rinsed away.

Certain synthetic detergents are also stable in acid and other chemical solutions and are thus useful for various industrial applications where not only detergency is required but also other properties such as wetting, dispersing and emulsifying. They are used, for example, in agricultural sprays, the wetting out of fabrics for dyeing and in the manufacture of light weight concrete by the entrainment of air bubbles.

The sodium alkyl aryl sulphonates are not as soluble as the sodium alkyl sulphates and therefore generally require the use of solubilizers such as alcohols, urea or nonionic surface-active materials to produce concentrated liquid detergents. They are used mainly as the basis of 'heavy duty' household detergents for which they are particularly suitable. As already mentioned, the conversion of the alkylate to the alkyl aryl sulphonate (often the dodecylbenzene sulphonate) is usually carried out by the manufacturer of the detergent powder. The powders contain, in addition to the synthetic detergent, (15–30%w), other ingredients known as 'builders' (30–50%w), usually phosphates and silicates, as well as perborates for bleaching, together with small quantities of foam stabilizers and fluorescent brighteners. The powders are produced in the form of small, free-flowing beads by a spray-drying process.

Primary sodium alkyl sulphates can also be used as base material for powders. The secondary alkyl sulphates tend to give sticky powders and are therefore used for the production of liquids such as Teepol containing 20–40%w alkyl sulphate in solution in water. They are used for 'light duty' household applications such as dish washing and washing fine textiles.

Fig. 181 Scrubbing an office floor with synthetic detergent

The nonionic detergents, being particularly stable and inert, are of value in textile processing. They are remarkably versatile, some being not only water soluble but also miscible with water-immiscible solvents. They are stable to acids and in this respect superior to soap and the alkyl sulphates. Selected nonionics are used as rinse aids in dish-washing machines and in controlled foaming detergents for use in clothes-washing machines.

Synthetic detergents are widely used in the household. Products suitable for washing clothes and household linen are in the form of powders whilst specially formulated liquid products are used for washing dishes, paint work, floors and carpets [Fig. 181].

Textile manufacturers are the largest industrial users of synthetic detergents. Wool, cotton, rayon and other synthetic fibres are scoured at various stages in their processing, from fibre to yarn and from yarn to woven or knitted fabric. The type of synthetic detergent used depends on the type of fibre, the type of soiling matter and the results required. Nonionics are being used to an increasing extent for wool scouring while the alkyl sulphates and alkyl aryl sulphonates find many uses in the processing of other fibres. Synthetic detergents and other surface-active agents are also used to wet out textiles prior to dyeing or bleaching, to disperse pigments, to promote even dyeing and various other applications [Fig. 182].

The laundry industry uses both synthetic detergents and soap. Detergents for laundering cotton goods are designed to be most effective at higher temperatures, and to be capable not only of removing soiling matter but of preventing its redeposition, and thus preventing the greying of cotton articles after repeated washing.

The engineering industry uses synthetic detergents, either alone or in combination with solvents or alkalis, for metal degreasing. Other industries, including mining, papermaking, leather, fur, building and food, use synthetic detergents for various processes. In mining they are used for dust laying and as wetting agents in ore extraction processes. In papermaking they assist in the pulping of raw materials and in the scouring of waste rags used for making high-grade papers. In the leather and fur industries their uses range from the scouring of skins and fleeces to their employment as wetting and penetrating agents in dyeing and finishing baths.

The rubber industry uses synthetic detergents as wetting and dispersing agents and as lubricants to prevent rubber sticking during processing.

The food processing industry is a large consumer. Not only must vessels and machinery used in the preparation of foodstuffs be kept scrupulously clean, but all containers – especially tins – must be made chemically and biologically clean prior to the packing of food. Similarly, in the manufacture of beers, wines, spirits and soft drinks, all vats, stills and bottles must be thoroughly cleaned. The choice of the synthetic detergent will depend on what is required of it. Liquid detergents such as Teepol, with their good water solubility, excellent wetting and suspending qualities, are extensively used, but low foaming nonionic detergents are sometimes preferred.

Ever increasing quantities of synthetic detergents are used in the general cleaning of every type of establishment, public and private offices, institutions, hospitals, schools, hotels, theatres and cinemas. Liquid detergents such as Teepol are ideally suited for this purpose.

Biodegradability

The extensive use of synthetic detergents in household and industrial processes has led to problems in sewage disposal. Sewage purification normally depends on biological degradation processes in which the organic matter is decomposed by bacterial action. Ordinary soap is readily decomposed in this way but some synthetic detergents are much more resistant. Hence the effluent from a sewage work may contain undecomposed detergent that causes troublesome foam on the river, canal or lake into which it is discharged. The situation is even worse where untreated sewage is discharged direct into such waters.

Fig. 182 Wool washing with synthetic detergent

Sodium alkyl sulphates are broken down readily enough but the alkyl aryl sulphonates are more resistant. It was found that the 'biodegradability' of such detergents depends on the type of side chains in the molecule, those with straight side chains are more readily broken down than those with branched side chains, and the more branched the chain the more resistant is the detergent. Resistant detergents are referred to as 'hard' detergents, readily degradable ones as 'soft' detergents.

This has led to the development of new types of alkyl benzenes and other base materials from which soft detergents are now made. The side chains are derived from olefins produced by the cracking of paraffin wax as opposed to the branched chains typical of the molecules of propylene tetramer benzene. Wax suitable for the purpose is obtained by urea dewaxing of petroleum fractions, whereby only straight-chain normal paraffins are extracted.

In some countries the use of soft detergents only has been made compulsory.

Synthetic resins–plastics

Synthetic resins, in which plastics are included, vary widely in chemical composition and physical properties. A vast number can be made, but relatively few have achieved commercial importance; about twenty different types represent well over 90 %w of those now being manufactured.

Synthetic resins are familiar to most people as plastics, but they have many other applications, such as paints, lacquers and adhesives. They consist in the main of high molecular weight polymers and, with synthetic textile fibres and rubbers, belong to a class of materials known as 'synthetic high polymers'.

The rapid growth of the synthetic high polymer industries has been made possible to a large extent by the ample supplies of the necessary raw materials provided by the cracking of petroleum fractions. They are today one of the fastest growing sectors of the petroleum-chemical industry. The abundant supplies of petroleum-based raw materials have so reduced costs that consumer goods can now be made synthetically to compete with those made from alternative materials, which they have in many instances displaced, due to advantages in performance, price or ease of manufacture. Moreover, synthetic materials have in many instances made possible the production of articles that could not be conveniently produced from other raw materials.

This chapter deals only with synthetic resins and plastics as such, leaving the closely related synthetic fibres and rubbers to succeeding chapters.

The word plastic refers to any kind of material that can be shaped or moulded while in a soft or plastic condition, and afterwards hardened to a rigid or semi-rigid state. Synthetic resins can be divided into 'thermoplastic' and 'thermosetting' materials. Thermoplastics, when heated, can be made to flow into a mould and, when cooled, regain their rigidity and retain their shape; they can be again softened and moulded by heating and cooling. Thermosetting material can be temporarily thermoplastic and moulded by heating and pressing, but they then set permanently by virtue of chemical reactions that take place in the mould; they cannot be softened and remoulded by heating.

Both types are composed of large molecules (macromolecules) and the difference in thermal behaviour is due to differences in internal structure. The large molecules of the thermoplastics have a long-chain structure with little branching. They do not link with each other chemically, although they may intertwine and form a cohesive mass ranging from hard solids to soft pliable materials, sometimes resembling rubbers. On being heated the long-chain molecules can move more or less freely in relation to each other, so that, without melting, the material softens and can flow under pressure and be moulded to any shape. On cooling, the moulded articles regain rigidity. Some resins require the addition of liquid plasticizers to improve their flow in the mould, the plasticizer acting more or less as a lubricant between the large molecules. In such cases the moulded articles are usually softer and more flexible than those made from unplasticized material.

The macromolecules of the thermosetting resins are usually strongly-branched chains which cross-link on heating to form a complex spatial network which prevents free movement of the molecules relative to each other and results in a permanently rigid structure.

Basic reactions

The synthetic macromolecules are built up by three types of chemical reaction, polymerization, polycondensation and polyaddition.

Polymerization

High polymers formed by polymerization are both more numerous and more important than those formed by the other two processes. They are usually made by joining together into long chains a number of molecules of the same kind with reactive carbon/carbon double bonds in their structure. The chains often consist of hundreds or thousands of the original molecules, (monomers). The manufacture takes place in two stages, production of the monomer, followed by polymerization. For example, polyvinyl chloride is produced in the two stages:

$$\underset{\text{acetylene}}{CH{\equiv}CH} + \underset{\text{hydrochloric acid}}{HCl} \longrightarrow \underset{\text{vinyl chloride (monomer)}}{CH_2{=}CHCl}$$

$$\text{n molecules } \underset{\text{vinyl chloride}}{CH_2{=}CHCl} \rightarrow \underset{\text{polyvinyl chloride}}{-CH_2-CHCl-CH_2-CHCl-CH_2-}$$

High polymers produced by polymerization are in general thermoplastic. However, in the case of similarly built polyacrylonitrile,

$$-CH_2-\underset{\underset{\displaystyle C{\equiv}N}{|}}{CH}-CH_2-\underset{\underset{\displaystyle C{\equiv}N}{|}}{CH}-CH_2-$$

the cyanogroups of neighbouring chain molecules influence each other so strongly (without forming a real chemical bond) that, on heating, the material decomposes before becoming sufficiently plastic. In some cases it is possible to form polymers from two, or even three, monomers of different structure, capable of linking end-to-end to form mixed chains. These are called 'copolymers' and are the basis of important types of synthetic rubber (p. 224).

Polycondensation

In this reaction two or more chemicals are brought together and the reaction is initiated by heating, by a catalyst or by both. The reaction proceeds with the elimination of water, an alcohol or hydrochloric acid, and the molecules join by chemical bonds to form macromolecules, either long chains of the thermoplastic type or spatial networks of the thermosetting type.

Examples of a thermoplastic condensation are the formation of polycarbonate resin by reaction of phosgene with the polyvalent phenol diphenylolpropane, with the elimination of hydrochloric acid:

$$COCl_2 + HO{-}C_6H_4{-}C(CH_3)_2{-}C_6H_4{-}OH \longrightarrow$$

phosgene diphenylolpropane

$$\left[{-}C(=O){-}O{-}C_6H_4{-}C(CH_3)_2{-}C_6H_4{-}O{-}C(=O){-}\right]_n$$

polycarbonate resin

and the formation of polyphenylene oxide (PPO), produced by General Electric, USA, by oxidation of 2,6-dimethylphenol, with the elimination of water.

$$n\ (CH_3)_2C_6H_3{-}OH \rightarrow {-}(CH_3)_2C_6H_2{-}O{-}(CH_3)_2C_6H_2{-}O{-}(CH_3)_2C_6H_2{-}$$

2,6-dimethylphenol polyphenylene oxide

An example of the thermosetting type is the condensation of a polyalcohol with more than two hydroxyl groups in the molecule, such as ethylene glycol, glycerol, pentaerythritol, with a dibasic acid to form alkyd resins. Maleic acid and the o-phthalic, isophthalic and terephthalic acids are generally used. The formation and growth of the three-dimensional network is due to the fact that the number of hydroxyl groups in the alcohol is not the same as the number of carboxyl groups in the acid so that there usually remains an active spot for further growth. Thus, in the formation of glycerol/o-phthalate resin the glycerol has three hydroxyl groups and the acid only two carboxyl groups.

$$HOH_2C{-}CH{-}CH_2 \quad CH_2{-}CHO{-}CH_2$$

(glycerol units linked through O–C(=O) ester groups to o-phthalate rings; one free COOH)

glycerol/o-phthalate resin

In the manufacture of thermosetting resins the chemical reaction is often arrested at an intermediate state of temporary thermoplasticity, and the resin is then set in its final shape by the application of heat and pressure or a 'hardener' or 'curing agent'. In this stage further interlinking of the molecules occurs, leading to rigid structures within the mould or, in the case of surface coatings, within the paint film.

Polyaddition

Polyaddition is the formation of a macromolecule either from monomers with reactive groups other than a carbon/carbon double bond in the molecule or by addition of active monomer molecules to such reactive groups.

Examples of the first type are the formation of polyethylene oxide from ethylene oxide:

$$n\ (CH_2)_2O \longrightarrow {-}CH_2{-}CH_2O{-}CH_2{-}CH_2O{-}CH_2{-}CH_2O{-}$$

ethylene oxide polyethylene oxide

and the formation of polymethylene oxide from formaldehyde:

$$n\ CH_2O \longrightarrow {-}CH_2{-}O{-}CH_2{-}O{-}CH_2{-}O{-}CH_2{-}O{-}CH_2{-}$$

formaldehyde polymethylene oxide

The plastic Delrin, developed by Dupont, is of this type.

An example of the second type is the reaction of a polyalcohol with a diisocyanate to form a polyurethane. The isocyanate group is —N=C=O, and the reaction is an addition of the alcohol to the N=C double bond. Tolylenediisocyanate is generally used.

$$O{=}C{=}N{-}C_6H_3(CH_3){-}N{=}C{=}O + HO{-}R{-}OH \longrightarrow$$

tolylenediisocyanate polyalcohol

$$O{=}C{=}N{-}\left[C_6H_3(CH_3){-}NH{-}C(=O){-}O{-}R{-}O{-}C(=O){-}NH{-}\right]_n C_6H_3(CH_3){-}N{=}C{=}O$$

polyurethane

The reaction of diisocyanate with a polyalcohol with two hydroxyl groups in the molecule leads to thermoplastic chain structures; with three or more hydroxyl groups, thermosetting spatial networks are formed. The polyurethanes are used in the lacquer and foam plastics industries.

Types of resins and plastics

It follows from the previous section that five types of material are possible:

Thermoplastic materials made by polymerization
Thermoplastic materials made by polycondensation
Thermosetting materials made by polycondensation
Thermoplastic materials made by polyaddition
Thermosetting materials made by polyaddition

Thermoplastic materials made by polymerization

This is at present the largest group, including polyvinyl chloride (PVC), copolymers of vinyl chloride and vinylidene chloride, polyvinyl acetate, polyethylene, polypropylene, polystyrene, and the polyacrylics.

Polyvinyl and polyvinylidene compounds

Polyvinyl and polyvinylidene compounds are formed by the polymerization of vinyl chloride or vinyl acetate.

One method for the preparation of vinyl chloride from acetylene and hydrochloric acid has already been mentioned (p. 212). Another method starts with the addition of chlorine to ethylene to form dichloroethane, which is then converted to vinyl chloride and hydrochloric acid by passing over hot pebbles.

$$CH_2{=}CH_2 + Cl_2 \longrightarrow CH_2Cl{-}CH_2Cl \longrightarrow CH_2{=}CHCl + HCl$$

ethylene	chlorine	dichloroethane	vinyl chloride	hydrochloric acid

The acetylene and ethylene routes are often combined so that no surplus hydrochloric acid is left.

A more recent and promising development is a process for the manufacture of vinyl chloride in which ethylene, air and hydrochloric acid are led together over a catalyst. The hydrochloric acid and oxygen form chlorine, which immediately reacts with ethylene to produce vinyl chloride and hydrochloric acid. This combination reaction is expected to lower the price of vinyl chloride.

Pure vinyl chloride can be polymerized in bulk by heating it under pressure to about 60°C (140°F). Alternatively, it can be polymerized as an emulsion in water to which certain catalysts (initiators) have been added. The process yields polymer in fine suspension, which is coagulated with chemical reagents. The coagulant is washed and dried and is then ready for further processing on normal plastics machinery, with or without plasticizers.

An analogous process, suspension polymerization, yields a coarser product that can be easily filtered off.

When vinyl chloride is reacted with chlorine and the reaction product is treated with caustic soda, vinylidene chloride is obtained, which also polymerizes very easily either as a comonomer or in copolymers with vinyl chloride.

Fig. 183 Manufacture of tubular polyethylene film by annular extrusion

$$CH_2{=}CHCl + Cl_2 \longrightarrow CH_2Cl{-}CHCl_2 \xrightarrow{NaOH} CH_2{=}CCl_2 + HCl$$

vinyl chloride — chlorine — trichloroethane — vinylidene chloride (monomer) — hydrochloric acid

Vinyl acetate is made by reacting acetylene with acetic acid.

$$CH{\equiv}CH + CH_3COOH \longrightarrow CH_3COOCH{=}CH_2$$

acetylene — acetic acid — vinyl acetate

A more recently developed combination process for the manufacture of vinyl acetate, worked out by ICI, reacts ethylene with air and steam in the presence of a catalyst, and gives promise of a cheap route. The ethylene is oxidized to ethylene oxide and acetaldehyde. Further oxidation of acetaldehyde gives acetic acid which, after reaction with ethylene oxide and subsequent dehydration, may form vinyl acetate.

$$CH_2{=}CH_2 + O \longrightarrow \begin{matrix} CH_2 \\ | \!\!> O \\ CH_2 \end{matrix} \rightleftarrows CH_3CHO \xrightarrow{O} CH_3COOH$$

ethylene — ethylene oxide — acetaldehyde — acetic acid

$$\begin{matrix} CH_2 \\ | \!\!> O \\ CH_2 \end{matrix} + CH_3COOH \longrightarrow CH_2OH{-}CH_2OCOCH_3 \longrightarrow$$

ethylene oxide — acetic acid

$$CH_2{=}CHOCOCH_3$$

vinyl acetate

Vinyl acetate readily polymerizes with itself or copolymerizes with other vinyl compounds. Flexible material is produced by the addition of plasticizers.

The vinyl resins are at present the most widely used of the thermoplastics. Produced in both flexible and rigid forms, polyvinyl chloride (PVC) is made into sheets, foil, extruded and moulded forms. It is also used as a coating compound, applied to other materials such as paper and fabrics. In this form it is used for making a very wide variety of everyday articles such as raincoats, curtains, upholstery, floor covering, handbags, shoes, wrapping film, piping, and toys. An important outlet in the UK is for the manufacture of conveyor belting for coalmines. PVC, produced by Shell since 1949 at Pernis, is sold as a fine powder under the trade name Carina.

Polyethylene, $-CH_2-CH_2-CH_2-CH_2-CH_2-CH_2-$

Very pure ethylene (99·9%) is the base material for polyethylene. Two processes, one high-pressure and the other low-pressure, have been developed industrially. The high-pressure process, developed by ICI, is carried out between 1000–2000 kg/cm² (14 200–28 400 lb/in²) in the presence of traces of oxygen as catalyst. About 20–25% of the ethylene is converted to high molecular polymer, and the unconverted ethylene is separated and recycled.

Two types of low-pressure process are applied commercially, the Ziegler process and the Phillips process, differing in their catalysts and pressures.

In the Ziegler process, ethylene is polymerized in a hydrocarbon solvent under moderate pressures (less than 20 atm) in the presence of a combination of titanium chloride and aluminium tri-ethyl.

In the Phillips process, ethylene is polymerized in a hydrocarbon solvent at pressures between 35–100 kg/cm² (500–1420 lb/in²) and temperatures from 175–260°C (350–500°F) with a mixture of molybdenum and chromium oxides as catalyst.

The Ziegler low-pressure polyethylene is a more or less crystalline product of relatively high specific gravity, caused by the close packing of the polyethylene chains practically without side chains. The ICI high-pressure polyethylene is a less crystalline product of lower specific gravity, the polyethylene chains being less closely packed because of the greater number of side chains.

Low-pressure polyethylene is used particularly for the manufacture of articles that are required to be rigid, insensitive to temperature and resistant to oxidation. Articles made from polyethylene are widely used in the household, such as pails, beakers, and washing-up bowls. It is used extensively for the manufacture of such articles as toys, bottles, tubes, films, electrical equipment, and bottle crates.

Both types of polyethylene are manufactured by Shell and sold under the trade name Carlona.

Polypropylene

Polypropylene, obtained by polymerization of propylene, is a recent important development. Impressed by the success of the Ziegler catalyst in the polymerization of ethylene, Natta used it for the polymerization of propylene, and found that the type of product depended on the nature of the catalyst. If propylene is considered as methylethylene (ethylene with a methyl group as a side chain) there are two possibilities in building up the polymer chain; the methyl groups can be situated either at random on both sides of the chain

$$\begin{matrix} CH_3 & & H & H & & CH_3 \\ | & & | & | & & | \\ -C- & CH_2- & C- & C- & CH_2- & C- \\ | & & | & | & & | \\ H & & CH_3 & CH_3 & & H \end{matrix}$$

or on one side of the chain only (stereospecific polymerization).

$$\begin{matrix} CH_3 & & CH_3 & & CH_3 & \\ | & & | & & | & \\ -C- & CH_2- & C- & CH_2- & C- & CH_2- \\ | & & | & & | & \\ H & & H & & H & \end{matrix}$$

This latter effect can be obtained by suitable modification of the catalyst, and the product then consists of regularly built chains, the structure of which is analogous to that of a crystal, the more symmetrical the structure, the higher the crystallinity of the product. These regularly built polymers are thermoplastics, but have higher softening temperatures than those of the polymers with a random structure.

Polypropylene has a low specific gravity, a high softening temperature, good mechanical strength and rigidity, good surface hardness and chemical resistance. Various grades are made for extruding and moulding, including non-inflammable and very tough types and types not easily charged with static electricity. It is used for the manufacture of transparent coloured articles, which find many household applications, and is also produced as fibre from which knitted goods are made.

Shell manufactures polypropylene both in Europe and in the USA, 10 000 tons/year at Pernis by Rotterdamse Polyolefinen Maatschappij NV, a Shell Montecatini combination, 5000 tons/year at Carrington, England, and 35 000 tons/year at Woodbury, USA. It is sold under the trade name Carlona P.

Polystyrene

The monomer styrene is made from benzene and ethylene by alkylation and dehydrogenation.

$$C_6H_6 + CH_2{=}CH_2 \rightarrow C_6H_5CH_2{-}CH_3 \rightarrow C_6H_5CH{=}CH_2 + H_2$$

benzene ethylene ethylbenzene styrene hydrogen

It can be polymerized in bulk or in emulsion to water clear polymers. It can easily be dyed, which makes it suitable for the manufacture of attractive, transparent, coloured articles. As an aromatic derivative, its refractive index is high and the refraction and reflection of light gives a lively impression, compared with which other polymers look dull. In itself it can be slightly brittle, but articles with a high impact strength can be obtained by incorporating rubber. The copolymer of styrene with butadiene is the most widely used synthetic rubber (p. 224). Copolymers of styrene and acrylonitrile or of styrene, butadiene and acrylonitrile (ABS polymers) have a high impact strength, particularly the latter. A wide variety of articles are made from polystyrene such as electrical fittings, buttons, brush handles, toothbrushes, toys, parts of washing machines and radios. Shell polystyrene is marketed under the trade name Carinex. A special type of polystyrene for making articles such as insulation sheets, flower pots and packaging material is sold under the trade name Styrocell.

Methacrylate resins

Methacrylate resins are polymers of esters of methacrylic acid, e.g. methylmethacrylate resins used as the well-known Plexiglass and Perspex. The base materials are acetone and hydrocyanic acid, which have already been described (pp. 203 and 196).

$$CH_2{=}C(CH_3){-}COOCH_3$$ methylmethacrylate

Polyacrylonitriles

Polyacrylonitriles are used as synthetic fibres and as copolymers in certain synthetic rubbers, both of which are discussed in subsequent chapters (pp. 222 and 224).

Copolymers

Certain copolymers recently developed by Shell as synthetic rubbers, and discussed under that heading (p. 224), may equally well be regarded as thermoplastic with applications outside the normal uses of rubber. They are Thermolastic, a copolymer of butadiene and styrene, and the ABS plastics, copolymers of acrylonitrile, butadiene and styrene.

Fig. 184 Injection moulding of acrylic plastics (domelights); (left) general view of plant (right) close-up of mould

Fig. 185 Pipes made from epoxide resin, reinforced with glass fibres

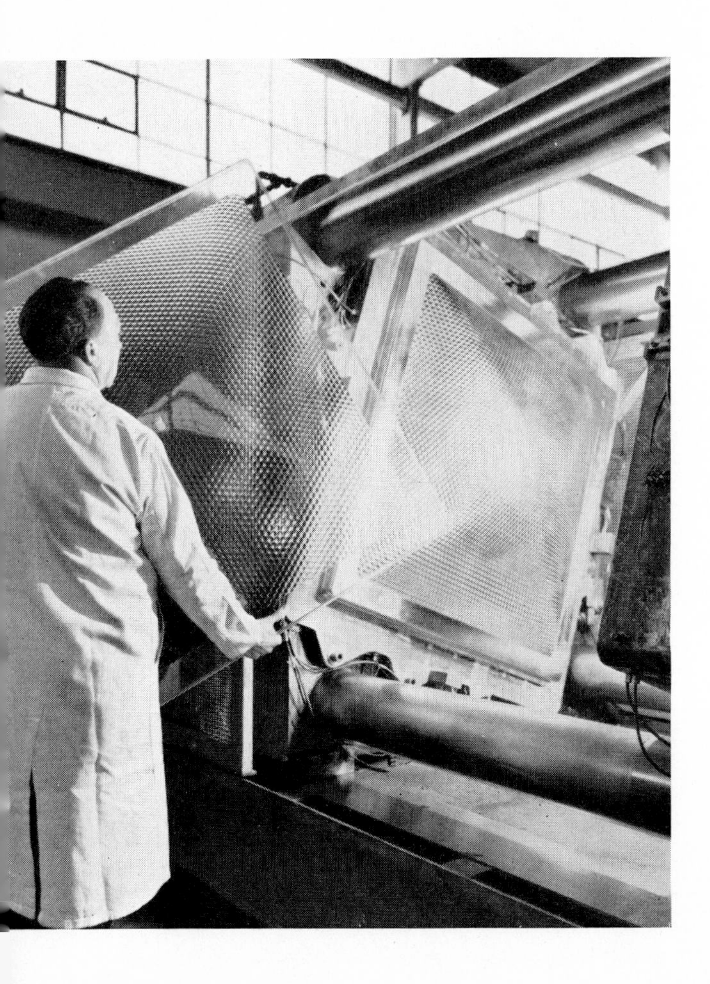

Thermoplastic materials made by polycondensation

These are of the polyester type, of which polycarbonate has already been mentioned (p. 213), and the polyamide type. Their main use is as synthetic fibres of the Terylene and nylon types which are discussed in the next chapter.

Thermosetting materials made by polycondensation

Alkyd resins

Alkyd resins, which have already been described (p. 213), belong to this group. They are of great importance in the paint and lacquer industry and are sold by Shell under the trade name Cardura.

Phenol/formaldehyde resins

Phenol/formaldehyde resins, such as Bakelite, are made by polycondensation of phenol and formaldehyde.

$$
\begin{array}{ccccc}
 & | & & | & \\
HO- & C_6H_2 & -CH_2- & C_6H_2 & -OH \\
 & | & & | & \\
 & CH_2 & & CH_2 & \\
 & | & & | & \\
HO- & C_6H_2 & -CH_2- & C_6H_2 & -OH \\
 & | & & | &
\end{array}
$$

Urea/formaldehyde resins

Urea/formaldehyde resins are made by polycondensation of urea and formaldehyde.

```
H2N—CO—NC—H2—N—CO—N—CH2—
        |       |       |
       CH2     CH2     CH2
        |       |       |
H2N—CON——CH2—N—CO—N—CH2—
```

Epoxide resins

Epoxide resins are usually made by condensation of epichlorohydrin (p. 231) and a polyvalent alcohol or phenol. The most commonly used phenol is diphenylolpropane, made by reaction of phenol with acetone. The reaction is carried out in the aqueous phase in the presence of an alkali. On completion of the reaction the separated resin is washed and dried, melted and run off into cooling trays.

```
     O                                CH3
    / \                                |
CH2 — CH2—CH2Cl  +  HO<benzene>—C—<benzene>OH  ——>
                                       |
                                      CH3
epichlorohydrin           diphenylolpropane
```

```
     O                    CH3                    OH                           CH3                          O
    / \                    |                      |                            |                          / \
CH2——CH2—CH2—[—O—<benzene>—C—<benzene>—O—CH—CH2—]n—O—<benzene>—C—<benzene>—O—CH2—CH2——CH2
                           |                                                   |
                          CH3                                                 CH3
```

Epoxide resin

The number n controls the various grades. The resin is applied with addition of a 'hardener' or 'curing agent' which reacts with the epoxy or the hydroxyl groups or with both to form a three-dimensional network. Diethylenetriamine is frequently used as the curing agent, but many others are also used such as acids, acid anhydrides, polyamides, polyamines, isocyanates, and mercaptans.

The resin can be used as a hard, corrosion resisting, strongly adhering lacquer film or as a product of great impact strength which, reinforced with glass fibres, can be used for light-weight high-strength pipes, tanks, boats and other structures [Figs 185 and 186]. Besides its use in industrial protective paints, it is used in adhesives, electrical insulating castings, flooring, laminates, and, in conjunction with bitumen, in highway surfacing. An important application is as paint for the cargo tanks of tankers transporting high-sulphur crudes or other corrosive cargoes. It can even be applied under water so that the hulls of boats, marine platforms and other underwater constructions can be painted *in situ* after cleaning by underwater sand blasting [Fig. 187].

The Shell trade name for epoxide resins is Epon in the USA and Epikote outside the USA.

Fig. 186 Sailing dinghy made of glass fibre impregnated with Epikote

Fig. 187 Underwater coating with Epikote

Thermoplastic and thermosetting materials made by polyaddition

Thermoplastic and thermosetting polyurethanes are the principal examples of this group. The thermosetting polyurethanes provide excellent lacquers, but require careful handling for indoor application, isocyanates being rather volatile toxic compounds. The terminal isocyanate groups of the polyurethanes are decomposed by water, forming carbon dioxide, which blows up the resin to a foam. Both flexible and rigid foams can be produced, the former from thermoplastic, the latter from thermosetting polyurethanes. Flexible foams are used for cushioning purposes, rigid foams for thermal insulation and as light-weight structural materials.

The Shell trade name for the base material for polyurethane foams is Caradol.

Processing of plastics

Thermoplastics can be shaped at temperatures above their softening point and retain their shape on cooling. They can be resoftened and reshaped by heating if desired. Thermosets, on the other hand, once set cannot be reshaped by heating, except at temperatures at which they would decompose. This difference in behaviour is due to differences in their molecular structure, as already explained, and is reflected in the difference in processing techniques applied to the two types.

A wide variety of processing techniques are applied to thermoplastics: injection moulding [Fig. 184], extrusion through an orifice, vacuum forming over a die, bottle blowing [Fig. 183], calandering, sintercoating, foaming, hot gas welding, heat sealing.

The methods for shaping thermosets are restricted to compression moulding, high pressure laminating, reinforcement with glass fibres and foaming.

The world production of plastics (1964) amounts to about eleven million tons a year, of which 70% thermoplastics and 30% thermosets. The major position of the thermoplastics is to a large extent due to their greater variety and greater ease of processing to end use applications.

Fig. 188 Blown-moulded plastic containers used in the petroleum industry

Fig. 189 Electrical components moulded from Epikote

Applications

The pattern of consumption

The level and pattern of consumption of plastics will naturally vary from country to country, and will depend largely on the level of national income and the degree of industrialization. The pattern in industrialized countries is shown in Table 20.

Table 20 Consumption of plastics

Application	Proportion used %w
Packaging	10–15
Electrical engineering	15
Domestic ware and consumer goods	15
Construction industry	20
Engineering, vehicles, instuments, etc	10
Paints	10–15
Adhesives	10–15
Miscellaneous	5

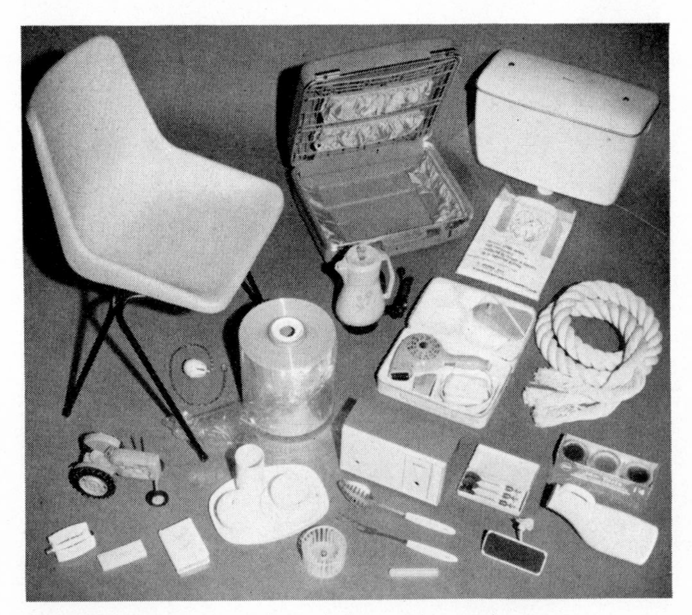
Fig. 190 Consumer goods made from polypropylene

Fig. 191 Expanded polystyrene insulating material

Fig. 192 Insulation of ducting with expanded polystyrene

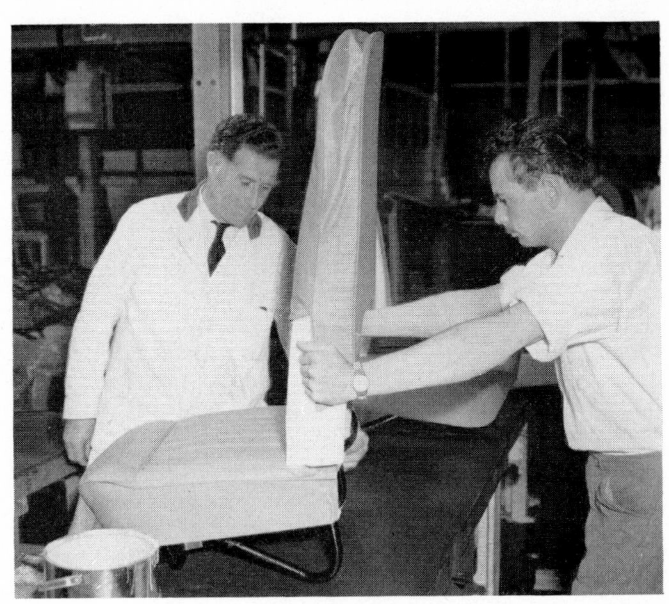

Fig. 193 Moulded polyurethane foam for the interior of car seat

Packaging

Until the early 1960s cellophane, derived from cellulose, was the major material used as a packaging film. Since then it has been largely replaced by polyethylene, the consumption of which now exceeds that of cellophane. Shrinkable films from polypropylene and hard plasticized PVC films are expected to gain more prominence over the next few years.

Blow moulded, injection moulded and vacuum formed plastic containers are in rapidly increasing use. Blown containers are used for packaging household detergents, bleaches, edible oils, fruit juices, and a host of other materials. Although high and low density polyethylenes have hitherto been favoured, rigid PVC bottles are now being used. Motor oils, hitherto packed in metal or fibreboard containers, are now supplied in polyethylene containers, and this usage is likely to increase rapidly over the next few years [Fig. 188].

Electrical engineering

The excellent electrical properties of many plastics have stimulated their use in the electrical engineering industry. Low density polyethylene and plasticized PVC are used for the sheathing and insulation of cables, the low power factor of the former and the non-inflammability of the latter being particularly attractive. Thermosetting resins are used extensively in the manufacture of electrical components [Fig. 189].

Domestic ware and consumer goods

Domestic ware such as bowls, cups and saucers, is manufactured in large quantities from thermoplastics, notably from polyethylene (both low and high density), and polypropylene. Plasticized PVC is used in many countries for the production of shoes and sandals, particularly in the less developed countries, where it can represent the major part of footwear sales. The toy industry uses large quantities of thermoplastics, polystyrenes and polyethylenes for injection moulded articles, and polyethylenes for blow moulded goods such as dolls and balls [Fig. 190].

Construction industry

The building industry in the major industrial countries accounts for 20% of plastics consumption, still only 2% of the value of its raw materials. The major use of thermoplastics has been in decorative finishes or in unloaded structures, but plasticized PVC is now being increasingly used in flooring, PVC and polyethylene in pipes, and laminates of plasticized PVC and metal as materials of construction. PVC, polyethylene and polystyrene are also used extensively as insulating material [Figs 191 and 192].

Motor vehicles

Realizing the considerable potential of the motor industry as a large-scale consumer, the plastics industry has vigorously promoted the application of plastics to motor vehicles. Plastics are attractive not so much on account of light weight or other physical advantages, but because they are cheaper and easier to fabricate than steel, cast iron, zinc alloys or wood. Car manufacturing costs are approximately 70% materials, 10% labour and 20% overheads, and on a cost per volume basis plastics are much cheaper than steel and zinc alloys.

The main use of plastics has been in decorative applications and interior trim, and plasticized PVC has been the predominant material, mainly for upholstery. However, newer materials such as polyamides and polypropylene are now used for 'under bonnet' applications, and moulded polyurethane cushions have been recently introduced [Fig. 193].

In the USA in 1962 the average use of plastics per car was approximately 12 kg and is expected to reach 24 kg by 1965. The Citroen AMI 6 weighs 640 kg and uses just over 17 kg of plastics. In the UK the consumption of plastics per car is estimated as approximately 20 kg and is expected to increase to about 35 kg by 1967.

Synthetic textile fibres

Synthetic textile fibres are made from synthetic resins and, as explained in the previous chapter, belong to the general class of synthetic high polymers.

Chemicals from petroleum have contributed considerably to the development of synthetic textile fibres. Already the precursors of the modern fully synthetic fibres, the semi-synthetic fibres derived from cellulose, such as cellulose acetate, cellulose nitrate (nitrocellulose) and regenerated cellulose (viscose), used large quantities of acetic acid, solvents and carbon disulphide, either for manufacturing or as spinning solvents. The Celanese Corporation in the USA developed a process for the manufacture of acetic acid by partial combustion of propane and butane.

Manufacture

Fully synthetic fibres are made by either polymerization or polycondensation of petroleum based materials. The fibres are formed by extruding the resin, either molten or dissolved in a volatile solvent, through a spinneret. The material, if molten, solidifies rapidly after extrusion, or, if in a solvent, is subjected to a current of warm air to evaporate the solvent [Fig. 194].

Polymerization

During the development of the high pressure polyethylene process, ICI spun fibres from the material, but the fibres had low tensile strength and bad dye acceptance. A stronger fibre was made from polypropylene, but the dyeing problem has not yet been completely solved.

An excellent fibre is made from polyacrylonitrile (Orlon, Dralon or Acrilan). Until recently the monomer acrylonitrile was produced by the reaction of hydrocyanic acid with either acetylene or ethylene oxide, both of which chemicals had to be prepared separately (Industrial chemicals, p. 227.)

$$CH{\equiv}CH + HCN \longrightarrow CH_2{=}CH{-}C{\equiv}N \longrightarrow \left[-CH_2-CH(C{\equiv}N)-\right]_n$$

acetylene + hydrocyanic acid → acrylonitrile → Orlon

or

$$\underset{\text{ethylene oxide}}{CH_2{-}CH_2 \text{ (O bridge)}} + \underset{\text{hydrocyanic acid}}{HCN} \longrightarrow \underset{\text{acrylonitrile}}{CH_2{=}CH{-}C{\equiv}N}$$

Although one would expect polyacrylonitrile to be a thermoplastic, decomposition sets in before adequate softening, so that it is impossible to spin fibres from the molten material. The product is dissolved in a highly polar solvent, dimethylformamide, from which it is spun.

Acrylonitrile is now manufactured by oxidation of propylene in the presence of ammonia (amino oxidation). This process gives excellent yields and has lowered the cost considerably. Acetonitrile, CH_3CN, is produced as a by-product for which a satisfactory outlet has still to be found.

Polycondensation

The polyesters (Terylene) and the polyamides (nylon) belong to this group. The ICI developed fibre Terylene, called Dacron in the USA, Terlenka in the Netherlands and Trevira in Germany, is a polycondensation product of ethylene glycol (or ethylene oxide) and terephthalic acid (or its methyl ester) [Fig 195]. Terephthalic acid is obtained by oxidation of para-xylene, by isomerization of the ortho- and isophthalic acids and by disproportionation of benzoic acid.

$$\underset{\text{glycol}}{CH_2OH{-}CH_2OH} + \underset{\text{terephthalic acid}}{HOOC{-}C_6H_4{-}COOH} \longrightarrow \underset{\text{Terylene}}{\left[-CH_2CH_2OOC{-}C_6H_4{-}COO-\right]_n}$$

The base material for nylon is adipic acid, which is condensed with hexamethylenediamine, also obtained from adipic acid. Adipic acid is produced from cyclohexane or phenol.

$$\underset{\text{phenol}}{C_6H_5OH} \xrightarrow{\text{hydrogenation}} \underset{\text{cyclohexanol}}{C_6H_{11}OH} \xrightarrow{\text{oxidation}} \underset{\text{adipic acid}}{COOH{-}(CH_2)_4{-}COOH} \longrightarrow$$

Fig. 194 Molten Terylene fibre emerging from spinneret

$$\begin{matrix} COONH_4 & & CONH_2 & & CN & & NH_2 \\ | & & | & & | & \text{hydrogenation} & | \\ (CH_2)_4 & \longrightarrow & (CH_2)_4 & \longrightarrow & (CH_2)_4 & \longrightarrow & (CH_2)_6 \\ | & & | & & | & & | \\ COONH_4 & & CONH_2 & & C{\equiv}N & & NH_2 \end{matrix}$$

ammonium salt — amide — adiponitrile — hexamethylene diamine

$$\begin{matrix} COOH & & NH_2 & \text{poly-condensation} & \\ | & & | & & \\ (CH_2)_4 & + & (CH_2)_6 & \longrightarrow & \left[HN(CH_2)_6NHCO(CH_2)_4CO \right]_n \\ | & & | & & \\ COOH & & NH_2 & & \end{matrix}$$

adipic acid — hexamethylene diamine — nylon 66

Starting from adiponitrile, both adipic acid and hexamethylene diamine can be made by hydrolysis and hydrogenation respectively. A new method for making adiponitrile from acrylonitrile has recently been developed by Dupont, applying electrolytic hydrogenation.

$$2\,CH_2{=}CH{-}C{\equiv}N + 2\,H \longrightarrow CN{-}(CH_2)_4CN$$

acrylonitrile — adiponitrile

Another polyamide fibre, nylon 6, is also made starting from phenol although recently various other routes have been developed.

phenol (C₆H₅OH) ⟶ cyclohexanol ⟶ cyclohexanone ⟶

$$C_6H_5OH \longrightarrow \underset{\text{cyclohexanol}}{(CH_2)_5CHOH} \longrightarrow \underset{\text{cyclohexanone}}{(CH_2)_5C{=}O} \longrightarrow$$

$$\underset{\text{cyclohexanone oxime}}{(CH_2)_5C{=}NOH} \xrightarrow{\text{isomerization}} \underset{\text{caprolactam}}{(CH_2)_5{-}CO{-}NH} \longrightarrow \underset{\text{nylon 6}}{\left[NH(CH_2)_5CO \right]_n}$$

Fig. 195 Terylene sails on Flying Dutchman racing dinghies

Synthetic rubbers

Natural rubber is obtained from the rubber tree, *Hevea brasillensis*. It is a chain polymer of isoprene (methylbutadiene) in which a certain number of double bonds remain and can react with vulcanizing agents such as sulphur, thus giving the rubber a more rigid structure due to the cross linking of the hydrocarbon chains.

Methlybutadiene $CH_2{=}CH{-}CH{=}CH_2$ (with CH_3 on the second carbon)

When the Germans were cut off from their overseas natural resources during World War I, they studied the the possibility of producing synthetic rubber, and already during the war they produced Methylkautschuk (methyl rubber) on a limited scale. It was made from dimethylbutadiene (methylisoprene) produced from acetone, but had a poor performance.

Dimethylbutadiene $CH_2{=}C{-}C{=}CH_2$ (with CH_3 on each of the two middle carbons)

The first commercial production of synthetic rubber was in Germany in the 1930s by copolymerization of butadiene with styrene (Buna S) or acrylonitrile (Buna N), and these products were considerably better than the earlier methyl rubber.

When, during World War II, the Japanese cut off the USA from their rubber supplies in South East Asia, the American chemical industry embarked on the large scale manufacture of synthetic rubber and produced GRS (Government rubber S) by copolymerization of butadiene with styrene. Most of the rubber was produced by commercial firms in Government-owned plants and after the war these plants were offered to industry on reasonable terms. Many firms, including Shell, took them over.

Since 1950 synthetic rubber has again become of great importance throughout the world because the demand for rubber has far outstripped supplies from natural sources. The annual consumption of synthetic rubber in the world outside the Sino-Soviet spheres is about 2·5 million tons, and has tripled between 1952–62. The corresponding consumption of natural rubber is about 1 million tons, which remained stationary during this ten-year period. The annual consumption in the Sino-Soviet spheres is estimated as 1·7 million tons of synthetic rubber and 0·6 million tons of natural rubber. The demand for synthetic rubber is continuing to increase steadily at a much higher rate than output of natural rubber, and it is evident that synthetic rubber will be required in ever greater quantities in the future.

Manufacture

Synthetic rubbers fall into two general classes according to their uses, the general-purpose rubbers and the speciality rubbers.

The most important general-purpose rubbers have been the SBR rubbers (the former American GRS and German Buna S types) made by copolymerization of butadiene and styrene. In the last few years, however, a new family of synthetic rubbers – the stereospecific rubbers – have been developed, based on the polymerization of diolefins such as butadiene by catalysts of the Ziegler/Natta type described in the chapter on Synthetic resins – plastics (p. 215). In this reaction, chains are built up by linking carbon atom 4 of one molecule with carbon atom 1 of another; the double bonds 1–2 and 3–4 disappear and a new double bond 2–3 emerges and is available for the formation of cross links. The polymer can then exist in either of two configurations, with the linkages of the carbon atoms 1 and 4 either on the same side of the plane of the new double bond (cis-configuration) or on opposite sides (trans-configuration).

$CH_2{=}CH{-}CH{=}CH_2$ (carbons numbered 1, 2, 3, 4)

cis: C1 and C4 on the same side of the C2=C3 double bond

trans: C1 and C4 on opposite sides of the C2=C3 double bond

Products with a cis-configuration are resilient and elastic, as is natural rubber, which is mostly a cis-polymer of isoprene. Products with a trans-configuration are hard and inelastic, as are the natural products guttapercha and balata, which also have a trans-configuration.

More recently, copolymers of ethylene and propylene, EP rubbers, have been developed. Being completely saturated polymers, they are very resistant to oxidation and the effect of light but do not readily vulcanize. Double bonds can be introduced by copolymerizing ethylene, propylene and hexadiene or cyclopentadiene to produce EPT rubbers (ethylene, propylene terpolymers).

Yet another synthetic rubber of the butadiene/styrene type has been developed recently by Shell in the USA under the trade name Thermolastic. It is transparent, resilient, abrasive resistant, waterproof and does not need vulcanization. Similar rubbers (ABS rubbers) are produced by copolymerization of the three monomers, butadiene, styrene and acrylonitrile.

These rubbers can also be classified as thermoplastics, with certain applications as plastics outside the normal uses of rubber. They are processed on normal thermoplastics machinery.

The speciality rubbers are of various types, of which the best known are butyl rubber, nitrile rubber and chloroprene rubber (Neoprene). Butyl rubber is made by polymerization of isobutylene, nitrile rubber is produced by a polymerization of butadiene and acrylonitrile, and Neoprene, developed by Dupont, by polymerization of chloro-

Fig. 196 Bale of synthetic rubber being removed from press

butadiene obtained by reacting vinyl acetylene with hydrochloric acid.

$$2\,HC{\equiv}CH \longrightarrow HC{\equiv}C{-}CH{=}CH_2 \xrightarrow{HCl} CH_2{=}\underset{\displaystyle Cl}{\underset{|}{C}}{-}CH{=}CH_2$$

acetylene — vinyl acetylene — Neoprene

Other speciality rubbers include polysulphide, polyether, polyurethane, acrylic and chlorosulphonated rubbers. Polysulphide rubber (Thiokol) is produced by condensing sodium polysulphide with ethylene dichloride or other dichloro compounds. Polyether rubbers are produced by copolymerization of propylene oxide and other unsaturated compounds. Chlorosulphonated rubber (Hypalon) is produced by the action of sulphur dioxide and chlorine on polyethylene.

The polymerization reactions involved in the production of synthetic rubbers are carried out in solution or in emulsion as described in synthetic resins–plastics (p. 214). By emulsion polymerization the rubber is obtained as a latex, similar to natural rubber latex, and can be used as such for the manufacture of foamed or dipped goods, or can be converted to crumb rubber by coagulation.

The general-purpose rubbers are produced not only as unmodified products but also mixed with mineral oil as extending material (oil-extended rubbers) or with carbon black (black masterbatches) [Fig. 196].

Base materials (monomers)

The price of the base materials, monomers, is an important feature in synthetic rubber manufacture. Ethylene and propylene are cheaply and abundantly available by cracking or steam-cracking petroleum fractions. Just before World War II, Shell developed a process for the manufacture of butadiene by first chlorinating the C_4 fraction (butanes/butylenes) of cracking gas to produce 2, 3-dichlorobutane which was then converted into butadiene by dehydrochlorination. But the process was never applied on a large scale. A lot of butadiene was produced during the early years of the war from ethyl alcohol by partly oxidizing it to acetaldehyde and condensing this with the alcohol.

$$CH_3CH_2OH \longrightarrow CH_3CHO + H_2$$

ethyl alcohol — acetaldehyde

$$CH_3CHO + CH_3CH_2OH \longrightarrow CH_2{=}CH{-}CH{=}CH_2 + 2\,H_2O$$

acetaldehyde ethyl alcohol — butadiene

Acetaldehyde may also be prepared from acetylene (p. 227) and then condensed with ethyl alcohol.

Butadiene is also produced by the catalytic dehydrogenation of n-butane or n-butylene. More recently it has been found possible to steam-crack hydrocarbon fractions in such a way as to produce large amounts of diolefins as well as olefins and this promises to become the cheapest process for the manufacture of butadiene.

Isoprene is produced by dehydrogenation of isopentane obtained by fractionation of straight-run pentane/isopentane.

Styrene is produced from ethylene and benzene as described in a previous chapter (p. 216).

Shell not only provides the basic raw materials for the production of synthetic rubbers but also has synthetic rubber plants in the USA (Torrance and Marietta) and in Europe (Pernis and Berre). The Shell rubbers are marketed under the trade name Cariflex outside the USA.

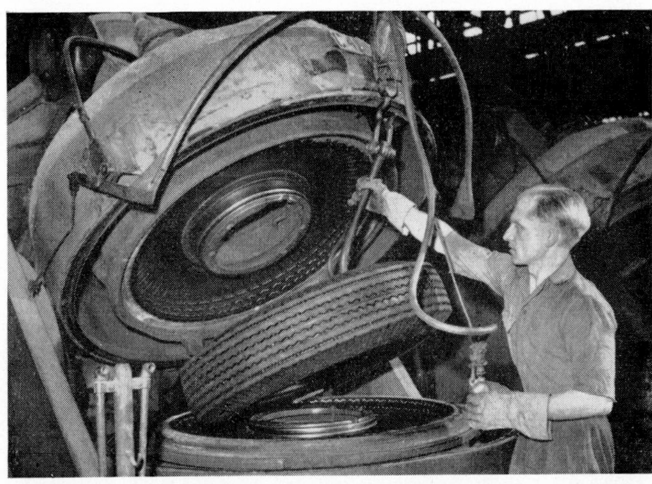

Fig. 197 Vulcanized tyre being removed from mould

Uses of synthetic rubber

The general-purpose rubbers can be used for most purposes for which natural rubber was formerly the only product available. They are used either alone or in blends with other materials, particularly carbon black, for the manufacture of car and truck tyres, mouldings, extrusions, footwear, belting, wire and cable covers, flooring and a whole range of domestic articles. Where necessary they are vulcanized with sulphur or other vulcanizing agents [Fig. 197].

The speciality rubbers have mostly been developed to achieve some particular property for specific applications for which general purpose rubbers would not be technically suitable. They are generally more expensive and are limited in use to the applications for which they are most suited by their individual characteristics such as resistance to high temperature, resistance to oil and solvents, and high flexural strength.

Butyl rubber is outstandingly impermeable to air and is accordingly widely used for inner tubes and curing bags. It also has good electrical properties and is used in wire and cable covers.

Nitrile rubbers are extremely resistant to mineral oils, including aromatic oils, and are used for hoses, tubing and gaskets that come into contact with oil products.

Neoprene is resistant to mineral oils other than aromatics; it is also resistant to ozone and is therefore an excellent material for cable covers. Its non-inflammability is important for applications in the building industry.

Ethylene-propylene rubbers, EPR, are outstandingly resistant to ozone and to ageing, and are used for the manufacture of weather strips and window sealings in cars and buildings.

Hypalon rubber is highly resistant to heat and chemicals and, being white, lends itself well to the manufacture of light-coloured articles.

Industrial chemicals

Apart from the chemicals produced for well-defined outlets described in preceding chapters, many others with a wide variety of applications are also produced from petroleum feedstocks. A description of all that have achieved commercial importance is beyond the scope of this book and only a few have been singled out for description. The choice has been made mainly on the basis of their present importance to industry, and because the outlets for most of them are unrelated to one another, no attempt has been made to group them according to their uses. Instead, they have been classified as far as possible on the basis of the number of carbon atoms in the hydrocarbon from which they are industrially derived, directly or indirectly. Since most of the products have many end-uses outside the main groups already described they are usually referred to as 'industrial chemicals'. This group includes those already described in the chapter on Solvents (p. 201).

Derivatives of methane (C_1)

Acetylene (ethine), C_2H_2, and derivatives

Various processes for the commercial manufacture of acetylene from natural gas have already been mentioned in the chapter dealing with the main primary conversions of base materials (p. 196).

Several important intermediates have been synthesized from acetylene, but a cheaper route via ethylene has been developed for many of them.

Acrylonitrile, $CH_2{=}CH{-}C{\equiv}N$, trichloroethylene, $CCl_2{=}CHCl$, and vinyl chloride, $CH_2{=}CHCl$, are produced from acetylene by reacting respectively with hydrocyanic acid, chlorine and hydrochloric acid. Their manufacture has already been described under Synthetic textile fibres (p. 222), Solvents (p. 201) and Synthetic resins – plastics (p. 212).

During World War II, I. G. Farbenindustrie in Germany developed a number of syntheses based on acetylene (Reppe chemistry), but after the war these processes were not competitive. Ethylene is now a cheap commodity and the field for acetylene as a base material has narrowed, leaving trichloroethylene and vinyl chloride as the main derivatives, although, for the latter, the new oxychlorination of ethylene promises to be cheaper.

Acetaldehyde, CH_3CHO

The production of acetaldehyde by oxidation of ethyl alcohol has already been mentioned (p. 225); the direct oxidation of ethylene is becoming commercially important, but much acetaldehyde is still prepared by addition of water to acetylene in the presence of a mercury salt as the catalyst.

$$C_2H_2 + H_2O \xrightarrow{\text{mercury salt}} CH_3CHO$$

acetylene water → acetaldehyde

Acetic acid, ethyl alcohol and butadiene can be manufactured from acetaldehyde.

Acetic acid, CH_3COOH, and acetic anhydride $(CH_3CO)_2O$

Although acetic acid can be obtained from propane and butane by direct oxidation, the important methods for commercial production are from acetaldehyde or from methanol, the manufacture of which from natural gas has been described under Solvents (p. 201).

The oxidation of acetaldehyde to acetic acid is carried out by a catalytic method using oxygen.

The synthesis from methanol involves the addition of carbon monoxide at 300 atm (4200 lb/in^2) and at a temperature of between 300–500°C (600–900°F) in the presence of a zinc oxide catalyst.

$$CH_3OH + CO \longrightarrow CH_3COOH$$

methanol, carbon monoxide → acetic acid

Acetic anhydride, which can be regarded as a combination of two molecules of acetic acid with the removal of one molecule of water, is commercially important as a raw material for cellulose acetate, employed for making both textile fibres and plastics. The anhydride is made by pyrolysis of acetic acid.

A new route, although not starting from natural gas, makes use of an important petroleum chemical, acetone, as the starting material. Acetone is pyrolyzed to yield a highly reactive intermediate ketene, which is then reacted with acetic acid to yield acetic anhydride.

$$CH_3COCH_3 \xrightarrow{\text{pyrolysis}} CH_2{=}C{=}O + CH_4$$

acetone → ketene + methane

$$CH_2CO + CH_3COOH \longrightarrow (CH_3CO)_2O$$

ketene + acetic acid → acetic anhydride

Hydrocyanic acid, HCN

Hydrocyanic acid, familiarly known as prussic acid, is produced from natural gas as already described (p. 196). It is used mainly to make nitrile compounds, such as acrylonitrile, for the plastics and synthetic resins industries (p. 216) and acetone cyanohydrin $(CH_3)_2COHCN$, an intermediate in the production of methylmethacrylate plastic (p. 216).

Ammonia, NH_3

Ammonia is manufactured by the direct combination of hydrogen and nitrogen under pressure over a catalyst [Fig. 198]. Much of the world's ammonia production is based on hydrogen obtained from coke ovens or by electrolysis,

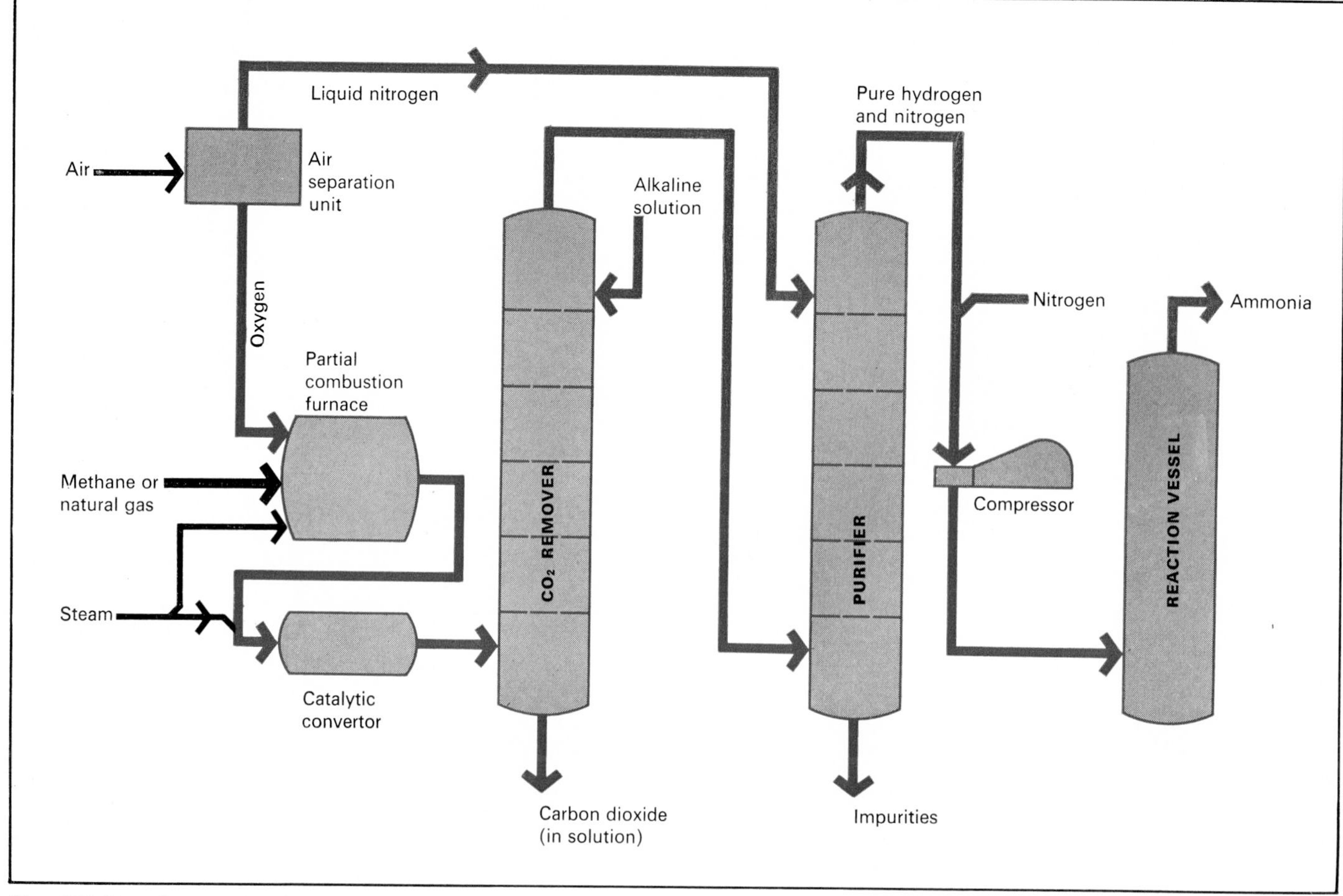

Fig. 198 Manufacture of hydrogen and ammonia

although in the USA over 80% of the synthetic ammonia production is now based on hydrogen produced from natural gas or liquid petroleum fractions, and these sources are now being exploited on a growing scale in Western Europe.

By burning methane or natural gas in a limited supply of oxygen and in the presence of steam, mixtures of hydrogen, carbon monoxide and carbon dioxide are obtained (p. 196). Carbon dioxide can be readily removed by absorption in alkali, but carbon monoxide cannot be removed in this way. It is therefore converted to carbon dioxide by passing it with steam over a catalyst at high temperatures, the resultant gas then consisting essentially of hydrogen and carbon dioxide. After absorption of the carbon dioxide in alkali the hydrogen still contains small amounts of water, carbon dioxide and hydrocarbons, all of which are removed by washing with liquid nitrogen.

Nitrogen is produced from the air by liquefaction and distillation, thereby separating it from the oxygen and other constituents.

The hydrogen and nitrogen are then combined to form ammonia according to the scheme shown in Fig. 198.

$$N_2 + 3H_2 \longrightarrow 2NH_3$$

nitrogen hydrogen ammonia

Several processes have been developed for this synthesis, all requiring the use of catalysts, high pressures (200–1000 kg/cm^2; 2840–14000 lb/in^2) and moderately high temperature.

The greater part of anhydrous ammonia production is used for the manufacture of nitrogenous fertilizers (p. 237), but it has many uses in other industries, for example textile, rubber, paper and metal ore processing; the manufacture of synthetic resins and explosives; chemical synthesis; and as a refrigerant.

Nitric acid, HNO_3

Nitric acid is manufactured by the high temperature oxidation of ammonia over a platinum or platinum/rhodium catalyst. It has many uses in industry and some of its salts are used as nitrogenous fertilizers (p. 237).

Urea, NH_2CONH_2

Urea is made by the reaction of carbon dioxide with ammonia at a pressure of 200 kg/cm^2 (2840 lb/in^2) and a temperature of 175C° (345°F), and it is now being manufactured in considerable quantities from petroleum raw material. It is used as a nitrogenous fertilizer (p. 237) and in the manufacture of plastics and resins (p. 217).

Carbon blacks, C

Carbon blacks are made from petroleum hydrocarbons as already described (p. 196) on a very large scale in the USA and to a lesser extent in the UK and elsewhere. They are used chiefly as reinforcing agents and fillers in tyre and rubber manufacture.

Derivatives of ethane and ethylene (C_2)

Ethyl chloride, C_2H_5Cl

Ethyl chloride can be made by chlorination of ethane or by addition of hydrochloric acid across the double bond of ethylene.

$$CH_3{-}CH_3 + Cl_2 \longrightarrow CH_3{-}CH_2Cl + HCl$$

ethane, chlorine, ethyl chloride, hydrochloric acid

$$CH_2{=}CH_2 + HCl \longrightarrow CH_3{-}CH_2Cl$$

ethylene, hydrochloric acid, ethyl chloride

Ethyl chloride is a volatile inflammable liquid; most of it is used in the manufacture of tetraethyl lead (TEL), the anti-knock compound for improving the ignition quality of gasolines. It is also used for the production of ethyl cellulose and as a local anaesthetic.

Dichloroethane, $CH_2Cl{-}CH_2Cl$

Dichloroethane, obtained by addition of chlorine to ethylene, is a base material for the manufacture of vinyl chloride as described in the chapter on Synthetic resins – plastics (p. 212).

Vinyl chloride, $CH_2{=}CHCl$

In the chapter on Synthetic resins – plastics mention is made of a new process for the oxychlorination of ethylene, producing vinyl chloride in one step from ethylene, hydrochloric acid and air.

Ethylene oxide, $CH_2{-}CH_2$ (bridged by O)

The tremendous growth in the use of ethylene and ethylene derivatives has been one of the most significant chemical developments of the past decade. Together with polyethylene and ethyl alcohol, ethylene oxide accounts for a large consumption of ethylene. Two processes are in use, although the older chlorohydrin route is being replaced more and more by the modern direct oxidation route, using either high purity oxygen or air as an oxidizing agent.

The chlorohydrin process starts with the formation of an intermediate, ethylene chlorohydrin, by direct combination of ethylene with hypochlorous acid. This reaction is carried out in towers, into which water and gaseous ethylene and chlorine are introduced. The resulting aqueous solution of ethylene chlorohydrin is mixed with a lime slurry and the ethylene oxide is driven off as a vapour by steam injection.

$$CH_2{=}CH_2 + HOCl \longrightarrow CH_2ClCH_2OH \xrightarrow[\text{slurry}]{Ca(OH)_2} CH_2{-}CH_2 \text{ (O bridge)}$$

ethylene, hypochlorous acid, ethylene chlorohydrin, ethylene oxide

The direct oxidation process is carried out by passing ethylene and air or oxygen over a silver catalyst at a temperature between 200–300°C (390–570°F). The use of oxygen of about 95% purity instead of air greatly reduces the size of the plant. The reaction is controlled in such a way as to minimize the formation of acetaldehyde (an isomer of ethylene oxide) carbon dioxide and water. The resulting ethylene oxide is absorbed in water, recovered by steam distillation and finally fractionated to give the purity required.

$$2\,CH_2{=}CH_2 + O_2 \longrightarrow 2\,CH_2{-}CH_2 \text{ (O bridge)}$$

ethylene, oxygen, ethylene oxide

Ethylene imine, $CH_2{-}CH_2$ (bridged by NH)

Ethylene imine is a new promising versatile product. It was initially manufactured from ethylene chloride and ammonia but recently a new process has been developed by which a mixture of ethylene, chlorine and ammonia is led over a catalyst.

(a) $CH_2Cl{-}CH_2Cl + 3\,NH_3$ (ethylene chloride, ammonia)

(b) $CH_2{=}CH_2 + Cl_2 + 3\,NH_3$ (ethylene, chlorine, ammonia)

$\longrightarrow$ $CH_2{-}CH_2$ (NH bridge) $+ 2\,NH_4Cl$ (ethylene imine, ammonium chloride)

Ethylene glycol, $CH_2OH{-}CH_2OH$

One of the main derivatives of ethylene oxide is ethylene glycol, which is obtained by reaction with hot water under pressure.

$$CH_2{-}CH_2 \text{ (O bridge)} + H_2O \longrightarrow CH_2OH{-}CH_2OH$$

ethylene oxide, water, ethylene glycol

Diethylene glycol, $HOCH_2{-}CH_2{-}O{-}CH_2{-}CH_2OH$, and triethylene glycol, $HOCH_2{-}CH_2{-}O{-}CH_2{-}CH_2{-}O{-}CH_2{-}CH_2OH$, are obtained by reaction of further quantities of ethylene oxide with ethylene glycol.

Mono-, di- and triethylene glycols are all colourless and slightly viscous liquids miscible with water and with organic solvents. They are employed to some extent as solvents but mainly as chemical intermediates. The principal use of monoethylene glycol is as a radiator antifreeze, for which it is very suitable because it depresses the freezing point of water, is inert and has low volatility.

Another important outlet is as an intermediate in the manufacture of the polyester synthetic resin from which Terylene is made (p. 222).

Diethylene and triethylene glycols are used as intermediates in the manufacture of alkyd resins and are widely employed as ingredients in paints, varnishes, lacquers and other surface coatings. They are also used in making plasticizers and as ingredients in various types of polyester resins used for making laminates and glass fibre reinforced articles.

Another outlet for diethylene and triethylene glycols is

in the manufacture of special dynamites, which have to withstand low temperatures without the risk of spontaneous detonation.

The glycols are further used as constituents of brake and other hydraulic fluids used by the automobile and engineering industries. Furthermore they find a use as humectants (moistening agents) in the preparation of many kinds of pharmaceuticals and cosmetics, as well as in the manufacture of cellophane.

Glycol ethers and esters

Glycol ethers are made by reaction of ethylene oxide with alcohols. Esterification of such a glycol ether with acetic acid gives the corresponding ester. They constitute a special class of solvents (p. 204).

Vinyl acetate, $CH_3COOCH{=}CH_2$

This monomer is obtained by direct oxidation of ethylene with air over a silver catalyst.

Ethanolamines (mono-, di-, and tri-)

The reaction of one, two or three molecules of ethylene oxide with one molecule of ammonia yields three ethanolamines.

$$NH_3 + \begin{matrix} \text{1 molecule} \\ \text{2 molecules} \\ \text{3 molecules} \end{matrix}\ CH_2\overset{O}{—}CH_2 \rightarrow \begin{matrix} H_2N—CH_2—CH_2OH & \text{mono-} \\ HN(CH_2CH_2OH)_2 & \text{di-} \\ N(CH_2CH_2OH)_3 & \text{tri-} \end{matrix}$$

ammonia   ethylene oxide   ethanolamines

These ethanolamines, separated by vacuum distillation, are clear viscous liquids above their melting points (0–40°C; 32–401°F). They are used as emulsifiers in the manufactur of cosmetics, polishes, metal cutting oils and horticultura sprays, and as corrosion inhibitors, plasticizers, foam stabil izers and intermediates for certain types of synthetic deter gents.

Monoethanolamine and diethanolamine are also usec for the absorption of acid gases, such as carbon dioxide ir the dry ice industry or hydrogen sulphide in natural anc refinery gases.

Derivatives of propane and propylene (C_3

Allyl chloride, $CHClCH{=}CH_2$

When a lower olefin such as propylene is treated witl chlorine, two different reactions may occur, either th addition of two chlorine atoms across the double bond, o the substitution of a hydrogen atom by a chlorin atom. At low temperatures the addition reaction takes plac preferentially, resulting in the formation of propylene di chloride.

$$\underset{\text{propylene}}{CH_3—CH{=}CH_2} + \underset{\text{chlorine}}{Cl_2} \xrightarrow{\text{addition}} \underset{\text{propylene dichloride}}{CH_3—CHCl—CH_2Cl}$$

At high temperatures the substitution reaction predomi nates, the double bond remaining intact. The main produc in this case is allyl chloride.

$$\underset{\text{propylene}}{CH_3—CH{=}CH_2} + \underset{\text{chlorine}}{Cl_2} \xrightarrow{\text{substitution}} \underset{\text{allyl chloride}}{CHClCH{=}CH_2} + \underset{\text{hydrochloric acid}}{HCl}$$

Fig. 199 Glycerine plant

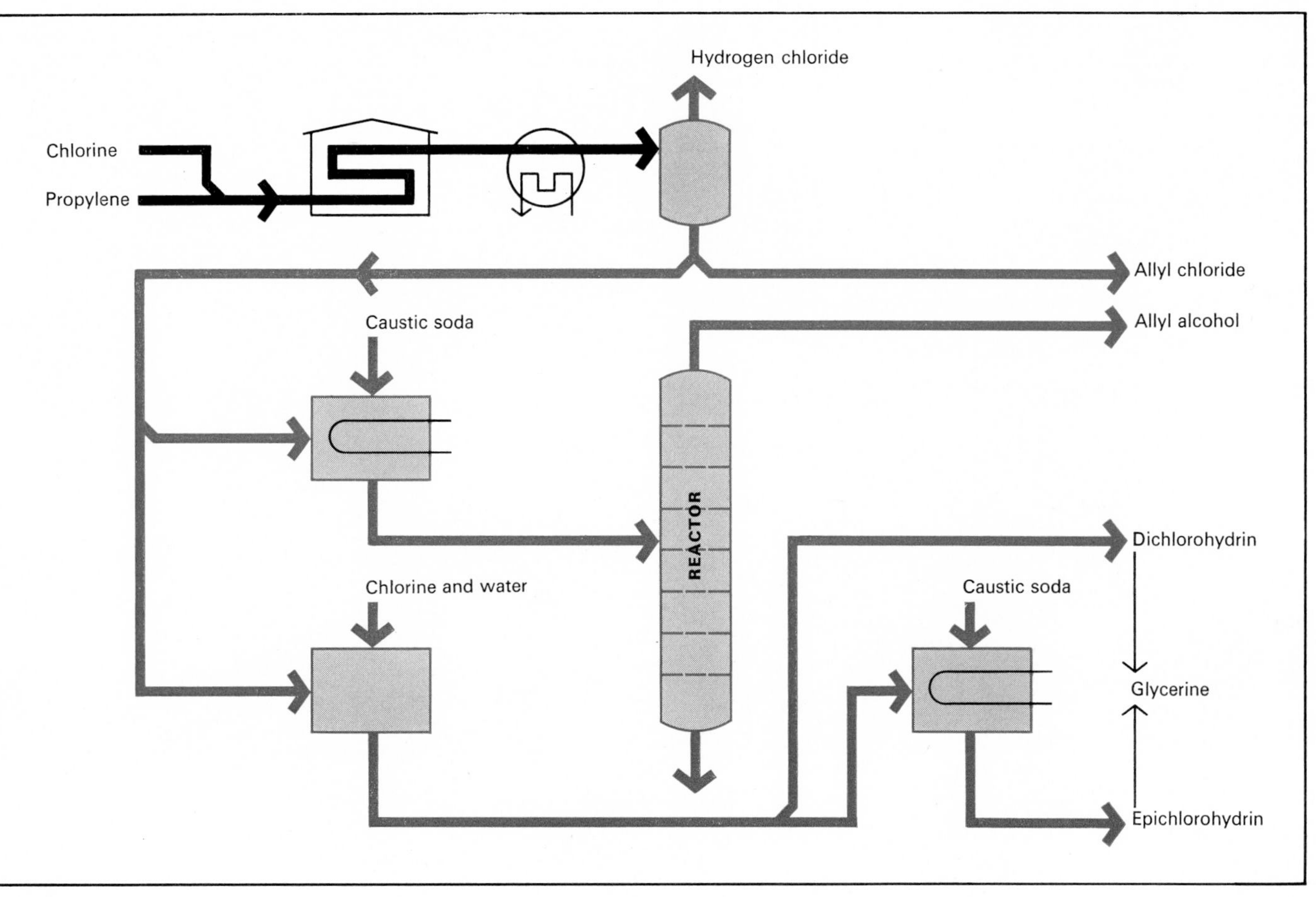

Fig. 200 Manufacture of glycerine and of chloro-derivatives of propane

The reaction is generally carried out at a temperature of about 500°C (930°F) and at a pressure slightly higher than atmospheric. The allyl chloride is separated from the other reaction products by distillation [Fig. 200]. Higher boiling products such as dichloropropylene and dichloropropane (D-D mixture) are used as soil fumigants (p. 242).

The manufacture of allyl chloride represents the first step in the synthesis of glycerol from propylene by a procedure devised by Shell Development Company and applied commercially in the USA since 1948 and in Europe since 1957.

Glycerol dichlorohydrin, $CH_2ClCHOHCH_2Cl$

The second step in the synthesis of glycerol involves the conversion of allyl chloride to glycerol dichlorohydrin by reaction with water and chlorine (hypochlorous acid).

$$\underset{\text{allyl chloride}}{CH_2Cl{-}CH{=}CH_2} + \underset{\text{hypochlorous acid}}{HOCl} \longrightarrow \underset{\text{glycerol dichlorohydrin}}{CH_2Cl\,CHOHCH_2Cl}$$

Epichlorohydrin, $CH_3Cl{-}CH{-}CH_2$ (with O bridging CH and CH_2)

The manufacture of this product may represent the third stage in the glycerol synthesis. It is obtained by heating a mixture of glycerol dichlorohydrin and lime. Besides being a possible intermediary in the glycerol synthesis, epichlorohydrin is also a base material for the manufacture of epoxide resins (p. 218).

$$\underset{\text{glycerol dichlorohydrin}}{CH_2Cl{-}CHOH{-}CH_2Cl} \xrightarrow[\text{slurry}]{Ca(OH)_2} \underset{\text{epichlorohydrin}}{CH_2Cl{-}\overset{O}{CH{-}CH_2}}$$

Glycerol, $CH_2OH{-}CHOH{-}CH_2OH$

Glycerol is finally obtained by hydrolyzing epichlorohydrin or glycerol dichlorohydrin with caustic soda [Figs 199 and 200].

$$\underset{\text{glycerol dichlorohydrin}}{CH_2Cl{-}CHOH{-}CH_2Cl} \;\text{or}\; \underset{\text{epichlorohydrin}}{CH_2Cl{-}\overset{O}{CH{-}CH_2}} \xrightarrow{+\,NaOH} \underset{\text{glycerol}}{CH_2OH{-}CHOH{-}CH_2OH}$$

At this stage the dilute glycerol solution is associated with sodium chloride and an excess of water. The bulk of the latter is removed in evaporators and after crystallization of the salt the resulting product, now having a purity of over

Fig. 201 Quarry blasting with dynamite made from glycerine

90%, is purified further by vacuum distillation. The final product is stored in nickel-clad steel tanks and shipped in aluminium tank cars.

This method of making glycerol requires the processing of strongly corrosive compounds and large amounts of chlorine. The chlorine either has to be bought from the electrochemical industry or made by the glycerol manufacturer, with consumption of expensive electrical energy.

An entirely different synthesis of glycerol from propylene has been evolved recently by Shell, in which propylene is oxidized to acrolein, which is in turn converted to allyl alcohol and thence to glycerol (see below).

Glycerol is familiar to the public as glycerine, a colourless, viscous, sweet-tasting liquid much used in pharmacy and cosmetics. It was formerly obtained solely as a by-product from the manufacture of soap and is still made in this way. In addition to its pharmaceutical uses it has many other applications on account of its solvent, plasticizing and moisture-retentive properties. It is used in food processing, in the preparation of tobacco, in the manufacture of cellophane and as an ingredient in pastes for various purposes. It is also the base material for the manufacture of nitroglycerine, the explosive used in dynamite [Fig. 201], and as an ingredient in manufacture of alkyd resins used in the paint, the varnish and lacquer industries.

Acrolein, allyl alcohol, glycerol

As mentioned above under glycerol, a Shell process involves the oxidation of propylene to acrolein by means of oxygen. The acrolein is converted into allyl alcohol by reaction with isopropyl alcohol, and the allyl alcohol is converted into glycerol by treatment with hydrogen peroxide, acetone being produced as a by-product.

$$\underset{\text{propylene}}{CH_3{-}CH{=}CH_2} \xrightarrow{\text{oxidation}} \underset{\text{acrolein}}{CH_2{=}CH{-}CHO} \xrightarrow[\text{isopropyl alcohol}]{CH_3CHOH\,CH_3}$$

$$\underset{\text{allyl alcohol}}{CH_2{=}CH{-}CH_2OH} \xrightarrow[\text{hydrogen peroxide}]{H_2O_2} \underset{\text{glycerol}}{CH_2OH{-}CHOH{-}CH_2OH}$$

This method offers advantages in locations where chlorine is not readily available. Hydrogen peroxide is normally produced by electrolytic oxidation of an ammonium sulphate solution to ammonium persulphate, followed by decomposition of the latter. As this process also requires considerable amounts of electric energy, the advantage of the method would be limited. Shell Development Company, however, succeeded in preparing hydrogen peroxide (and acetone) by oxidation of isopropyl alcohol under special conditions.

$$\underset{\text{isopropyl alcohol}}{CH_3CHOH\,CH_3} + \underset{\text{oxygen}}{O_2} \longrightarrow \underset{\text{hydrogen peroxide}}{H_2O_2} + \underset{\text{acetone}}{CH_3COCH_3}$$

The process is applied by Shell on a commercial scale at Norco Refinery (New Orleans) in the USA.

Acrylonitrile, $CH_2CHC{\equiv}N$

Acrylonitrile is produced by the propylene/ammonia

oxidation process of Standard Oil Company of Ohio, acetonitrile, CH_3CN, being produced as a by-product.

$$\underset{\text{propylene}}{C_3H_6} + \underset{\text{ammonia}}{NH_3} + \underset{\text{oxygen}}{O_2} \xrightarrow{\text{catalyst}} \underset{\text{acrylonitrile}}{CH_2{=}CH{-}C{\equiv}N}$$

Propylene oxide, $CH_3{-}CH{-}CH_2$ (with O bridging the two CH groups)

Although methods have been worked out for the manufacture of propylene oxide by direct oxidation of propylene with oxygen or air, the yields are rather poor and the manufacture is better carried out in two stages by the chlorohydrin method as for ethylene oxide. Propylene is reacted with hypochlorous acid to give propylene chlorohydrin from which hydrochloric acid is removed by means of a lime slurry to provide propylene oxide.

Propylene glycol and isopropanolamines can be prepared from propylene oxide and used for the same purposes as the ethylene oxide derivatives, but are less toxic.

Derivatives of butane and pentane (C_4/ C_5)

Isobutylene and diisobutylene

Isobutylene is used in the manufacture of butyl rubber; diisobutylene for the same purpose as other higher olefins (see below).

Butadiene and isoprene

Both products, base materials for synthetic rubber, are discussed in the chapter on Synthetic rubber (p. 224).

Before the modern process of steam-cracking oil fractions developed to an important source of butadiene, the diolefin was chiefly obtained by dehydrogenation of normal butylene over a silicate catalyst.

$$\underset{\text{n-butylene}}{CH_3{-}CH{=}CH{-}CH_3} \longrightarrow \underset{\text{butadiene}}{CH{=}CH{-}CH{=}CH_2} + \underset{\text{hydrogen}}{H_2}$$

Supplies of n-butylene are often limited, and for this reason butadiene was frequently manufactured by catalytic dehydrogenation of n-butane. In both processes the hot gases leaving the reactor are rapidly cooled and subsequently passed to a butadiene recovery and purification system.

Isoprene is similarly manufactured from isopentane.

Sulfolene and sulfolane

When butadiene is reacted at a relatively low temperature with sulphur dioxide, SO_2, a cyclic addition compound is formed which can be hydrogenated to sulfolane.

$$\underset{\text{butadiene}}{CH_2{=}CH{-}CH{=}CH_2} + \underset{\text{sulphur dioxide}}{SO_2} \longrightarrow \underset{\text{sulfolene}}{\begin{matrix} CH{=}CH \\ | \quad | \\ CH_2 \; CH_2 \\ \diagdown \diagup \\ SO_2 \end{matrix}} \xrightarrow{H_2} \underset{\text{sulfolane}}{\begin{matrix} CH_2{-}CH_2 \\ | \quad | \\ CH_2 \; CH_2 \\ \diagdown \diagup \\ SO_2 \end{matrix}}$$

Sulfolane, a polar compound, is used as a selective solvent in solvent extraction processes, for example in the separation of aromatics from aliphatics (p. 91).

Derivatives of higher olefins (C_6—C_{18})

Synthetic higher alcohols (OXO alcohols)

By addition of carbon monoxide and hydrogen (synthesis gas) across the double bond of an olefin in the presence of a catalyst, primary alcohols with one more carbon atom in the molecule are obtained (OXO alcohols).

$$\underset{\text{olefin}}{C_6H_{13}CH{=}CH_2} + CO + H_2 \longrightarrow \underset{\text{OXO alcohols}}{\begin{matrix} C_6H_{13}CH{-}CH_3 \\ | \\ CH_2OH \end{matrix}}$$

These alcohols are base materials for plasticizers for vinyl resins.

Synthetic carboxylic acids

By addition of carbon monoxide and water to the double bond of a higher olefin under the influence of sulphuric acid as a catalyst, carboxylic acids with one more carbon atom in the molecule are obtained.

$$\underset{\text{olefin}}{C_6H_{13}CH{=}CH_2} + CO + H_2O \longrightarrow \underset{\text{acid}}{\begin{matrix} C_6H_{13}CH{-}CH_3 \\ | \\ COOH \end{matrix}}$$

These acids are used as base materials for plasticizers and paint dryers. They are supplied under the Shell name Versatic.

Pivalic acid, $C(CH_3)_3COOH$, manufactured from isobutylene on a commercial scale at Pernis, is used in the manufacture of polymerization catalysts.

Derivatives of aromatics

Benzene, toluene and the xylenes

The manufacture of these aromatic hydrocarbons from petroleum hydrocarbons is dealt with under Raw materials and primary conversion processes (p. 196). They are also produced from coal tar.

Ethyl benzene and styrene

Benzene can be alkylated with ethylene to give ethyl benzene, from which styrene, an aromatic olefin, may be obtained by catalytic dehydrogenation.

$$\underset{\text{benzene}}{C_6H_6} + \underset{\text{ethylene}}{CH_2{=}CH_2} \longrightarrow \underset{\text{ethyl benzene}}{C_6H_5{-}CH_2{-}CH_3} \longrightarrow$$

$C_6H_5-CH=CH_2 + H_2$

styrene hydrogen

The dehydrogenation product is subjected to a number of distillations for the recovery and purification of the styrene.

Phenol

Phenol is an important base material for many synthetic resins and industrial chemicals. Although at one time wholly obtained as a by-product of coal tar manufacture, supplies from this source are no longer adequate and the product is therefore now made synthetically in various ways, starting from benzene. In a recently developed process benzene and propylene are reacted to give isopropyl benzene (cumene); this is oxidized to cumene hydroperoxide, which is then split into phenol and the by-product acetone.

$$C_6H_6 + CH_3-CH=CH_2 \longrightarrow C_6H_5-CH(CH_3)_2 \xrightarrow{O_2}$$

benzene propylene cumene

$$C_6H_5-C(CH_3)_2-O-O-H \longrightarrow C_6H_5-OH + CH_3-CO-CH_3$$

cumene hydroperoxide phenol acetone

Phenol is used as an intermediate for the manufacture of synthetic resins, nylon, herbicides and disinfectants. The Shell product Ionol, ditertiary butylmethylphenol, is used as an anti-oxidant and anti-rust compound in lubricating, hydraulic, transformer and turbine oils, in aviation and automotive fuels and brake fluids. It is also used as a non-staining anti-oxidant in natural and synthetic rubbers.

Bisphenol A

Bisphenol A is made from acetone and phenol.

$$CH_3-CO-CH_3 + 2\ C_6H_5OH \longrightarrow$$

acetone phenol

$$HO-C_6H_4-C(CH_3)_2-C_6H_4-OH$$

bisphenol A

It is an intermediate in the manufacture of epoxide resins (Epikote) and polycarbonate resins (p. 213).

Cresylic acids

Most of the cracked and reformed distillates contain derivatives of phenol known as acid oils or cresylic acids. They can be extracted by alkaline solutions and recovered from these by acidification.

Phthalic acids

The xylene fraction boiling between 135–155°C (275–310°F) contains four aromatic hydrocarbons of the same chemical composition, but different chemical structure: ortho-, meta- and para-xylenes and ethyl benzene. They can be separated by fractional distillation and crystallization and may be oxidized to the corresponding phthalic acids (o-, m- and p-). As mentioned in the chapters on Synthetic resins–plastics and on Synthetic textile fibres, the first two are important base materials for alkyd resins, the third, also called terephthalic acid, is used in the manufacture of the synthetic fibre Terylene.

Aromatic luboil extracts

These are products gained by distillation of certain extracts obtained by solvent refining (Solvent extraction, p. 89) of lubricating oil distillates, e.g. furfural extract. Well-known examples of such extracts are the Shell Dutrex products. They have two valuable properties: they are compatible with high polymers, such as rubber, and they dissolve insecticides.

They are used in the rubber industry to facilitate manufacturing operations and as plasticizers and extenders; in agriculture as solvents in the formulation of insecticides containing aldrin, dieldrin, DDT or BHC, and as base oils for herbicides. They can also partly replace linseed oil in printing inks.

Naphthenic acids

Naphthenic acids are present in gas oil and the light lubricating oil fractions (distillates of certain crude oils) from which they can be extracted by treatment with dilute aqueous solutions of caustic soda. The sodium naphthenate solutions so formed are acidified to set free the crude naphthenic acids. These may be used in this form or may be further purified by distillation. The lower molecular naphthenic acids form oil-soluble lead, cobalt and manganese salts, used as paint driers (siccatives). Zinc and copper naphthenates are rot-proofing agents for textiles and wood.

Sodium naphtha sulphonates

The manufacture of transformer oils and technical white oils involves treatment with oleum (fuming sulphuric acid) for the removal of the final traces of aromatic compounds (p. 110). The aromatics associated with paraffinic side chains are converted by oleum into a mixture of sulphonic acids, some of which are soluble in the oil phase and others in the sulphuric acid phase. The oil-soluble acids, called 'mahogany' acids on account of their colour, are the more valuable products and are recovered from the oil phase by extraction with an alcoholic alkali solution.

This solution is then evaporated for the recovery not only of the sodium naphtha sulphonates, but also of the alcohol, which is re-used.

The water soluble acids, known as 'green' acids, may be separated from the sulphuric acid phase, the sulphuric acid sludge. Dilution of the free sulphuric acid content of the sludge to 70% concentration liberates the sulphonic acids which may then be separated and converted into sodium sulphonates.

Sodium naphtha sulphonates are used as emulsifiers in metal working oils, rust preventives, textile oils, dry-cleaning soaps and agricultural sprays. Hyperbasic calcium naphtha sulphonates are used for the manufacture of dispersant additives for lubricating oils.

Lubricating oil additives

As already mentioned when discussing the application of lubricants and related products (p. 118), various types of additives are customarily used to improve their performance. Many of these additives are themselves derived from petroleum, particularly dispersants, VI improvers and anti-oxidants.

Dispersants

Dispersants are used to keep in suspension the oxidation products formed during the use of a lubricating oil, particularly in engines. Typical examples are Tergol and AC additives.

Tergol is a basic (containing excess alkali) calcium salt of a high molecular weight sulphonic acid. Sodium naphtha sulphonates are converted by means of calcium chloride into neutral calcium naphtha sulphonates, which are then treated with calcium hydroxide (slaked lime) to form the basic salts.

AC additives (alkylation-carboxylation) are basic calcium salts of alkylsalicylic acids. An aliphatic side chain is first introduced into the benzene nucleus by alkylating phenol with a higher olefin. Sodium alkylsalicylate is then formed by introducing one molecule of carbon dioxide into one molecule of the alkylated phenol in the presence of caustic soda. By treating with slaked lime, the sodium salt is converted firstly into the neutral calcium salt and then, with excess lime into the basic salt.

$$C_6H_5OH + C_{14}H_{28} \longrightarrow HO{-}C_6H_4{-}C_{14}H_{29} \xrightarrow{+\ CO_2\ +\ NaOH} HO{-}C_6H_3(COONa){-}C_{14}H_{29}$$

phenol olefin alkylphenol sodium alkyl salicylate

The basicity of these additives can be varied according to the amount of excess lime used and the highly basic (superbasic) additives of this type, in addition to their use as dispersants, are very effective in neutralizing the acids formed by combustion of the fuel in an engine.

VI improvers

A high VI (viscosity index) denotes a flat viscosity/temperature curve of a lubricating oil, i.e. little decrease in viscosity with increase in temperature. The VI of an oil can be increased by dissolving certain high polymers in it and polyacrylonitrile, polyacrylates and polyvinyl pyridine, all derived from petroleum, are used.

Anti-oxidants

Ionol, ditertiary butylmethylphenol, already mentioned on p. 234, and the AC additives described above as dispersants are use extensively as anti-oxidants.

Anti-statics

Anti-static additives are used to prevent the generation of static electric charges in aircraft fuel during high-speed fuelling operations (pp. 138 and 272). The additive adds enough metal ions to the fuel to give it a sufficiently high electrical conductivity to allow the charge to leak away before sparking can occur. Complex metal salts of alkylsalicylic acids are used for this purpose.

Sulphur and sulphuric acid

Some crude oils contain appreciable amounts of sulphur compounds, and in cracking operations part of this sulphur is converted into hydrogen sulphide, which has to be removed from the cracking gases. Hydrogen sulphide also occurs, often in large amounts, in certain natural gases, from which it is also removed by alkaline absorption.

Hydrogen sulphide is converted into elemental sulphur by partial combustion with air (Claus plant), bauxite being used as a catalyst.

$$2\,H_2S + O_2 \longrightarrow 2\,H_2O + 2\,S$$

hydrogen sulphide oxygen water sulphur

The sulphur vapour is condensed and the molten sulphur is run off into tanks where it solidifies. It is then broken into lumps for shipment. Liquid sulphur is also transported in heated tank cars, and even in tankers.

Petroleum derived sulphur is extremely pure; it is used in the manufacture of sulphuric acid, in the production of carbon disulphide for the rayon industry, for agricultural uses and for rubber vulcanization.

Sulphuric acid may also be produced by burning hydrogen sulphide to sulphur dioxide, which is converted into sulphuric acid by oxidation over a vanadium oxide catalyst.

Hydrogen peroxide

The manufacture of this product on the basis of isopropyl alcohol is described on p. 232. Hydrogen peroxide is used for bleaching and disinfection and as a source of oxygen for rocket fuels.

Agricultural chemicals

The term 'agricultural chemicals' embraces fertilizers, pesticides and various miscellaneous products used by farmers and gardeners. Fertilizers and pesticides provide a very important means of increasing food production in a world in which the population is increasing at a phenomenal rate.

There are at present (1965) 130 000 more births per day than deaths; it has also been estimated that for every seven people in the world twenty years ago there are now ten, and that in twenty years' time there will be sixteen. The problem of producing enough food to feed these extra mouths, let alone to improve standards of nutrition, is probably the biggest challenge of the mid-twentieth century and one that makes improvement in agricultural production techniques so essential.

In this task, fertilizers and pesticides are complementary to one another – it is no use growing bigger crops by using fertilizers if these are destroyed by pests – and to other methods of increasing food production, such as the use of improved seed and, where rainfall is insufficient at the right season, irrigation.

Insect pests and fungus diseases are believed to cause a 20% loss in agricultural crops during growing and harvesting and a further 10% loss during storage, and weeds and nematodes are also responsible for very heavy losses. A large part of these losses can be prevented and higher yields obtained by the correct use of pesticides and fertilizers.

To some extent the growth in world population is the result of the enormous decrease in the number of deaths caused until fairly recently by insect-borne diseases such as malaria. This decrease has in large measure been brought about by the use of insecticides to kill the insect carriers of disease.

The interest of the oil industry in agricultural chemicals stems from the time before World War II, when petroleum oils were among the most important pesticides in use. Although these oils still have certain uses as sprays, the most important contribution now made by petroleum to agriculture is as a source of hydrogen for the manufacture of ammonia and of various oil fractions for use as solvents for synthetic organic chemical pesticides, some of which may also be made from petroleum products.

Fig. 202 Maize crop in Venezuela with fertilizer on left and right, without fertilizer in centre

Fig. 203 Citrus crop being sprayed with insecticide

Fertilizers

The available cultivable area of the world is strictly limited, and the adoption of more intensive methods of cultivation is essential to achieve increased production of crops. A greater use of fertilizers is probably the most important means of doing this [Fig. 202].

The three main plant nutrient elements are nitrogen (N), phosphorus (P) and potassium (K), and fertilizers supply these in varying proportions according to the requirements of the crop and soil to be treated. Other elements are also necessary for plant growth, but are usually present in the soil in adequate amounts. Where they are lacking, fertilizers containing them may be applied, but such products still represent a relatively small part of the industry.

The main contribution of the petroleum industry to the fertilizers industry is in the supply of nitrogen in the form of ammonia. The manufacture of ammonia (NH_3) by the direct combination of hydrogen (from petroleum and natural gas) and nitrogen (from the air) is described under Industrial chemicals (p. 227).

Ammonia can be used directly as a fertilizer in the form of liquefied ammonia, and two novel techniques were developed for this purpose by Shell in the USA. In the first (nitrogation), liquid ammonia is injected into irrigation water, in the second (nitrojection), which is rapidly superseding the first, the gas from liquid ammonia is injected into the soil by means of a tractor-drawn injector. The more usual method of using ammonia, however, is in the form of its salts, such as ammonium sulphate or ammonium phosphate; in the form of salts of nitric acid, such as calcium ammonium nitrate or magnesium ammonium nitrate; or as urea. Both nitric acid and urea are manufactured from ammonia as described in the chapter on Industrial chemicals (p. 227).

Pesticides

The main groups of pesticides are: insecticides and acaricides, herbicides, fungicides, and nematicides.

Most of these are complex organic compounds, only partly or not at all derived from petroleum, and it would be beyond the scope of this book to discuss the details of their manufacture or indeed to describe them all. Some of the more important are discussed in the following sections.

Insecticides and acaricides

Insecticides and acaricides are used to kill insects and mites in certain phases of their life cycles [Figs 203, 204]. At one time petroleum oils were widely used for this purpose but today nearly all the products in current use are synthetic organic chemicals, some of which are based on materials derived from petroleum and nearly all of which are formulated with petroleum solvents.

These synthetic products, of which rather more than eighty are in current use, can be divided into three chemically distinct groups: chlorinated hydrocarbons, organophosphates, and carbamates, of which the first two groups are by far the larger.

A number of natural products, for example extracts of pyrethrum, derris root and tobacco, which were extensively used before the days of synthetics, are still used, but are limited in supply and activity.

Petroleum spray oils

Petroleum spray oils have been widely used for many years for the control of insects and mites in citrus and deciduous fruit orchards. Such oils are available to the grower in two forms: as 'stock' emulsions, concentrated oil-in-water

Fig. 204 Coffee crop being sprayed from the air with insecticide

emulsions to be diluted in the field, or as 'emulsifiable oils', consisting of oil plus emulsifiers ready for final dilution in the spray tank. The base oils vary with season of application, pests to be controlled and crops.

Spray oils are used in the form of winter grades and summer grades. Winter grades are applied while fruit trees are dormant, to kill the over-wintering eggs of insects and mites. Straight spindle oils are sometimes used but oil alone will not always control all the insects present in dormant trees and the oil is fortified with dinitro-ortho-cresol (DNOC).

Summer grade spray oils are applied to deciduous trees in leaf and to citrus trees, to kill the eggs and adults of spider mites and scale insects. There is a greater danger of damaging trees in leaf than dormant trees, so more highly refined oils have to be used. They are usually more volatile and have a higher unsulphonatable content than winter grade base oils to minimize the risk of phytotoxicity, associated with aromatic (sulphonatable) content.

Organophosphate insecticides (p. 240) have taken over many applications of spray oils, but because insect resistance problems are not normally encountered with spray oils, and because of their low mammalian toxicity, their use is likely to continue.

In some countries summer spray oils are added as 'stickers' to insecticides and fungicide sprays in order to obtain improved retention on leaf surfaces. Heavier grades of oil than are normally used for summer sprays can be used for this purpose.

Chlorinated hydrocarbons

The discovery of the insecticidal properties of DDT (dichloro diphenyl trichloroethane) initiated the era of modern pest control and chlorinated hydrocarbons have continued to dominate the world insecticide market. DDT, already synthesized in 1874, but recognized as a powerful insecticide only in 1939, is prepared from chloral (trichloro acetaldehyde) and chlorobenzene.

CCl_3
Cl–⟨ring⟩–CH–⟨ring⟩–Cl

DDT

DDT was soon followed by BHC (benzene hexachloride or hexachlorocyclohexane) made by the addition of chlorine to benzene. Various isomers are possible, distinguished by the relative positions of the chlorine atoms in respect of the plane of the six-membered carbon ring. The insecticidal activity depends on these positions, and the gamma isomer, also known as lindane, is the most active.

Cl Cl Cl Cl Cl Cl (ring)

BHC

During the early 1950s an important family of insecticidal chloro-compounds, the diene insecticides, was obtained from cyclopentadiene, a cyclic diolefin present in light fractions from coal tar distillation, as well as in those obtained in the course of deep cracking of gasoline. These insecticides include aldrin, dieldrin and endrin. Their chemical structures are complicated, for example:

Aldrin

Dieldrin

Aldrin is synthesized in two stages. Acetylene and cyclopentadiene are reacted to form a product which is then combined with a highly chlorinated derivative of cyclopentadiene. Dieldrin is closely related to aldrin and obtained from it by reaction with hydrogen peroxide. Endrin is similarly obtained by the action of hydrogen peroxide on a product formed by reacting acetylene or vinyl chloride with hexachlorocyclopentadiene and combining the resultant product with cyclopentadiene. Endrin is stereo-isomeric to dieldrin.

These chlorinated hydrocarbon insecticides are highly active against a wide range of insect pests. They are solids, almost insoluble in water, and are easily formulated as dusts, granules, wettable powders or emulsifiable concentrates. While they are closely related chemically, they differ sufficiently in biological characteristics to be complementary in use.

Aldrin is best known and most widely used as a soil insecticide. A single treatment, which can be made in various ways early in the season, will protect the underground parts of the crop right through from sowing to harvest. Aldrin sometimes enables land which would otherwise be useless, to be brought into cultivation (as in the case of ant control in Brazil). Increased yields of 20%, coupled with improved crop quality, are typical. The farmer's production costs are reduced, his efficiency is increased and he has a assured and secure living.

The eradication of certain serious and deadly insect-borne diseases from large areas only became a practical proposition with the introduction of the chlorinated hydrocarbon insecticides. Until quite recently malaria affected 250 million people and killed three million a year. However, the use of DDT, BHC and dieldrin in co-ordinated campaigns has been highly successful in many regions and the malaria death roll is now reduced to about one million people a year.

There are many other human diseases carried by insects, for example yellow fever (mosquito-borne), dysentery (carried by the house fly), sleeping sickness (tsetse fly) and plague (transmitted by rodent fleas) which can be controlled by the proper use of insecticides.

Following the successes in malaria control, increasing attention is being paid to combating other diseases, and dieldrin is used to control 'Chagas' disease (transmitted by a triatomid bug) and sleeping sickness. A successful means of controlling the insect vector of filariasis (in many countries second only to malaria in importance) is still being sought, but the use of insecticides against the vector mosquito is likely to play an important role.

Another international field in which dieldrin has played and important role is the control of the desert locust. Control operations since the 1950s have been extremely successful against this pest, whose threat of crop destruction and possible famine to 300 million people is now greatly reduced [Fig. 205].

Dieldrin has proved exceedingly valuable for the control of many other pests, including, for example, the shot hole borer, Ceylon's major tea pest, for which it is the only reliable insecticide. In addition, it is highly effective against termites and widely used to protect buildings, timber and underground electric cables. If properly applied, it will protect timber from termites for at least fourteen years.

Fig. 205 Desert locusts (left) on the march (right) dead, after treatment with dieldrin

Endrin is highly effective against the most important cotton pests in all major cotton growing areas. Cotton produces lush growth that harbours a great variety of insect pests which, if not controlled, greatly reduce yield and quality of lint and oilseed.

Organophosphates

Many organophosphate compounds exhibit anticholinesterase activity on insects and mites and some of them have become widely used as insecticides, for example the thiophosphate compounds known as parathion and malathion. The vinyl phosphate compounds include active insecticides such as Phosdrin and Bidrin.

$(CH_3O)_2P(=O)-O-C(CH_3)=CH-C(=O)OCH_3$

Phosdrin

$(CH_3O)_2P(=O)-O-C(CH_3)=CH-C(=O)N(CH_3)_2$

Bidrin

These two compounds are manufactured in the form of water-miscible liquids and are diluted with water immediately before spraying to control insects on foliage. Both compounds are 'systemic' – i.e. they are absorbed by and carried throughout the plants in the sap. Insects feeding on these plants will ingest the poisonous compounds. Phosdrin and Bidrin control a wide range of biting, boring and sucking insects, including caterpillars, leaf-miners, beetles, thrips, aphids and mites.

Phosdrin is unique among systemic insecticides in the rapidity with which it is broken down in plants to harmless decomposition products. It is also notable for its rapid 'knockdown', or ability to kill insects within minutes of being sprayed. These characteristics are essential in protecting edible and forage crops from insect damage in the days immediately preceding harvest. Bidrin is more persistent in plants and gives control of insects for several weeks after spraying.

Vapona is another vinyl phosphate insecticide, the active ingredient of which is dimethyldichlorovinyl phosphate (DDVP).

$(CH_3O)_2P(=O)-O-C(H)=CCl_2$

DDVP

It is a volatile liquid, the vapour of which is a highly active insecticide. It is used in aerosol packs to control insects in enclosed spaces, e.g. in greenhouses, warehouses and domestic dwellings [Fig. 207]. Although DDVP is quickly lost from the site of application, continuous control of insects over a period of months can be achieved with a formulation of Vapona in plastic strips which release DDVP vapour slowly [Fig. 206].

Carbamates

Like organophosphates, some carbamates, derivatives of carbamic acid, NH_2COOH, inhibit essential enzymes of

Fig. 207 Vapona aerosol spray for household use

Fig. 206 Vapona strip in butcher's shop

insects and are thus effective insecticides. Relatively few carbamates have as yet been marketed but one, naphthyl-N-methylcarbamate, has been widely used under the name carbaryl.

O—CO—NH
CH_3

carbaryl

Insecticides for animal health

The world's most acute nutritional problem is a gross shortage of animal protein – meat, milk and eggs. Livestock diseases are a very important factor in this shortage, not only through the direct losses they cause but also by inhibiting more intensive production. It has been estimated that world-wide losses due to animal disease cost over £5000 million per annum – nearly 20% of the value of total production. These losses could be much reduced by making greater use of chemical control of parasites and diseases.

Pesticides have an important role to play in this field, for insect and mite parasites cause enormous losses in livestock, either directly through loss of condition and death of the animals, or indirectly by transmitting diseases. For example, the ticks that plague cattle in Africa can transmit a variety of disease organisms such as those causing east-coast and red-water fevers.

Such chlorinated hydrocarbon insecticides as DDT, BHC, aldrin and dieldrin have been instrumental in keeping many of these parasites under control, and these are now supplemented by a range of organophosphate insecticides. Of these, Vapona, already described in the previous section, is uniquely suited, by virtue of its rapid action in the vapour phase, to the control of parasites in animal housing or for short-term protection of animals from biting and sucking insects. Two other organophosphorus compounds suitable for the longer term control of parasites of animals, including livestock on range, are Ciodrin and Supona. The former is ideal for the protection of dairy cattle because it does not appear in the milk, and the latter is outstanding in its spectrum of activity against the parasites, such as blow flies, ticks, keds and lice, which attack livestock and domestic animals.

Herbicides (weedkillers)

The use of chemical weedkillers is increasing rapidly. This is largely due to the discovery of more selective weedkillers for use in agricultural and horticultural crops and to the acceptance of total (non-selective) weedkillers by government authorities and industry [Fig. 208].

Petroleum oils are gradually being replaced by synthetic organic compounds. However, white oils and kerosines still play an important role in selective weed control in cotton, vegetables and tree nurseries, while heavy fractions of low volatility and viscosity but high aromatic content are used as solvents and emulsifiers in formulations containing synthetic organic weedkillers.

Since World War II, developments in chemical weedkillers have been impressive. The first important group were the phenoxy acids, both cheap and effective in the

Fig. 208 Weedkiller being sprayed onto crop of sugar cane

control of broad-leaved weeds in cereal crops and pasture. The most widely known of these selective hormone type weed-killers are 2,4-dichlorophenoxyacetic acid (2,4–D) and methylchlorophenoxyacetic acid (MCPA). The phenoxy acids are absorbed through the leaf.

Later followed the discoveries of substituted urea compounds (monuron and diuron) and the triazines (simazine and atrazine), both of which groups are applied to the soil and will kill germinating weed seeds. They are all of low water solubility and possess marked residual activity, maintaining the soil in a weed-free condition throughout an entire growing season.

OCH_2COOH

—Cl

Cl

2,4–D

Dalapon, a chlorinated aliphatic acid, sold by Shell as Gramevin (sodium 2,2-dichloropropionate) has found widespread use, particularly in tropical plantation crops, as a systemic leaf-absorbed grass killer. In contrast to the phenoxy acids, this compound kills the majority of grass species, leaving many broad-leaved crops unaffected.

CH_3CCl_2COONa

Dalapon

Shell have recently developed Prefix, a new soil-acting herbicide, which controls a wide range of both broad-leaved and grass weeds, and finds use in a wide range of perennial tree crops, such as orchard fruit and vines and in irrigated rice.

The product is synthesized from 2,6-dichlorobenzonitrile, in itself a good herbicide, and H_2S.

It is proving to be a highly successful total weedkiller and is being widely used for railways, roadsides and around refineries and petroleum depots.

NH_2

C=S

Cl— —Cl

Prefix

Fungicides

Fungus diseases account for considerable losses in crops. Disease-causing fungi are themselves parasitic forms of plant life and for this reason it is not easy to find chemicals capable of eradicating diseases in or on crop plants without harming the crop. Fungicides are used mainly to protect crops from disease. They act by killing the fungal spores as they germinate on the sprayed plant surfaces. Repeated applications of fungicides are therefore necessary in order to maintain a protective covering of the chemical over the plant surface while the crop is susceptible to disease attack.

The fungicides used most widely throughout the world are inorganic materials based on copper salts and sulphur

Fig. 209 Injecting nematicide into soil prior to planting

and their cheapness has prevented their general replacement by more modern organic fungicides. However, since the use of organic fungicides can, in some applications, lead to higher crop yields because of lower phytotoxicity or greater fungicidal activity, they are replacing the inorganic fungicides in some instances.

Notable among the organic fungicides are the dithiocarbamates, such as zinc- and manganese-ethylene dithiocarbamates, zineb and maneb, which are replacing copper fungicides.

Several antibiotics have been found to be fungicidal, but only the antibiotic blasticidin is being used extensively, in Japan, as a curative measure against blast disease of rice.

Fungicides vary widely in the range of diseases they are able to control. No one currently available fungicide can control all known fungus diseases, although copper salts and dithiocarbamates have a wide range of activity.

Non-volatile petroleum oils, in addition to their use as insecticides and carriers for fungicides, are also used to control leaf spot disease of bananas. Suitable refined oils when applied at low volume at frequent intervals are capable of arresting the growth of fungus on the leaf. Large quantities of these are used as 'banana spray oils', generally applied by helicopter or fixed-wing aircraft. The oil may be applied alone or mixed with fungicides and water.

Nematicides

Among the many minute organisms living in the soil are eelworms or nematodes. These are thread-like creatures,

Fig. 210 Healthy tobacco crop resulting from treatment with nematicide

not normally visible to the naked eye, some of which feed on plant roots and are major pests throughout the world, attacking a wide variety of crops such as tobacco, potatoes, tomatoes, flower bulbs, pineapples, citrus fruits and bananas. It has been estimated that nematodes rob farmers of 5% of the value of all they grow. The most practical way of controlling nematodes is the application of volatile nematicides to the soil, a technique to a large extent pioneered by Shell. The soil fumigants are injected into the soil, where they diffuse, the vapours killing the nematodes. Ideally a soil fumigant should be nonphytotoxic (harmless to plants), but most of the products available will damage plants and therefore have to be injected before planting [Figs 209 and 210].

The nematicides most widely used are ethylene-dibromide (EDB), mixtures of dichloropropylene and dichloropropane, such as Shell D-D, and 1,2-dibromo-3-chloropropane (DBCP), marketed by Shell under the trade name Nemagon. The latter, developed by Shell in the 1950s, represents a major advance, as it is not phytotoxic to the majority of perennial crops.

$CH_2ClCHBrCH_2Br$

Nemagon

D-D, the first commercially important nematicide, is now used exclusively as a pre-plant treatment for many economically important crops, including vines, pineapples and a wide variety of vegetables. D-D is a yellowish inflammable liquid normally applied to the soil at 20–40 gal/acre. For the best effect the soil temperature should be in the region of 10–25°C (50–80°F). After application, the soil is immediately sealed in order to retain the vapour long enough to kill the nematodes. Before planting, the soil is aerated by cultivators to allow any remaining vapour to escape.

EDB, a colourless liquid, is similar in use to, and competitive with D–D in most markets; it is mainly used for tobacco.

Nemagon can be applied to the soil around living plants. It has been found particularly valuable for treating bananas, citrus and stone fruit trees. Normally it is applied as an emulsifiable concentrate, but it can also be formulated as a granular solid for incorporation into the soil without specialized equipment. Since it is less volatile than D-D, the soil temperature should be 20–25°C (70–80°F). It can also be applied by using flood irrigation water as a medium.

Research is now being directed to the development of systemic nematicides which, sprayed on to a crop, would be absorbed and carried by the sap into the roots.

Marketing

Marketing

The scope of marketing

Marketing – the selling and delivery of oil products and chemicals to the ultimate user – is the last link in the long chain of operations, starting with exploration, which are described in this book. But it earns much of the revenue that finances all other phases of the business and provides funds for further investment.

The value of any commodity depends on the relation between the number of people prepared to buy it and the available supply. Oil products and chemicals are no exception to this rule. Whether it be crude oil at well head, refined oil product ready for the market, chemical intermediate or finished chemical product, it is worth nothing unless someone will buy it.

Oil products and chemicals are not like novelties, which can for a time be sold by persuading customers that they want what is being produced; a genuine technical requirement must be satisfied in order to obtain a long-term sales outlet.

The only sure way to successful marketing of oil products and chemicals is to determine the customers' needs as accurately as possible in terms of product and service, and to supply them as efficiently and cheaply as possible.

The marketing company must continually study its market so that it knows not only what the customers want now, but also what they are likely to want next week, next month, and over the coming years. Distribution and selling facilities must be planned with future expansion in mind.

Each marketing company must therefore accurately forecast the requirements of its territory in respect of all the various oil products and chemicals that it markets. In particular it must estimate the energy requirements of the country, including automotive fuels, and assess the probable share to be provided by petroleum fuels and the volume it should be able to sell in the face of competition, not only from other oil companies but from other sources of energy.

It must use market research to determine the true underlying needs of each type of customer in terms of both product and service. Many classes of customer must be considered, the motorist, the householder, the farmer, the manufacturer, the civil engineer, the builder, the international transport operator and many others. The needs of each class will be very different.

It is impossible, within the scope of this chapter, to discuss all these categories, but a few of the more important are described by way of example, as well as the place of advertising, sales promotion and market research in satisfying consumer demand.

The domestic heat market

The term 'domestic heat market' embraces households, public administration buildings, institutions, offices, commercial premises of various sorts, and small factories; of these, households are probably the largest energy consuming segment and the most easily identifiable. The variety and importance of end-uses depends basically upon climatic conditions and income levels with heating predominating, particularly where incomes are high and temperatures low.

The competition between alternative fuels in the domestic market is dictated by local conditions of fuel availability and price, income levels and consumer habits. Kerosine can be used for space heating, cooking, lighting and water heating and needs only a relatively simple type of burner with good heating efficiency. Distillate fuel oils, which have a low sulphur content, are used for small central heating units in individual dwellings (40 000 – 120 000 Btu/hr) although residual fuels are normally used for larger units in industrial and communal systems where the larger offtake makes price considerations more important.

The range of domestic heating equipment is very extensive, with kerosine stoves and oil-fired central heating systems predominating. Millions of the former are in use in Asia and Africa while central heating, already well established in North America, is a rapidly growing outlet throughout Europe.

In addition to individual home-heating systems, 'central oil storage', by which oil is piped from a central point to a number of dwellings, and 'district heating', by which an oil-fired steam raising plant distributes steam, hot water or even hot and cool air to a number of homes, are both evoking considerable interest.

The marketing trend is to more complete 'package deal' schemes whereby a home comfort service is supplied directly by the fuel supplier, be it gas or electricity authority or oil company. All indications point to more direct involvement of the supplier with the customer and to an expanding and challenging market.

The automotive retail market

The development of the motor vehicle over the last fifty years has resulted in spectacular growth in private motoring and the emergence of the passenger car as the most favoured means of personal transport for both business and recreation.

Identifying and satisfying the needs of the motoring public has therefore become one of the prime tasks of the oil industry. This mass market, made up of an aggregation of individuals with similar needs and buying habits, is termed the 'automotive retail market'. It accounts for more than two-thirds of all motor gasoline sales and is supplied through filling stations and service stations, known throughout the industry as 'retail outlets'.

In the period of transition from the horse-drawn carriage to the motor vehicle, automotive fuels and lubricants were frequently sold from erstwhile blacksmith's shops in tins and drums. From this humble beginning, the retail outlet progressed through the multi-brand kerbside outlet, specializing in dispensing gasoline from underground storage tanks by manually operated pumps, to the one brand filling station, and now to today's service stations which are a familiar sight all over the world in towns and along highways.

Retail outlets are designed to meet the needs of many types of motorists but in the main are located to serve either a local trade area or the motoring public travelling between centres on main or arterial roads. In some cases a retail outlet, strategically placed, can satisfy requirements of both types of buyers.

While the filling station, selling only automotive fuels and lubricants, still has an important part to play in a retail network, it has become apparent that, as the motor car has developed, the needs of the motorist are extending far beyond the supply of fuels and lubricants. Tyres, batteries, accessories and spare parts must now be supplied and fitted, and the vehicle must be maintained in a safe and roadworthy condition. The motor vehicle has become such an essential part of both business and social life that servicing and preventive maintenance to ensure that it is on the road for the maximum possible time is now a vital necessity.

The modern retail outlet is therefore often designed as a service station with facilities to meet all these needs. The spacious forecourt is designed to enable a number of vehicles to be serviced simultaneously with gasoline, oil, air and water and to allow each of them to enter and leave the site without impeding the safe and easy access of other vehicles.

Electric pumps, many with cash totalisors or computers, dispense gasoline and frequently gas oil. A comprehensive range of crankcase and transmission lubricants and of speciality products such as anti-freeze and polishes is marketed. A sales area is provided for the display and merchandising of such products, as well as tyres, batteries and accessories. A lubrication bay for lubrication and safety check services, and one or more bays for mechanical services are also provided. In many instances car washing facilities are also incorporated.

The extensive maintenance and servicing work calls for a great deal of specialized equipment, such as an hydraulically operated hoist, lubricant dispensers, and equipment to test and diagnose faults in a motor vehicle with the least possible delay to the motorist. Such equipment, much of it electronic, enables a fault to be detected before it immobilizes the vehicle, and is therefore the key to preventive maintenance.

The importance of the service station, as opposed to the filling station, is increasing with the growing tendency of the motorist to obtain all his requirements at 'one stop'. With increasing traffic and parking problems, the motorist is less inclined to make several stops to obtain his needs, the filling station for gasoline and oil, a tyre merchant for tyres and batteries, another shop for parts and accessories, a garage workshop for servicing. This trend is now extending beyond the needs of the car to the needs of the motorist himself by the provision of rest rooms, toilets, snack bars, restaurants and accommodation in the shape of motels.

This broadening in customer approach necessitates greatly increased skills in service station management and greater salesmanship on the part of the dealer and his staff. The major oil companies assist the retailer by providing training for him and his employees in all the techniques of retail selling, including the effective use of credit. Retailers new to service station operation are given initial training, followed up by refresher courses supported by practical, on-the-job instruction, in subjects ranging from selling techniques to accounting methods and stock control.

As in other markets, changes are continually taking place in the pattern of retailing. Automatic vending and self-service have been established in many countries and pumps designed to dispense any given blend of gasoline grades have been introduced. Many other innovations are continually being tried, all designed to meet the ever growing needs of the motorist.

Industrial and commercial markets

The automotive retail market and the domestic heat market are mass markets in the sense that they comprise a very large number of individual customers having similar requirements for a limited number of petroleum products and services. Compared with these, the industrial and commercial markets comprise a relatively small number of individual customers purchasing between them many hundreds of different products for an extremely wide range of applications. Because of the smaller number of customers of each type and their wide variety of product and application requirements, marketing to industrial and commercial customers is very different from marketing automotive or domestic products. For example, in the industrial field, there tends to be much more direct contact between the petroleum company salesmen and the ultimate customer, and much less use of mass media advertising, than in the automotive retail market. The following paragraphs describe some of the characteristics of a few of the groups of customers that can be identified within the total complex of the industrial and commercial markets as having similar product and service needs.

Agriculture

In all countries, at whatever stage of agricultural development, the farmer can benefit from the use of oil and chemical products. He may need fuels and lubricants for tractors, plant and machinery, fuels for crop drying, the heating of greenhouses, incubators and animal quarters, as well as for domestic applications in the farmhouse, bitumen for road surfacing, lining irrigation canals or various building applications. He will also need weedkillers, insecticides, fertilizers and other specialized chemical products, Farms are usually scattered over wide areas and consequently the agricultural market consists of a larger number of relatively small consumers, often in remote locations. Efficient distribution is thus difficult to achieve and is made even more difficult by the seasonal nature of the demand for many products and by its dependence on weather conditions. The agricultural market thus calls for an intimate knowledge of farming problems and the establishment of a widespread distribution network that can meet the farmers' needs promptly and efficiently.

Civil engineering

Construction and civil engineering contractors, like farmers, are usually widely dispersed geographically. Unlike farmers, however, they are mobile and therefore need to be assured of the availability of products wherever the construction site may be. This may involve the petroleum company in setting up temporary storage facilities for the fuels and lubricants used in earth-moving equipment and contractors' plant or accurate scheduling of deliveries of bitumen to plants preparing materials for road construction. Contractors are usually committed to stringent time schedules and the effect of delays in product deliveries or of breakdowns of machinery or vehicles can be very serious.

Government departments

In many countries the Government and the armed forces are large buyers of petroleum products. In general they are interested in securing the availability of products to meet rigorously standardized requirements at the lowest cost and over a wide geographical area. Accordingly most Government and military purchasing agencies have established comprehensive product specifications against which all purchases are made, and contracts are generally awarded on the basis of the lowest prices tendered. To meet this situation the petroleum marketer must be able to provide a range of products that have been approved by the authorities as conforming to the official specifications. In some fields of application, particularly in the aviation and marine fields, military equipment tends to be technically in advance of commercial equipment and military specifications may establish new product performance requirements that may later be adopted by industrial users.

Manufacturing and process industries

These industries embrace a varied group of markets with a growing demand for petroleum fuels, lubricants and other products in wide variety.

In many countries coal production cannot keep pace with the demand for power, and the electricity generating industry has become one of the largest users of fuel oil which, in some instances, is delivered by pipeline.

In the iron and steel industry there are many processes in which petroleum fuels have technical or economic advantages. The injection of fuel oil into blast furnaces is now well established as resulting in reduced coke consumption and increased iron output.

Some large industrial users of petroleum products establish product specifications and invite competitive quotations. The petroleum marketer, while constantly aiming at meeting these requirements, is also interested in offering improvements in product quality which may lead to greater overall efficiency for the customer.

Many customers have very specialized requirements for relatively small volumes of a wide variety of oil products, some of which may be used as raw materials in manufacturing processes and require special qualities quite unrelated to those usually specified.

Transport

The four main transport industries concerned with the movement of people and goods by road, rail, sea and air, present their own special problems to the petroleum marketer. In these industries the cost of fuel and the maintenance of equipment represents a significant element of the total costs of operation, much more so than in many manufacturing industries.

Availability of suitable products must be assured along the transport routes. In the case of sea and air transport particularly, these routes may cross many national territorial boundaries and much of the petroleum business may be covered by international contracts.

International sales

For reasons of efficiency it is obviously preferable for an international airline or a shipping company to negotiate one contract with a multi-national organization such as a major oil company rather than many contracts with local organizations in as many different countries. While the problems involved in dealing with these two classes of international customer are not identical, the availability of the expertise, service, quality and continuity of supply which an international oil company can offer is equally important.

As an example of what can be offered, Shell companies are established in more than 100 countries throughout the world, with facilities for the supply of aviation fuel at over 1000 airports, and for the supply of bunker fuels at over 350 seaports.

International aviation sales

An airliner flying from Tokyo to London may call at Hong Kong, Bangkok, Calcutta, Karachi, Beirut, Rome and Frankfurt within the space of 24 hours, to pick up and set down passengers and, where necessary, to fuel. At every stop, the right equipment to deliver the fuel to each particular type of aircraft must be readily available as the aircraft touches down. Also, however far the fuel has had to be brought from the refinery and by whatever means of transport, at the moment it enters the aircraft it must be true to a rigid set of specifications and free from all impurities.

These requirements will be covered by a contract between the airline and the oil company's operating company in the country in which the airline is domiciled, but the terms of the contract will be the result of close and detailed co-operation between the oil company's central organization and its operating companies in all the countries in which the airline operates. For instance, the world-wide requirements of KLM (Royal Dutch Airlines) are covered by a contract with Shell Nederland Verkoopmaatschappij but the terms of the contract are the result of co-operation between Shell International Petroleum Company in London and the Shell operating companies in the countries in which KLM operates.

In addition to aviation fuels and engine lubricants, some thirty other special aviation products are provided, including hydraulic fluids, instrument oils, compass fluids, high and low temperature greases, rust preventives and de-icing fluids.

International marine sales

Ships may call at many ports in the course of a voyage and facilities must be available at the main ports for the supply of fuels (bunkers) and lubricants, and service or technical advice may be required at any of them. Such facilities and service can most readily be provided by an international oil company and, as with international aviation business, it is a convenience for the shipping company to have but one contract with such a company instead of a multiplicity of contracts, and yet be able to rely on a consistent supply of products throughout the world.

For instance, the Group offers shipowners a comprehensive chain of bunkering stations throughout the world and, through its operating companies, technical service is available at almost every port. Moreover, as operators of a tanker fleet, the largest single fleet in the world, comprising vessels of all sizes and types of propulsion, the Group is in a particularly advantageous position to give technical advice.

Most of the Group companies' bunker trade is covered by contracts issued in the name of Shell International Petroleum Company Limited but the major part of the trade is assigned to the operating company by whom the bunkers are delivered and forms part of its overall business.

These contracts cover a wide range of customers from large liner operators to tramps of all sizes and even small motor ships. Different shipowners have very different requirements for fuel, ranging from light fuels of say 250 sec. Red I at 100°F to heavy fuel of up to 6 500 sec. Red I at 100°F. This range of demand is met by the widespread use of blending equipment at the Shell bunkering installations, thus enabling 'tailor-made' fuel of the required viscosity to be delivered.

The chemicals market

The chemicals market is not an entity but consists of a large number of individual markets, or groups of industries, some of long standing, others of post-war development. Moreover, the chemical industry is its own biggest customer, for example Shell purchase large quantities of raw materials or process chemicals from chemical manufacturers such as ICI who in turn obtain their requirements of certain chemicals, such as glycerine and xylene, from Shell. Apart from the chemical industry, important markets are in the paint, varnish, printing, plastics, textiles and rubber industries, in agriculture, in pharmaceuticals, antibiotics, detergents and so on. Taken together these markets can for convenience be referred to as the 'chemicals market'.

Each of these various markets has its own characteristics. Some chemicals (detergent alkylates) are sold to few customers, and more than two thirds of the tonnage may be sold to three international customers. Other chemicals are sold to a very large number of customers and industries. Some chemicals may be sold for resale as such, either in their original concentrated form or suitably diluted, or to a processing industry, or as an intermediate for further chemical synthesis. Some chemicals are very cheap, others very expensive, ranging from a few pounds per ton for sulphur to several thousands of pounds per ton for insecticides. The problems of marketing will vary from field to field; they will be completely different and unrelated, for example, in such fields as selling synthetic rubber to the major international tyre companies and selling insecticides to widely dispersed farming communities.

Petroleum based chemicals have made possible the creation of new markets and the penetration of established markets either with new products or with chemicals produced more cheaply and more abundantly from petroleum than from other raw materials. Petroleum based chemicals fall into two categories; 'specification' chemicals, chemicals manufactured to a rigid specification and whose properties and uses are a matter of common knowledge, and 'performance' products, products designed to do a specific job.

The marketing of specification chemicals is largely a matter of price and availability in which their production from cheap and abundant petroleum feedstocks confers an advantage. The marketing of performance products, however, demands a thorough knowledge of the industry aimed at so that sales may be promoted and sustained by first-class technical service.

Advertising, promotion and research

As an aid to marketing it is necessary to inform the various consumer groups of the availability and benefits of the products and services available to meet their needs. This is the task of advertising in the broadest meaning of the word and includes the use of mass media advertising, sales promotion and publicity.

These are all means of communication operating at different levels and with different aims but all geared to the primary objective of helping a marketing company to trade profitably.

Mass media advertising is usually directed at the general public through channels of communication that are impersonal, purchased, seen or heard by millions, and equally available to competitors, e.g. newspapers, cinemas, radio, TV and roadside hoardings.

Sales promotion on the other hand is generally a more exclusive and restricted form of communication, directed to a smaller, more clearly defined audience, such as dealers or agents, or through them to their own local customers or potential customers. The advantages of this form of advertising are: it is through media under the control of the advertiser, it is less easily neutralized by competitors and it is often cheaper.

Publicity is the dissemination of information or ideas for public relations and/or marketing purposes. It is achieved not only through paid advertisements but also through unpaid space or time, i.e. through editorial or other free mention. The aim of publicity is usually to create a favourable atmosphere for selling rather than to put over a direct selling appeal to the consumer.

Advertising is only one of the many factors in marketing that help selling, but it is perhaps the most flexible and, in terms of reaching a mass market, one of the least expensive. Its role is relatively more important in the marketing of mass consumption products than in that of products sold to industrial and other large scale consumers.

Advertising must be not only closely geared to marketing objectives and sales targets but also carefully attuned to the needs and desires as well as the tastes and motivations of the consuming public.

In all systems of distribution and selling there must be a two-way channel of communication between buyer and seller. In one direction the seller communicates what he has to offer and in the other the buyer what and how he wants to buy. This second aspect – finding out what the consumer wants and why – is the concern of market research. Marketing research employs various techniques, such as statistical analysis, consumer research, motivation research, product and advertising testing, to obtain marketing information that will enable management to make decisions on marketing policy.

Transport, distribution and storage

Tankers

Trunk pipelines

Distribution of oil products and chemicals

Installations and depots

Measurement and loss control

Tankers

History and development

When the economic history of the twentieth century comes to be written, the amazing developments in the transport of oil by sea will form an interesting chapter. We who are living during the course of these changes cannot see the whole picture, and he would be a bold man who would say that the limits of progress have been reached; but a brief survey of developments up to the present day will give a sufficient indication of the revolutionary changes which have taken and are taking place.

When oil first entered into international trade about one hundred years ago its transport by sea was, like that of most other cargoes, effected in specially made containers. At first wooden barrels were used, but these were subsequently replaced by large iron tanks fitted into the hull of the ship. As the economies of bulk transport became evident, the idea was conceived of using the hull of the vessel itself as the oil container. This necessitated the use of iron ships, instead of the wooden vessels previously employed, and constituted the main principle in the development of the tanker as we know it today.

Probably the first ocean-going vessel constructed on these lines was the ss *Glückauf* built in 1885, with a gross tonnage* of 2307 tons. The use of steam machinery and coal-fired boilers in a vessel engaged in oil transport was still in its infancy and was attended by grave risks in view of the highly inflammable nature of the cargo; but such risks are the lot of the pioneer, and subsequent experience showed that running them was well worth-while.

The next landmark was the passage of the Suez Canal by a fully laden tanker, the first Shell tanker, ss *Murex*, of 5010 dwt, built in 1892 at West Hartlepool. After lengthy negotiations with the Canal authorities she undertook her maiden voyage from Batum on the Black Sea to the Far East. The passage through the Suez Canal was completed without incident, despite fears that she might prove a danger to other shipping using the Canal. From this small beginning some seventy years ago, the annual quantity of oil moving through the Canal has continually increased and reached 138 million tons in 1963.

In the early years of the present century the pattern of the oil trade underwent an important change owing to the opening up of the Sumatra and Borneo oilfields. Whereas previously oil was carried only from west to east and dry cargo on the return voyage, the new requirement for oil movements from the East Indies to Europe made it possible to employ vessels exclusively for the carriage of petroleum. This resulted in a change of tanker design and encouraged

* References are made in this chapter to gross and deadweight tonnages. Gross tonnage, broadly speaking, represents the total capacity of all enclosed spaces in the ship, measured in 'tons' of 100 ft^3. Deadweight tonnage (dwt) represents the weight of the cargo, stores, bunkers and water which the ship can lift, expressed in tons of 2240 lb. It is customary when referring to merchant shipping generally to express tonnage figures in terms of gross tons, but statistics relating only to tankers are more often quoted in deadweight tons which is the measurement used in this chapter except where otherwise stated. With a normal tanker of average size, the gross tonnage is usually about two-thirds of the deadweight tonnage.

Fig. 211 Shell steam tanker *Volute*, 5670 dwt, built in 1893, a sister ship of ss *Murex*

Fig. 212 Shell motor tanker *Vulcanus*, 1215 dwt, built in 1910

some increase in size. At the beginning of the century the total tanker tonnage was half a million tons with an average of 5000 dwt per tanker; by 1914 the total tonnage had increased to 2 million dwt with an average of something over 6000 tons per tanker.

During this period preceding World War I a further development, in which the Royal Dutch/Shell Group played an important part, was the construction of the first ocean-going motor vessel of any kind, the Shell tanker *Vulcanus*, built in 1910. Although only a small vessel of 1215 dwt, she amply proved the advantages of motor propulsion and was the forerunner of a very large number of motor tankers which today represent half the vessels in the world tanker fleet.

The years between the wars were characterized by a policy of consolidation and gradual development in size, speed and technical improvements. The size of the standard tanker rose to 10 000 dwt and later to 12 000 dwt with a speed of 11 knots. Half-hearted attempts were made to push the maximum size up to more than 20 000 dwt but very few large vessels were built. By 1939 the world tanker fleet had grown to more than 1500 vessels totalling 16½ million dwt, of which over 1½ million dwt were owned by Group companies.

The vital need for oil during World War II gave a tremendous impetus to tanker building. The lead was taken by the USA which, having developed a standard tanker of 16 600 dwt with a speed of 14½ knots, proceeded to turn out such vessels in very large numbers. During the years 1942–5 nearly five hundred of these ships, known as T2, were built. Thus, despite heavy war losses, the world tanker fleet by the end of the war had risen to a total of 24 million dwt.

Thereafter began one of the most spectacular advances of shipping history. A number of influences were at work. The growth of the Middle East as a producing centre, the new policy of building refineries in the consuming areas instead of near the oilfields, the enormously increased demand for oil in the industrialized regions and the growing realization of the economies to be secured from the use of larger vessels, all combined to establish a revolution in outlook. Gradually at first, and then at a quickened tempo, tanker owners began to build bigger ships. From 24 000 dwt, claims were made for the world's largest tanker by successive stages at 32 000 dwt, 45 000 dwt, 84 000 dwt and 132 000 dwt; and even larger tankers were planned and ordered. The era of the mammoth tanker had arrived. The output of the world's shipyards increased by leaps and bounds; in 1964 over 8 million dwt of tankers were delivered. By the end of that year, out of a total tanker tonnage of nearly 82 million dwt (more than a third of all merchant shipping throughout the world) about 25 million dwt represented ships larger than 45 000 dwt. In the upper ranges, tankers of more than 70 000 dwt totalled 6 million dwt, with another 8 million dwt of this size group on order. The effect of this growth in tanker size on the shape of the world fleet is illustrated in Table 21.

Table 21 World tanker fleet (2000 dwt and over)

	Percentage of total carrying capacity			
Year	Up to 25 000 dwt	25 to 45 000 dwt	45 to 70 000 dwt	Over 70 000 dwt
1951	93	7	—	—
1956	78	21	1	—
1961	50	37	11	2
1966 (estimated)	30	29	28	13

Group companies, keeping pace with world expansion, owned or managed at the end of 1964 a fleet of 171 vessels aggregating 4·1 million dwt, and had a further 8·8 million dwt on charter. The total operated fleet represented nearly

16% of all world tanker tonnage. Vessels still to be built for Group ownership at the same date amounted to over 1 300 000 dwt for delivery in the years 1965–7, and included two ships of over 110 000 dwt each. Early in 1965 further orders placed by the Group included four crude carriers of about 165 000 dwt each, the dimensions of which exceeded those of any merchant ship afloat or on order throughout the world at that time.

Classes of tanker

In the drive for ever larger tankers, owners could not, of course, ignore the limitations imposed by port and drydock facilities or by the maximum permitted draft for Suez Canal transit. The tendency in recent years has been to concentrate on three main classes of ocean tanker in conformity with the emerging pattern of trade and the port facilities available.

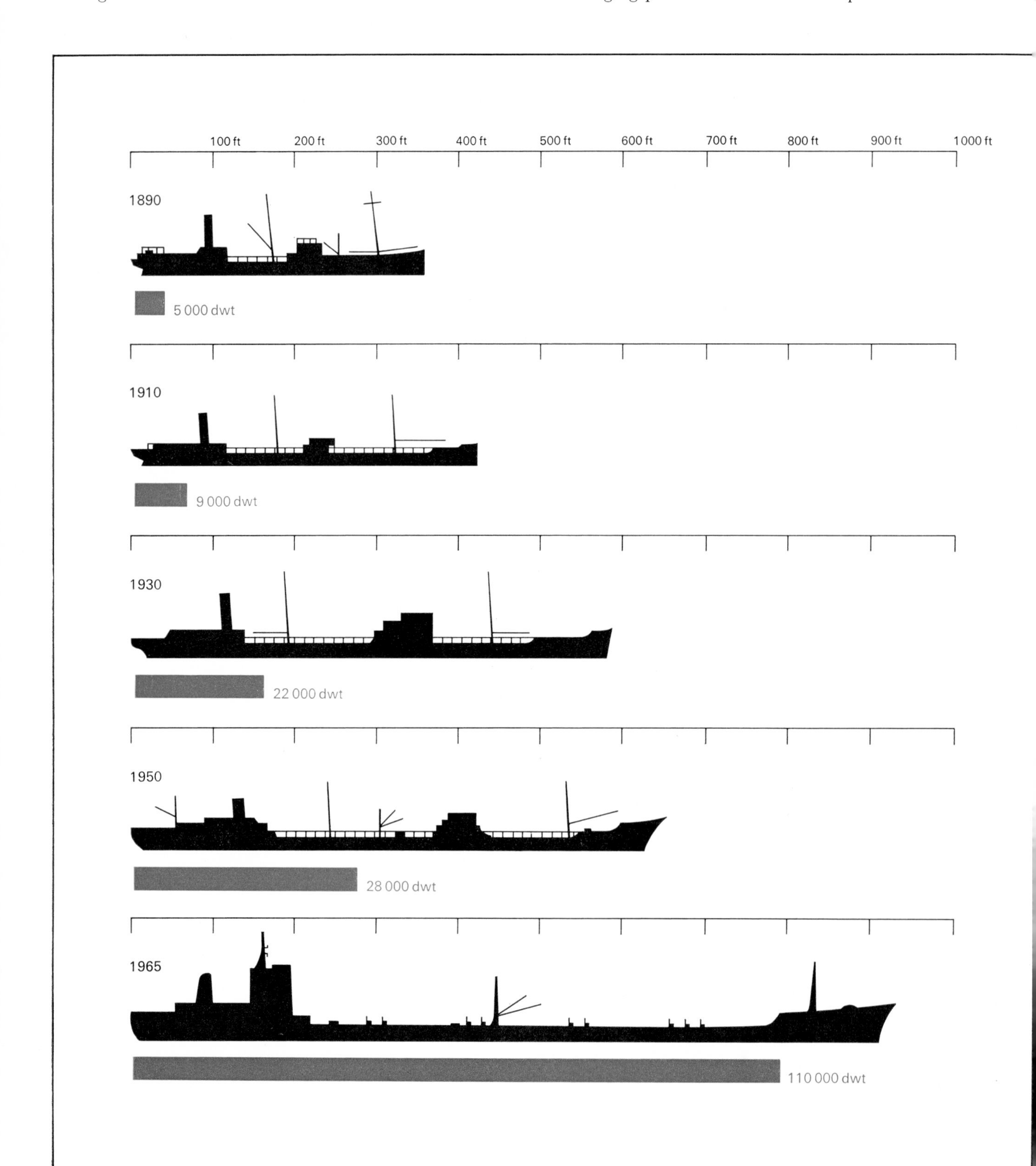

Fig. 213 Development in size, capacity and characteristic appearance of the ocean tanker

Fig. 214 ss *Solen*, 67 848 dwt, built in 1961

Firstly, the general-purpose ship of 15 000–25 000 dwt and 14–15 knots, which can be accommodated at most oil ports and carries all the more important types of oil cargo, mainly refined products. Secondly, for the ferrying of crude oil in large quantities from oilfields to distant refineries, the 'work-horses' of up to about 70 000 tons and 16 knots; at present the majority of these are around 30 000–40 000 dwt but as the new, larger ships come into service, the average size will move towards the upper ranges. Thirdly, the crude carriers of over 70 000 dwt which cannot pass through the Suez Canal on full draft and can enter only a limited number of loading and discharging ports. These ships tend to be employed regularly on the same run and may be described as the 'liners' of the oil trade.

The tanker market differentiates between two types of trade, referred to respectively as 'white' and 'black', or 'clean' and 'dirty'. This has no reference to the cleanliness of the ships – the Master of a tanker trading dirty would justifiably resent any suggestion that his ship was not spick and span – but merely indicates the type of oil cargo which she is carrying. Clean cargoes, which are mainly carried in general-purpose tankers, consist of the highly refined products such as aviation and motor gasoline; dirty cargoes include crude oil, fuel oil and diesel fuels. Dirty tankers are usually fitted with heating coils in the cargo tanks in order to maintain a sufficiently high temperature to keep the oil in a fluid state for easy discharge. Formerly it was the practice to commit a products tanker to clean oil trading for a number of years and then transfer her to the black oil trade because the steel cargo tanks were more vulnerable to corrosion by clean oils than by black oils. Great progress has since been made in corrosion control by tank painting and other techniques in place of, or supplementary to, cathodic protection and it is no longer necessary to transfer from clean to black solely for corrosion prevention. Transfers from one class of trade to the other may sometimes be necessary for operational reasons, but a switch from black to clean is avoided as far as possible because of the expense and delay involved in tank cleaning, without which the highly refined cargoes would be ruined by residues left from the previous black oil cargo. Moreover, only a limited number of ships are suitable for white oil trading.

These classifications are extremely important for the tanker-operating companies. Having made a close estimate of the requirements of their trade for as far ahead as is deemed necessary, they endeavour to have available a fleet which is closely matched to those requirements, both in total quantity and in classes of tonnage. As an illustration of the respective proportions of each type which may be employed, Fig. 215 shows how the carrying capacity of the Royal Dutch/Shell ocean-going fleet was composed and utilized in 1965.

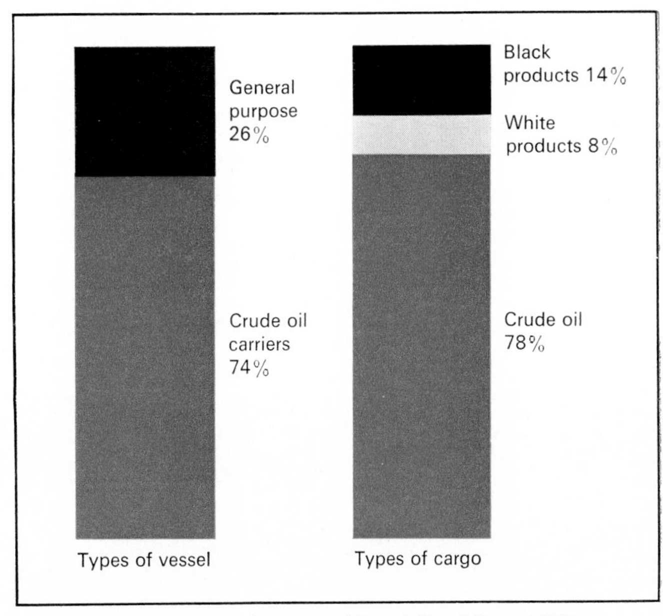

Fig. 215 Composition of the Royal Dutch/Shell fleet, 1965

Specialized tankers

In addition to the main classes of ocean tanker, comprising well over 90% of the total tanker tonnage operating commercially, there is a segment consisting chiefly of ships employed in localized or coastal trades but also including a number of vessels designed for the carriage of particular cargoes.

Bitumen, for example, is solid or nearly solid at normal temperatures and must be carried in ships capable of keeping the cargo at a high temperature during the voyage to ensure that it can be pumped easily on discharge. Lubricating oil, of which there are many grades, requires handling with the greatest care to keep it free from contamination, and if carried in a general-purpose tanker for one voyage only this necessitates expensive tank cleaning before loading and, in some cases, after discharge, and ships may therefore be restricted to this type of cargo for long periods. The transport of chemicals demands a high degree of purity which may call for specially protected tanks and, with a large number of comparatively small parcels of different grades, completely segregated pipelines and pumps.

The size and number of liquefied petroleum gas (LPG) carriers, chiefly for the transport of propane and butane, have increased over the past few years, mainly because of development in the use of 'cooling' techniques. Previously, the only method used to liquefy the gas, and thus to reduce its volume to manageable proportions for transport by sea, was to compress it into cylindrical containers (often described as 'bottles') in ships specially constructed for the purpose. Most of the vessels engaging in this type of transportation are small, seldom greater than about 3000 tons gas carrying capacity.

A more recent method of transporting LPG is to maintain it at ambient atmospheric pressure by reducing its temperature. Commercial butane liquefies at +6°F (−14·5°C), and commercial propane at −55°F (−48·4°C), both at ambient pressure. There are now a number of LPG carriers in service which carry liquefied gas at low temperatures in insulated tanks. Generally, the gas is cooled in shore refrigeration plants but some ships of this type have plant to cool the cargo as it is loaded (a slow process, however) and most have plant capable of reliquefying the 'boil-off'. For the transport of large quantities over long distances, refrigeration is more economical than pressurization because of the weight of steel saved and the relatively lower cost of the cargo tanks per gas volume. For middle distances and comparatively small quantities, techniques utilizing a combination of both pressure and cooling are often adopted, while for very small quantities the original pressurized method is the most economical.

An important development in marine transportation is the carriage of liquefied natural gas (LNG). Natural gas can be liquefied only by an extreme reduction in temperature, i.e. down to −258°F (−161°C). The very difficult technical problems involved in the ocean transport of a liquid at such a low temperature have been overcome in recent years and the validity of the techniques was established by the prototype vessel ss *Methane Pioneer* in 1959–60, carrying 2000 tons of LNG. Following upon this initial success, the ss *Methane Princess* and the ss *Methane Progress*, each of 12 000 tons capacity, came into service in 1964 as the world's first commercial natural gas carriers. Due to the low specific gravity of the liquefied gas, i.e. 0·42 or roughly half that of crude oil, and also due to the need for completely separate ballast spaces, these vessels have dimensions comparable to those of a crude oil tanker of 28 000 dwt. With a speed of 17¼ knots, they were planned to make about thirty round voyages a year each between Arzew on the North African coast and Canvey Island in the UK, with a combined

Fig. 216 ss *Methane Princess*, built in 1964, designed to carry refrigerated LNG

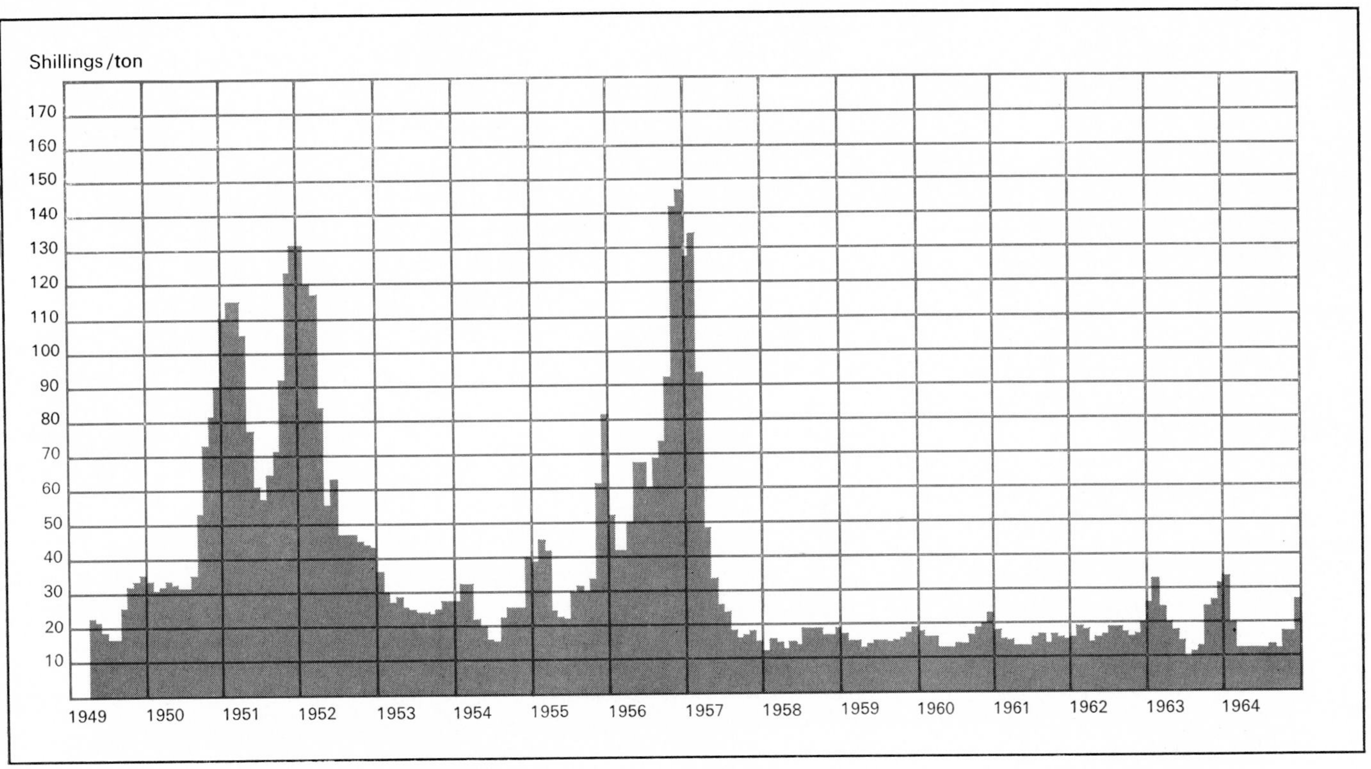

Fig. 217 Tanker single voyage freight rates, 1949-64

annual delivery of 700 000 tons of liquefied gas – some 10% of Britain's gas consumption. Owned respectively by Conch Methane Tankers Ltd, and Methane Tanker Finance Ltd, the ships are operated by Shell Tankers (UK) Ltd, under the British flag. (The handling of LNG is further described under Natural gas, p. 70.)

Organization of the world's tanker fleets

Nearly two-thirds of the world's tanker tonnage operates under the flags of five countries. Before World War II the British and Commomwealth flag fleets were larger than those registered under any other flag, but the severe losses sustained by British owners during the war, coupled with the very large quantity of wartime tanker tonnage constructed in the USA, brought the latter country into top place by 1945. Subsequently, there were large transfers of American tonnage to other flags with the result that by 1965 the USA had dropped to fourth place with 11% of the world total. Norway and Britain held second and third places respectively with 15% and 14%. Japan, with virtually no tanker tonnage after World War II, had risen to fifth place with 5 million tons or 6%, and was still rapidly increasing her tanker fleet. The really striking change of recent years, however, has been the emergence of Liberian flag, from nothing at all in 1945 to first place with 15½ million dwt in 1965, representing 19% of the total. The practice of registering ships under so-called flags of convenience, such as Liberian, which is due to the taxation advantages enjoyed by the owners of ships so registered, has been the subject of much controversy in shipping circles.

Apart from considerations of flag, the three main classes of owner are: the oil companies, who run their ships as part of a fully integrated industry; independent owners without any other stake in the oil industry; and Governments which, in addition to requiring tankers for use as fleet oilers, in some cases desire, for reasons of internal policy, to control the commercial transport of the oil which they import or to engage in international trade with national flag ships.

Before World War II more than 50% of the total world tanker tonnage was owned by the oil companies, but the rapid post-war expansion in the demand for oil, with its consequent heavy burden of capital expenditure in all segments of the industry, made a reduction in this proportion almost inevitable. Many independent shipowners were quick to foresee the new situation and, with complete confidence in the future, took steps to increase their share of the tanker trade. As a result, in 1965 commercial oil companies owned about 34% of the total fleet, independents 57% and Governments 9%.

The role of the independent owner is a vital one. In making their long-term plans for the provision of tonnage, the oil companies, after taking account of their own ships, proceed to charter from the independents the balance of their requirements up to perhaps 90% of the whole, this chartering being done on a period basis for five, seven or even ten or more years. By leaving the remaining, say 10%, unchartered, the oil companies give themselves room for manoeuvre in circumstances of fluctuating demand, and as the actual deficit of tonnage becomes apparent in a short-term review, they secure it, again from the independent owner, by chartering ships for single or consecutive voyages. This system provides the flexibility essential to an industry which is particularly susceptible to seasonal fluctuations and other factors causing rapid swings in demand.

For all that, the system has its demerits, since the law of supply and demand falls upon a comparatively small amount of marginal tonnage with the result that tanker freight rates for these ships are subject to violent changes [Fig. 217]. In 1951–2 and again in 1956, when world requirements tended to outstrip tanker availability, rates rose to very high levels; on each occasion large new building programmes, which in the aggregate proved larger than necessary, were put in hand during the time of shortage, with a resulting surplus of tanker tonnage in the following years, and a consequent slump in rates. No valid solution has yet been offered which will ensure a measure of equilibrium between the demand for tankers and their availability, although in 1963 a number of independent owners pinned their hopes to the Tanker Recovery Scheme, launched by the International Tanker Owners Association. The aim of this scheme was to counteract the continuously depressing effects on tanker freights of a surplus of tonnage, by paying cash allowances out of members' contributions as an inducement to lay-up or scrap eligible tonnage. At the time of writing there was some doubt whether the scheme had attracted sufficient support to ensure its success. Despite the problems of the tanker market, however, the success of the oil companies' operating machinery is evident by the fact that under normal conditions oil consumers all over the world can obtain their supplies as and when required.

This demands frequent and careful reviews of the ever-growing tanker requirements. The oil companies are obviously in a better position than the independent owners to undertake such reviews and thus implement them by placing orders for new ships or by contracting to charter vessels of the size and type required, which independent owners undertake to build or may already have available or on order. The independent owner who elects to build without a charter-party in his pocket is, of course, running the risk that when his ship is ready she may not be able to find employment; but on the other hand there is always the possibility that delivery of the ship may coincide with a tonnage shortage and correspondingly high freight rates.

Obsolescence must naturally be considered in these reviews. For some years after World War II tankers were scrapped, on the average, after a life of about thirty years, but with changed conditions resulting from the rapid expansion in tanker size, most forward estimates regard twenty years as the useful life. As a ship gets older her repair bills tend to become extremely heavy, and a very careful comparative study of costs and potential earnings has to be made as each four-year special survey becomes due. When tanker freights are low it may be cheaper to lay up a vessel than to run her at a loss; or there may be for the independent shipowner the possible alternative of conversion from an oil carrier to a carrier of dry cargo in bulk, depending upon the state of the tramp market. In recent years some two hundred tankers have been converted to dry cargo carrying at an average age of fifteen years per ship, and many others have been temporarily employed in the grain trade when unable to obtain an oil cargo.

Economics of tanker operation

It goes without saying that the relationship between costs and earnings is a matter of prime importance to any shipowner. The vagaries of the tanker freight market, on which earnings depend, have been touched upon in the preceding section. The factors affecting tanker freighting costs are complex, covering as they do the original purchase price of the ship, its size, speed, mode of propulsion, type of fuel, pumping capacity and manning scale. The general rule is that a large ship freights more cheaply than a small one, since building and operating costs do not rise proportionately with increase in size, but the descending curve of freighting costs tends to flatten out when the very large tonnage ranges are reached.

Building costs can vary considerably, not only as regards the cost per deadweight ton for various sizes of ship but also according to the state of the market at the time an order is placed. In the middle 1950s there was not sufficient shipbuilding capacity to meet the great surge in demand for new ships, and owners placing orders at that time had sometimes to wait several years before the ship could be delivered – a seller's market in which prices were high. Ten years later

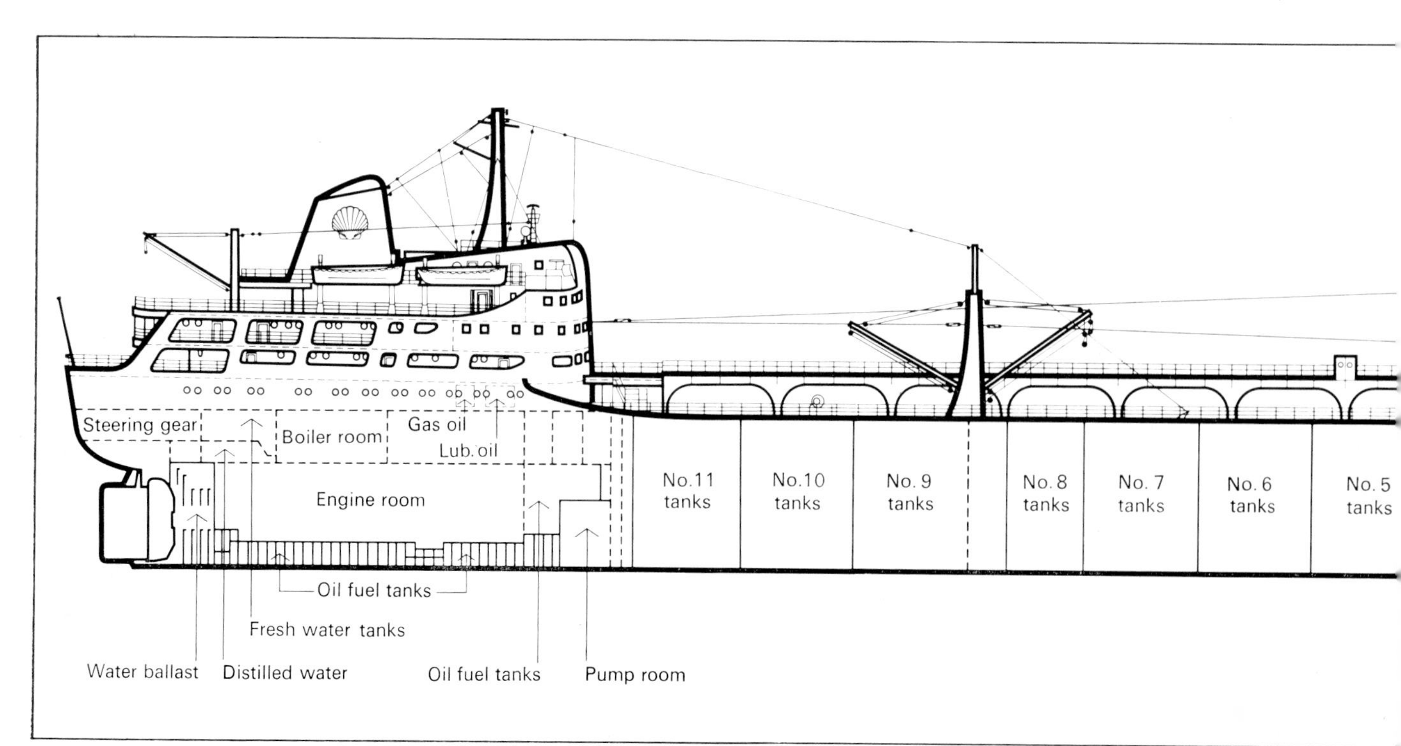

Fig. 218 Profile of a modern 22 000 dwt general-purpose motor tanker

shipbuilding capacity had increased to such an extent that theoretically one-tenth of the entire world merchant fleet could have been replaced every year; consequently competition became fierce and prices slumped. As an illustration of extremes in price fluctuation (a small ship in a dear market and a large ship in a cheap market), the cost of building an 18 000 dwt tanker in a European shipyard in 1956 was over £75/dwt, whereas a 65 000 dwt tanker building in Japan in 1964 cost less than £37/dwt. But even in 1964, the small ship would probably have cost well over £60/dwt.

Whether motor ships are more economical than steam-propelled ships is a question to which there is not at present any final answer; the contest between the two modes of propulsion has continued unabated during the post-war years. Whereas in 1947 only 32% of world tanker tonnage consisted of motor vessels, the proportion had risen to 46% by 1955. With the coming of the large crude carrier, however, the tendency was to change over to steam-propelled ships and relatively few large tankers on order in the middle 1950s were designed as motor ships. Since that time the pendulum has swung again and spectacular development in the 'large bore' diesel field has once more challenged the turbine. For powers up to approximately 25 000 shp either steam or diesel engines are available with the latter claiming more attractive fuel rates. Linked closely with this question is that of the type of fuel consumed. Diesel fuel, formerly the normal fuel for motor vessels, is considerably more expensive than fuel oil, but in recent years marine diesel engines have been able to burn the cheaper oil, largely as a result of the development of improved lubricants.

The pumping capacity of a tanker contributes largely towards the speed of her turnround in port. Having regard to the fact that the daily operating cost of a general-purpose tanker is about £1000 and of the largest crude carrier over £2000, it is clear that all unnecessary port delays must be avoided and the ship must proceed as quickly as possible on the next voyage to help earn her keep. In very general terms, it can be said that tanker owners have tended to give their ships discharge capabilities roughly equivalent to 10% per hour of the cargo capacity; however, this is by no means a rigid criterion as the equipment of individual ships, as well as the shore receiving facilities, must be related to the economics of the particular trade.

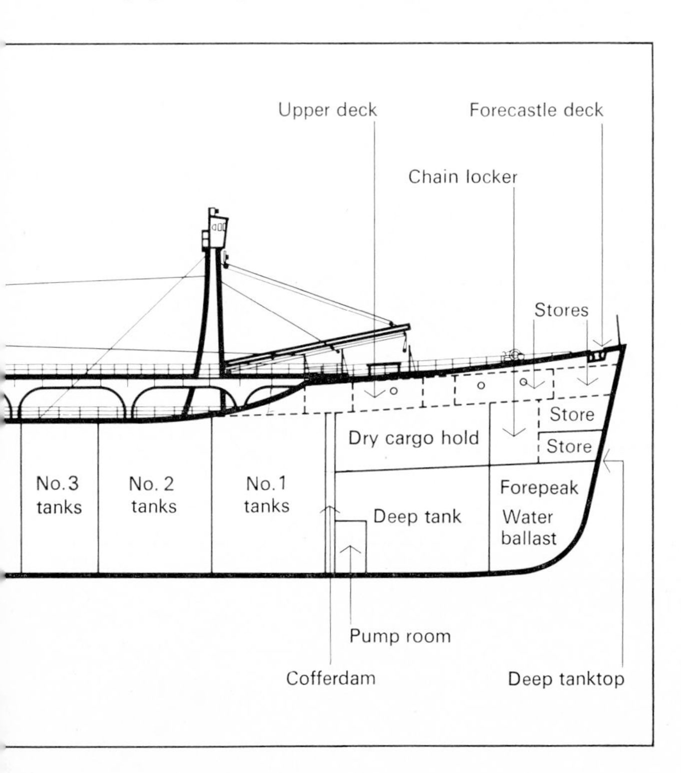

The problem of unremunerative ballast-runs is one which must be faced by every tanker operator. Oil companies with a world-wide trade are sometimes able to reduce the loss of earning time by programming their ships on triangular voyages. Thus, a tanker may carry crude oil from Venezuela to a port in north-west Europe, followed by fuel oil from the United Kingdom to the Canary Isles. This represents a considerable saving in ballast time compared with the employment of two tankers, one on each of the voyages mentioned. With the same object in view, there has in recent years been an expansion in both the number and the size of dual-purpose vessels, designed to carry oil on one leg of a voyage and iron ore on another.

From time to time oil companies have had to consider the relative cost of pipelines and tankers. Over the same distance, tankers can generally be operated more cheaply than a pipeline, but where the pipeline runs more or less as the crow flies while the tanker voyage describes an arc, the pipeline may well be cheaper. A classic example is the line running from the Saudi Arabian oilfields to the Eastern Mediterranean over 1000 miles of country. This can reduce the tanker round voyage by 6000 miles, and also save the expensive Suez Canal dues. However, political problems, and the fact that a pipeline has no alternative uses such as are available to a tanker, can have an important bearing on the issue.

Tanker design and equipment

From the earliest days the propelling machinery of a tanker has nearly always been situated at the after end, as this location avoids the need for an oil-tight propeller shaft tunnel running through the cargo space and thus simplifies design and assists in reducing the initial building cost.

For many years this characteristic made the tanker's silhouette instantly recognizable. Gradually, however, dry cargo shipowners followed suit and silhouettes became remarkably similar; only such features as size, freeboard or decks cluttered with cargo derricks or cranes led a trained eye to differentiate between the two types of ship. By the middle 1950s development had gone a stage further, with the removal of the navigating bridge and accommodation, traditionally maintained amidships, to a position at the after end above the machinery space. Again, this was primarily on grounds of achieving economies in building costs, but with the advent of improvements in navigational aids, cargo handling and mooring arrangements, it was seen as a logical stage in the development of automation and remote control.

Early experience gained with all-aft ships in the smaller general purpose class showed such arrangements to be satisfactory, and larger ships quickly followed the same pattern. All-aft arrangements are now common in all classes of cargo ships and tankers alike, and there are already such tankers of over 100 000 dwt in service.

As can be seen from Fig. 218, the cargo tanks are isolated from the machinery space by a virtually empty space called the pump room. A similar empty space, which traverses the

Fig. 219 Engine control centre on Société Maritime Shell's ss *Sivella*, 79 327 dwt, built in 1963

whole breadth of the vessel, and which is termed a cofferdam, may isolate the cargo space from the fore part of the ship, if a permanent ballast tank is not fitted in this position.

The cargo space is sub-divided transversely, and a further sub-division is provided by two longitudinal bulkheads between the forward cofferdam and the pump room. In the particular case illustrated in the diagram, this results in thirty-three separate compartments.

On this ship, in common with most modern tankers, not all of the space is utilized for cargo carrying. Four wing tanks, isolated from the cargo system, are used solely for clean sea-water ballast. As they do not contribute to the cargo-carrying capacity, they are generally exempt from tonnage charges. By reducing the need for carrying ballast in empty cargo tanks, they form a most useful adjunct to the measures employed in combating oil pollution of the sea. Permanent ballast tanks also assist in minimizing delays and reducing turn round times at loading and discharging ports, since the ship can start loading cargo as soon as she moors, or can sail immediately the cargo discharge is completed. In the larger ships currently entering service, empty ballast tanks amidships materially assist in reducing the sagging stresses in large loaded tankers.

A general-purpose tanker such as that shown in the diagram is designed to carry several different grades of cargo. A complex system of cargo pipelines, located at the bottom of the ship, permits a number of grades to be stowed and correctly segregated, and to be loaded or discharged simultaneously without contamination. Loading and discharging are effected from manifolds, generally placed amidships, by means of which shore flexibles can be connected to the ship's pipeline system. The flow of oil into or out of each cargo tank is controlled by valves mounted in the pipeline. The remainder of the pipeline valves and the cargo pumps are usually situated in the cargo pump room, and where this is located adjacent to the engine room the cargo pump prime movers are normally found there. Gas-tight seals are fitted to the pump drive shafts at the engine room/pump room bulkhead.

Larger tankers are basically constructed and equipped in the same way. When only homogeneous cargoes such as crude oil are carried, however, present practice is to simplify the design still further by the introduction of fewer, but much longer cargo tanks. No stability difficulties have been encountered on such ships, and the problem of oil surging in long tanks has been satisfactorily resolved. Cargo-handling methods have also advanced and cargo pipelines are tending to be used to a lesser extent on crude carriers, free-flow systems being adopted in their place. Here openings in the steel walls at the bottom of the tanks take the place of the conventional pipeline valves, and cargo flows from tank to tank through these openings, controlled, again from the deck above, by sluice valves. Droplines from the midships loading connexion permit cargo to flow both forward and aft when loading. When discharging, the cargo flow is directed to the after end, where large pumps situated in the pump room take suction from the aftermost tank and discharge the cargo ashore through the midships manifold. With such systems, high capacity pumps are capable of very fast pumping speeds, and 120 000 tonners are able to discharge a full cargo in under 10 hours.

Centralized cargo control systems are being increasingly

adopted with automatic operaiton of valves and pumps linked with or controlled by remote reading ullage gauges at the cargo control centre. Controls of main engine and certain principal auxiliary machinery, together with comprehensive instrumentation and safety monitoring equipment, are being progressively concentrated in a control centre to enable the entire watch-keeping operation to be undertaken from one point. Electronics figure largely in these developments, and also in improved communication and navigational systems. Data loggers to monitor machinery performance automatically, telex over radio to transmit communications between ship and shore anywhere in the world, facsimile recorders for the reception of weather charts, and radar sets incorporating automatic plotting arrangements and great circle course computers; these are among the electronic aids which assist the navigator in the task of guiding the tanker smoothly, speedily and safely across the sea.

Safety measures have progressed in recent years with the introduction of considerably improved gas-freeing systems and fire-fighting methods. Mooring and unmooring operations are now performed more smoothly and more quickly by the installation of automatic tensioning winches.

Despite the reduced manning resulting from these and other innovations, the crew will always play a most essential part in tanker operation. Since the ship, apart from repair periods, spends a very short time in port, and returns to the home port are irregular, every effort is made to provide the staff and crew with compensating amenities by way of accommodation and 'off-time' activities. The modern tanker has a separate cabin for each member of its complement and many owners permit the officers to take their wives away with them indefinitely or for trips in home waters according to their rank. Spacious and comfortably furnished smoke and recreation rooms are available for both officers and crew and all the accommodation is air-conditioned. A swimming pool is provided and facilities are installed for film shows. The leave arrangements are generous and every endeavour is made to grant leave at reasonably short intervals and on the date it becomes due.

Single buoy mooring

A recent Shell development, single buoy mooring, is designed to overcome the difficulty of inadequate facilities for large tankers. A large buoy is securely and permanently anchored to the sea bed at a convenient distance offshore to give sufficient depth of water and swinging area, and is linked by submarine pipelines to the shore installation. Floating hoses provide a connexion between the buoy and the tanker's manifolds. The moored tanker can swing freely through 360° as wind and tide dictate, thus minimizing mooring forces.

Single buoy mooring is not intended to supersede normal berthing facilities but only to provide an attractive solution to the problem of large tankers requiring accommodation in difficult locations. The system has been operating successfully in the open sea since 1960 and has weathered many a storm without serious damage.

Fig. 220 (above) shows such a buoy with the ship's hawsers (centre) and the floating hose pipes (left) connected to the buoy's pipelines and (below) a tanker attached to the buoy, with the floating hoses ready to be pulled aboard for attachment to the ship's manifolds.

Anti-pollution of the seas

The serious results of pollution of the seas by oil caused much concern in post-war years and attempts were made to deal with the problem by inter-governmental conferences in 1954 and again in 1962, although without any great success.

Although tankers were not wholly responsible for this pollution, it was clear that the practice of discharging crude oil tank washings and dirty ballast into the sea was contributing very largely to it; in fact, it was estimated that by the early 1960s a million tons of crude oil was being dumped into the sea by tankers every year. Shell's marine experts had given much thought to the problem and by 1962 they had developed a method, known as the 'load-on-top' system, of collecting the tank washings into one of the ship's tanks, allowing the water to separate from the oil, then discharging the water overboard, leaving the oil residues and a very small amount of water in the tank. The next crude oil cargo was loaded on top of the residues.

The efficacy of the load-on-top system having been proved, it was later adopted by other oil companies and by the end of 1964 was in operation for some 60% of international crude oil movements. Although not providing an answer to the problem of persistent oil already in the sea, it is hoped that universal adoption of the system will eventually lead to the removal of the menace of oil pollution.

Fig. 220 Single buoy mooring

Trunk pipelines

Most industrialized countries have long had large networks of pipes for the distribution of water and gas, but pipelines as a means of moving commodities over long distances originated in the oil industry about 100 years ago. The first successful crude oil pipeline was built in 1865 in Pennsylvania, a screwed cast-iron pipeline 2 in. diameter and six miles long. Its life was short for it was torn up by the infuriated teamsters it had put out of work. But it demonstrated the feasibility of the method.

The three basic functions of trunk pipelines in the oil and natural gas industries are:

To transport crude oil from oil fields to ocean terminals and from ocean terminals to refineries or, where no sea voyage is necessary, from oilfields direct to refineries.

To carry refined products from refineries or tanker terminals to consumers or local distribution depots.

To transport natural gas from the fields to local distribution centres or direct to large consumers.

Since pipelines are unaffected by climatic conditions and other natural hazards, such as floods, fog and frost, their use helps to avoid congestion on inland waterways, railroads and highways. The total length of trunk and gathering pipelines in the world (excluding the Sino-Soviet spheres) amounts to some 900 000 miles (190 000 miles for crude oil, 650 000 miles for natural gas and 70 000 miles for products). About 90 000 miles have been constructed in the last five years (Table 22).

Crude oil pipelines in Western Europe

Before World War II there were no pipelines of importance in Western Europe, because refineries were located near the coast and oil products were transported from them by rail, road or inland waterways. By the middle 1950s oil consumption in the inland areas had increased so much that conventional transport of products was becoming difficult and costly. Mainly on economic grounds, it was decided to build inland refineries served by crude oil pipelines from the coast rather than to expand coastal refineries with product pipelines to the interior.

Since the inauguration of the first 240 mile crude oil trunk pipeline from the North Sea to the Rhine/Ruhr area in 1959, an increasing number of large diameter crude oil pipelines from the North Sea and the Mediterranean have been constructed, and more will be built in the near future. The main European pipelines are shown in Fig. 221. The four large crude oil lines taken into service from 1959–64 can carry more than 25 000 million ton/miles of oil, a transport service equivalent to all the goods carried by the river Rhine.

Oil products pipelines

Although commonplace in the USA, where they have for over thirty years played an important role in distributing refined products, pipelines for finished petroleum products are only now becoming significant in the rest of the world. As oil companies expand their operations they must transport more products to more places more quickly than ever before. With rising transport costs, pipelines of all types have become a necessity. Some cater for a wide range of products, others are more specialized, for example moving aviation fuels from refineries or depots to airports, or carrying industrial fuels to power stations or feedstocks to chemical plants.

Multi-product pipelines generally need a minimum throughput of 500 000–1 000 000 tons/year to compete with conventional transport. But because distances by rail, road and river are usually greater than by pipeline, and because loading and unloading containers add to the cost, pipelines may well compete at lower throughputs than those indicated. Nevertheless, movements of oil by conventional methods will continue on a large scale because they are more flexible and economically attractive for the movement of smaller quantities; they are also extensively used for viscous products, such as heavy fuels and luboils.

The operation of multi-product pipelines is similar to that of crude lines, but is a little more complex because quality control is more important. Since a whole range of products may be carried, ranging from aviation gasoline to light fuel oils, proper sequence of product batches is necessary to reduce contamination to a minimum. Rubber spheroids or similar barriers may be inserted between batches to minimize interfacial mixing. To speed up the scheduling of product intake and delivery, electronic computers have entered into the picture.

Natural gas pipelines

For the transport of natural gas, pipelines had no rival until the recent advent of refrigerated methane tankers, and during the last thirty years gas pipeline mileage in the USA rapidly overtook that of oil pipelines.

Following the North American example, pipeline systems have been built to handle natural gas in South America, USSR, France, Italy, Pakistan and North Africa, and a large diameter network is under construction in the Netherlands. In the not-too-distant future pipelines drawing their supplies from the Netherlands or North Africa are expected to extend throughout Western Europe (including the UK) to supply natural gas for both domestic and industrial purposes. Similar developments are taking place in Eastern Europe.

An interesting possibility is the proposal to carry Saharan gas by pipeline under the Mediterranean. The technical problems involved are on the way to being solved, but the economics as compared with liquefaction and transport by methane tanker still remain to be resolved.

The economics of gas pipelines differ somewhat from those of oil lines, as gas lines do not generally operate in competition with other forms of transport, but form an even more completely integrated part of the business of getting the gas from the well head to the consumer. In this, natural gas is

Table 22 Some noteworthy pipelines

Year	From	To	Length miles	Diameter inches	Capacity	Carrying	Remarks
1865	Pithole City Pennsylvania (USA)	Millers Farm Pennsylvania (USA)	6	2	1800 b/d	Crude	First recorded crude, gas and product lines
1870	Newton Pennsylvania (USA)	Titusville Pennsylvania (USA)	5·5	2	—	Gas	
1897	Baku (Russia)	Batum (Russia)	117	4	1700 b/d	Kerosine	
1911	Matadi (Congo)	Léopoldville (Congo)	244	4	1550 b/d	Gas oil	Still in use
1934	Kirkuk (Iraq)	Tripoli (Lebanon)	531	12	43000 b/d	Crude	
1934	Kirkuk (Iraq)	Haifa (Palestine)	617	12	43000 b/d	Crude	Now inoperative
1942	Longview, Texas (USA)	Bayway, New Jersey (USA)	1254	24	300000 b/d	Crude (now gas)	'Big Inch' line
1942	Baytown, Texas (USA)	Bayway, New Jersey (USA)	1475	20	235000 b/d	Products (now gas)	'Little Inch' line
1942	Comodoro Rivadavia (Argentina)	Buenos Aires (Argentina)	1000	10	35000000 ft^3/d	Gas	
1951	Abqaiq (Saudi Arabia)	Sidon (Lebanon)	1068	30/31	320000 b/d	Crude	'Tapline'
1952	Kirkuk (Iraq)	Banias (Syria)	556	26/30/32	371000 b/d	Crude	
1953	Edmonton, Alberta (Canada)	Sarnia, Ontario (Canada)	1765	16/18/20/30	214000 b/d	Crude	'Interprovincial'
1953	Edmonton, Alberta (Canada)	Vancouver, BC (Canada)	718	24	150000 b/d	Crude	'Trans-Mountain'
1953	Le Havre (France)	Paris (France)	143	10	44000 b/d	Products	
1955	Sui (West Pakistan)	Karachi (West Pakistan)	350	16	10000000 ft^3/d	Gas	
1959	Hassi Messaoud (Algeria)	Bougie (Algeria)	411	24/22	300 000 b/d	Crude	SOPEG – first Saharan crude oil trunk line
1959	Burstal, Alberta (Canada)	Montreal (Canada)	2294	34/30/24	800000000 ft^3/d	Natural gas	Trans-Canada pipeline
1959	Wilhelmshaven (Western Germany)	Wesseling (Western Germany)	242	28	360 000 b/d	Crude	NWO – Europe's first crude oil trunk line
1960	In Amenas (Algeria)	La Skhirra (Tunisia)	482	24	240000 b/d	Crude	Compagnie des Transports par pipelines au Sahara – a subsidiary of CREPS
1960	Pernis (The Netherlands)	Frankfurt (Western Germany)	285	24	200000 b/d	Crude	RRP – Europe's first international crude oil line
1960	Texas (USA)	Milwaukee/ Minneapolis (USA)	2175	10/8	60000 b/d	LPG	Mid-America pipeline
1960	Campo Duran (Argentina)	Buenos Aires (Argentina)	1083	24/22	243000000 ft^3/d	Natural gas	YPF – Yacimientos Petroliferos Fiscales – Argentine state oil company
1961	Hassi R'imel (Algeria)	Arzew (Algeria)	327	24/20	400000000 ft^3/d	Natural gas	SOTHRA – first Saharan natural gas trunk line
1961	Ciudad Pemex (Mexico)	Mexico City (Mexico)	487	24	550000000 ft^3/d	Natural gas	
1962	Alberta (Canada)	California (USA)	1366	36/30	415000000 ft^3/d	Natural gas	Pacific, Gas & Electricity
1963	Lavéra (France)	Karlsruhe (Western Germany)	485	34	500000 b/d	Crude	Société du pipeline sub-Européen – biggest pipeline in Europe
1963	Gazli (USSR)	Sverdlovsk (USSR)	1360	40	675000000 ft^3/d	Natural gas	First of twin lines
1964	Houston (USA)	New York area (USA)	2600	36/30	600000 b/d	Products	Colonial pipeline – by far the world's biggest oil products line
1964	Comodoro Rivadavia (Argentina)	Buenos Aires (Argentina)	1045	30	350000000 ft^3/d	Natural gas	YPF – Argentine state oil company
1964	Volga-Ural fields (USSR)	Hungary East Germany Poland Czechoslovakia	3300	40/32/28 24/20	400000 b/d	Crude	Comecon pipeline

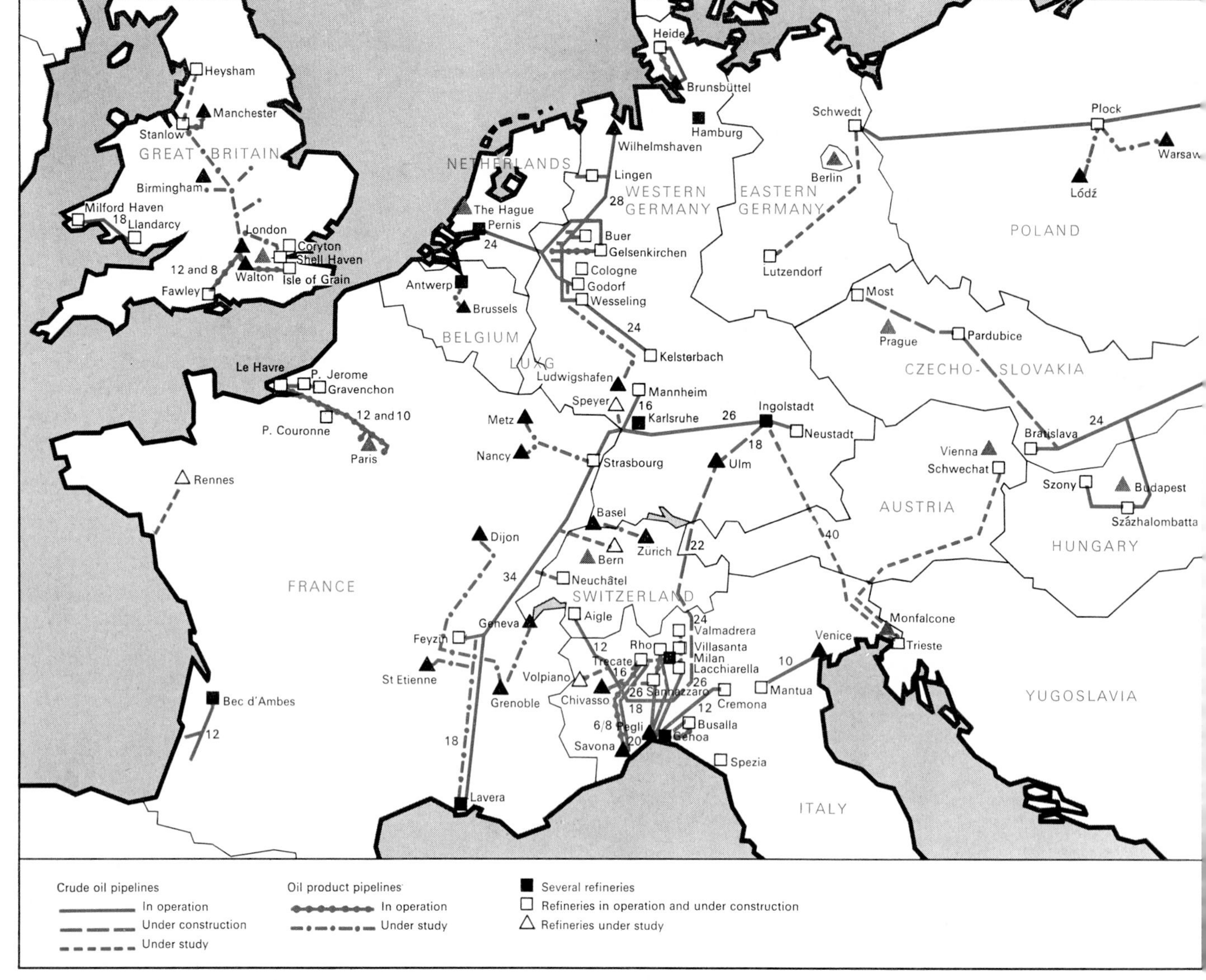

Fig. 221 Main European pipelines

at a disadvantage compared with oil because its energy content per unit of volume is far lower; a gas pipeline of given size can transport only about one quarter of the calorific value compared with a similar pipe carrying oil. Compressor stations are more costly to install, and absorb more power than pumping stations on oil lines. Total costs depend largely on the initial pressure of the gas at source and on whether it is discharged into atmospheric or high pressure storage at the receiving end.

The economics of oil pipelines

Capital costs for pipelines increase directly as the diameter of the pipe, but capacity increases somewhat more than in proportion to the square of the diameter. Large diameter pipelines therefore save capital per unit of capacity. The present cost of pipeline construction (excluding ancillary equipment) can vary from £1000–£3500 per mile per inch of pipe diameter, according to the nature of the terrain. The cost of ancillary equipment and indirect costs may increase this figure by 50–75%.

These large capital (fixed) costs are offset by low operating (variable) costs, since pipeline operation requires little labour. Fig. 222 shows that for a typical pipeline, operating at optimum throughput, fixed costs may be about 80% of the total. It also shows that for throughputs above and below the optimum, unit costs rise steeply as throughput drops, but fairly gradually as it increases. Continuity of throughput is therefore desirable since, if throughput drops temporarily, tariff revenue immediately decreases in proportion while costs are only slightly reduced.

Fig. 223 shows total costs for lines of various sizes, and these must be analysed before a diameter can be chosen for a particular project. The broad principle in selection is to combine the largest possible diameter with maximum use over the expected life of the line. Since the economic life of a pipeline is usually at least twenty years, accurate long-term forecasts of demand are required.

In order to take advantage of the lower transport costs, competing oil companies often join together in the building of pipelines. A separate company is usually formed to design, construct and operate the line on behalf of all participants, each owning shares in the company in proportion to their throughput requirements. A further advantage of a joint company is that a large part of the investment is usually borrowed direct from the money market.

The tariff charged by a pipeline company for transport and ancillary services includes operating and maintenance costs, depreciation, interest on borrowed capital, taxes and profit. The ancillary services include marine and storage facilities, reception of tankers, inspection and handling of cargoes, quantity measurement and quality control.

Pipeline legislation

Although in many countries the construction and operation of pipelines is still subject to general legislation, the increasing use of pipelines has led to a growing tendency for specific pipeline legislation dealing with such matters as rights of way, technical aspects of construction and operation, transport for third parties and government control or assistance.

Planning and preparation

Specialized pipeline engineering contractors are frequently employed for the design and construction of pipelines. Basic data on which the choice of line size and location of pumping stations is made include the quantity and characteristics of the oil, the average and extreme temperatures to be encountered, and the length and profile of the line.

Selecting the route is a vital part of planning. As soon as adequate surveys have been made, permits are obtained from the authorities, and rights of way are negotiated. Special permits are often required for the crossing of railways, roads and rivers, and this usually involves the submission of detailed maps, drawings and specifications.

Finally, the necessary materials and equipment have to be selected, specified and ordered, and the construction contract awarded.

Materials and equipment

Pipe steel is by far the most costly item of pipelines; it may constitute some 35–45 % of the total cost. Bending apparatus and welding skills have improved greatly in recent years, and tensile strength has been greatly increased without sacrifice of bending and welding qualities. Today, steel with a tensile strength of up to 60 000 lb/in² can be used economically, allowing thinner wall pipe to be employed, so that total weight, and therefore costs, can be reduced. The improvement is partly due to the addition of small quantities

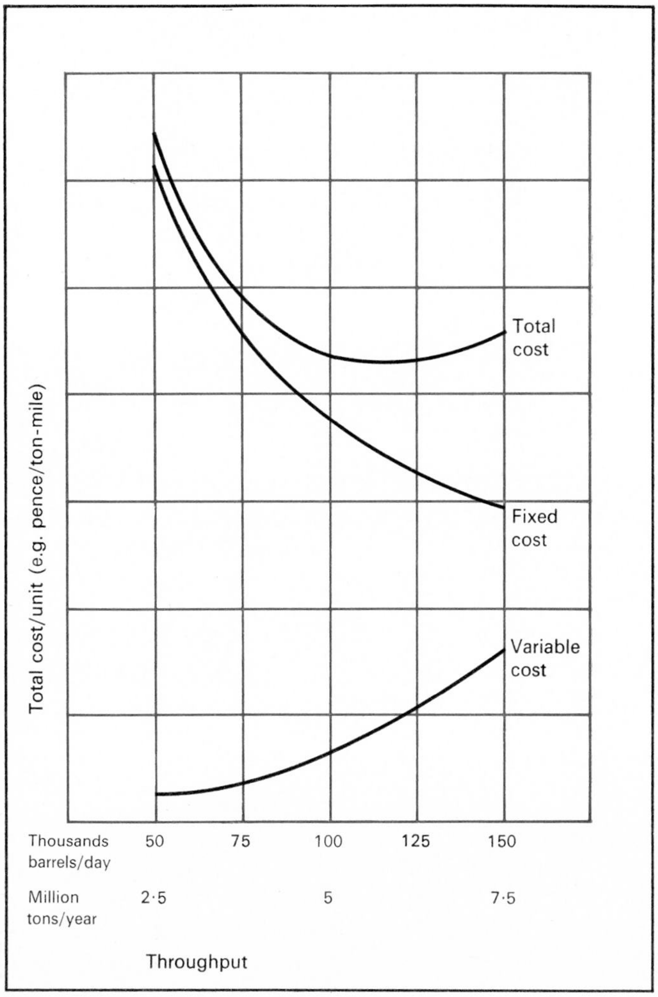

Total cost
Fixed cost
Variable cost
Total cost/unit (e.g. pence/ton-mile)
Thousands barrels/day
50
75
100
125
150
Million tons/year
2·5
5
7·5
Throughput

Fig. 222 Capital and operational costs of pipelines

10 in.
12 in.
14 in.
16 in.
18 in.
20 in.
22 in.
24 in.
26 in.
28 in.
30 in.
Total cost/unit (e.g. pence/ton-mile)
Thousands barrels/day
50
100
150
200
250
300
350
Million tons/year
2·5
5·0
7·5
10·0
12·5
15·0
17·5
Throughput

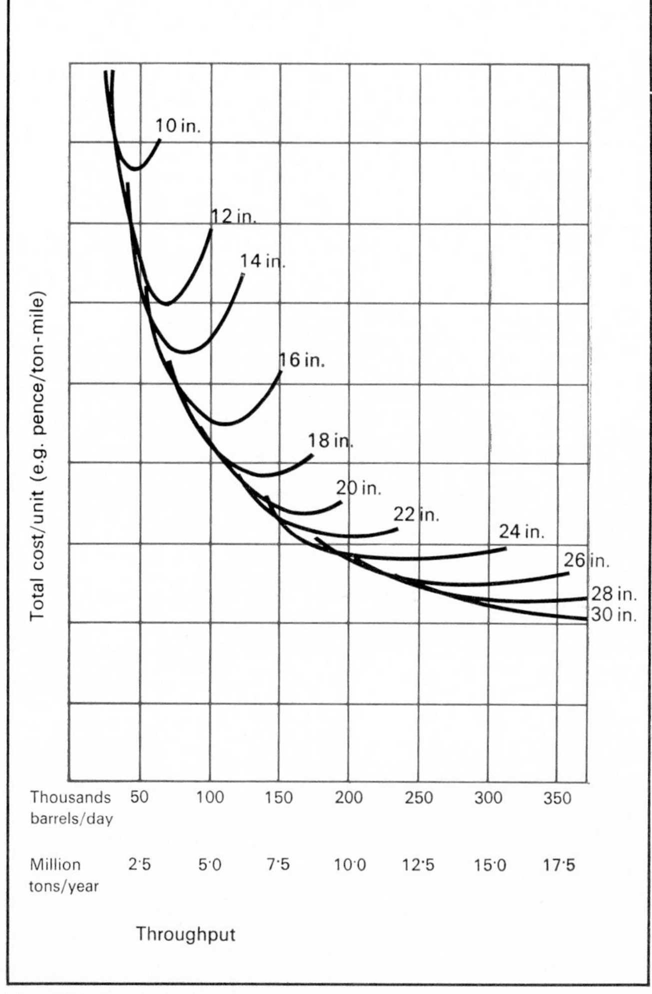

Fig. 223 Total pipeline costs according to size

of such metals as columbium, titanium and vanadium, and partly due to better manufacturing techniques.

Steel pipes for trunk lines may be seamless or welded, welding being particularly applicable for large diameter pipes. During the last few years advances have been made in the employment of spiral weld pipe formed from steel strip spirally wound with the edges joined by submerged arc welding.

Aluminium has some technical advantages over steel, such as lower friction factors, resistance to certain types of corrosion and lighter weight (30–35% less than steel). However, since the joint factor for welding is lower than that of steel, and the limited yield strength makes it essential to have heavier wall pipe than for high yield strength steels, aluminium has not so far been able to compete economically with steel under normal pipeline conditions.

Plastic pipes also have advantages, such as low density, resistance to corrosion and chemicals, and ease of handling, but they are still inferior to metal pipes in their ability to withstand extremes of temperature and pressure.

Valves are installed at intervals along the pipeline so that sections of the line can be isolated when necessary. 'Full opening' valves are used to permit the use of scrapers to clean the line at intervals.

As a rule, liquids have to be pumped and gas forced through a pipeline. For low viscosity oils, centrifugal pumps are almost invariably used as these allow some flexibility in throughput. For high viscosity oils, a positive displacement type of pump is usually preferred, and multi-stage, high-speed reciprocating pumps are generally used. For gas, reciprocal or centrifugal compressors are used. Depending on the circumstances, almost any type of prime mover may be used: electric motors, gas turbines, steam turbines, diesel engines and gas engines. With the availability of strong thin-wall pipe in larger sizes, the trend nowadays is to space trunk line stations farther apart for both oil and gas lines.

Fig. 224 South European pipeline under construction

Construction

Construction of pipelines is a spectacular job comparable with the building of railways in the past. Construction is generally carried out by a number of self-contained groups or 'spreads' each working on a separate section of the pipeline. The size of a spread is governed mainly by the diameter of the pipe and the type of country being traversed. Under reasonably good conditions a spread for laying 'big-inch' (16 in. or larger) pipe averages a mile per day and may achieve as much as $1\frac{1}{2}$ miles.

The construction phases consist of: clearing and grading the right of way, hauling and 'stringing' the pipe, ditching, bending, lining-up and welding, inspecting welds, cleaning, priming, coating and wrapping, lowering in, backfilling and cleaning up, pressure testing. Extra phases of construction are entailed whenever roads, railways or rivers have to be crossed.

A great deal of specialized equipment and machinery has been developed for use in pipeline construction. There are special vehicles for transporting and stringing; sideboom tractors for lifting and handling; machines for bending, cutting, bevelling, cleaning, aligning, welding, coating and wrapping; machines for trenching and backfilling and special barges for laying submarine pipelines.

Since it is very costly to immobilize all this equipment and the crew, especially the welders, for even a day, rights-of-way and permits must be procured well in advance.

Although pipelines are sometimes laid on the surface in desolate country, practically all modern pipelines are buried. Buried lines offer physical protection from interference, especially in congested areas, while stresses due to temperature fluctuations are much reduced.

Submarine pipelines in estuaries, wide rivers and even in the sea are being laid in steadily increasing numbers, and in water as deep as 300 ft. Submarine pipelines are generally three to five times as expensive as pipelines on land.

Practically all lines laid nowadays have welded joints. The electric arc welding process is used almost exclusively. Automatic welding would offer substantial savings but has so far failed to give consistently sound welds. Radiographic inspection of welds, especially at vulnerable points such as major water crossings, is normal practice. Fig. 224 shows welding operations in progress on the South European pipeline in eastern France. The unwelded sections lie ahead adjacent to the trench in which the pipeline will eventually be buried.

Without special protection, buried pipelines would be subject to corrosion, which is essentially electro-chemical in nature. The steel of the pipeline and the chemicals in the soil may cause electric currents to flow from the pipe to the soil at certain points (anodes) and from the soil to the pipe at others (cathodes). Corrosion takes place where the currents leave the pipe. Buried lines are therefore coated with layers of bitumen or coal tar, asbestos felt and/or glass fibre, the exact type of wrapping depending on local conditions. Synthetic plastic coatings are relatively new, but tapes made from polyethylene or butyl rubber appear promising.

In recent years the increased use of cathodic protection has reduced external corrosion to negligible proportions. In this method an electric current is made to flow towards the surface to be protected; that is to say, the whole pipeline is rendered cathodic.

Corrosion may also occur internally, though crude oil lines are generally immune. Rust and scale, which build up inside refined products lines, reduce their capacity and are dealt with by chemical inhibitors and by cleaning the line with brush type scrapers.

Operation

A dispatcher co-ordinates operations of the pumping stations and storage tanks in order to move oil through the line on schedule. Dispatching orders govern starting or stopping of units, raising or lowering of pressure, opening or closing of important valves, utilization of tankage and sampling of oil.

Whilst different crude oils may be either mixed or kept separate, refined products should always be kept separate, because only a small percentage of one product can be blended with another without affecting its specifications. As long as oil in a pipeline moves fast enough, mixing between two adjacent product batches amounts to only a fraction of 1%. Recently, elastomer spheroids have come into use in some pipelines for separating batches more effectively and thus reducing interfacial mixing.

The operation of a pipeline, especially one with several points of origin and destination, requires careful planning and control, for which a good system of communication is essential. Modern pipeline systems make extensive use of micro-wave transmission, telephone, telegraph and teletype for intercommunication. Control systems are widely used, including automatic remote control of pumping and take-off stations with the aid of telemetering systems. High speed digital counters are commonplace on new pipeline systems. Various types of modern computers are used to assist in planning and programming for the most economic operation.

Maintenance crews keep the lines and ancillary facilities operating at high efficiency and at minimum cost, with as little loss of operating time as possible. Pipelines, if properly welded, coated and cathodically protected, require little maintenance.

Safety measures

The oil industry's need for safe, reliable and efficient pipelines to serve terminals, refineries and depots coincides with the need to ensure the safety of the public. Pipeline safety is ensured in many ways, but the main emphasis must always be on building a well-designed pipeline to the best engineering practices to avoid possible failures.

To ensure that all materials and equipment incorporated in a pipeline system are suitable and safe for the conditions under which they are used, they must comply with strict specifications and standards.

It is a standard rule for pipe manufacturers to inspect and test the tubes continuously throughout the process of manufacture. Construction, too, is carried out with the most careful inspection, supervision and testing procedures. In addition, many types of control systems are used, including automatic remote control of pumps and valves, which largely removes human error from these operations.

In addition to visual inspection of the completed pipe, it is standard practice to test the pipeline coatings electrically for breaks or pin holes, known as 'holidays', before burying the line. All this means that the chance of a leak is infinitesimal.

Great importance is attached to fire and accident prevention.

The future of pipelines

Notwithstanding considerable improvements in pipeline techniques in the last two decades, ample room is left for further developments on which research is now being conducted. In the field of materials and equipment, the objectives are new coatings, higher strength materials, and improved pipe laying machinery. Recently a mobile pipe mill has been developed, rolling, welding and stringing pipe on site as it moves along.

Efforts are being made to achieve better separation techniques, so that crudes and products can be handled interchangeably. New techniques for transporting extremely viscous oils without heating, and the design of completely automated centrally controlled pipelines are being developed.

Anything that can be made to flow can be piped. Pipeline transportation of commodities other than oil and gas, such as coal, gilsonite, nickel-copper concentrates, clay, potash, phosphates, woodpulp, etc, will certainly be extended. There have been proposals for piping butter, milk, cereal grains, orange juice, parcel post and even people. A new avenue of technical research, that of enclosing the solid material in capsules and pumping these in a liquid is also being explored, so that the outlook is bright for a continuing high rate of pipeline activity.

Distribution of oil products and chemicals

The pattern of distribution

One of the main functions of an organization marketing oil products and chemicals is to distribute the products from their source at the refinery or chemical plant to their destination at the point of sale. The details of a distribution system naturally vary with circumstances, but the general pattern is from refinery or chemical plant to installations, from installations to depots, and from depots to the customer or retail outlet. Nevertheless, where more convenient, customers or retail outlets may be supplied direct from refinery, chemical plant or installation.

Bulk distribution from refineries to installations can be made by tanker (generally the cheapest means of transport), by trunk pipeline, rail or road. The operation of tankers and trunk pipelines is often entrusted to separate companies and these means of transport are discussed earlier in this section. The policy of siting refineries near to areas of consumption and importing crude oil to them has considerably reduced the amount of product distribution by tanker from refineries to distant installations, although this is still the normal method of supply to installations in overseas markets where refineries do not exist.

The local marketing companies distribute products from installations and depots by a combination of road and rail transport, sometimes supplemented by product pipelines and by coastal and inland water transport. The pattern of distribution depends on the size and topography of the marketing area; larger areas will require more installations and depots, countries rich in waterways will use more water transport.

The pattern is also affected by special features of the products or of methods of marketing. Chemicals, for example, call for methods of storing, handling and distributing different from those employed for oil products; LPG and bitumen require quite different facilities; aviation fuels demand special techniques of supply to aircraft, and automotive fuels and lubricants are mainly delivered to the customer via what are known as 'retail outlets'.

These various means and systems of distribution are described below.

Fig. 225 Bulk tank lorry (for chemicals)

Installations and depots

An installation is a main centre of distribution equipped with all necessary facilities for receiving supplies from the refinery and storing, blending and issuing them in smaller quantities within a marketing area. Installations are supplied by ocean-going or coastal tankers, or by pipeline, rail or road. Usually an installation supplies customers and retail outlets within a convenient distance by direct deliveries, but supplies more distant points via depots.

Depots are secondary centres of distribution which receive supplies from an installation by road, rail, water or pipeline, store them and issue them in smaller quantities throughout a limited local marketing area.

Installations and depots and their facilities are described in more detail in Installations and depots, p. 275.

Road transport

Road transport plays a very large part in the distribution of petroleum products. By far the greater proportion of petroleum products are delivered to the customer in bulk tank lorries, but packed trucks are also used, mainly for lubricating oils and chemical products.

Bulk lorries range in total capacity from 1000 to 12 000 UK gal (4550 to 54 550 litres) the size used depending on restrictions imposed by road conditions, legislation and the nature of the distribution network. Every effort is made to use the maximum size of vehicle as the unit cost of delivery decreases as the capacity increases.

Various types of chassis are used for bulk lorries, including rigid vehicles without trailers, rigid vehicles with trailers, and articulated vehicles consisting of tractors and semi-trailers. The type selected, the number of axles used and whether a gasoline or diesel engine, depend entirely on local operating conditions [Fig. 225].

Modern bulk lorries are designed either as general-purpose vehicles or as special-purpose vehicles. The general-purpose vehicle is usually divided into compartments as in many countries the quantity of gasoline that can be carried in a single compartment is limited by law and ranges from 800 to 2000 UK gal (3650 to 9100 litres). The tanks are fitted with sumps to ensure complete draining, and in the case of mild steel tanks the internal surfaces are lined with Epikote resin to ensure cleanliness. Tanks are increasingly being made of aluminium alloy as this enables more product to be carried for a given vehicle weight, and in some countries the aluminium tank has almost superseded the conventional mild steel variety. However, aluminium needs special techniques to repair, and in areas where no such repair facilities are available, mild steel, although heavier, is still the best material.

Tanks made of polyester resin, reinforced with glass fibre, are being increasingly used, especially for the middle range of distillates, as they require little maintenance and are light and strong. Their more general use has so far been restricted by their thermal susceptibility; they cannot be used at temperatures above 120°C. Where vehicles are intended for use with return freights, stainless-steel tanks are sometimes used because they can be cleaned easily, but the use of stainless steel is restricted by its high cost.

Bulk lorries are usually filled through open manholes on top of the tank, with quantities either metered in or filled to a fixed ullage level. Discharge is generally through tank bottom connexions with a flexible hose from the tank outlet pipe to the inlet of the receiving tank, and deliveries are made where possible by full compartment parcels and more preferably by full tank loads. When products have to be discharged to a level higher than the lorry tank, or when more viscous products such as heavy fuel oils are being delivered, the lorries can be fitted with discharge pumps.

For deliveries of domestic heating oils to houses, or of small parcels of products to dealers, lorries have meters fitted in the outlet system to measure quantities delivered.

The use of large capacity vehicles has led to more rapid filling and discharge arrangements so as to get the maximum number of trips from a vehicle. Discharge by gravity has been accelerated by use of larger outlet pipelines and, where this is not possible, by battery electric pumping. With heavy traffic congestion in some cities, deliveries are frequently made at night, the driver controlling the delivery in the absence of the customer, and this has led to more intensive use of vehicles.

Special-purpose vehicles are used where general-purpose vehicles are not suitable, e.g. bitumen vehicles which can also be used for fuel oil and for sulphur, provided the tanks are internally lined with aluminium. These products need to be heated, and the tanks are therefore equipped with flame tubes or steam coils and are lagged with non-conductive material. Discharge is usually by air pressure, the most rapid and simple method, but pump discharge is used in some countries as this enables a less robust tank to be used.

LPG also requires specially designed vehicles. Stronger tanks are required, almost double the weight of similarly sized mild steel tanks for non-pressurized products, but high-tensile steel tanks are being introduced to reduce the tank weight. LPG tanks are not fitted with compartments and the liquid is discharged to customers' storage via a meter and by means of a pump driven from the vehicle engine. Bridging delivery vehicles are discharged by static pumps or compressors. No insulation is provided for LPG tanks. Safety relief valves on the tanks are set to a pressure in excess of any that may be encountered under extremes of climatic conditions in the country in which the vehicle operates.

Other products, such as ethylene, require to be refrigerated as well as compressed before they are transported, and tanks similar to LPG tanks are used with up to five inches thickness of insulation, which limits the temperature rise to about 0·5°C (1°F) per hour. Special fittings are required for refrigerated products due to the risk of moisture freezing on them and rendering them inoperative.

Chemicals also require specialized tank materials to maintain their purity and to resist corrosive or solvent action, and stainless steel is able to cope in these respects with most of the chemicals that have to be transported. Discharge is usually by pump, also made of stainless steel or similar corrosion resistant material that will ensure complete purity of the products.

Rail transport

In many countries, the railways are still the mainstay of the internal distribution system. Products are distributed in bulk by rail wagons from refineries or ocean terminals to installations or depots, or in some cases direct to customers.

Bridging of large quantities of products from refineries or ports to installations is now being undertaken in some countries by liner trains made up entirely of bulk tank wagons, and these operate at high speeds with rapid turn-round at each end achieved by large capacity loading and discharge arrangements. Although freight tariffs for liner trains are much lower than for single wagons, much higher capital investment is required at loading and discharge points, and liner trains made up of bulk tank wagons have to be equipped with brakes and running gear designed to operate at high speeds.

Rail tank wagons vary in size from 15 to 80 tons and some experimental wagons are in service of up to 150 tons pay load capacity. The tendency is to increase the size of wagons up to the limit permitted by the rail system, usually determined by the axle loading and rail gauge, so as to obtain the maximum pay load to tare ratio [Fig. 226].

Bulk rail tank wagons are designed to carry only one product at a time and the tanks are not divided into separate

Fig. 226 Rail tank wagons (for bitumen)

compartments. Tanks are normally cylindrical in shape and are fitted with a top manhole for filling or to provide access for cleaning and repair, and usually have discharge pipes from the bottom of the tank. These bottom connexions can also be used for filling. When wagons are used to carry volatile products the tanks are fitted with pressure/vacuum relief valves.

Rail tank wagons may be grouped into three main classes, according to their use, for white oils, black oils and bitumen, and LPG, although by far the largest number are employed in white and black oil traffic. White oils are light and clean products which require no heating. Black oils and bitumen, being heavier, require smaller tanks than white oils for a given weight, and tanks are usually insulated and provided with internal flame tubes fed by oil burners to heat the cargo. Steam or oil coils are sometimes used where wagons ply between places equipped with steam or hot oil facilities.

Modern white oil wagons are usually provided with a bottom discharge, protected by an internal foot valve, to make them self-draining and so that they can be switched from one product to another quickly and safely. Internal tank baffles are now being reduced in number or totally eliminated, thus giving a clean bore tank that is easy to clean, and the internal surfaces are sprayed with either Epikote resin or aluminium in order to maintain a high standard of cleanliness. Aluminium lining is used only where steam cleaning is employed.

Special high-tensile steels are used for the construction of LPG wagons. Due to the light weight of LPG, tanks to carry the maximum weight permitted by railway axle loading become very large, and self-supporting tanks without the usual underframes are sometimes used. Discharge of LPG is through high pressure hoses connected to the liquid and vapour spaces, using a compressor or a pump. Tanks are fitted with internal valves that automatically limit the discharge rate, and remote controlled internal valves are sometimes fitted to close the discharge in case of emergency.

Water transport

Water transport is comparatively cheap and, where geographical conditions permit, is widely used for distributing products. The use of ocean-going tankers is discussed under Tankers, p. 252. In coastal waters small tankers are used varying in capacity from 500 to 6000 tons. Such vessels supply ports that are inaccessible to larger tankers, or where it is more economic to supply in comparatively small lots.

On inland waterways and estuaries, barges of 50–1500 tons capacity are used in a similar way. They may be self-propelled, differing from small tankers only in details of construction, or 'dumb' barges without propelling machinery, towed or pushed by a tug, often in trains of several barges. Such barge trains can amount in total capacity to 25 000 tons.

Fig. 227 Self-propelled bunkering lighter

Self-propelled and dumb barges of 150 to over 1000 tons capacity are also used in harbours and roadsteads for supplying bunkers to vessels that cannot come alongside a wharf or jetty. Bunker craft are equipped with hose handling gear or flow booms and pumps capable of delivering oil at rates up to 400 tons an hour. These craft also usually carry small bulk stocks of lubricating oil for ship's machinery and of gas oil for ships' galleys and auxiliaries. A typical modern bunkering craft is illustrated in Fig. 227.

Product pipelines

Product pipelines are used only where there is a large, concentrated market area to be fed from a refinery. The high capital cost of a pipeline can then be justified by savings in transport cost over conventional means of transport. Under normal conditions a pipeline can transport at about one quarter of the cost of a comparable movement by rail and with even greater savings over road transport. Pipelines can also compete economically with all types of inland barge

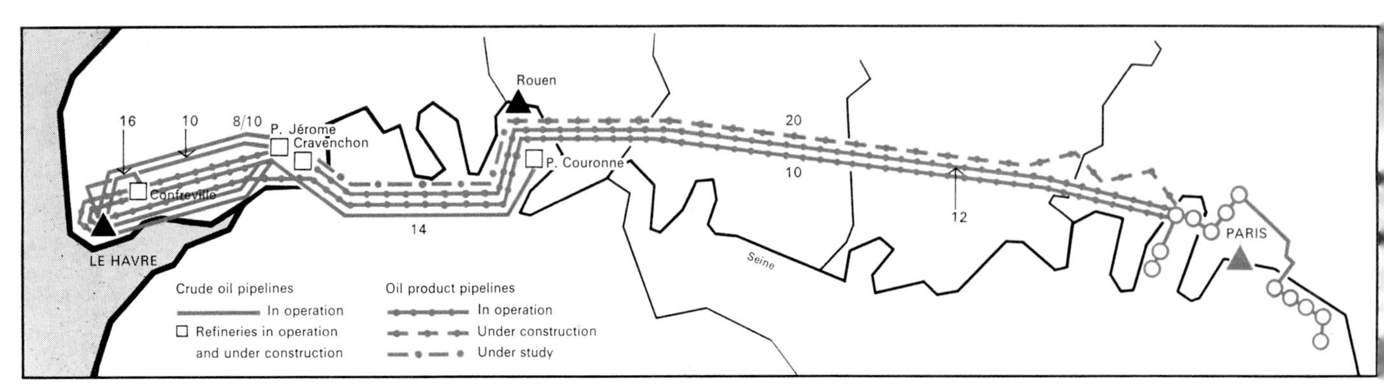

Fig. 228 The Trapil pipeline

movements. The use of trunk pipelines is described under Trunk pipelines, p. 262.

An example of a product pipeline is the Trapil line connecting four separate refineries near Le Havre with some thirty depots in the Paris area [Fig. 228]. A 10 in. diameter line was commissioned in 1953, when the traffic through the line was 300 000 tons/annum. By 1961 this traffic had become 2 000 000 tons, and by that time a second line of 12 in. diameter was being installed. A third 20 in. diameter line is being commissioned running parallel to the other lines, and meanwhile the traffic has grown to about 3 500 000 tons/annum, divided between some forty different products (taking into account the diversity of origin and characteristics). This pipeline has not eliminated conventional water transport on the Seine, but has shown the two methods of transportation to be complementary; water transport alone could not have dealt with the tremendous increase in product demand over the past decade.

Retail outlets

Large customers often draw supplies of oil products or chemicals direct from an installation or depot, or have them delivered to their premises, but for the general public the last link in the chain of distribution is the retail outlet (p. 246).

Retail outlets are of various types, ranging from small dealer-owned premises selling in tins and drums to large company- or dealer-owned filling and service stations where several grades of gasoline and automotive gas oil are dispensed through electric pumps, and lubricants and special products are available in lithographed tins. The small outlet is being steadily superseded by the more complex service or filling station that is now a familiar sight in towns and on highways all over the world.

Service stations differ from filling stations in that, in addition to selling oil products, they provide facilities for lubricating and washing vehicles and also supply tyres, batteries and accessories. Service and filling stations are an increasingly important part of the distribution system (p. 247) and, apart from their direct value as selling points, have a high publicity value [Fig. 229]. Special attention is given to their design and siting to make them attractive in appearance, easy of access and convenient in use, and to their clean, efficient operation and maintenance.

Aviation fuelling

The delivery of fuel into the tanks of civil aircraft is an important function of petroleum marketing in most countries.

Mobile fuellers are commonly used for fuelling aircraft and comprise special tank lorries fitted with pumps, filter/water separators, meters and the necessary hose gear. As the demands of aircraft for jet fuels have grown, so have mobile fuellers increased in size. A modern fueller is

Fig. 229 A typical service station

Fig. 230 Aircraft fuellers servicing a Boeing 707

illustrated in Fig. 230. Fuellers of this type, together with a trailer, provide the flexibility required by large airfields. The fueller illustrated has a capacity of 4000 UK gal (18 200 litres) and is designed to tow a trailer of up to 6000 UK gal (27 300 litres) capacity; it is capable of delivering fuel into aircraft at 500 UK gal (2300 litres) per minute. Two such fuellers with trailers are sufficient for fuelling any aircraft operating today.

Hydrant fuelling systems, as an alternative to mobile fuellers, have been installed at many large airfields throughout the world. Basically, this system consists of a battery of storage tanks from which fuel is pumped through filter/water separators to pipelines laid under the parking apron to a series of fixed hydrant valves, suitably placed, from which the fuel is delivered into the aircraft's tanks by dispensing trolleys. Fig. 231 illustrates a mobile dispensing trolley fuelling a VC10 aircraft. The dispensing trolley carries a filter/water separator, meters and hoses through which fuel is delivered into aircraft at 500 UK gal (2300 litres) per minute. A separate pump and pipeline system is provided for each grade of aviation fuel. The whole system is usually automatic or semi-automatic in operation and incorporates all necessary safety devices.

Although large quantities of fuel are easily handled by a hydrant system it does not give the same flexibility as mobile fuellers because the aircraft parking positions are fixed, and these can vary considerably with the introduction of new aircraft.

With modern dispensing trolleys and mobile fuellers control of the pressure during under-wing fuelling of aircraft is obtained by the hose end pressure controller which incorporates the aircraft coupling unit at the end of each hose. Fig. 232 illustrates a hose-end pressure controller on a mobile fueller.

Distribution of liquefied petroleum gas (LPG)

Liquefied petroleum gas is normally distributed in pressure vessels from which it is allowed to vaporize, by reduction of pressure, only at the point of usage. With the ever increasing demand for this product the pattern of distribution has changed from purely local distribution in small pressure containers to distribution in bulk in large pressure vessels over long distances by road, rail and sea. The pressures involved in such vessels range from 110 lb/in^2 for butane to 275 lb/in^2 for propane.

Reference has already been made to the bulk transport of LPG by road (p. 269) and by rail (p. 270). This has increased tremendously in recent years, not only in the amount transported, but in the size of containers. The maximum size of both road and rail tanks is generally about 20 tons although in North America rail tank wagons up to 80 tons (50 000 US gal) are used. LPG is similarly transported by sea in large pressure containers.

In North America LPG is commonly moved over long distances through pipelines linking refineries and gas wells to large customers and utilities. In other areas, however, the use of pipelines is at present generally limited to shorter runs between refineries and chemical plants or utilities. However, the proven techniques of pipelining LPG between parcels of light products such as gasoline may result in the wider use of pipelines for this purpose outside North America.

Outside North America the steel cylinder remains the most important package for the delivery of LPG to the domestic, commercial and light industrial user. Cylinder sizes normally range from 5 to 50 kg of product. In the past the tendency has been to fill cylinders at large central filling plants, but the tendency now is to a multiplicity of small local plants situated in centres of high consumption, economies being achieved in the number of cylinders required for a particular market and in their handling, transport and storage.

Automation and the more extensive use of mechanical handling equipment have considerably improved the efficiency of cylinder filling plants. In one particular market the number of cylinders filled per man employed in the filling plants has almost doubled, and cylinders are untouched by hand from the moment of collection from the distributor, through the stages of transporting, painting, filling, weighing, leak testing and delivery back to the agent.

Instead of being handled under pressure at atmospheric temperature, LPG can be handled at atmospheric pressure if cooled to its boiling point, and can then be stored in relatively light-weight insulated tanks. This is economically possible with large quantities as the cost of refrigeration is less than the additional cost of the heavier pressure vessels required for storage at atmospheric temperature. Alternatively the refrigerated LPG can be stored in frozen pits, covered with a light, but gas tight roof, similar to those described in the chapter on Natural gas (p. 67). In North America, where the quantities involved are sufficient to make it economic, LPG is also stored in underground mined caverns, washed out salt domes and depleted oil wells. LPG is transported by sea in the refrigerated state in much the same way as is described for natural gas (p. 70). Whereas until a few years ago it was moved by sea in pressure vessels in parcels of hundreds of tons, it is now moved world-wide in the refrigerated state in parcels of tens of thousands of tons.

Distribution of chemicals

Chemicals manufactured from petroleum may be solid, liquid or gaseous at normal temperatures and pressures. They have a wide range of value and are mainly sold to strict specifications calling for a very high degree of purity. Many are highly inflammable while others possess toxic or corrosive properties and require very careful handling. These characteristics call for methods of storage, handling and distribution different from those normally employed for oil products. Moreover, the quantities of chemical products handled are small compared with those for oil products, and this limits the methods used in transporting.

The diversity of chemical products is reflected in the variety of packages used: paper, jute and plastic bags and sacks, tins, lined and unlined steel and fibre drums and various types of semi-bulk containers such as aluminium bins and portable tanks.

In recent years there has been an increasing trend towards bulk supply of certain liquid chemicals due to growth in tonnages sold, rising packaging and packed freight costs, increased experience in the techniques of bulk transport and storage, and greater availability of suitable bulk carriers. Overland transport in bulk lorries and rail tank wagons is already a well-established practice for the distribution of chemicals. Distribution in bulk by sea, however, has only become feasible with the appearance of a new species of

Fig. 231 Hydrant fuelling trolley

Fig. 232 Hose-end pressure controller

tanker. Conventional oil tankers require extensive cleaning and modification before being used for chemicals, and the expense can seldom be justified by the size of the chemical cargoes available. It is more usual, therefore, to charter one of the growing number of tankers specially designed for the carriage of chemicals. These vessels provide complete segregation for a number of different grades, and each of their cargo tanks, which are usually either of stainless steel or lined with a protective paint, is served by a separate line and pump. In size they range from that of small coasters up to tonnages comparable with the general-purpose oil tanker (Tankers p. 255).

In step with this development, suitable facilities are being installed in various parts of the world for the reception of bulk chemicals. Some have been established at existing installations in countries where requirements are now sufficient to justify the import of certain grades in parcels that are large by chemical standards, and others at installations from which the bulk supply can be drummed off for re-distribution to neighbouring countries whose individual requirements are at present insufficient to justify direct bulk import.

Improved facilities and increasing experience have combined to reduce the risk of contamination inseparable from bulk movements of pure chemicals, but have not lessened the need for extreme care and strict control at all stages between the plant and the ultimate customer.

Planning a distribution system

Much of the cost of marketing a product is attributable to distributing costs; it is therefore important to have an efficient and economical distribution system. Though simple in theory a distribution system may be very complex in practice; it cannot be allowed to grow up haphazardly, but must be planned at every stage of its development.

As a distribution system develops – as it often does from small beginnings – many problems require solution; the size and location of individual installations, depots and retail outlets, the methods of transport to be used in each link of the distribution chain, the design of each item of plant and equipment, and the techniques and methods to be followed. These problems cannot be viewed in isolation, but must be considered against the background of the system as a whole. Nor is it sufficient to consider merely the immediate situation, the planner must look ahead and try to foresee the changes likely to take place five, ten or even twenty years ahead.

Planning is influenced by many factors: the geography and climate of the market, the distribution of population and industry, the relative prosperity of different districts, the available means of communication, variations in consumption, the location of sources of supply, the activities of competitors, the availability of finance and so on. Many of these factors are constantly changing and the distribution system must be flexible enough to change with them.

Installations and depots

Both installations and depots have the same essential functions: to receive products in large quantities, to store them and to issue them in smaller quantities. In general, therefore, the nature of the plant and equipment provided to carry out these functions is much the same at both; installations, however, operate on a much larger scale than depots, and consequently the size and range of their facilities are generally greater. Moreover, individual installations and depots vary greatly in size and scope; some handle only 'white' products, some only 'black' products, some both. Again, some handle products only in bulk, others partly in bulk and partly packed, while depots may handle only packed products. The actual plant and equipment required in any particular case are determined by the range of products handled, the volume of the trade and the nature of the operations carried out.

For handling products in bulk, facilities are required for unloading from tankers, rail tank wagons or bulk lorries and for filling into small craft, rail tank wagons, bulk lorries, drums or small packages; pipelines and pumps are required for moving products, and tanks for storing them. For handling packed products, means are required for unloading, moving and stacking packages and for loading them onto transport for despatch, and sheds and yards must be provided for storage. Fig. 233 shows a typical small installation.

Means for measuring and controlling stocks are required (Measurement and loss control, p. 282) and an office for administration. Various auxiliary facilities may also be needed, especially at installations, for example:

A laboratory for checking the quality of incoming and outgoing products, and for controlling blending operations.

A drum-reconditioning plant, if second-hand drums are used.

A tin-making and case-making plant, when such packages cannot be obtained locally.

Boiler plant, if steam is required for heating tanks in which viscous products are stored or for blending operations.

Electric power plant, if no public supply is available.

Workshops for maintenance of plant and vehicles.

Garages, general stores, etc.

Where special products such as LPG, chemicals or bitumen are stored and handled, or where blending of lubricating oils or the formulation of insecticides is carried out, an installation must be appropriately equipped.

Both installations and depots require amenities for staff and labour, ranging from the usual washrooms, canteens, etc, customary in any factory, to living quarters and services for a complete community in an isolated location.

The organization of an installation must be such as to ensure that the demands of the market are promptly and efficiently met, stocks of products are maintained at an adequate but not excessive level, the quality of products is up to specification, losses are eliminated as far as possible, plant and equipment are maintained in good condition, safety measures are observed and costs are kept as low as possible.

The manager of an installation is in contact not only with his own staff and the local branch office of his company but also with labour unions and staff associations, the officers of tankers, the officials of transport organizations, contractors, and numerous local authorities such as police, fire, public health, factory inspectorate, customs, weights and measures, harbour board, etc. In addition he often becomes virtually

Fig. 233 A typical small installation

the unofficial mayor of the installation community. The duties of the superintendent of a depot are similar, though, of course, on a smaller scale.

Pipelines

Whenever possible installation and depot pipelines are laid above ground, both to save cost and to simplify maintenance, but lines sometimes have to be laid underground, to cross a road, or under water, to cross a river. Above-ground pipelines are protected from corrosion by painting; buried and submerged pipelines are wrapped with fabric and coated with bitumen; where corrosion conditions are severe they may also be given cathodic protection (Trunk pipelines, p. 267). As a rule product pipelines require no internal protection, but lines that may occasionally contain water (for example tanker discharge lines that are cleared with water) may be protected internally by galvanizing or by lining with cement.

Pipelines are required at all installations and depots for moving products from the points where they are discharged to the storage tanks, and from the storage tanks to the filling points. Pipelines may account for a large proportion of the total cost of an installation or depot, and economy in their design and layout is therefore essential. Nevertheless, since even slight contamination by certain products may put other products off grade, the pipeline system must ensure adequate segregation of products. Moreover, the system should be highly flexible, it should be easy to pump a product from the discharge point to any tank, from one tank to any other tank, and from any tank to a given filling point.

These requirements are met by using common pipelines for two or more products, whenever this can be done safely, and by arranging for all lines to converge on a central valve manifold or hose exchange near the pumphouse. In this way a pipeline can be readily connected to any other via a pump, in a manner analogous to the operation of a telephone switchboard. Valve manifolds are more expensive than hose exchanges, and are less positive in product segregation, but they are generally preferred as they require less labour to operate, are cheaper to maintain, and eliminate loss and risk through spillage. Where a high degree of flexibility is necessary, each storage tank can be provided with its own remotely controlled pump situated close to the tank. Although this can be expensive in pumps it eliminates the need for a pump house and requires only a comparatively simple manifold.

The pipelines are invariably constructed from lengths of steel pipe. For pipes up to about 3 in. diameter, screwed joints, valves and fittings are generally used; for larger diameters, welded joints and flanged valves and fittings are used. The pipes, valves and fittings are nearly always in accordance with the standards of the American Petroleum Institute (API) which are generally accepted by the petroleum industry throughout the world.

Where the flexing of pipelines might cause excessive stress, it is possible to use couplings that relieve the stress by permitting a limited degree of movement at the joint. Such couplings are used, for example, to connect a pipeline to a storage tank so as to take care of possible settlement of the tank. It is not generally necessary to make any special provision for expansion or contraction due to changes in temperature since the normal bends and offsets in a line provide sufficient flexibility. However, when hot products are handled it may sometimes be necessary to provide special expansion bends, especially on long straight runs.

Heating is advisable with viscous products such as some lubricating oils and fuel oils to reduce their viscosity and facilitate pumping; it is essential with bitumen. The products are usually heated in the storage tanks and generally it is only necessary to lag the pipelines, although, in some cases, particularly with long lines, it may be necessary to heat them. This is done either by running a smaller steam or hot-oil line alongside the product line and wrapping both together in the same lagging, or by steam-jacketing, i.e. running the product line inside a larger, lagged steam line.

Discharging facilities

Where installations or depots receive their bulk supplies of products by tanker or barge, the cargoes are discharged through one or more pipelines leading to the manifold or hose exchange. If the vessels can come alongside there is nothing unusual about these pipelines, but if the vessels have to moor offshore it is necessary to provide either a submarine pipeline from the shore to the mooring point or a floating pipeline that can be launched and towed into position when required. The connexion between a vessel and the pipeline is made by means of flexible hoses.

Tanker discharge lines are usually fairly long and have to be reasonably large (with capacities up to 2000 tons/hour) to reduce discharge time and to speed tanker turnround. It would therefore be very expensive to provide a separate line for each product and generally only two lines are required, for 'black' and 'white' products respectively. Segregation of individual white oils is usually ensured by pumping water between successive grades. This causes no difficulty as the water rapidly settles to the bottom of the shore tank and is periodically drawn off. Black oils cannot be handled in this way as they form fairly stable emulsions with water. They are therefore generally pumped product to product and the small amount of down-grading due to mixing at the interface is accepted. Whenever possible, tanker discharge lines are left full of product, otherwise white oil lines are cleared with water and black oil lines with compressed air.

Some products, such as bitumen and LPG, require special handling and have their own separate discharge lines. Other products such as lubricating oils need special care to prevent contamination and may require separate lines, either one for each grade or one for each group of compatible grades. Lubricating oil lines are always cleared with compressed air and never with water.

When installations or depots are supplied by road or rail the discharge lines are generally short and fairly small and it is usual to ensure segregation by providing a separate line for each product.

Pumps

Pumps are used for all movements of oil through installations and depots. Reciprocating, duplex, double acting pumps (pumps with two cylinders and using both sides of the piston), were at one time the most widely used, but are being replaced to an increasing extent by centrifugal pumps which have the advantage of a smooth instead of a pulsating flow. Moreover, they are simpler to operate and maintain and are better adapted to direct drive by individual electric motors and to automatic methods of control. There is quite a large clearance between the impeller and the casing in the ordinary centrifugal pump so that there is always a certain amount of 'slippage' of product. The slippage is the greater the higher the viscosity of the liquid until, with viscosities over about 1500 sec. Red. I (1700 SSU, 48° Engler) it becomes uneconomical to use a centrifugal pump. Rotary, positive displacement pumps, which have a very fine clearance between impeller and casing, are then used and can efficiently handle liquids with viscosities up to about 3500 sec. Red. I (4000 SSU, 113° Engler) at the pumping temperature. With products of still higher viscosity it is generally more economic to reduce viscosity by heating than to use more powerful pumps.

Centrifugal pumps run at high speed and are generally coupled directly to electric motors and form very compact, efficient units of low initial cost. Rotary pumps, however, are most efficient at comparatively low speeds and therefore need reduction gearing when driven by electric motors. Electric motors are usually the most suitable form of drive though diesel engines are sometimes used. Diesel engines are also often used to drive large-capacity pumps that operate infrequently, as in bunkering operations, to avoid the high standing charges incurred by large electric motors.

The capacity of each pump depends on the service required; for filling packages it depends on the capacity of the filling machine; for filling bulk lorries and rail tank wagons a filling rate of about 15 minutes per vehicle is generally aimed at. The individual pumps are usually capable of dealing with two filling points at a time; when larger throughputs are required two or more pumps are used in parallel. Pumps are often operated by remote control and when two or more are used in parallel they may be arranged to start or shut down automatically in sequence according to the demand at the filling points. For filling barges and small coastal tankers, and for bunkering, pumping rates up to 500 tons/hour or more may be needed. Bunkering pumps are generally controlled by an operator who receives instructions by telephone from the bunkering point but remote and automatic controls are also used to an increasing extent.

Storage tanks

Since the earliest days of the industry cylindrical tanks have been used for the bulk storage of crude petroleum and its products. Within the Royal Dutch/Shell Group the types and sizes of tanks have long been standardized. Such tanks are of all-steel construction with butt-welded shells and lap-welded bottoms and roofs. For most purposes vertical tanks are preferred and are constructed in capacities up to 100 000 cubic metres (22 million UK gal). Horizontal tanks are also used, especially when tanks have to be buried, and vary in capacity from 50–260 m³ (11–52 thousand UK gal). Fig. 234 shows a typical vertical storage tank.

For storing non-volatile, high flash-point products, such as gas oil, lubricating oil, fuel oil, tanks are operated at atmospheric pressure, but for storing volatile, low-flash products, such as gasoline and certain chemicals, it is necessary to maintain a slight pressure in the vapour space of the tank to reduce evaporation losses or, alternatively, to eliminate the vapour space by the use of a floating roof or plastic blanket (Measurement and loss control, p. 288).

The fixed roofs of standard tanks are conical and self-supporting, i.e. there are no internal columns supporting the roof. The roof consists of thin steel plates welded together at the edges, resting on a supporting steel framework and attached to the tank only at the top of the shell. This ensures that in the event of an explosion in the tank the roof sheets will blow off at the periphery, thus acting as a safety valve and avoiding damage to the roof framing or tank shell.

Floating roofs consist either of a single deck supported by pontoons or of a double deck over the whole surface of the tank. The roof floats on the surface of the liquid and rises or falls with the level of the product in the tank. Fig. 235 illustrates a floating-roof tank. Details of other types of vapour

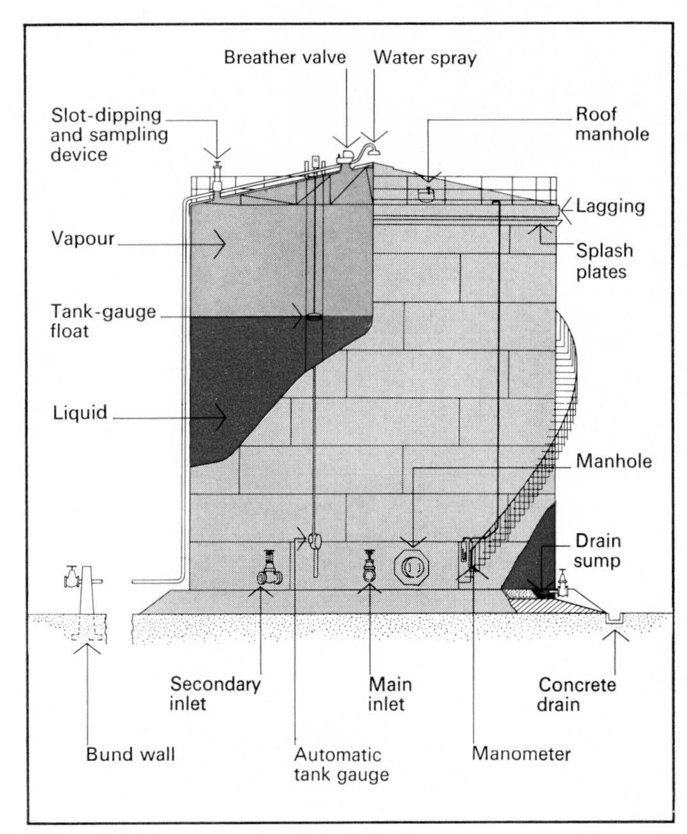

Fig. 234 Vertical storage tank

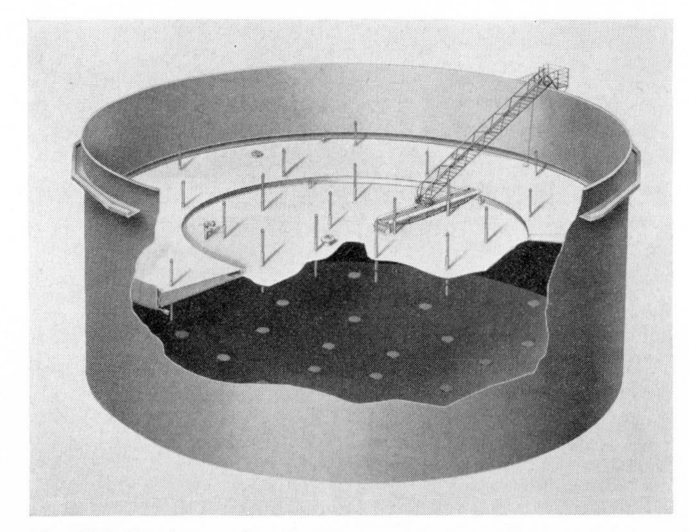

Fig. 235 Floating-roof tank

Fig. 236 Pressure vessels for storage of LPG

conservation tanks are given under Measurement and loss control, p. 282.

Standard tanks are not suitable for the storage of LPG owing to the very high pressures required to keep it liquid, about 85 lb/in² (6 kg/cm²) for butane and 250 lb/in² (18 kg/cm²) for propane. Pressure vessels are used, either long, heavily built, small-diameter horizontal tanks with rounded ends, or spheres [Fig. 236].

Unlike other steel structures, storage tanks do not usually require concrete or masonry foundations. Except on the very poorest soils, tanks are usually erected on a simple foundation of consolidated rubble covered with a layer of sand about 10 in. thick and finished off with a 2 in. layer of sand-bitumen mix which seals the foundation against weather erosion and protects the underside of the tank bottom against corrosion. The foundation raises the bottom of the tank 30 in. above ground level. On poor soils it may be necessary to limit the load on the foundation by using a shallower tank of greater diameter. Where this is not practicable a concrete raft foundation supported on piles may be required.

Tank fittings and accessories

Dip hatches

All storage tanks are provided with various fittings according to the products stored. Every tank has one or more dip-hatches on the roof through which the height of liquid in the tank can be measured and samples extracted. On floating roofs and non-pressure fixed roofs the dip-hatch is merely a hole with a hinged lid, but on pressure roofs a gas-tight fitting must be used to permit gauging and sampling without loss of internal pressure. The use of remote-reading automatic gauging devices is becoming more common, but they supplement rather than replace dip-hatches since 'dipping' remains the most accurate method of measurement (Measurement and loss control, p. 282).

Vents and manholes

The roof of every tank is also provided with one or more vents to permit air to escape when the tank is being filled and to enter when it is being emptied; otherwise the tank might be damaged by an excessive difference between internal and external pressure. The size and number of vents depend on the rate of pumping into or out of the tank. On non-pressure roofs open vents are used, protected only by a cowl to keep out rain and wire gauze to keep out birds. On pressure roofs the vents are fitted with pressure/vacuum relief valves that allow air or vapour to escape when the internal pressure rises to a certain limit or to enter when it falls to a certain vacuum. On the Shell standard tanks these limits are $2\frac{1}{2}$ in. water gauge pressure and $2\frac{1}{2}$ in. water gauge vacuum for diameters up to 64 ft, and 8 in. water gauge pressure and $2\frac{1}{2}$ in. water gauge vacuum for diameters up to 128 ft.

Tank roofs are provided with one to three manholes which are normally kept shut and are opened only to ventilate the tank before cleaning or repairing. One or more manholes are also fitted in the bottom course of the steel plates of vertical tanks for ventilation when necessary, and to give access for internal cleaning and maintenance.

Pipeline connexions

On vertical tanks the pipeline connexions are made through the bottom course of steel plates; on horizontal tanks they may be either through the bottom or the end of the tank or through a top manhole. At least one pipe connexion must obviously be made to each tank, but it is more usual to have two so that separate lines can be used for filling and emptying, thus reducing the risk of water contamination when the filling line is cleared with water. Two connexions also permit the tank to be used for blending as well as for storage.

One of the two pipeline connexions is sometimes provided with a swing pipe inside the tank, i.e. a length of pipe attached to the connexion by a swivel joint and provided with hoisting gear so that its free end may be raised or lowered to any level. A swing pipe is extremely useful when blending since it enables the contents of the tank to be drawn off from the top and returned to the bottom or vice versa, thus speeding up the mixing. It also permits good quality oil to be drawn from the top when a layer of wet or dirty oil is lying at the bottom. A variant of the same idea is the 'floating suction' used in aviation fuel tanks where it is particularly important to avoid water contamination. It consists of a swing pipe the inlet end of which is kept just below the liquid surface by floats.

The bottom of every tank is fitted with a sump and a drain connexion for removing water.

Steam coils

Tanks used for the storage of heavy oils and bitumen are provided with steam coils to keep the tank contents warm enough to be easily pumped. The coils usually consist of rows of steam pipes, connected at alternate ends by hairpin bends, situated in a horizontal plane a few inches from the bottom of the tank.

Compound or fire walls

Storage tanks are usually surrounded by oil-retaining walls known as 'bund' or 'compound' walls. Tanks containing high flash-point products need only walls high enough to prevent leaking oil from draining on to adajacent land, but tanks containing low flash-point products or hot products must have walls high enough to enclose a volume sufficient to contain any oil likely to leak or boil over should a tank catch fire. Usually there are local regulations fixing the size of compound in relation to the capacity of the enclosed tanks. For protection against normal risks a compound capable of holding the contents of the largest tank plus 10% of the capacity of the other tanks in the enclosed space is considered sufficient.

Bulk filling

One of the main operations at nearly every installation and depot is the loading of products in bulk into small craft, rail tank wagons, or bulk lorries for deliveries to depots, retail outlets or customers. The delivery of bunkers to vessels lying alongside is also a bulk filling operation. To ensure segregation it is usual to lay a separate pipeline for each product from the manifold or hose exchange to each bulk filling point.

For filling small craft and for bunkering, the filling point at the jetty is connected to the pipeline aboard the vessel by a flexible hose. Filling is usually to an ullage mark although increasing use is being made of meters.

Rail tank wagons usually come in on a siding, and the filling lines for the various products run parallel to the tracks with branches fitted with control valves at intervals corresponding roughly to the length of a tank wagon. If the tank wagons are filled from the bottom, the end of the appropriate branch is connected to the bottom inlet of the tank by a flexible hose. If the wagons are filled from the top, the branches are carried to the top of a platform running parallel to the rail track and level with the tops of the tank wagons. Filling is done either by lowering flexible hoses or articulated filling arms connected to the branches into the open manholes of the tanks or by connecting flexible hoses to filling tubes in the manhole lids. Filling is usually to a fixed mark inside the tank although meters may also be used.

Bulk lorries are usually similarly loaded from overhead. The lorries run either underneath a gantry carrying the filling lines or alongside a filling platform similar to that used for rail tank wagons [Fig. 237]. Filling is generally through articulated filling arms or flexible hoses lowered into the open manholes of the lorry tanks or through hoses connected to filling tubes in the manhole lids; bottom loading is sometimes carried out through flexible hoses with quick-acting, self-sealing coupling. Lorries are often filled to an ullage mark, though meters, often with preset stop valves, are increasingly used.

Drums and small packages

Bulk storage and transport are the most economical means of handling oil products and chemicals, but the ultimate delivery to the customer is frequently required in relatively small quantities contained in drums or small packages. To retain the advantages of bulk handling as far as possible, the filling of packages is carried out in the last stage of the distibution, i.e. at the installation or depot. Many different sizes and types of packages are used, especially for

Fig. 237 Loading bulk lorries

lubricants, chemicals and special products, but by far the commonest packages for all products outside the USA are the 46 UK gal (209 litre) drum and the 4 UK gal (18 litre) tin.

Drums

Drums are generally made of mild steel, though for certain chemicals other materials such as aluminium are used. 'Non-returnable' drums are made of light, 18 gauge material, the 'returnable' drums from heavier, 14 gauge, material. The former, in spite of their name, can usually be re-used a good many times before being scrapped, the latter naturally have a much longer life. Drums are usually painted externally and may be lacquered or metallized internally. Returnable drums are sometimes galvanized both internally and externally.

Drums may be filled by volume or by weight. Weight filling machines consist essentially of a platform weighing machine, on which the drum rests during filling, and a filling nozzle controlled by a pneumatically or electrically operated valve. The tare weight of the drum may be set on the machine either manually or automatically. The filling nozzle is usually opened manually and shut automatically when a preset weight of product has been filled. Modern machines incorporate a two-stage device that allows for initial rapid filling with a slower rate of topping up. Low viscosity products handled at ambient temperatures are normally volume filled by means of preset positive displacement meters.

Even the smallest drum filling plant incorporates some form of simple mechanical conveyor system to facilitate handling of drums both before and after filling. In plants with a large number of filling points, comprehensive conveyor systems are employed, comprising both gravity and powered conveyors, in order to move both empty and full drums as efficiently as possible with the minimum of manhandling.

Drums inevitably get knocked about in use and need periodical reconditioning. The work is done by outside contractors where possible, but often has to be done at the installation. Minor leaks are repaired by welding, chimbs (the junctions of bodies and ends) are straightened and sealed in rolling machines, dents are removed by hydraulic pressure, and paintwork is touched up or the drums are completely repainted.

The most common method of marking drums is by the use of silk or nylon screen stencils. This method is rapid and relatively cheap, the markings have a good appearance and they stand up well to handling and exposure. When screen printing cannot be justified, owing to small throughput, simple cut-out stencils are used and the paint applied by roller, spray-gun or brush.

Tins

The 4 UK gal tin, made of tin plate, is approximately 10 in. square by 14 in. high. It has been the traditional package of the petroleum industry for some sixty years and is still widely used in many parts of the world, especially in the Middle East, Africa, India, Pakistan and the Far East, where the tin itself has a considerable re-sale value. Even today, with increasing bulk distribution, millions of tins are used each year. At one time kerosine was distributed almost entirely in tins, and tins are still used mainly for kerosine and to a much smaller extent for other products.

Fig. 238 Drums being stacked on pallets by fork-lift truck

Tins may be filled either by weight or by volume by means of semi-automatic filling machines. The filling hole may be closed by a screw cap, an expanded cap, or a press cap, applied by a capping machine.

Many other types of small tins, especially lithographed tins, are used for marketing lubricants and various special products. For the most part they are packed and distributed in cases or cartons. The packages are normally filled at installations by means of semi-automatic or fully automatic high-speed filling machines. A typical modern high-speed filling line comprises automatic machines for filling and seaming, carton packing, gluing, sealing and palletizing, the machines being linked by gravity and powered conveyors and elevators to provide a fully automatic flow from start to finish.

Plastic packages

Of recent years the use of thermoplastic resins as packaging materials has developed rapidly. Conventional packaging materials, glass, tinplate and mild steel, are being replaced by synthetic materials such as PVC (polyvinyl chloride), polyethylene and polystyrene in the form of tubes, bottles, jerricans and even drums. These new packages have the advantages of lightness, corrosion resistance and good impact strength. Plastic packages, mainly high-density polyethylene, are used for a wide variety of products including lubricating oils, kerosine, detergents and other chemical products.

Storage of packages

Practically every installation and depot handles part of its throughput in packages, some in very large quantities. The movement and storage of these packages can easily require much labour and storage space. To save labour the maximum use is made of mechanical handling devices, e.g. roller conveyors, hoists, drum trucks, tractor-trailer trains and fork-lift trucks. Fork-lift trucks are generally used in conjunction with pallets, i.e. rectangular platforms on each of which a number of drums or small packages are stacked and handled as a unit. Small packages are stored under cover, but drums are generally stacked in the open. Whether stored inside or outside, packages are stacked as high as safety and convenience permit in order to make best possible use of available space. High stacking is made possible by the use of pallets and fork-lift trucks [Fig.238].

Storage and handling of special products

To an increasing extent products such as LPG, lubricants and bitumen, which at one time were invariably filled into packages at refineries and so distributed, are now distributed in bulk. Installations may therefore require facilities for receiving and storing these products in bulk and for blending and filling them for distribution to the market, either packed or in bulk.

Additives are increasingly blended into products at installations, and facilities for this purpose are usually required. Various additives, for example ignition control additive (ICA) may be blended into gasoline at the installation, but anti-knock additives (TEL/TML) are more usually added at the refinery.

Special facilities are required where chemicals are stored and handled in bulk. Chemicals are generally expensive, and may be rendered unfit for use by even the slightest contamination; segregation and the utmost cleanliness are therefore essential in their handling and storage. In general, separate equipment is required for each chemical handled in bulk. For solvents, much the same facilities as are used for gasoline are suitable. For corrosive products, especially those that attack steel, tanks and equipment must be lacquer lined or suitably metallized (coated with aluminium, zinc or nickel) or even made of aluminium, or stainless steel. For toxic products special measures for dealing with dust or fumes are necessary. Air conditioning may be necessary to exclude moisture from powdered or granular chemicals.

Workshops, stores and power supply

All the varied storage and handling equipment at installations and depots requires careful maintenance to ensure long life and trouble-free operation. The general policy is to concentrate on preventive maintenance, i.e. a system of regular inspection and adjustment which will ensure that any deterioration is detected and dealt with before it can cause trouble. However, certain facilities are required to deal with the inevitable, if occasional, emergencies. As much maintenance as possible is generally entrusted to outside contractors, especially work of a specialized or irregular nature, but it is desirable to be able to carry out a certain minimum of the most essential work with one's own resources, and for this reason most installations have a small workshop and a few skilled craftsmen.

Every installation has a general store to supply its day-to-day requirements of materials for operation and maintenance. Certain materials such as steel pipes can be stored in the open, but the majority must be stored under cover. The installation store, therefore, usually includes both a yard and a warehouse in which materials can be arranged on racks and shelves. Standard procedures for ordering, storing, issuing and accounting have been adopted throughout the Group, and the materials themselves have been classified, coded, and to a large extent standardized.

Every installation and depot requires power to operate its equipment. Electric power is preferred since electrical apparatus is convenient, adaptable, and generally more economical than other forms. Electric power is usually purchased from the local electricity supply undertaking, but when there is no reliable and economic source an installation or depot may generate its own supply. Power is chiefly needed for pumping, but electricity is also needed to drive machinery, to provide light, and to operate inter-communication and control systems. Other forms of power are sometimes necessary; steam is used for tank heating and may also be used for pumping; diesel engines are used for portable equipment, and gasoline engines are often used for emergency fire pumps.

Safe operating practices

Although installations and depots may appear to be dangerous places because of the type and large quantities of products handled, rigorous observation of The Institute of Petroleum's *Code of Safe Practice* has achieved an enviable safety record.

The dangerous feature of volatile oil or chemical products is the inflammability of their vapours. These vapours, however, burn only if mixed with air in the correct proportion and if ignited by a flame, a spark, or incandescent metal. A spark with sufficient energy for ignition can be caused not only by an electric circuit but by static electric charges generated within the product and released on the liquid surface during or shortly after transfer of the product from one container to another. The safety measures at installations and depots are based on the elimination of all possible sources of ignition from all areas where dangerous concentrations of inflammable vapours are at all likely.

The emphasis is thus on the prevention of fires rather than on their extinction, but since fires may nevertheless occur, each installation and depot is provided with 'first aid' fire-fighting equipment of various sizes at stategic points for dealing with small outbreaks. Fire extinguishers used in installations and depots may contain foam, soda/acid, carbon dioxide, dry chemical or vaporizing liquid, each type being suitable for a particular purpose. Facilities are generally provided for producing large quantities of foam for extinguishing larger fires in storage tanks.

Areas surrounding possible sources of inflammable vapour are designated 'restricted areas', the size of the area depending on the type of products handled. Within restricted areas all possible sources of ignition are eliminated by rigid rules against smoking, carrying matches, lighting fires; by the use of flameproof or intrinsically safe electrical equipment, engines and machinery and the exclusion of all non-flameproof equipment and vehicles.

Where toxic or corrosive chemicals are handled, suitable safe operating practices are applied including, for example, the provision of suitable protective clothing.

Measurement and loss control

Careful measurement of crude oil, refined petroleum products and chemicals within clearly defined limits of accuracy is essential, not only to ensure that quantities are correctly invoiced, and that duties, taxes and royalties are accurately assessed, but also to enable an adequate control to be kept on storage, handling and transport losses.

Measurement standardization

In order to keep pace with rising costs and increased duty payments, improvements are constantly being sought in the procedures and apparatus used in measurement so that greater accuracy can be achieved and the required labour reduced. Apart from the work carried out by the oil companies, various national standardization bodies such as The Institute of Petroleum (IP) in England, the American Society for Testing and Materials (ASTM) and the American Petroleum Institute (API) are continuously engaged in the standardization of methods of measurement, and the major oil companies are actively represented on their committees. More recently, the standardization of methods for chemicals is being undertaken by the British Standards Institution (BSI) whilst some work is also being done in the USA.

The oil measurement procedures recommended by the ASTM and the IP, or equivalent methods, are now widely used throughout the world. Joint ASTM–IP Petroleum Measurement Tables, covering the British, USA and metric systems, have been recommended by the International Standards Organization (ISO) for adoption by national authorities for calculating oil quantities. It is now possible, therefore, to ensure that quantities of oil are measured in international transactions with the same precision, whatever the system of weights and measures used.

Measurement by volume and by weight

Crude oil and oil products are customarily measured by volume rather than by weight. The expansion or contraction in volume due to changes in temperature is ignored when dealing with small quantities measured at or near ambient temperature since the effects are small compared with the accuracy of measurement. For larger bulk quantities, however, the change in volume with temperature may be appreciable, and it is usual to take it into account. This may be done by buying or selling at an agreed standard temperature, for example 60°F or 15°C. If the liquid is not exactly at the standard temperature at the time of measurement, its actual temperature is recorded, and the volume at the agreed temperature is calculated by means of volume correction tables, the most accurate of which are in the ASTM–IP Petroleum Measurement Tables.

Since the weight of a given volume of any liquid remains constant whatever the temperature, it might be thought that measurement by weight would be simpler than measurement by volume. This is true for small quantities that can be weighed directly on a weighbridge or scales, but for larger quantities weights have to be determined indirectly. In practice the volume at standard temperature is calculated and then multiplied by the appropriate weight per unit volume factor, which is related to the specific gravity or density of the liquid. Tables giving weights per unit volume, entered against specific gravity at 60/60°F or density at 15°C are also included in the ASTM–IP tables.

Crude oils, and most refined light products, are usually sold by volume at standard temperature, whilst black oils and chemicals are usually sold by weight. Generally speaking, freights are calculated on a weight basis.

Gauging

The process of measuring the bulk quantities of crude oil, oil products or chemicals is known as 'gauging'. The various steps in the process are described briefly below, and involve the accurate measurement of volume, temperature, specific gravity or density and the calculation of volumes at standard temperature, or of weights.

Special techniques are necessary for measuring liquids stored and handled under pressure or at low temperatures, such as LPG and refrigerated natural gas (LNG), but the same general principles apply.

Tank calibration and measurement of volume

Large tanks are provided with tank capacity tables showing volumes corresponding to various depths of liquid. In smaller tanks, for example on vehicles, the volume to a fixed reference mark may be all that is required. In either case accurate calibration of the tank is necessary. By 'calibration' is meant the whole process of compiling a table showing how much liquid is in the tank at any level.

Small and irregularly shaped tanks are most conveniently calibrated by filling in known volumes of liquid and recording the depth after each addition. Large, regularly shaped tanks are usually calibrated by mensuration methods from the measured dimensions of the tank and internal fittings. In the 'strapping' method, external circumferences of each course of tank plates are measured and corrected for plate thickness; alternatively a large number of internal diameters may be measured. Ships' tanks, in view of their complex shape, may be calibrated more readily from the builder's drawings, but where greater accuracy is required, as for bunkering vessels, direct internal measurement is employed.

Once a tank has been calibrated, the quantity of liquid it contains is determined by taking a 'dip' or 'innage' measurement, i.e. by measuring the height of liquid from the bottom of the tank to the liquid surface. Alternatively the 'ullage' or 'outage' (the distance between the liquid surface and the tank top) may be measured. The latter method is used most

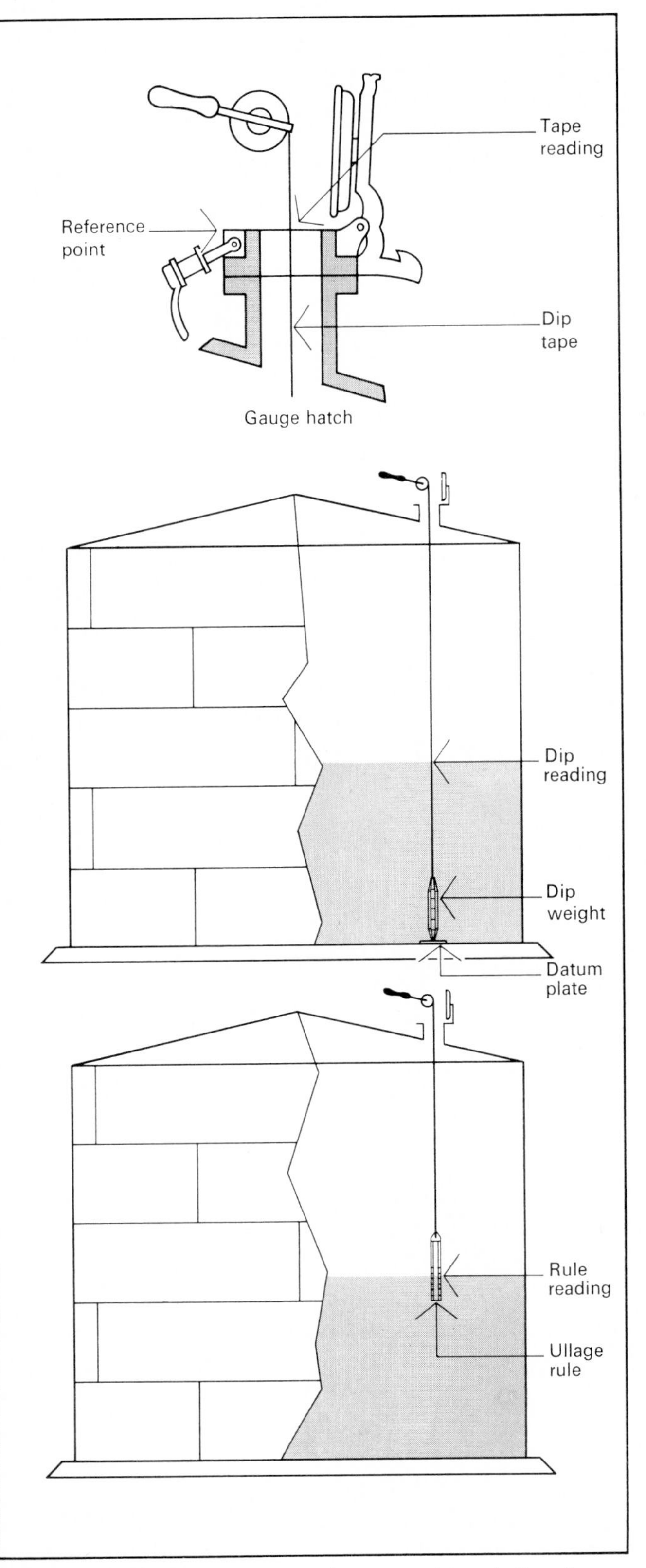

Fig. 239 Measurement of products in storage; (above) dip or innage measurement, (below) ullage or outage measurement

frequently in ships, where the frames and fittings on the tank bottoms would interfere with accurate dipping. In both cases, either a standardized weighted steel measuring tape (dip-tape), or a 'dipstick' calibrated in units of either length or volume may be used according to the size of the tank [Fig. 239].

The liquid depth so measured will include any free water, sludge or sediment on the tank bottom or suspended in the liquid, for which allowance must be made. Water is measured by coating the dip-tape or dipstick with a water-sensitive paste, by using water-finding paper attached to a special rule or by detecting the water level electrically by a special dip-weight and tape fitted with a miniature ammeter, as in the Aquoil instrument developed by the Group. Sludge and sediment are most accurately measured by taking a number of samples from the tank bottom and submitting them to laboratory analysis.

Sampling

Samples of the tank contents are required for the determination of temperature, specific gravity, sludge and sediment. Since the contents of large tanks are not necessarily uniform throughout their depth, more than one sample is usually taken, the number depending on circumstances and the purpose for which the samples are required. For large tanks containing refined oil products three samples are usually sufficient, taken at one-sixth, one-half and five-sixths of the oil depth. The samples are usually drawn by lowering a weighted, corked can to the required depth, jerking out the cork fastened to the lowering cord, and allowing the can to fill.

Temperature measurement

The usual method of measuring the temperature of the contents of a tank is to draw several samples and average their temperatures, using a mercury-in-glass thermometer. Since small temperature variations have an appreciable effect on the volume contained in a large tank, accurate figures are essential, and considerable skill is needed to achieve them.

Density, specific gravity and API gravity

The density of a substance is its mass per unit volume. Since the volume will change with temperature it is necessary to specify the temperature at which the density is determined, and in the oil industry this is normally 15°C. Specific gravity is the ratio of the density of the substance to that of water, and it is again necessary to specify the temperatures to which these densities refer. In the British system it is customary to take 60°F as the standard temperature for both product and water, specific gravities being reported at 60/60°F. In the metric system 15°C and 4°C respectively are most commonly employed (SG 15/4°C), the result being numerically equivalent to the density at 15°C. In the chemical industry, however, 20/20°C and 25/25°C scales are frequently used.

In the USA an arbitary scale divided into °API is used for oil products, the scale being related to specific gravity 60/60°F as follows:

$$°\text{API} = \frac{141{\cdot}5}{\text{SG } 60/60°\text{F}} - 131{\cdot}5$$

The 60/60°F, 20/20°C and 25/25°C scales are, however, used for chemicals.

API gravity, specific gravity or density of liquid petroleum products and chemicals is usually determined by a hydrometer made of glass, scaled in 0·1° API or 0·001 units of

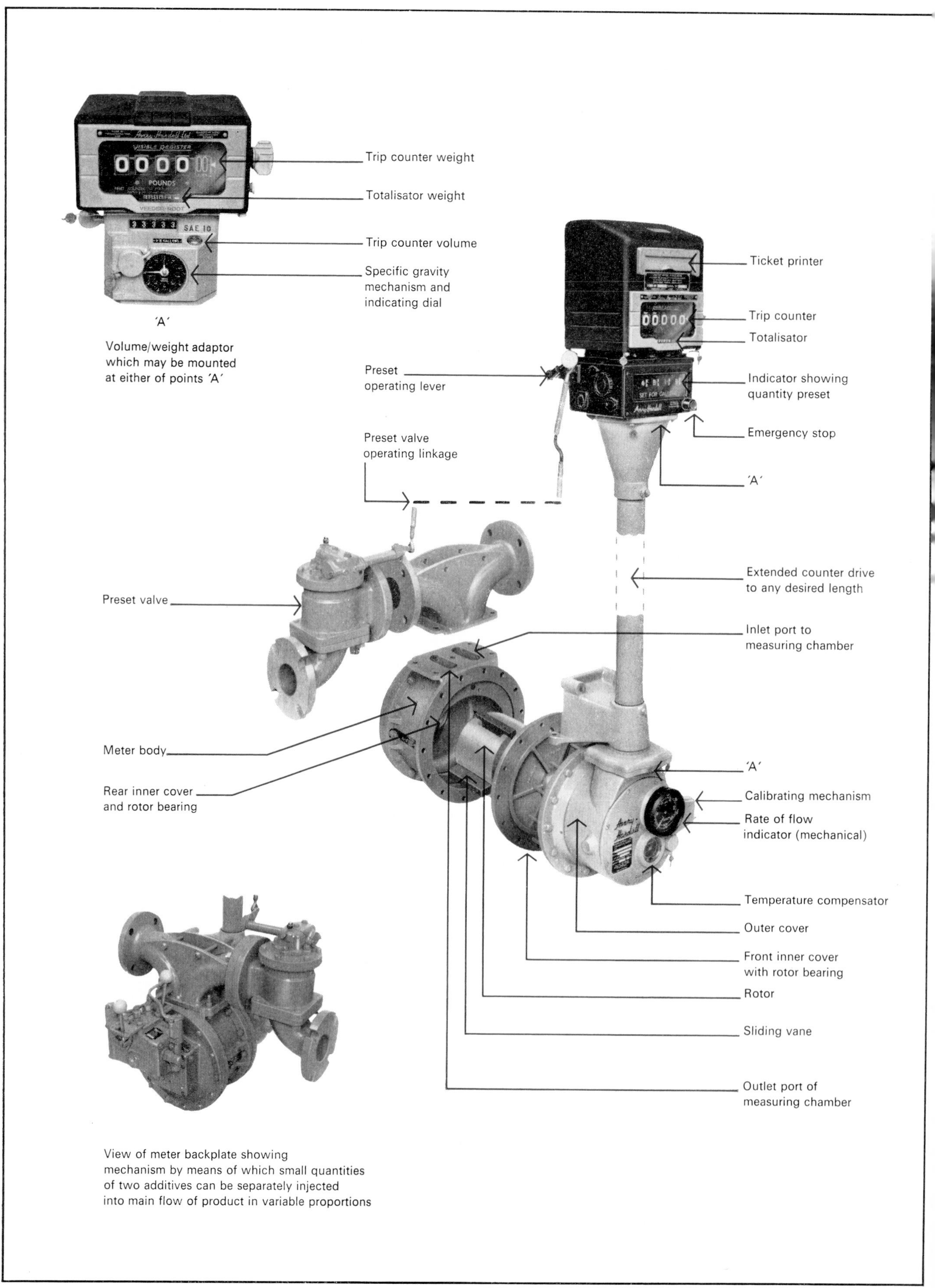
Trip counter weight
Totalisator weight
Trip counter volume
Specific gravity
mechanism and
indicating dial
'A'
Volume/weight adaptor
which may be mounted
at either of points 'A'
Ticket printer
Trip counter
Totalisator
Preset
operating lever
Indicator showing
quantity preset
Emergency stop
Preset valve
operating linkage
'A'
Extended counter drive
to any desired length
Preset valve
Inlet port to
measuring chamber
Meter body
Rear inner cover
and rotor bearing
'A'
Calibrating mechanism
Rate of flow
indicator (mechanical)
Temperature compensator
Outer cover
Front inner cover
with rotor bearing
Rotor
Sliding vane
Outlet port of
measuring chamber
View of meter backplate showing
mechanism by means of which small quantities
of two additives can be separately injected
into main flow of product in variable proportions

Fig. 240 Positive displacement meter

specific gravity or density, and standardized at the appropriate reference temperature. Readings are taken with the instrument immersed in the liquid which can be maintained at either the standard temperature or at any other convenient and measured temperature. In the latter case, the readings are corrected to standard temperature using the appropriate ASTM–IP petroleum tables or similar tables prepared for particular chemicals.

Automatic measuring instruments

Considerable development has taken place in recent years in the design and application of equipment that will enable the measurement of oil movement and stocks to be carried out automatically. Although the manual methods described still provide the reference standard, automatic measurement is now accepted in many instances for fiscal and custody transfer purposes. An inherent advantage of automatic equipment is that besides giving local indication of the measurements at the point where they are made, for example the tank, or the vehicle filling gantry, the readings can be transmitted to other points by direct land lines, teleprint circuits or short-wave radio. In the more elaborate systems the measuring equipment can be used to control directly the operation of pumps and valves, whilst the measurement data can be encoded and fed to a computer for automatic stock accounting, invoicing and operational data processing.

Automatic tank gauges are of two kinds, those that detect changes in the liquid level by a float, displacer or sensing head, and hydrostatic gauges that measure the pressure exerted by the head of liquid. The former can be very precise, can be fitted with remote indication and can be readily adapted to automatic control and data processing schemes. Electrical resistance thermometers form an integral part of the gauging system and are so arranged as to give the average temperature of the tank's contents.

Hydrostatic gauges are generally less flexible in their applications, are less precise and are more suitable for smaller tanks, particularly those of regular cross section. They can be calibrated directly to give the weight of the product in the tank, and temperature measurement is then not required. For this reason, they are used extensively for measurements in ships' bunker tanks and also in small tanks in blending plants to simplify the preparation of blends on a weight basis. They are not suitable when water bottoms may be present in the tank. A special adaption of hydrostatic gauge for the automatic control of tanker loading and discharge is now available, but this principle is not as suitable as a level-sensing device for more elaborate automation schemes.

Automatic sampling, density and BS and W determination

Manual methods for sampling and for the determination of density and bottom sediment and water (BS and W) still have to be used for tanks where the contents are not homogeneous. Equipment is however available for production and pipeline applications. The accuracy obtained with automatic densimeters (gravitometers) and automatic BS and W apparatus depends principally on the adequacy of the samples which are drawn continuously or intermittently from the flowing stream, and a number of problems associated with such automatic sampling still have to be resolved. Besides their use for quantitative purposes, densimeters are also used to detect the interface between products during product-to-product pumping operations in pipelines.

Meters

Positive displacement meters, so called because a fixed volume of liquid is displaced for every cycle of the meter, are used for many different operations. They range in size from less than 1 gal (5 litres)/h, used for the measurement of fuel consumption in power plants and for centralized domestic fuel supplies, to 700 000 gal (3200 m³, 20 000 barrels)/h, used for loading tankers at crude oil terminals and for pipeline applications. Various principles are employed but in essence a meter consists of (a) a measuring element that divides the liquid into segments as it moves through the measuring chamber, (b) a counter registering in units of volume, and (c) a calibrating device [Fig. 240].

During the passage of the liquid through the meter a small quantity will leak past the measuring element without being registered and the accuracy will depend on this 'slippage' as well as on various other factors, such as the speed of the meter, the temperature, pressure and viscosity of the liquid. Meters must therefore be calibrated and used under well-defined conditions, and can then be very accurate. They must be re-calibrated if any of these conditions are changed, and in any case at fairly frequent intervals, since wear tends to increase error.

Ancillary equipment used with meters includes air eliminators to prevent the measurement of air or vapour which might be present in the liquid, filters to protect the meter, flow-control devices and rate-of-flow indicators. Special types of counter mechanisms can be fitted, such as trip and totalizator registers, price computers, ticket printers, and presets. Presets automatically shut the outlet valve when a pre-determined quantity has been measured, and may be used to deliver varying quantities or to measure repeatedly the same quantity, as in package filling meters.

Meters may be fitted with temperature compensators which, with an appropriate coefficient of expansion setting, will automatically adjust the calibration according to the liquid temperature, giving read-out in terms of volume at standard temperature. Used in conjunction with an auxiliary computing counter on which the specific gravity or density at standard temperature can be set, such meters can be used to indicate weight, and these are finding increasing use in bunkering and other operations.

Meters are also widely used for in-line blending, ranging from the injection of small quantities of additives into the metered liquid by proportioning pumps directly driven or indirectly controlled by the meter, to the blending of two or more components. In the latter application, the meter may adjust the flow of the components through an electrical control device, or two or more meters may be mechanically linked through a differential to maintain the measurement of the components in a desired ratio.

Remote indicating or recording counters and presetting devices are available for control, data processing or blending operations.

Turbine meters are also being used for oil measurement. In these meters, an impeller fitted with angled blades is mounted axially in the pipe and rotates at a speed proportional to the liquid velocity. The impeller may be geared to a mechanical counter or the meter may be fitted with a pick-up coil which senses changes in the magnetic field or in electrical capacitance as the impeller rotates beneath it, and transmits a series of electrical pulses to an electronic counter. These meters have the advantage that they are very compact whereas positive displacement meters are heavy and cumbersome in the larger capacities. However, they are less accurate than positive displacement meters over a similar wide range of flow rates and are particularly sensitive to viscosity (and hence temperature) changes in the liquid. Although viscosity changes can be partially compensated, the meters are not yet accepted generally for the measurement of smaller quantities. However, when the flow rate, viscosity, and temperature, of the liquid stream remain fairly constant over long periods, as in some pipeline operations, turbine meters are being accepted for custody transfer purposes.

Although the use of specially calibrated proving tanks of fixed volume for the checking and calibration of meters still remains as a reference standard, methods incorporating Group patents which utilize a calibrated section of the pipeline are fast becoming the preferred method, particularly as they are very suitable for inclusion in automated schemes.

In these systems, a series of electrical pulses produced by a generator on the meter and proportional to the volume delivered, is fed to an electronic counter, the pulse train being started and stopped by the passage of a solid plug in the line as it passes detector switches fitted at each end of the calibrated section. The volume equivalent to the number of pulses counted is compared after each run with the known volume displaced by the plug between the two detector switches.

Lease automatic custody transfer (LACT) systems

Increasing use is being made of automatic measuring methods in production leases where sustained accuracy of measurement is required for custody transfer purposes and royalty assessment. LACT systems must be capable of operating unattended for long periods under very rigorous conditions. Two methods of measurement are employed, one using positive displacement meters and the other incorporating 'dump tanks' which are calibrated containers arranged to fill and empty automatically, the total number of fillings being counted and recorded. Both systems include gas and water separation equipment and may incorporate temperature compensation and BS and W monitoring.

Package filling

Drums and smaller containers may be filled either by volume or by weight. In the former case, local regulations may insist that the volume shall be correct at a standard temperature.

Manually operated volumetric fillers of the duplex type, consisting of two containers, the volume of which can be fixed within narrow limits, and so arranged that one fills as the other empties into the package, were formerly widely used. They are now largely replaced by automatic volumetric filling machines fitted with a multiplicity of filling points operated on a time cycle, or for larger quantities, by positive-displacement meters fitted with repeating presets, and sometimes incorporating a temperature compensating device.

Automatic weight fillers, which are frequently electrically controlled, are now more often used for filling tins and small packages than for drums. In these machines the flow of oil, which can be started manually or automatically, is automatically cut off when the weight reaches a predetermined figure, the machine incorporating an adjusting device for the tare of the container.

Loss control

The general rise in world prices in recent years has focused attention on the need for reducing all handling losses to the minimum. Small losses are inevitable, particularly with volatile products, but careful operation and 'good housekeeping' can do much to keep these losses at an economic level.

The first stage in loss control is the keeping of accurate stock records. Real losses may be masked by temperature variations, and it is therefore essential that oil accounting should be on a basis of weight or of volume at standard temperature, and in such detail as will enable losses to be determined at each stage of the operations. Errors in accounting or invoicing may sometimes occur but can usually be detected and corrected immediately if the correct stock accounting procedure is adhered to.

An apparent loss through faulty measurement at one stage may be balanced by a corresponding gain at another stage, but if the errors are large, real losses may be hidden. If a similar error is made in buying or selling, a real loss or gain will occur. Accurate measurement is essential to avoid such events. Small differences will inevitably occur from time to time but these can be estimated statistically, allowing the more serious systematic errors, in tank or meter calibration or in measuring instruments, to be determined and corrected.

Losses by leakage or spillage can be prevented or minimized by careful operational procedure, adequate plant maintenance and staff training. The seriousness of even a small leak is illustrated by the fact that a leak of only one drop per second undetected for a year would cause a loss of about 410 UK gal (492 US gal, 1860 litres).

Careful drainage of ships' tanks, and road and rail vehicle tanks is essential, especially with viscous products such as fuel oils, lubricating oils, bitumens and crude oils, particularly those of a waxy nature. Many tons of crude oil may be left in the bottoms and on the sides of ships' tanks, although these cargoes are usually heated to facilitate pumping and to assist drainage. Large quantities of oil were formerly lost through this cause, the residues being pumped overboard with ballast water. The Group has played a leading part in devising means to combat the menace of sea pollution and contamination of beaches arising from this practice. The tanks of all Group tankers, and those of many of the larger tanker owners, are now washed at sea, the oily water is collected and allowed to settle, and the clear water is then pumped overboard and the oil retained on board (p. 261).

In many operations, particularly those connected with tanker discharge, some loss by down-grading of products is inevitable, especially when one pipeline is used for more than one product. Down-grading does not involve loss of product but can represent a serious loss of money. It can be minimized by careful control of pumping operations.

Losses by evaporation represent the biggest single category of loss for volatile products, and as such merits more detailed consideration.

Evaporation losses

The quantity of liquid that will evaporate into the vapour space of a container is governed by the surface temperature of the liquid, its vapour pressure at that temperature, and the total pressure in the vapour space. Vapour pressure increases with temperature and the higher the vapour pressure the more readily will the liquid evaporate. In a closed container evaporation will continue until equilibrium is reached when the air/vapour mixture above the liquid becomes saturated.

Other factors influencing evaporation losses are:

The relation of the liquid volume to the capacity of the container.

The type and size of container and the surface area of the liquid.

The range of pressures over which the pressure/vacuum relief valve in a storage tank works.

Climatic conditions.

The temperature variations in both the liquid and the vapour spaces of the container.

The quantity of liquid pumped into or out of the container and the rate of pumping.

The time during which the product remains in the tank.

The molecular weight of the liquid, which governs the volume of vapour produced by the complete evaporation of unit volume of the liquid.

The significance of these factors is discussed under the following three headings.

Filling losses

During the filling of a container, some of the liquid will evaporate into the air space in the container. As the liquid level rises, air/vapour mixture will be displaced to atmosphere and the remaining mixture will become progressively richer in vapour until, towards the end of the operation, it will reach saturation. The rate of increase in vapour content is proportional to the degree of turbulence of the liquid, and filling losses therefore may be minimized by avoiding splashing. This is done by using a filling pipe that extends to the bottom of the container, or by filling through a bottom connexion. The loss by submerged filling of an average gasoline into a bulk lorry should be less than 0·1 %v, but with splash loading it could be as high as 0·25 %v. Higher losses may be experienced in drum filling, where it is not practicable to use completely submerged filling, especially if the velocity of the emerging air/vapour mixture is sufficiently high to entrain liquid droplets. The remedy is to reduce the speed of filling.

Displacement losses

Conversely, when a container is emptied, fresh air is drawn in, which in time becomes saturated with vapour. In large storage tanks evaporation will continue for some days after pumping has ceased before saturation is reached. Subsequently, when the tank is refilled, the vapour will be displaced to atmosphere and lost. Displacement losses may be less than 0·1 %v in tanks where the emptying-filling cycle is very short but normally for gasoline a loss from about 0·15 %v to 0·20 %v will occur according to its vapour pressure and temperature.

Both displacement and filling losses can be reduced by using a closed vapour-return system in which the vapour spaces of the container being filled and of the tank from which it is being filled are interconnected by pipework. The vapour is thus displaced from the one container into the other, reducing filling and displacement losses by about two-thirds. The system is suitable only in small compact depots, in larger installations the cost of the piping is prohibitive. Displacement losses from many storage tanks may also be reduced by using floating roofs, floating screens or special types of tanks, which are described in more detail later.

Breathing losses

So far, only losses incurred in product movement have been discussed. Evaporation also takes place in standing storage, and high losses may occur through the phenomenon known as 'breathing'. During the daytime the vapour space of a tank becomes heated by the surrounding atmosphere or by the direct rays of the sun. The air/vapour mixture in it therefore expands and is expelled to the atmosphere. At night the vapour space cools and fresh air is drawn in. This air takes up more vapour, and the mixture will again be expelled on the following day when the tank is again warmed. Vapour is thus lost as the cycle is repeated. Apart from the major changes between day and night temperatures, rain and cold winds will also have an effect.

In-fixed roof tanks used for storing gasoline and other volatile oil products or chemicals, pressure/vacuum relief valves are fitted, the roofs being strengthened to withstand small inward or outward pressures. During the heating period of the breathing cycle, loss of vapour is prevented until the pressure rises above the pressure-valve setting and, conversely, during the other part of the cycle, the vacuum valve prevents air from being sucked in until the vacuum setting has been reached.

Two types of fixed-roof tanks are in use within the Group for volatile products, one operating over a pressure range of 10½ in. water gauge (26·5 g/cm²), the other over pressure ranges up to 24 in. water gauge (60 g/cm²). The roofs of the former type are often lagged with cork slabs or other suitable insulation, which decreases the temperature variations in the vapour space. This, together with the effect of the relief valves, reduces the breathing losses by about 75 % as compared with a freely ventilated, uninsulated tank. The breathing losses from the higher pressure range tanks, which are limited to diameters not exceeding 64 ft, may be even less although roof insulation is not used with them.

The cost of tanks rises very sharply with increase in working pressure so that, except in special circumstances, it is not economic to build gasoline tanks to operate at higher pressures.

Breathing losses may also be prevented, or reduced, by other methods. In the floating-roof tanks described on page 277 there is no vapour space, and breathing takes place only above the roof seal. The losses from the standard seal are about equal to the breathing loss from a standard tank, operating at 8 in. water gauge pressure/2½ in. water-gauge vacuum, but lower losses are claimed for certain special seals whilst the floating roof also prevents displacement losses.

In the variable vapour-space tank, the volume of the space contained by the roof can change, thus allowing vapour to expand into it. This type of roof construction is costly, and maintenance charges are usually higher than for fixed-roof tanks. Extravagant claims are sometimes made for these tanks but it is doubtful whether they offer any real advantage over standard tanks. The three main types of variable vapour-space tanks are (a) the vapour-dome tank fitted with a flexible balloon-like synthetic rubber membrane which inflates [Fig. 241]; (b) the lifter-roof tank on which the roof moves up and down like a gasholder [Fig. 242]; and (c) the balloon-roof tank in which the roof, made of thin flexible steel plates, can inflate. Sometimes the vapour spaces of a number of fixed-roof tanks are connected with a variable vapour-space tank or with a vapour holder.

In addition to roof lagging, cooling of the vapour space may be effected by fitting a water spray. This system suffers from the disadvantage that frequent re-painting of the roof and shell is necessary to prevent corrosion, and unless the system is automatically controlled, over-cooling may take place, with increase in breathing loss. Water cooling is not often used nowadays for shore tanks but is used most successfully for the control of losses from barges and small tankers operating in tropical waters.

The paint used on tanks has a marked effect on losses; highly reflective paints such as aluminium or titanium white paint give the best results.

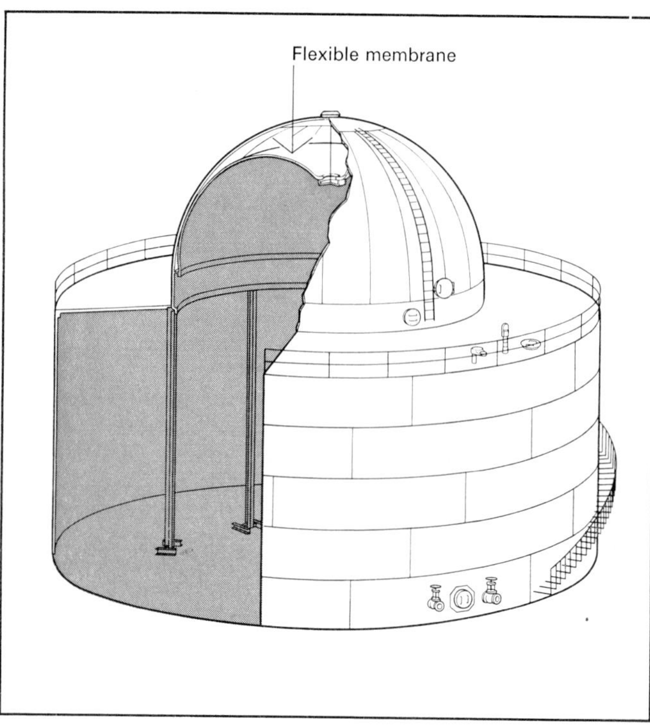

Fig. 241 Vapour-dome tank

Floating screens

In recent years a number of conservation methods have been tried, based on similar principles to those of the floating-roof, but intended for use in fixed-roof tanks. These have included 'microballoons', minute hollow spheres of phenolic resin resembling a coarse powder, which form a plastic layer on the oil surface; 'plastic blankets' consisting of sheets of PVC supported by a cellular layer of the same material, the whole resembling a floating-roof; and similar blankets or screens made of resin-bonded fibreglass, aluminium or thin sheet steel.

Although microballoons are effective initially in comparatively thick layers when used for crude oil, the material is expensive, wastage is high and there is risk of product contamination. Plastic blankets were similarly effective in reducing evaporation losses, but rapid deterioration of the blanket occurred in service, particularly with aromatic-rich products. These methods have therefore given place to fibreglass and metallic screens, but these are generally expensive, and their use cannot be economically justified in

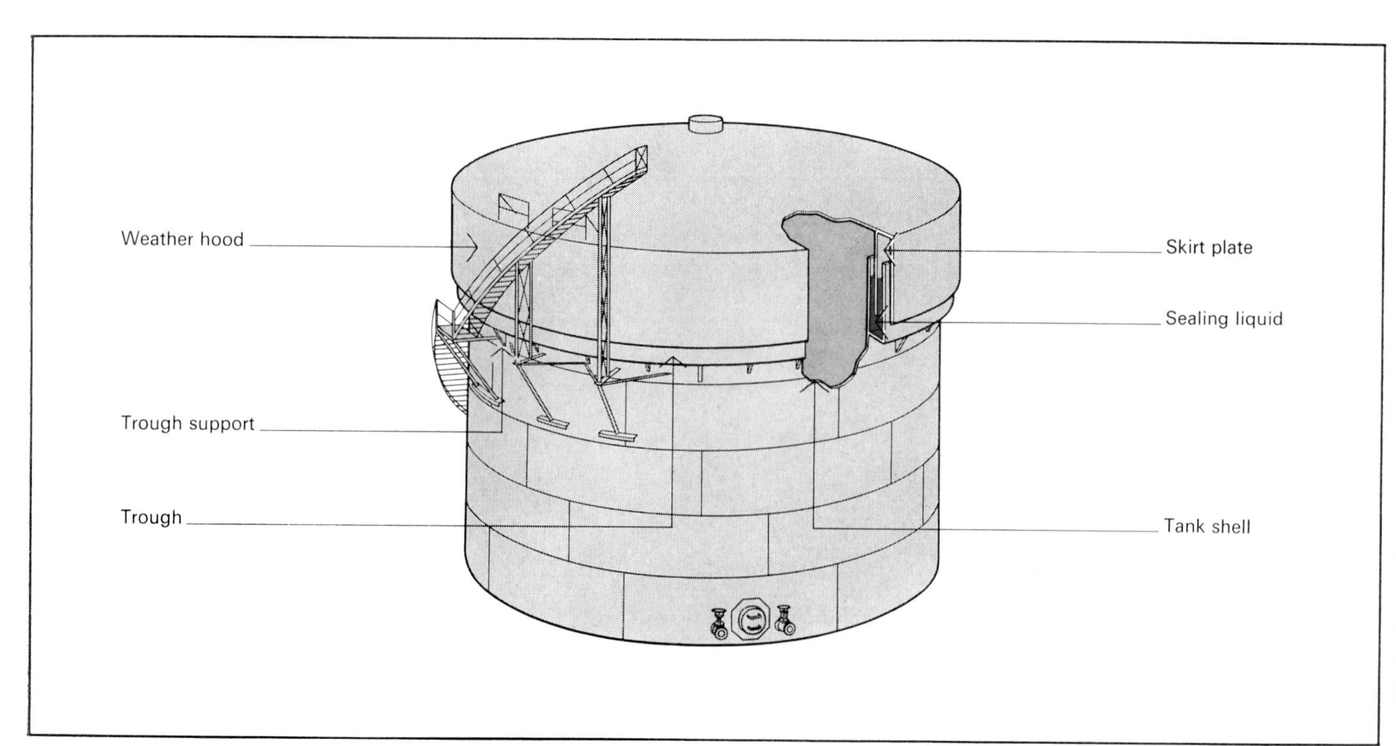

Fig. 242 Lifter-roof tank

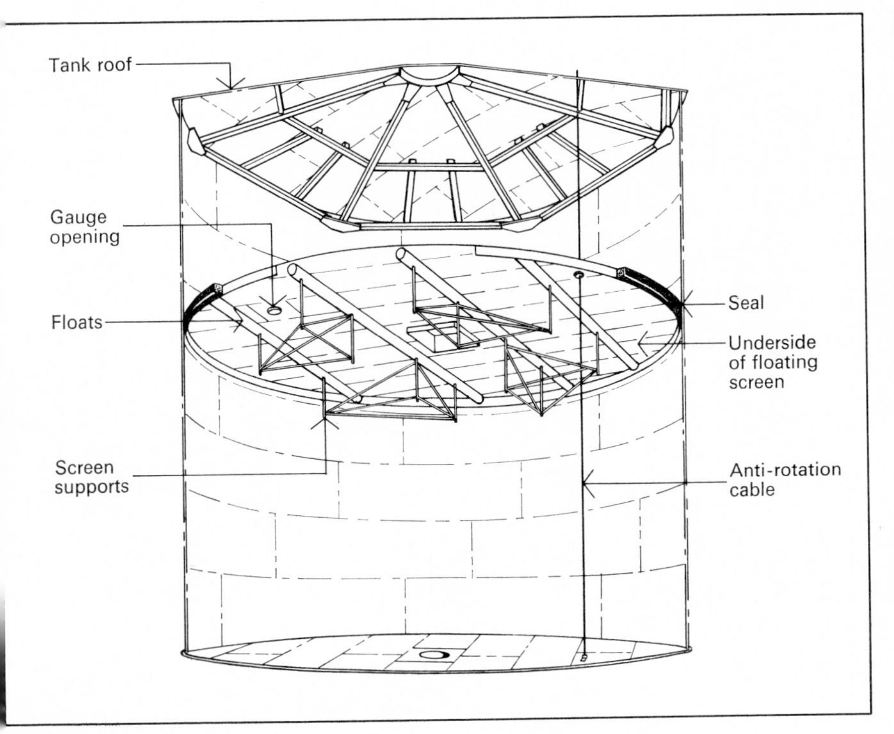

Fig. 243 Floating-screen tank

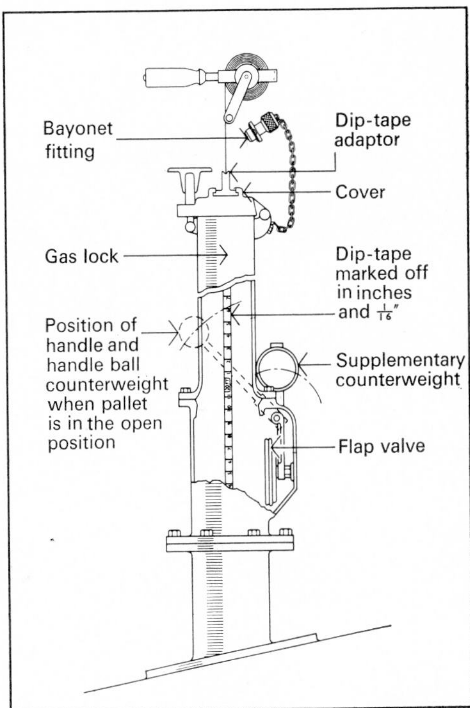

Fig. 244 Slot dipping device

many cases. However, one form of aluminium screen, designed by the Group, can be constructed more cheaply than similar proprietary equipment and is being used successfully in several installations [Fig. 243]. Quite apart from their use as vapour conservation devices, screens are installed in tanks containing aviation turbine fuels to reduce hazards from static electricity.

Precautions

In order to take full advantage of the saving afforded by the various vapour-conservation methods, it is essential that tank roofs should be kept vapour-tight by adequate maintenance of all roof fittings. Unnecessary loss of vapour should be avoided; tanks should not be opened frequently for sampling, gauging, etc, and gauge hatches and manhole covers must not be left open. Special dipping devices, such as the slot dipping device designed by Shell [Fig. 244], enable tanks to be manually gauged whilst under pressure. In this apparatus, designed for pressures up to 24 in. water gauge (60 g/cm^2), the dip-tape is passed through a narrow slot through which only a very small quantity of vapour can escape, and samples can be taken through a gas-lock. For tanks operating at higher pressures, a totally enclosed dipping and sampling head is used. Automatic tank gauging equipment also permits measurements to be made while the tank is under pressure and special designs are available for LPG and LNG tanks.

Research and development

Research and development

Industrial research is not an isolated activity, but is an integral part of the whole industrial organization. The oil and chemical industries are based on technology, and the responsibility of industrial research is to provide new technology as required. Results should be available at the right time and in the right quantity for use by the operating functions. For optimum benefit the research programme should be geared to the operating structure and objectives of the enterprise, and consequently the planning of research is a very important and almost continuous activity.

In striving for the goals set by the research programme, scientific knowledge and method are applied to a large extent.

Scientific knowledge has been accumulating over many centuries, but the systematic research now commonplace in industry is a comparatively new activity. It developed extensively during the nineteenth century, but growth in the present century has been prodigious.

Since the middle of the nineteenth century the research activities of industries and governments have expanded tremendously, stimulated to a large extent by inter-company and inter-state competition. Whilst it is difficult to reach a reliable figure for present-day expenditure on research, the amount in 1960 was certainly well in excess of £7000 million in the western world alone. In the United Kingdom, government and industry between them spent considerably more than £600 million in 1962 on research and development, whilst the figure for the United States was well over £6500 million.

There are great differences in the uses of research by different industries. On the one hand, there are the industries firmly based on scientific and technical knowledge acquired by research, like the aviation, chemical and oil industries. These and other industries could not maintain their position without continuous research. On the other hand, there are old-established craft industries whose operations have been based on practical knowledge acquired over a long period of time; these have been slow to embark upon research, partly on account of their conservative attitude and partly because of the expenditure involved. However, most of these industries now realize the benefits to be obtained from research and, by joining together to form research associations or by making use of semi-official or private research institutions, the smaller concerns, typical of these craft industries, are beginning to take advantage of modern research methods.

A great change in research methods has come about in consequence of the more and more complex problems with which modern industry has to contend. Barely fifty years ago, research was confined to a few creative minds. In those days scientists worked very much alone, on their own initiative, aided by only a few assistants. They were guided largely by their intuition and were more concerned with advancing fundamental knowledge than with developing practical applications of this knowledge. Today there is an emphasis on practical application and there has consequently been a far-reaching change in the approach to research. Industrial research is now tackled by organized teams to investigate a particular problem systematically.

Although this system brings a massive attack to bear on a problem, it involves an extra level of scientific administration to organize and direct the effort of specialists and to co-ordinate their results in order to arrive at useful solutions. Additionally, various services are required to support the research teams, ranging from workshops for making specialized experimental equipment to a publications section for disseminating the final reports.

Whilst such teamwork has produced striking results – an outstanding example being the enormous strides made in the development of nuclear energy over a period of ten or twelve years – there still remains the need for advancing fundamental and basic knowledge. A certain proportion of the budget of a large industrial research laboratory is therefore devoted to fundamental research.

Fundamental research, embracing both theoretical and experimental work, generally provides new knowledge and techniques in a particular field of interest; sometimes new insights are acquired leading to entirely new ideas.

Research in the oil industry

The oil industry invests heavily in research. It is usual to express research expenditure as a percentage of the net sales of a company or industry. The expenditure of the Royal Dutch/Shell Group on oil and chemical research, including experimental activities of certain operating companies, currently stands at about 1% of net sales. The amount involved in 1964 was well over £30 million, while the activity embraced more than 7000 people.

In the United States, the largest producer and consumer of petroleum products, the oil industry spends enormous sums of money on research, as shown by the following approximate figures:

1955 £60 million
1958 £80 million
1961 £100 million

In relation to net sales, the US oil industry, including chemical activities, also spends about 1% on research and development. For comparison, the figure for many chemical industries throughout the world ranges around 4–5%, and there are other industries which spend even more in relation to their sales, although in such cases there is often a strong measure of state aid. There are other industries, however, which spend less.

It has been estimated that research expenditure by the world petroleum industry outside the Sino-Soviet spheres has more than tripled during the last decade from £38 million in 1953 to approximately £125 million in 1963. During recent years, major oil companies have spent on average about equal proportions of their research funds, i.e. 25%, on exploration and production, oil manufacturing methods, oil product development, and chemicals.

Because of the number and diversity of products derived

from petroleum, and the complexity of the many operations involved, from exploration to marketing, only the larger oil companies can afford to undertake comprehensive research and that undertaken by the Royal Dutch/Shell Group can be taken as an example of what is involved.

Organization of research in the Royal Dutch/Shell Group

The operations of a fully integrated oil enterprise such as the Royal Dutch/Shell Group may be divided broadly into four main sections: Exploration and Production; Manufacturing and Marketing Oil; Manufacturing and Marketing Chemicals; Transport and Storage.

Research activities fall naturally into these same categories but attention is also given to research concerned with advancing general knowledge. Accordingly research activity within the Group is concerned with Exploration and Production; Oil Processes and Products; Chemical Processes and Products; Transport and Storage; and Fundamental Research.

Group Research, including experimental activities of certain operating companies, is located in some twenty-five laboratories spread over various countries (the Netherlands, United Kingdom, France, Germany, United States of America and Canada).

Exploration and production research

Exploration research is largely concerned with methods for discovering new sources of crude oil. As most of the oil-bearing structures that are more or less sharply outlined against their surroundings, either geologically or geophysically, have now been found, the search for new oil reservoirs is becoming increasingly difficult. In order to find the less-defined structures, new and more accurate exploration methods have to be developed, and the accuracy, selectivity and conclusiveness of the existing methods improved.

Furthermore, a better understanding of factors affecting the occurrence of oil underground is required. Many aspects of the genesis, migration and accumulation of oil are not yet fully understood. In order both to solve these problems and to provide a basis for the development of new exploration methods and the improvement of existing exploration techniques, extensive and costly fundamental research is essential. Exploration research extends over many subjects and comprises studies in geophysics and geochemistry – sciences concerned with the physics and chemistry of the earth as a whole and of its component parts; palaeontology and palynology, sciences concerned with fossil flora and fauna; sedimentology – a science concerned with the deposition, composition and configuration of sedimentary rocks; and a number of other related sciences (Exploration, p. 20).

Production research concerns itself with the problems of drilling for oil and of bringing it to the surface as effectively and cheaply as possible. Drilling costs are increasing, not only because of mounting labour and equipment costs but also on account of the increased depths at which oil is now being discovered, particularly in the USA, and because more wells are being drilled in less accessible locations. It is therefore of the greatest importance that the efficiency of drilling techniques should be improved as much as possible (Drilling, p. 33).

Fig. 245 Sea-bed sampling device for use in offshore exploration

A great deal of this research is done in the field, but much also in laboratories. The principal subjects under investigation are: the factors influencing the drilling rate, and the development of more efficient drilling fluids for general use, or of fluids suitable for use in drilling at great depths when conditions are such that normal drilling fluids cannot be employed. Techniques, such as electric, radioactive and sonic logging methods used for the identification and appraisal of strata penetrated by the drill, are being perfected, and improved methods of interpreting the data obtained by these means are being devised. In co-operation with field organizations, new drilling methods, equipment and materials are being developed and tested, particularly for offshore operations, the present highly developed state of which is very much due to research [Fig. 245].

The problem of obtaining the maximum possible yield from a field is receiving continued attention. It is not possible to extract all the oil that a producing formation contains; the percentage that can be recovered depends not only on the original conditions in the reservoir but also on the production methods employed. Accordingly constant study is made of drainage conditions in reservoir rocks and improved methods of producing and gathering the oil. Subjects of study are, for instance, formation pressure/volume/temperature relations, acidizing of impervious rock, sand consolidation, emulsion dehydration, gas and oil separation, just to mention a few.

Much oil is, however, often retained in the oil-bearing strata, held like liquid in a sponge, after normal production has ceased. Of particular importance are therefore 'secondary recovery' methods, such as repressuring, artificial water drive and the newer methods, involving the introduction of heat into a reservoir, either by injecting hot water or steam, or by underground combustion, in cases where the high viscosity of the oil would restrict flow through the producing formation.

In general, investigation of these problems in the laboratory is concerned with physical properties of reservoir rocks, while relative movements of the oil, gas and water which they contain are studied mathematically and experimentally. Tests are carried out on samples of various kinds of reservoir rock but, in addition, use is made of models of ingenious design which allow reproduction on a small scale of the movement of fluids that would take place when oil is being produced from an actual reservoir formation. In such models the development of flow patterns and changes in pressures, which would take years in an actual reservoir under normal conditions, are accomplished in much less time, thereby making it possible to predict the behaviour of a field in practice.

Oil process and product research

The task of process research is to develop new processes and to improve existing ones, as well as to reduce manufacturing costs. It also aims at developing, from the various crude oils available, new and better products to meet ever changing demands.

Research is continuous on the various separation, conversion and treating processes described under Manufacture, p. 78. Separation processes, the earliest of refinery operations, have long been practised but are continually under review by research to improve their techniques. The conversion processes are of more recent origin and are the outcome of research that has brought about great changes in the industry. Apart from raising the whole level of quality, they have enabled the industry to meet the changing relative demands for the various products.

Fig. 246 A complex laboratory apparatus for studying catalytic gas reactions

In support of the research directly concerned with process development, fundamental studies are made on the activity, selectivity and life of various catalysts, on a variety of phenomena concerned with the mixing of fluids, including heat transfer, and on the properties and characteristics of the construction materials to be used for building the final plant [Fig. 246].

Research is also carried out on equipment for the control of plant operation. The processes in modern refineries are often so complicated that manual control is no longer possible or advisable, so that techniques of automatic control are continually being developed and used. Great advances have been made in this direction, and automation is highly advanced and successfully applied in many branches of the petroleum industry. A considerable research effort is still devoted to improving and developing new control techniques, making use of modern mathematical methods.

A major phase of process research concerns pilot plant work. If a laboratory investigation shows promise, development work is carried out in pilot plants, which are small versions of the full-scale plant. This step is necessary because, when a process has been worked out in a small laboratory apparatus, it is not possible to transfer it directly to an industrial scale without running considerable risks. In pilot plants not only can the process be worked out and improved, but products can be prepared in the same way as in the future industrial plant, and their quality evaluated. The complexity of a pilot plant is illustrated in Fig. 247.

Oil product research is concerned with product performance and the development of products suitable for given applications. Research here is closest to the user or the customer and, therefore, to the sales side of the business.

The main objectives of this type of research are:

To maintain products in the forefront of quality by developing new or improved products to meet the marketing demands.

To establish the standards of quality and the test methods needed to ensure these standards.

To cope with new developments in equipment.

To detect and overtake any competitive advance as rapidly as possible.

To provide technical service to customers.

To build up the prestige and goodwill of the Group in technical circles.

Engineering research and development is leading continuously to the operation of equipment at higher speeds, temperatures and pressures and to the use of new constructional materials, all of which make the oil product requirements more exacting. Consequently, oil product research is continually directed to new goals and is becoming more specific in its aims. Exceptions arise when development ceases in some field of engineering. For example, no research is now done on aviation gasoline because the piston aero-engine, though still in use, has been static in design since the introduction of the gas turbine engine. These new performance requirements have to be translated into scientific and technological terms. For example, a lubricant may need improved oxidation stability; a gasoline may need an improved octane number for certain new high compression ratio car engines. Only when such translations have been carried out can the procedures for examining the behaviour of the product be decided. When the critical requirement is related to a recognized physico-chemical property, such as oxidation stability, it can be studied in simple glass equipment such as is available in any chemical

Fig. 247 Pilot plant for investigating processes involving hydrogen under pressure (hydroprocesses)

laboratory. When, as more often happens, the physico-chemical property in question is the result of a complex combination of a number of factors, it is usually necessary to isolate, simulate and perhaps exaggerate the critical requirement in specially designed equipment. A typical example is a high-speed gear rig in which steel gears can be run at the highest speeds, tooth-loadings and temperatures likely to be encountered in existing or foreseen equipment.

Sometimes, the research can be carried out in the actual equipment in which the oil product is used. This is done if the equipment is relatively cheap and compact; for instance, normal domestic refrigerators are used for developing refrigerator oils. Even if equipment is neither cheap nor compact, it may still have to be used for research if the performance characteristics are so complicated that simulation would be impossible. This is one of the reasons why the anti-knock properties of gasolines are now mainly investigated in cars on the road or test-track instead of in laboratory engines.

When a new product has been formulated, performance trials are essential. If the preliminary work has been carried out in simulations rigs or chemical apparatus, the product is then evaluated in more realistic equipment, but still in conditions that are only a simulation of normal use. Thus engine oils may be tested in single-cylinder versions of normal commercial multi-cylinder engines, modified to impose severe conditions of operation. The object of this procedure is to accelerate deterioration of the product so that the test

Fig. 248 An engine test laboratory for assessing fuels and lubricants

differentiates between different products within a reasonably short period [Fig. 248].

The more promising formulations are tested under progressively more realistic conditions until some can be put forward for full-scale trials under actual service conditions. These trials may take place anywhere in the world; they may extend over as long as two to five years, since climatic and storage conditions, as well as immediate performance, have to be taken into account.

Chemical process and product research

The incentive for chemical process and product research arose when the introduction of cracking to increase gasoline production resulted in the simultaneous production of large quantities of unsaturated hydrocarbons which are potential raw materials for the manufacture of chemicals. However, the chemical side of the industry has grown so rapidly that its raw material requirements far exceed the availability of unsaturated hydrocarbons as by-products from oil refining, and major plants are now used for the production of unsaturated hydrocarbons and aromatics, gasoline being the by-product.

The chemical business is still based to a very large extent on unsaturated hydrocarbons (olefins) and much research is devoted to the discovery of new products that can be produced from them and to the invention of new processes for the manufacture of such products.

The lower olefins such as ethylene, propylene and the butylenes, together with dienes such as butadiene, are produced by cracking light petroleum fractions, and the higher olefins – C_6 to C_{18} – are produced by cracking wax. Much research is devoted to extensive studies of the chemistry of olefins, dienes and the many products that can be made from them. Processes have been developed for the production of alcohols from the corresponding olefins, and from these a wide range of solvents and other chemicals and intermediates can be produced. Research on olefin chlorination revealed that, instead of the classic addition reaction across the double bond, a substitutive chlorination of one of the hydrogens on the double bond could be achieved, and this has led to the development of a process for the production of allyl chloride and, from it, allyl alcohol and glycerol. With this process, the Royal Dutch/Shell Group was the first discoverer of an economic synthetic route to glycerol which previously had been available in commercial quantities only from natural sources. From allyl chloride, epichlorhydrin, a key raw material for the production of Epikote resins, can also be produced.

Research on olefin oxidation has led to the Shell Direct Oxidation process for the production of ethylene oxide and to a process for the production of acrolein from propylene. Only a decade ago, acrolein was a laboratory curiosity; it is now an important industrial intermediate with a considerable commercial potential. It is the starting material for an entirely new route to synthetic glycerol and further research is being devoted to extending its uses as an intermediate. A new route to hydrogen peroxide by the oxidation of isopropyl alcohol and a new process for the catalytic oxidation of hydrochloric acid to chlorine have been developed as a result of this type of research.

Research pioneered the development of synthetic detergents and continues to be active not only in developing new detergents but in investigating the problems resulting from their use. This has led to the development of biologically soft detergents – detergents that break down into simple compounds under the action of bacteria and therefore do not cause foam on rivers and waterways when effluent containing such detergents is discharged into them.

Considerable research is devoted to the development of plastics and the processes by which they are made. A process using the chlorination of ethylene, followed by the dehydrochlorination of the dichloroethane thereby produced, has been developed for the production of vinyl chloride from which polyvinyl chloride is manufactured. Research has also developed processes for the production of polyethylene and polystyrene from ethylene, and polypropylene from propylene.

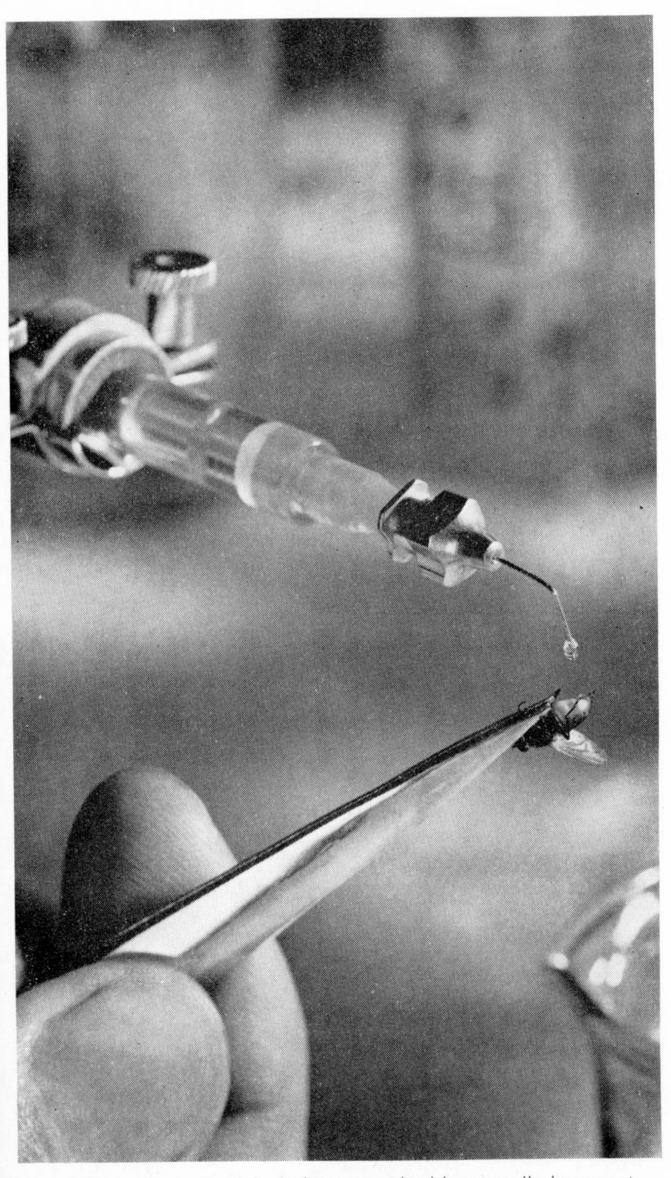

Fig. 249 Anaesthetized fly being treated with controlled amount of insecticide

Research continues on synthetic rubbers. The first commercial process for the large scale production of butadiene was developed during World War II but work is still going on in this field – indeed a new and unique process for the low cost production of this key raw material has recently been developed. Other results of this research have been the development of polyisoprene, a synthetic rubber closely approaching natural rubber both in chemical structure and in properties, and polybutadiene, a new type of synthetic rubber with specialized properties and applications.

Research is not devoted solely to the exploitation of raw materials that are easily available, or can be made at low cost, but extends to all fields of interest to the chemical industry. Particularly in the field of agricultural chemicals, a considerable research effort is being devoted to the development of new biocides – insecticides, fungicides, herbicides, etc – irrespective of the source of raw materials [Fig. 249]. Research is also devoted to seeking new applications for existing products, to improving the quality of those products, and to increasing the operating efficiency of the processes whereby they are made.

The development of biocides entails investigation of their toxicity to ensure not only that they are effective biocides but that they create no undue hazard to man. This in turn necessitates a considerable amount of background toxicological research and specialized laboratories.

Another field of interest, directly linked with oil product research, is the search for and manufacture of additives to improve the qualities of fuels and lubricants to which reference is made under Oil products – applications, p. 113.

It is the results of research such as outlined above, together with the less spectacular results of the whole support effort of the research laboratories, the technical service laboratories, and the manufacturing technological departments, which have helped to put the petroleum industry in the position in which it finds itself today as a major manufacturer of chemicals.

Research on transport and storage

The transport and storage of products give rise to their own special problems. These relate to improved methods of transport and storage, losses, corrosion of equipment, contamination, and hazards during transport and storage.

Much of the work is carried out in the field, since full-scale experiment is often necessary, but a considerable amount of supporting research is nevertheless done in the laboratory. Mock-up distribution systems are sometimes constructed to study problems under controlled conditions, for example in the case of hydrant re-fuelling systems for airfields. Before laying down such equipment at airfields it is clearly desirable to solve the problems which may arise in practice.

Corrosion in all its phases costs Group companies enormous sums of money annually and means for its alleviation are continuously under investigation.

Static electricity has been responsible for a number of fires and explosions during the handling of petroleum products and a great deal of successful activity has already been devoted to ways of overcoming this hazard.

Marine research connected with a tanker fleet constitutes a special part of this type of research. Tank cleaning; prevention of tank corrosion by cathodic protection, by special

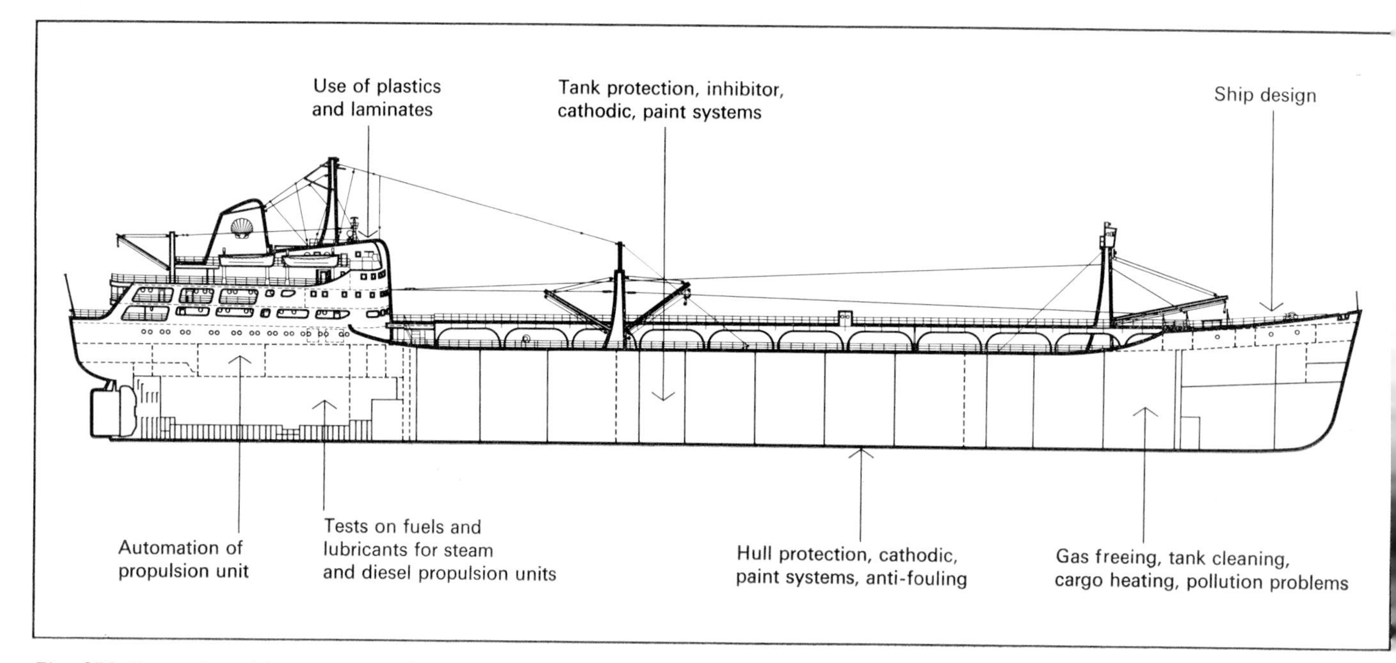

Fig. 250 Research problems connected with the tanker

paint systems and by inhibitors; transport by tanker of liquified petroleum gas; all these are typical examples of marine research [Fig. 250].

Research is also being carried out to solve problems emanating from the increased use of pipelines for the transport of crude oil and products.

This type of research is carried out in most laboratories, depending upon the nature and location of the particular problem, and not in a central specialized laboratory, but central co-ordination ensures effective utilization of research facilities.

Fundamental research

There was a time when it was the practice for industry to 'obtain from books' the basic knowledge necessary for the solution of its problems, and the establishment of this knowledge was almost exclusively the province of the universities. However this is no longer the case; the increasing complexity of the problems in the oil and other industries has created so great a need for basic knowledge that it can no longer be satisfied by the universities. Therefore a certain part of the Group's research effort is concerned with fundamental research. This comprises research in practically every department of chemistry, organic, inorganic, analytical, physical and colloid; in many departments of physics, such as the structure of liquids and solids, spectroscopy, physical measuring methods, thermodynamics, physical technology, rheology, geophysics and optics; in mathematics, for example in mathematical statistics and numerical analysis; and in biology, including microbiology and biochemistry [Fig. 251].

Problems that can be solved only by long-term efforts, and for which a specialized knowledge of mathematics and theoretical methods is necessary, are becoming of increasing importance. In order to master the very extensive calculations which are often necessary, use is made of modern computers, without which many fields of investigation would remain inaccessible [Fig. 252].

Fig. 251 The rotating cryostat used to isolate organic free radicals for further study

Fig. 252 The analogue computer enables the chemical engineer to carry out complex simulated experiments rapidly and cheaply

While industry now devotes a notable effort to fundamental research, it should perhaps be emphasized that this is in no way intended to displace the valuable work done in the university laboratories; in fact it supplements it. Indeed, by means of grants for post-graduate research and donations to building funds, industry is supporting these institutions and encouraging their research activities. There is a considerable amount of collaboration, and industrial staff are frequently seconded to universities and institutes to acquire knowledge in special fields.

Patents

Throughout the oil industry it is the general practice to patent a large part of the inventions arising from research and development work. As a result, competitors know about each other's inventions at an early stage, duplication of research effort is avoided and technical progress in the oil industry is expedited. The general willingness, particularly in the field of oil processing, to grant licences to others under one's own patents further contributes to this progress, especially as the existence of a patent enables valuable know-how, unpatentable in itself but broadly protected by the patent, to be included in the licence.

Very many refinery processes are available under licence and it would be fair to say it is possible to build a modern refinery by purchasing the required processes and the attendant operating information without it being necessary to have a large research and development organization. Obviously, in such cases, the royalties to be paid to the more advanced organizations which have been responsible for the development of the processes, will take the place of the research costs which must otherwise be borne. The larger the operations grow, however, the greater becomes the economic advantage of development of technical knowledge and consequent patenting, quite apart from the additional advantage of gaining time in the modernization and optimization of the operations.

A similar attitude on licensing is generally taken with respect to the fields of exploration and production, general equipment, pollution and safety. However, where the results of research contribute to the appeal which a company's product has for its customers, the company generally wants to keep the results exclusively to itself, in accordance with the aim of the patent system. Understandably such policy is the more necessary where the size of such markets or the price structure could not bear competition. In general, this policy is more applied in the fields of oil and chemical products. However, as patents have a limited life and the invention of alternatives might circumvent the exclusivity, these subjects also ultimately become available to the industry at large.

The Group's activity in patents is in broad lines very similar to that of the whole of the industry; it generally patents its inventions. To this end its patent organization keeps in close contact with research and technological work conducted in laboratories and plants and when novel and useful inventions are made, the machinery for patenting them is put into motion. Since each patent is only effective in its own country this means that a series of patents for an invention may have to be taken out in a number of countries; an important invention may thus be patented in some thirty or more countries. The aggregate of patent applications filed annually lies between three and four thousand.

The converse of this task is to prevent competitors obtaining patents of unduly broad scope which may become a hindrance for one's own operations. As court litigation is usually highly time and labour consuming and excessively costly, many countries have instituted opposition proceedings in which the public can intervene in the grant of patents and thus effectuate a control with respect to the decisions of the Patent Offices. About 10 000 patent specifications have to be screened for this purpose annually.

A major task of the patent organization is to see that when plans are being made for the introduction of new or improved processes and products no conflicts will arise with patents held by others. It advises on their scope and validity, on the possibility of overcoming such patent obstructions or on the necessity of seeking licences.

As already mentioned, patents form a valuable source of technical information and may also give an early indication of new developments initiated by competitors. A continuous stream of such patents are published all over the world and the most interesting information therefore is extracted by the patent organization for dissemination within the Group. In this fashion about 2000 inventions in the petroleum field and 6000 in the chemical field are annually called to the attention of those concerned, a selection of the odd 40 000 patents which are annually added to the patent library, which constitutes the most extensive catalogue of the state of the art available to the Group. In the handling, storage and retrieval of this accumulating information modern processing through mechanical and electronic equipment is now being used.

In addition to these aspects of the work, the patent organization contributes to the gradual improvement of the patent laws and international arrangements and conventions by studying the problems thereof, co-operating in efforts made by professional and business institutions and advising where appropriate. Finally it is charged with the task of preventing unauthorized use of the Group's patents or infringement of the exclusivity it may enjoy through being licensed by others.

Bibliography

The petroleum industry

Beaton, K. F.
Enterprise in Oil: A History of Shell in the United States
(Appleton-Century-Crofts, New York, 1957)

Dunstan, A. E. *et al* (eds)
The Science of Petroleum, 6 volumes
(Oxford University Press, London, 1938–55)

Forbes, R. J., O'Beirne, D. R.
The Technical Development of the Royal Dutch/Shell, 1890–1940
(Brill, Leiden, 1957)

Gerretson, F. C.
Geschiedenis der Koninklijke, 3 volumes
(N. V. A. Oosthoek's Uitgevers Maatschappij, Utrecht, 1942)
History of the Royal Dutch, 4 volumes. (English edition of above)
(Brill, Leiden, 1953–57)

Hartshorn, J. E.
Oil Companies and Governments
(Faber and Faber, London, 1962)

Henriques, R.
Marcus Samuel
(Barrie and Rockliffe, London, 1960)

N. V. Koninklijke Nederlandsche Petroleum Maatschappij: 1890, 16 Juni 1950; Gedenkboek uitgegeven ter gelegenheid van het Zestig Jarig Bestaan
(N. V. Koninklijke Nederlandsche Petroleum Mij., s'Gravenhage, 1950)
The Royal Dutch Petroleum Company (N. V. Koninklijke Nederlandsche Petroleum Maatschappij): 1890, 16 June 1950; Diamond Jubilee Book
(Royal Dutch Petroleum, The Hague, 1950) (English edition of above)

Odell, P. R.
Economic Geography of Oil
(Bell, London, 1963)

Sells, G.
The Petroleum Industry
(Oxford University Press, London, 1963)

Production

American Geological Institute
Glossary of Geology and Related Sciences
(American Geological Institute, Washington, DC, 2nd edition 1960)

Brantly, J. E.
Rotary Drilling Handbook
(Palmer Publications, Los Angeles, 6th edition 1961)

Carson, G. B. (ed)
Production Handbook
(Ronald Press, New York, 1958)

Dobrin, M. B.
Introduction to Geophysical Prospecting
(McGraw–Hill, New York, 2nd edition 1960)

Haun, J. D., Le Roy, L. W. (eds)
Subsurface Geology in Petroleum Exploration
(Colorado School of Mines, Golden, Colorado, 1958)

Illing, V. C. (ed)
The Science of Petroleum, Volume VI
(Oxford University Press, London, 1953)

Landes, K. K.
Petroleum Geology
(John Wiley, New York, 2nd edition 1959)

Levorsen, A. I.
Geology of Petroleum
(Freeman, San Francisco, 1954)

Moody, G. B. (ed)
Petroleum Exploration Handbook
(McGraw–Hill, New York, 1961)

Nind, T. E. W.
Principles of Oil Well Production
(McGraw–Hill, New York, 1964)

Pratt, W. E., Good, D. (eds)
World Geography of Petroleum
(American Geographical Society, Special Publication No. 31, Princeton University Press, 1950)

Russel, W. L.
Structural Geology for Petroleum Geologists
(McGraw–Hill, New York, 1955)

The chemistry of petroleum

Astle, M. J.
The Chemistry of Petrochemicals
(Reinhold, New York, 1956)

Hatch, L. F.
The Chemistry of Petrochemical Reactions
(Gulf, New York, 1955)

Brooks, B. T. *et al*
The Chemistry of Petroleum Hydrocarbons, 3 volumes
(Reinhold, New York, 1954)

Dunstan, A. E. *et al* (eds)
The Science of Petroleum, 6 volumes
(Oxford University Press, London, 1938–55)

Natural gas

Dunstan, A. E. *et al* (eds)
The Science of Petroleum, Volume II
(Oxford University Press, London, 1938)

Katz, D. L. *et al*
Handbook of Natural Gas Engineering
(McGraw–Hill, New York, 1959)

Lawrie, J.
Natural Gas and Methane Sources
(Chapman and Hall, London, 1961)

Medici, M.
Les Utilisations du Gas Naturel
(Dunod, Paris, 1959)

Schnidman, L. (ed)
Gaseous Fuels
(American Gas Association, 1954)

Stephens, M. M., Spencer, O. F.
Natural Gas Engineering
(Pennsylvania State University, 1957)

Oil products – manufacture

Alders, L.
Liquid–Liquid Extraction
(Elsevier, Amsterdam, 2nd edition 1959)

Dunstan, A. E. *et al* (eds)
The Science of Petroleum, 6 volumes
(Oxford University Press, London, 1935–55)

Gruse, W. A., Stevens, D. R.
Chemical Technology of Petroleum
(McGraw–Hill, New York, 1960)

Gurwitsch, L., Moore, H.
Scientific Principles of Petroleum Technology
(Chapman and Hall, London, 1932)

Institute of Petroleum
Modern Petroleum Technology
(Institute of Petroleum, London, 3rd edition 1962)

Kalichevsky, V. A., Kobe, K. A.
Petroleum Refining with Chemicals
(Elsevier, Amsterdam, 1956)

Kobe, K. A., Meketta, K. A.
Advances in Petroleum Chemistry and Refining, 10 volumes
(Interscience, New York, 1958–65)

Nelson, W. L.
Petroleum Refinery Engineering
(McGraw–Hill, New York, 4th edition 1958)

Robinson, C. G., Gilliland, E. R.
Elements of Fractional Distillation
(McGraw–Hill, New York, 4th edition 1950)

Treybal, R. E.
Liquid Extraction
(McGraw–Hill, New York, 1951)

Oil products – applications

General

Guthrie, V. B.
Petroleum Products Handbook
(McGraw–Hill, New York, 1960)

Have, van der, Verver, C. G.
Petroleum and its Products
(Pitman, London, 1957)

Institute of Petroleum
Glossary of Petroleum Terms
(Institute of Petroleum, London, 3rd edition 1961)

Institute of Petroleum
Modern Petroleum Technology
(Institute of Petroleum, London, 3rd edition 1962)

Dunstan, A. E. *et al* (eds)
The Science of Petroleum, 6 volumes
(Oxford University Press, London, 1938–55)

Engines

Ashton, R. L.
The Diesel Locomotive
(Thames & Hudson, London, 1957)

Broeze, J. J.
Combustion in Engines
(De Technische Uizgeverij H. Stam N. V., Haarlem, 1964)

Constant, H.
Gas Turbines and their Problems
(Todd, London, 1953)

Cox, H. Roxbee (ed)
Gas Turbines, Principles and Practice
(George Newnes, London, 1955)

Heldt, P. M.
High-Speed Combustion Engines; Design, Production, Tests
(Chilton, Philadelphia, 16th edition 1956)

Judge, A. W.
Modern Gas Turbines (1950)
High-Speed Diesel Engines (5th edition 1957)
Modern Smaller Diesel Engines (1965)
Modern Petrol Engines (1965)
(Chapman & Hall, London)

Lichty, L. C.
Internal Combustion Engines
(McGraw–Hill, New York, 6th edition 1951)

Maugham, E., Peace, A.
Jet Engine Manual
(George Newnes, London, 2nd edition 1956)

Molloy, E. (ed)
Automobile Diesel Engines
(George Newnes, London, 2nd edition 1958)

Pounder, C. C.
Marine Diesel Engines
(George Newnes, London, 2nd edition 1960)

Ricardo, H. R.
The High-Speed Internal Combustion Engine
(Blackie, London, 4th edition 1953)

Robertson, E. C.
The Industrial Gas Turbine
(Temple Press, London, 1951)

Shepherd, D. G.
Introduction to the Gas Turbine
(Constable, London, 2nd edition 1960)

Smith, G. G.
Gas Turbines and Jet Propulsion for Aircraft
(Flight, London, 6th edition 1955)

Smith, D. H.
The Modern Diesel
(Iliffe, London, 1959)

Schmidt, F. A. E.
The Internal Combustion Engine
(Chapman and Hall, London, 1965)

Fuels

Brame, J. S. S., King, J. G.
Fuel
(Edward Arnold, London, 1955)

Francis, W.
Fuels and Fuel Technology, 2 volumes
(Pergamon Press, Oxford, 1965)

Johnson, A. J., Auth, G. H. (eds)
Fuels and Combustion Handbook
(McGraw–Hill, New York, 1951)

Ministry of Fuel and Power
Efficient Use of Fuel
(HMSO, London, 1958)

Schnidman, L. (ed)
Gaseous Fuels
(American Gas Association, 1954)

Williams, D. A., Jones, G.
Liquid Fuels
(Pergamon Press, Oxford, 1963)

Lubricants

Bastian, E. L. H.
Metalworking Lubricants; their Selection, Application and Maintenance
(McGraw–Hill, New York, 1951)

Boner, C. J.
Manufacture and Application of Lubricating Greases
(Reinhold, New York, 1954)

Boner, C. J.
Gear Transmission Lubricants
(Reinhold, New York, 1964)

Bowden, F. P., Tabor, D.
Friction and Lubrication of Solids, Parts I and II
(Clarendon Press, Oxford, Part I 1954, Part II 1964)

Braithwaite, E. B.
Solid Lubricants and Surfaces
(Pergamon Press, Oxford, 1964)

Brewer, A. F.
Basic Lubrication Practice
(Reinhold, New York, 1955)

Evans, E. A.
Lubricating and Allied Oils
(Chapman and Hall, London, 4th edition 1963)

Forbes, W. G.
Lubrication of Industrial and Marine Machinery
Revised by C. L. Pope and W. T. Everitt
(Chapman and Hall, London, 2nd edition 1954)

Georgi, C. W.
Motor Oils and Engine Lubrication
(Reinhold, New York, 1950)

Groff, J. L. E.
ABC du Graissage, 3 volumes
(Editions Technip, Paris, 1961)

Gunderson, R. C., Hart, A. W. (eds)
Synthetic Lubricants
(Reinhold, New York, 1962)

Hobson, P. D.
Industrial Lubrication Practice
(Industrial Press, New York, 1955)

Institution of Mechanical Engineers
General Discussion on Lubrication and Lubricants 1937
Conference on Lubrication and Wear 1957
Lubrication and Wear Convention 1963
(Institution of Mechanical Engineers, London)

Morton, I. S., Perry, A. L. H.
Friction, Lubrication and Cutting Fluids
(Cleaver-Hume, London, 1957;
reprinted from H. Wright Baker [ed]:
Modern Workshop Technology,
Part II [2nd edition])

Thomsen, T. C.
The Practice of Lubrication
(McGraw–Hill, New York, 4th edition 1951)

Zuidema, H. H.
Performance of Lubricating Oils
(American Chemical Society Monograph Series; Reinhold, New York, 2nd edition 1959)

Wax

Warth, A. H.
The Chemistry and Technology of Waxes
(Reinhold, New York, 2nd edition 1956)

Bitumen

Abrahams, H.
Asphalts and Allied Substances, 5 volumes
(Nostrand, New York, 6th edition 1960)

Asbeck, Baron W. F. van
Bitumen in Hydraulic Engineering, 2 volumes
(Vol. 1 Shell International Petroleum, London, 1959)
(Vol. 2 Elsevier, Amsterdam, 1964)

Pfeiffer, J. Ph.
The Properties of Asphaltic Bitumen
(Elsevier, Amsterdam, 1950)

Road Emulsion Association Limited
Modern Road Emulsions
(Road Emulsion Association, London, 1958)

Traxler, R. N.
Asphalt, Its Composition, Properties and Uses
(Reinhold, New York, 1961)

Test methods

American Association for Testing and Materials, ASTM, Philadelphia
ASTM Standards–Volumes 17 and 18 (annual editions)
Significance of ASTM Tests for Petroleum Products (1957)
Manual for Rating Motor Fuels by Mohr and Rekardi Methods (1956; 1957)

Institute of Petroleum, IP, London
IP Standards for Petroleum and its Products
Part I *Methods for Analysis and Testing* (annually; 24th edition 1965)
Part II *Methods for Rating Fuels–Engine Tests* (2nd edition 1960)
Part III *Methods for Assessing Performance of Crankcase Lubricating Oils–Engine Tests* (2nd edition 1964)
Part IV *Methods for Sampling* (2nd edition 1962)

Ellis, E. G.
Lubricant Testing
(Scientific Publications, London, 1953)

Chemicals – manufacture and applications

Petroleum-chemical industry

Astle, M. J.
The Chemistry of Petrochemicals
(Reinhold, New York, 1956)

Goldstein, R. F.
The Petroleum Chemical Industry
(Spon, London, 2nd edition 1958)

Hatch, L. F.
The Chemistry of Petrochemical Reactions
(Gulf, New York, 1955)

Shreve, R. N.
The Chemical Process Industries
(McGraw–Hill, New York, 1956)

Steiner, H. (ed)
Introduction to Petroleum Chemicals
(Pergamon Press, Oxford, 1961)

Topchiev, A. V. *et al*
Synthetic Materials from Petroleum
(Pergamon Press, Oxford, 1962)

Waddams, A. L.
Chemicals from Petroleum, an Introductory Survey
(John Murray, London, 1962)

Solvents

Curme, G. O., Johnston, F. (ed)
Glycols
(Reinhold, New York, 1952)

Doolittle, A. K.
The Technology of Solvents and Plasticisers
(John Wiley, New York, 1954)

Durrans, T. H.
Solvents
(Chapman and Hall, London, 7th edition 1957)

Mellan, I.
Industrial Solvents
(Reinhold, New York, 1950)

Tysall, L. A.
Industrial Paints, Basic Principles
(Pergamon Press, Oxford, 1964)

Detergents

Durham, K.
Surface Activity and Detergency
(Macmillan, London, 1961)

Moilliet, J. L., Collie, B., Black, W.
Surface Activity
Spon, London, 2nd edition 1961)

Osipow, L. I.
Surface Chemistry
(Reinhold, New York, 1962)

Price, D.
Detergents, What They Are and What They Do
(Chemical, New York, 1952)

Schwartz, A. M., Perry, J. W.
Surface Active Agents; their Chemistry and Technology
(Interscience, New York, 1958)

Synthetic resins – plastics; Synthetic textile fibres; Synthetic rubbers

Barron, H.
Modern Plastics
(Chapman and Hall, London, 2nd edition 1949)

Boundy, R. H., Boyer, R. F.
Polystyrene, its Polymers, Copolymers and Derivatives
(Reinhold, New York, 1952)

Briston, J. H., Miles, D. C.
Polymer Technology
(Temple Press, London, 1965)

Couzens, E. G., Yarsley, V. E.
Plastics in the Service of Man
(Penguin, Harmondsworth, 1956)

Hill, R.
Fibres from Synthetic Polymers
(Elsevier, Amsterdam, 1953)

Macfarlane, G. B.
Technology of Synthetic Fibres
(Fairchild, New York, 1953)

Moncrieff, R. W.
Artificial Fibres
(National Trade Press, London, 2nd edition 1954)

Morell, R. S., Langton, H. M. (eds)
Synthetic Resins and Allied Plastics
(Oxford University Press, London, 1951)

Renfrew, A., Morgan, P. (eds)
Polythene, the Technology and Uses of Ethylene Polymers
(Iliffe, London, 1960)

Roff, W. J.
Fibres, Plastics and Rubbers
(Butterworths, London, 1956)

Stern, H. J.
Rubber, Natural and Synthetic
(MacLaren, London, 1954)

Whitby, G. S. (ed)
Synthetic Rubber
(Chapman and Hall, London, 1954)

Industrial chemicals

Faith, W. L., Keyes, D. B., Clark, R. L.
Industrial Chemicals
(Chapman and Hall, London, 2nd edition 1957)

Fieser, L. F., Fieser, M.
Organic Chemicals
(Reinhold, New York, 3rd edition 1956)

Goldstein, R. F.
The Petroleum Chemical Industry
(Spon, London, 2nd edition 1958)

Kirk, A. E., Othmer, D. F.
Encyclopaedia of Chemical Technology
(Interscience, New York, 1947–55)

Leffingwell, G., Lesser, M. A.
Glycerin, Its Industrial and Commercial Applications
(Chemical, New York, 1945)

Morgan, Sir G. T., Pratt, D. D.
British Chemical Industry – Its Rise and Development
(Edward Arnold, London, 1946)

Agricultural chemicals

Audus, L. J.
The Physiology and Biochemistry of Herbicides
(Academic Press, London, 1964)

Fisher, E. H. (ed)
Entoma: A Directory of Pesticide Materials-Equipment-Service
(Department of Entomology, University of Wisconsin, 14th edition 1961–62)

Laverton, Sylvia
The Profitable Use of Farm Chemicals
(Oxford University Press, London, 1962)

Martin, H. H. (ed)
Insecticide and Fungicide Handbook for Crop Protection
British Insecticide and Fungicide Council
(Blackwell, Oxford, 1963)

Martin, H.
The Scientific Principles of Crop Protection
(Edward Arnold, London, 5th edition 1965)

Robbins, W. W., Crafts, A. S., Raynor, R. N.
Weed Control
(McGraw–Hill, New York, 3rd edition 1962)

West, T. F., Hardy, J. Eliot
Chemical Control of Insects
(Chapman and Hall, London, 2nd edition 1961)

Transport, distribution and storage

Tankers

King, G. H. B.
Tanker Practice
(Maritime, London, 1960)

Lamb, J.
Oil Tanker Cargoes
(Charles Griffin, London, 1954)

Trunk pipelines

Bell, H. S.
Petroleum Transportation Handbook
(McGraw–Hill, New York, 1963)

Hicks, T. G.
Pump Selection and Application
(McGraw–Hill, New York, 1957)

Katz, D. L. *et al*
Handbook of Natural Gas Engineering
(McGraw–Hill, New York, 1959)

Lester, C. B.
Hydraulics for Pipelines
(Bayonne, 1958)

Minchin, L. T.
Famous Pipelines of the World
(Muller, London, 1964)

Oil Pipe Line Transportation Practices
Vol. 2 – Construction and Maintenance (1964)
Vol. 4 – Pumping Station Operation (1956)
(University of Texas, Austin)

Parker, M. E.
Pipeline Corrosion and Cathodic Protection
(Gulf, Houston, 1962)

Oates, J. A. (ed)
Pipes and Pipelines, Manual and Directory
(Pipes and Pipelines, London, 1962)

Scheel, L. F.
Gas and Air Compression Machinery
(McGraw–Hill, New York, 1961)

Measurement and loss control

American Petroleum Institute (API), New York
ASTM/API Code for Installation, Proving and Operation of Positive Displacement Meters, Code 1101 (1952)
Symposium on Measuring (Transactions, 1954)
Code for Measuring, Sampling and Testing Crude Oil, Code 2500 (1955)

American Society for Testing and Materials, Philadelphia/Institute of Petroleum, London
Petroleum Measurement Tables (1953)
Petroleum Measurement Tables (Metric, 20°C) (1963)
Petroleum Measurement Manual, Parts I, VI, VII, IX (1), Available (1965)
Parts II, III, IV, V, VIII, IX(2), X, XI, In preparation (1965)
Report on Development, Construction, Calculation and Preparation of the Petroleum Measurement Tables (1960)

Index

Figures shown in bold refer to primary references in text
and those enclosed within square brackets refer to illustrations

1742/1.66/67.5m

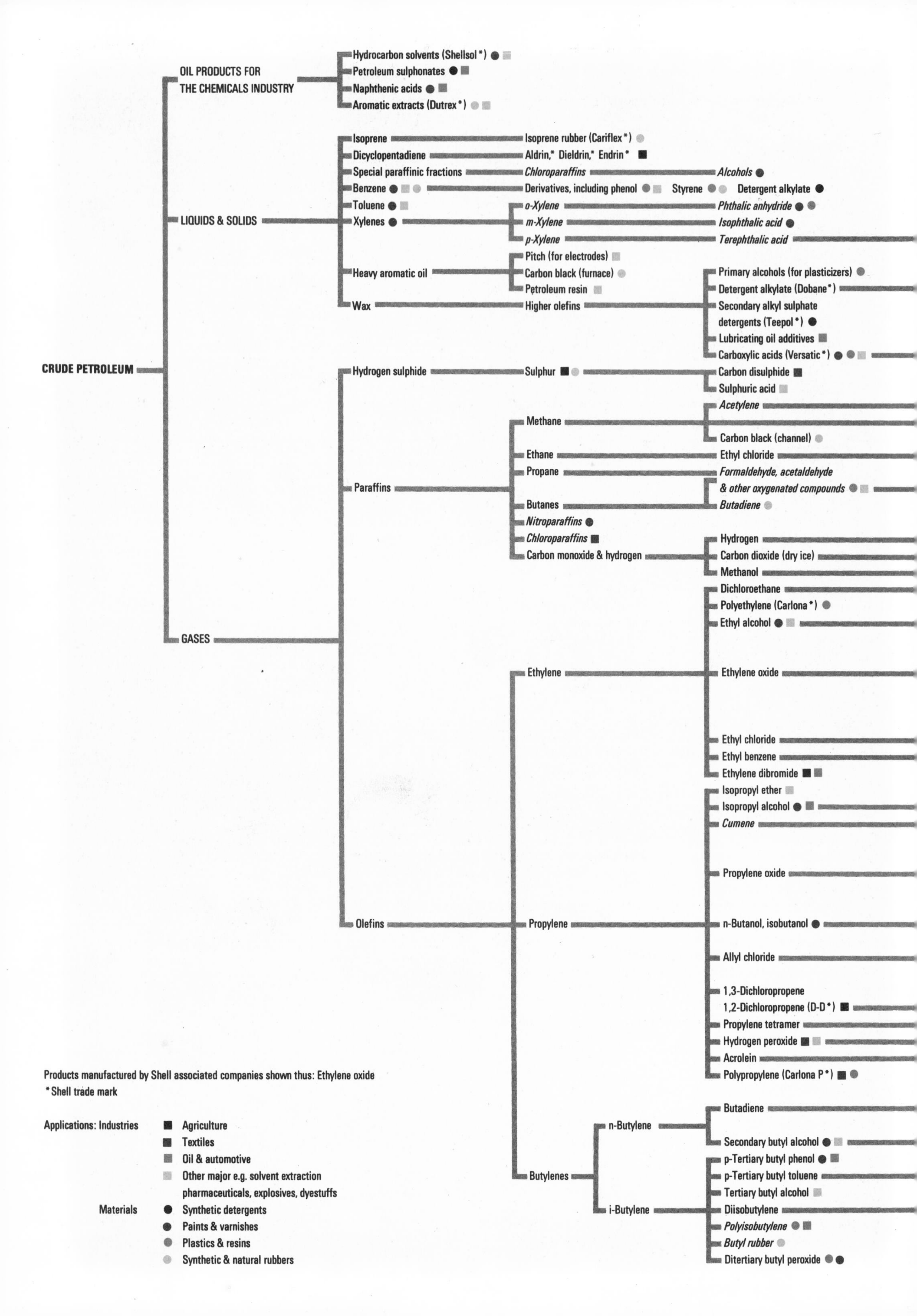
CRUDE PETROLEUM
OIL PRODUCTS FOR THE CHEMICALS INDUSTRY
Hydrocarbon solvents (Shellsol*)
Petroleum sulphonates
Naphthenic acids
Aromatic extracts (Dutrex*)
LIQUIDS & SOLIDS
Isoprene
Isoprene rubber (Cariflex*)
Dicyclopentadiene
Aldrin,* Dieldrin,* Endrin*
Special paraffinic fractions
Chloroparaffins
Alcohols
Benzene
Derivatives, including phenol
Styrene
Detergent alkylate
Toluene
Xylenes
o-Xylene
Phthalic anhydride
m-Xylene
Isophthalic acid
p-Xylene
Terephthalic acid
Heavy aromatic oil
Pitch (for electrodes)
Carbon black (furnace)
Petroleum resin
Wax
Higher olefins
Primary alcohols (for plasticizers)
Detergent alkylate (Dobane*)
Secondary alkyl sulphate detergents (Teepol*)
Lubricating oil additives
Carboxylic acids (Versatic*)
GASES
Hydrogen sulphide
Sulphur
Carbon disulphide
Sulphuric acid
Paraffins
Methane
Acetylene
Carbon black (channel)
Ethane
Ethyl chloride
Propane
Formaldehyde, acetaldehyde & other oxygenated compounds
Butanes
Butadiene
Nitroparaffins
Chloroparaffins
Carbon monoxide & hydrogen
Hydrogen
Carbon dioxide (dry ice)
Methanol
Olefins
Ethylene
Dichloroethane
Polyethylene (Carlona*)
Ethyl alcohol
Ethylene oxide
Ethyl chloride
Ethyl benzene
Ethylene dibromide
Propylene
Isopropyl ether
Isopropyl alcohol
Cumene
Propylene oxide
n-Butanol, isobutanol
Allyl chloride
1,3-Dichloropropene
1,2-Dichloropropene (D-D*)
Propylene tetramer
Hydrogen peroxide
Acrolein
Polypropylene (Carlona P*)
Butylenes
n-Butylene
Butadiene
Secondary butyl alcohol
i-Butylene
p-Tertiary butyl phenol
p-Tertiary butyl toluene
Tertiary butyl alcohol
Diisobutylene
Polyisobutylene
Butyl rubber
Ditertiary butyl peroxide
Products manufactured by Shell associated companies shown thus: Ethylene oxide
* Shell trade mark
Applications: Industries
Agriculture
Textiles
Oil & automotive
Other major e.g. solvent extraction pharmaceuticals, explosives, dyestuffs
Materials
Synthetic detergents
Paints & varnishes
Plastics & resins
Synthetic & natural rubbers